James Lee

40

wed. noon
Robert Pahl
WA 9361

Agricultural Science Series

L. H. BAILEY, EDITOR

THE NATURE AND PROPERTIES OF SOILS

THE MACMILLAN COMPANY
NEW YORK · BOSTON · CHICAGO · DALLAS
ATLANTA · SAN FRANCISCO

MACMILLAN AND CO., Limited
LONDON · BOMBAY · CALCUTTA · MADRAS
MELBOURNE

THE MACMILLAN COMPANY
OF CANADA, Limited
TORONTO

THE NATURE AND PROPERTIES OF SOILS

A COLLEGE TEXT OF EDAPHOLOGY

by T. LYTTLETON LYON
Late Professor of Soil Technology, Emeritus, Cornell University

and HARRY O. BUCKMAN
Professor of Soil Technology, Cornell University

FOURTH EDITION
Revised by
HARRY O. BUCKMAN

NEW YORK · THE MACMILLAN COMPANY · 1949

Preface to the Third Edition

This volume is designed for the student who is interested in the nature and properties of soils and their relationships to higher plants. A working knowledge of inorganic chemistry and elementary physics is presupposed as well as some understanding of the colloidal state of matter. A background of general geology and biology will be exceedingly helpful.

References are cited for two purposes, to establish authority and to assist the student who may wish to verify or read more deeply into the various phases of pedology and edaphology. Further than this, citations from the exceedingly voluminous literature are not attempted.

T. L. L. *and* H. O. B.

Cornell University
February, 1937.

Preface to the Fourth Edition

Because of the rapid advances in soil science the author has found it increasingly difficult to cover, even in an introductory text, so broad a field. The additional attention required by the physics of soil moisture, by the chemistry of the colloidal state, and by soil genesis and classification, have of necessity lessened the emphasis on topics that once were deemed worthy of more extended consideration. It is hoped that in bringing the book abreast of research, the viewpoint presented is still a well-balanced one.

This volume is dedicated to the memory of T. Lyttleton Lyon, the late senior author, to whose judgment and scholarly discrimination the modest success of the previous editions of this book was due in no small part. It is the hope of the present author that this, the fourth edition, is as well received.

H. O. B

Cornell University
February, 1943.

Table of Contents

vii

Chapter I. The Soil in Perspective

Before beginning a detailed examination of the many and varied phases of soil science, it is well to view this natural body we call the *soil* in a broad yet critical way. A well-balanced concept, if attained, should prevent many misinterpretations of scientific data and forestall serious misconceptions in respect to things of practical import. Two methods of approach, or better two attitudes of mind, respecting the soil immediately present themselves — that of the *pedologist* on the one hand and the *edaphologist* on the other.

Certain phases such as the origin of the soil, its various characteristics, and its classification and description are embraced in what is designated as *pedology*.[1] Pedology considers the soil purely as a natural body and has little regard for its practical utilization. It is soil science in its most restricted form. A pedologist must be a systematist.

While pedology has yielded much valuable information, soil investigation to satisfy the average man must be pushed into wider and more practical fields. Since all animal and human food comes directly or indirectly from the soil, crop-production knowledge is ever in demand. Hence soil study, in the final analysis, must yield information of an agricultural and economic nature. *Edaphology*,[2] an examination of the soil from the standpoint of higher plants, covers this broader but no less scientific aspect of soil inquiry. The ultimate, if not the immediate objective, of the edaphologist is crop production.

It is into this wider field that the reader is invited. Here the origin, the properties, and the classification of soils are viewed in an edaphological light. Here are studied the many interrelations of soils and plants, the principles of fertility maintenance, and the application of such principles to everyday problems. Even hypothesis and specula-

[1] Pedology from *pedos* meaning soil or earth.
[2] Edaphology from *edaphos* referring to the soil or earth as a foothold for higher plants.

1

tion will not be found wanting as explanations are sought for phenomena arising from the interaction of soil and plant and climate.

1. *Soil genesis — a biochemical phenomenon*

Land surfaces almost everywhere are covered with <u>unconsolidated debris</u> called the *regolith*. This mantle above the bedrock may be negligibly shallow or it may be hundreds of feet in thickness. Moreover, its physical condition and chemical composition may vary not only horizontally but also vertically, and its geological origin is not always the same even within restricted areas. The regolith has attained its position either through transportation and deposition by water, wind, or ice, or by the weathering in place of the country rock.

Since the upper part of this variable regolith is in contact with the atmosphere, weathering readily occurs. Hydrolysis, hydration, oxidation, carbonation, and solution accompany the physical changes that are taking place. And when microorganisms and higher plants have gained a foothold, organic matter tends to accumulate on and in the surface layer. It is at this point that soil genesis really begins. In fact a true soil cannot be formed without the presence and decay of some organic matter. Mere physical and chemical weathering of rocks should not be confused with soil formation. As a result most soil processes are directly or indirectly biological in nature. The soil is thus a natural body, distinct from, yet transitional to, the parent material with characteristics both obvious and unique. It is the

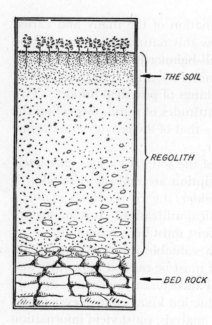

FIG. 1. Diagram showing the relative positions of the regolith, its soil and the underlying country rock. Sometimes the regolith is so thin that it has been changed entirely to soil, which, in such a case, rests directly on bed rock.

upper, weathered, and biologically molded part of the regolith. (See Fig. 1.)

2. *The soil profile*

If a section downward through a soil is examined, a layering, often well defined, will usually be found. Such a section is called a *profile* and the individual layers are regarded as *horizons*. Every well-developed undisturbed soil has its own distinctive profile. Profile characteristics are made use of in soil classification and survey and are of great practical importance.

The upper layers of a soil profile generally contain considerable amounts of organic matter and are usually darkened appreciably because of such an accumulation. Layers thus characterized are conveniently referred to as the *A* horizons and when plowed and cultivated, make up the familiar surface soil or furrow-slice. Below the surface soil lies the subsoil, also markedly weathered but usually containing comparatively little or no organic matter. Its various layers are referred to as the *B* horizons and attain an indefinite but moderate depth below the surface. A depth of 3 or 4 feet is representative for temperate-region soils. Here the noticeably modified subsoil gradually merges with the original regolith or *soil material*. This part of the profile is called the *C* horizon. It is usually weathered, sometimes markedly so, and its upper portion is about to become a part of the lower subsoil. (See Fig. 2.)

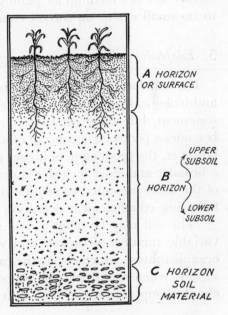

Fig. 2. A representative soil profile. The *A* horizon is relatively high in organic matter and becomes the furrow-slice when the land is plowed. The *B* horizon, while markedly weathered, usually contains but little organic matter. At variable depths it merges gradually into the soil material designated as the *C* horizon.

The soil is thus conceived to be a natural body formed by weathering, supplemented by certain biotic influences, and evolving from the original regolith by well-defined physical, chemical, and biological changes. For any particular soil [1] the various horizons are characteristic and greatly influence the growth of higher plants. This is especially true of the *A* horizon and the upper subsoil. In these layers maximum root extension occurs. Even when roots do not penetrate deeply into the subsoil, its permeability to air and water and its chemical nature may favorably or unfavorably influence the surface soil as a medium for plant growth. Soil productivity depends to no small extent on subsoil characteristics.

3. *Edaphological characterization of the soil*

The soil has already been designated as the "upper, weathered, and biologically molded part of the regolith." This is a rather formal statement, but when expanded into a profile and horizon study, it becomes a pedological concept of soil origin and characterization. If, however, the production of higher plants is to be a part of the picture, a broader and more inclusive statment must be offered. In the light of the ideas presented respecting the general function of the soil, the following edaphological definition is suggested:

"The soil may be defined as a natural body, engendered from a variable mixture of broken and weathered minerals and decaying organic matter, which covers the earth in a thin layer and which may supply, when containing the proper amounts of air and water, mechanical support and in part sustenance for plants."

4. *Four soil components*

The soil, as ordinarily conceived, especially when it is in an optimum condition for the growth of higher plants, consists in a broad way of four components or fractions; namely, *mineral materials, organic matter, water,* and *air*. These in the main are in a rather fine state of subdivision and are intimately mixed. In fact the contact is often so close as to render satisfactory separation rather difficult.

The more solid part of the soil is made up of mineral fragments in

---

[1] *A soil*, as distinguished from *the soil*, is merely a well-defined subdivision based on profile characteristics and is practically identical throughout its lateral range.

various stages of disintegration and decomposition. Mixed with these inorganic substances is to be found a variable amount of organic matter depending on the horizon under examination. Normally the largest amount of organic matter is in the surface soil.

The mineral material, which is generally in the ascendancy, has its genesis in the regolith or soil material. Some of the soil minerals have persisted more or less unchanged, while others have developed as the regolith weathered, either before or during soil formation. Naturally various sizes of particles occur, ranging from those that are comparatively coarse, such as gravel and sand, to those, such as silt and clay, that are in a very fine state of division.

The organic matter represents the accumulation of plant and animal residues and is generally in an active state of decay. Such material, because it readily succumbs to the attack of microorganisms, is a rather transitory soil constituent and requires constant renewal. A furrow-slice sample of a dry upland soil may contain from 2 to 5 per cent of total organic matter compared with 95 to 98 per cent of inorganic substances. With lowland soils, the organic matter is often much greater.

An examination of any soil will reveal the presence of pore spaces of varying sizes. These occur not only between the large, solid particles but also between and within the clumps and aggregates which the finer particles tend to form when the soil is in a suitable physical condition for plant growth. These pore spaces, variable as to continuity, local dimensions, and total volume, are occupied in large part by water and air, the proportion depending on the character of the soil and the conditions under which it is functioning.

Water, the third component of the soil, is held within these pore spaces with varying tenacity due to certain surface forces. Some passes readily from place to place, while some moves hardly at all. In all cases, surface contacts are paramount. Due to the action of the water itself and also to the carbon dioxide and other substances which it always carries, solution occurs continuously even though the soil solids, especially the mineral portions, are not always easily dissolved. Soil water for this reason carries many soluble salts.

The principal gases of the soil air, the fourth component, are nitrogen, oxygen, and carbon dioxide. The first is very inert and enters into chemical reaction only when appropriated by certain bacteria, called *nitrogen fixers*. By them it is built into complex organic compounds. Oxygen is, of course, essential for all life forms, whether the roots of higher plants or the tiniest bacteria. The carbon dioxide by reacting with the soil water produces carbonic acid, one of the most important acids found in soils. Carbon dioxide also creates anaerobic conditions in certain parts of the soil and serves as a source of carbon for special types of microorganisms. This mixture of nitrogen, oxygen, and carbon dioxide not only varies inversely with the amount of water present in the soil but also is extremely variable as to the ratio of the gases present.

5. *Mineral versus organic soils*

The soil as above described obviously may be low or high in organic matter, as the case may be. Soils low in organic matter are conveniently referred to as *mineral soils* since the inorganic constituents greatly predominate. Most soils are of this nature. But in swamps, bogs, and marshes, conditions are often such as to encourage the accumulation of much organic matter. This gives rise to peat deposits and peat soils in which the organic content may range as high as 95 per cent. Perhaps 80 per cent of organic matter and 20 per cent of minerals are reliable representative figures for such deposits used as field soils. As such they are referred to as *organic soils*. As might be expected, peat soils are markedly different from mineral soils in many important respects and their practical handling presents problems that are both distinctive and unique. In spite of their smaller area these soils are very important for certain crops, especially those of a specialized nature.

Since mineral soils are of wider area, better known, and are in general more important agriculturally than organic soils, they will receive major attention. Moreover, pedological and edaphological studies are based for the most part on mineral soils. The origin, characteristics, and agricultural use of peat deposits will be treated later. (See Chap. XIV.)

6. *The volume composition of mineral soils*

Once the identity of the four soil constituents is established, the question as to their relative proportions is sure to be raised. As to this, the surface soil will be considered first, leaving the subsoil for later examination. For simplicity of statement the representative surface soil when dry may be considered to contain by weight approximately 4 per cent of organic matter and 96 per cent of mineral material. But this leaves entirely out of consideration the air and water, a serious omission since these constituents have so much to do with the activity of a normal soil. If a quantitative concept, truly significant, is to be realized, the volume basis of representation must be used.

A silt loam surface soil will be considered as more or less representative. When such a soil is in optimum condition for plant growth, it contains approximately 50 per cent of solids and 50 per cent of pore space. The pore space will be somewhat less for sandy soils and somewhat greater for soils of a more clayey nature. The 50 per cent of solid space is occupied by about 45 per cent of mineral and 5 per cent of organic substances by volume. At optimum moisture for plant growth, the 50 per cent of pore space possessed by this representative silt loam is divided roughly into 25 per cent of water space and 25 per cent of air. The proportion of air and water is, of course, subject to great fluctuations under natural

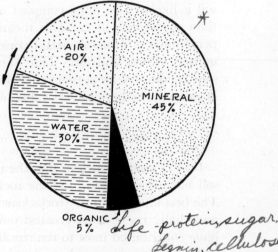

Fig. 3. Volume composition of a silty loam surface soil when in good condition for plant growth. The air and water in a soil are extremely variable, and their proportion determines in large degree its suitability for plant growth.

conditions, depending on the weather and other factors. (See Fig. 3.)

In presenting such an arbitrary volume representation of a surface mineral soil, it must be emphasized that the four main components of the normal soil exist for the most part in a finely divided and very intimately related condition and that very complex reactions occur with surprising ease and rapidity within and between the groups. Contact, or *interface*, reactions are especially important. Unless such interactions take place, this complex heterogeneous mass cannot long remain in a condition, either physically or chemically, to support plant life.

No attempt will be made to establish even a tentative volume composition for the subsoil. Suffice to say in many cases, especially with soils inclined to be clayey, the pore space is much less than that of the surface soil and the individual interstices are smaller. This is to be expected as there usually is little organic matter to promote porosity and thereby offset natural compaction. The downward movement of clay also tends to fill up the pore spaces, sometimes resulting in a decidedly impervious condition called a *clay pan*. All in all, the subsoil is likely to be more compact and less pervious to air and water than the furrow-slice. This means, on the volume basis, a higher percentage of minerals and a considerably lower content of organic matter, water, and air. Thus the aeration and drainage of clayey soils becomes of great practical concern and should not be overlooked in judging the agricultural value of land.

7. *The mineral constituents of the soil*

It is, of course, obvious that the inorganic constituents of a mineral soil have their origin from the rocks common at the earth's surface. The best known country rocks,[1] such as limestone, granite, sandstone, and shale, present the greatest outcrop surface. Of necessity, they have contributed most to the regolith and to soil formation.

Two types of minerals are present in the soil: those that have persisted more or less unchanged from the parent regolith, and those that have been formed by the weathering of less resistant minerals as the regolith developed and soil formation progressed. The former are called *original* minerals and the latter, *secondary*. For example, the quartz grains of a soil almost always come directly from the original rock, as do particles of feldspar, mica, hornblende, and apatite. On the other hand, hematite, limonite, gypsum, and such clay minerals as kaolinite, beidellite, and montmorillonite, as well as other sec-

---

[1] Some of the more common country rocks are as follows:

Igneous	*Sedimentary*	*Metamorphic*
Granite	Limestone	Gneiss
Syenite	Dolomite	Schist
Diorite	Sandstone	Slate
Gabbro	Shale	Quartzite
Peridotite	Conglomerate	Marble

ondary silicates, seem to have originated in most cases through the weathering of some of the primary minerals.[1]

The mineral particles of the soil may be classified according to size under four heads as follows:

1. Very coarse	Visible to the naked eye	Stone and gravel
2. Coarse	Visible to the naked eye	Sands of various sizes
3. Fine	Visible under ordinary micro-scope	Silt particles
4. Very fine	Visible satisfactorily only under electron-microscope	Clay particles — highly colloidal

The last three grades are the most desirable as components of arable soils and commonly predominate. They are referred to collectively as *fine earth*. While sand grains usually are quartz, other minerals may occur such as hornblende, augite, mica, garnet, and magnetite. (See Fig. 7.) Among the larger sand particles, fragments of sandstone, shales, granite, and other rocks are commonly found. Stone and gravel are seldom made up of single minerals, but are usually rough or rounded fragments of bedrock.

The clayey material because of its fineness of division, the great amount of surface presented, and its intimate relationship to the soil water, is in a highly colloidal condition. It is viscous and gelatinous when moist, but hard and cohesive when dry. It, therefore, endows

---

[1] The more important soil minerals may be listed as follows:

Primary Origin [a]

1.	Quartz	SiO_2
2.	Microcline and orthoclase	$KAlSi_3O_8$
3.	Plagioclase feldspars	Ca and Na, aluminum silicates
4.	Muscovite and biotite	K, Mg, Fe, and H aluminum silicates
5.	Hornblende and augite	Ca, Mg, and Fe aluminum silicates
6.	Calcite and dolomite	$CaCO_3$ and $(Ca, Mg)CO_3$
7.	Apatite	Apatite, $Ca_5(PO_4)_3 \cdot (Cl, F)$

Secondary Origin [b]

1.	Various clay minerals	Complicated aluminum silicates
2.	Hematite	Fe_2O_3
3.	Limonite compounds	Typified by limonite $2Fe_2O_3 \cdot 3H_2O$
4.	Secondary calcite	$CaCO_3$
5.	Secondary gypsum	$CaSO_4 \cdot 2H_2O$
6.	Secondary phosphates	Oxy-, hydroxy- and carbonate-apatites
7.	Secondary mica	Typified by sericite

[a] Other minerals of primary origin are garnet, zircon, magnetite, rutile, epidote, tourmaline, and olivine.
[b] Other minerals that may be of secondary origin are serpentine, chlorite, epidote, talc, etc.

Some of these so-called secondary minerals may have become in course of the geological cycle a part of the bed rock. They are nevertheless still secondary in a geologic sense and will be so considered pedologically. Thus hematite is a weathering product whether its formation was coincident with the development of the regolith and its accompanying soil or formed long before in some other cycle of weathering.

the soil with outstanding physical properties that are well recognized in practice. Moreover, its adsorptive power, one of the notable characteristics of all colloidal matter, has much to do, not only with the retention of nutrients, but also with their speed of reaction. The catalytic property thus imparted to the soil by such finely divided material hastens a great variety of chemical reactions and renders the complex and rather insoluble mineral mass highly dynamic.

The silt particles, as to origin, are in large part original. Their interior is generally more or less unweathered, while their outer portion is coated with clayey matter. As a result, unwashed silt is somewhat plastic, cohesive, and adsorptive, but much less intensively so than is typical clay.

Thus it is evident that the representative mineral soil is a mixture of particles differing in size, in chemical composition, in mineralogical nature, and in physical and chemical properties. The particular group of particles that dominates an individual soil, as well as the proportionate amounts of the others present, determine the characteristics of that soil and have much to do with its fertility and its successful crop production.

8. *The organic matter of the soil*

One of the essential differences between a fertile soil and a mere mass of rock fragments lies in the organic content of the former. But the amount of organic matter present is so small — only about 4 per cent in the case of the representative mineral soil — that its importance might be considered of minor significance, especially in comparison with the 96 per cent of mineral materials present. In answer to this, it is only necessary to state that organic matter is necessary for soil genesis. Moreover, practically all of the nitrogen and the sulfur of the soil are held in organic combinations. Therefore, when the organic matter begins to fail, these elements, essential for the development of higher plants, must of necessity become critical.

Again the organic matter has much to do with the physical condition of soils, especially those of a clayey nature. It promotes the granulation of the soil, increases its water-holding capacity, and makes the creation of a satisfactory seedbed more easy and rapid. In addition, the organic matter is the main source of energy for soil microorganisms. Without it, biochemical activity would come practically to a standstill.

For convenience, the soil organic matter may be considered to consist of three general types: (1) original tissue, (2) partially decomposed materials, and (3) humus. The original tissue includes the more or less undecomposed additions that are constantly being made. Normally these additions are mostly of plant origin — the roots and tops of higher plants, as well as microorganic remains — although some animal tissue is received from rodents, earthworms, protozoa, and the like.

If conditions are at all favorable, soil organisms, both of plant and animal nature, vigorously attack the added organic matter using it as a source of energy and as a tissue-building material. The original additions and the resultant intermediate products are thus rapidly resolved to humus — the black or brown incoherent and amorphous material so noticeable in surface layers of most soils. In reality, humus is a synthesized residue of microorganic activity and is very complex. It is the more resistant portion of the soil organic matter.

Concomitant with the synthesis of humus is the appearance of many simple compounds of great importance. Carbon dioxide is evolved at all times in large quantities, while at certain stages, nitrates, sulfates, and other rather soluble and available products are much in evidence. At the same time, energy from organic matter is liberated as heat as well as made use of freely by soil organisms. In fact, most of the tangible energy of the soil is that of the organic matter.

In common with other types of matter in the colloidal state, the soil humus exhibits adsorption and catalysis to a very unusual degree. In its capacity to attract and hold water, gases, and salts in solution, humus, pound for pound, greatly excels the clayey colloids. Small amounts of humus augment tremendously the dynamic characteristics of a soil.

9. *The soil solution*

As water circulates through the intimately mixed mass of decomposing mineral and organic matter of the soil, it of necessity becomes a solution bearing at least traces of every element present in the soils. However, the mistake is often made of considering this soil solution in its relationships to higher plants as a simple water culture such as is used in botanical laboratories. The latter presents a continuous liquid body not greatly influenced by undissolved solids and, therefore, is rather homogeneous. The soil solution, however, is in marked contrast. It is greatly dispersed and exists, in part at least, in minute subdivision. Moreover, it suffers intense adsorption as it contacts the immense surfaces exposed by the colloidal solids. Thus some is held tightly and has little movement, while some is free to adjust readily from place to place. Also the concentration due to the adsorption of the solute is greater in the immediate neighborhood of the colloidal surfaces. The soil solution may, therefore, be characterized as heterogeneous in position, in movement, and in concentration.

Moreover, the soil solution is highly dynamic both as to amount and concentration. Rain, evaporation, and plant action obviously tend to vary its total amount. When such fluctuations are accompanied by varying rates of solution, losses of nutrients to higher plants and to drainage, radical changes in concentration are sure to occur. Additions of fertilizers, lime, and farm manure intensify rather than lessen these dynamic tendencies.

In such a fluctuating medium, higher plants as well as microorganisms must accommodate themselves to a great variety of conditions. And such adjustments are often difficult as they involve an accommodation not only to the amount of the solution and to its concentration in total but also to concentrations and proportions of particular elements both essential and nonessential for growth. The soil solution is thus unique and by no means comparable to an ordinary water culture. Deductions from one to the other should be made with caution.

10. *The soil air*

One of the common misconceptions is to consider the soil air as merely a continuation of the ordinary atmosphere into the soil. In the first place the soil air is not a continuous gaseous body as is the lower atmospheric air but is highly dispersed and adsorbed by the soil colloids. Moreover, an appreciable proportion of it is dissolved in the soil water. Again its humidity usually approaches 100 per cent, a condition especially favorable for the growth of fungi, bacteria, and other soil organisms.

Although the soil air, like the atmospheric air, is a mixture of oxygen, nitrogen, carbon dioxide, and certain minor gases, the proportions are strikingly different. Quantitatively, carbon dioxide is especially plentiful in the soil. This gas, given off in large volume by decaying organic matter, tends to dominate the mixture, the nitrogen and especially the oxygen decreasing as the carbon dioxide is evolved. The air of the larger pore spaces may contain several hundred times more carbon dioxide than the air above the soil, for which 0.03 per cent by volume is a representative figure. And the atmosphere of the minute spongelike interstices is often almost pure carbon dioxide. This is of great chemical and biological significance since this carbon dioxide pressure tends to increase the H-ion concentration of the soil solution and at the same time enhance anaerobic conditions.

As a result of its peculiar associations, the soil air is markedly heterogeneous as to position, as to movement, and as to composition. Some is adsorbed by the colloidal surfaces and thus is in close contact with the soil solids. Such air is very high in carbon dioxide and has slow, if any, movement at all. Some occupies the larger interstices, is free to move from place to place, and contains considerable quantities of oxygen and a minimum of carbon dioxide. Besides this heterogeneity, the atmosphere of the soil is dynamic, changing constantly in amount and composition. A fluctuation in the soil water automatically varies the amount of air present, while any condition that increases or decreases carbon dioxide production must certainly modify the proportion of the various gases present.

The soil air because of its varying amounts of carbon dioxide and oxygen presents to the roots of higher plants and to microorganisms an atmosphere suited to almost any type of biochemical activity. Aerobic and anaerobic organisms flourish side by side while reduction and oxidation may occur simultaneously in the same soil. The dynamic nature of such an atmosphere is such as to force rapid adjustment upon any plant or animal that attempts to function within it. This is a phase that must be reckoned with in biological studies of natural soils.

11. *The biological nature of the soil*

The representative mineral soil, bearing as it does so much available energy in organic form, harbors a varied population of living organisms. Nature is most lavish in this respect. Indeed the life of the soil plays such a prominent and indispensable role in the changes constantly occurring, that no discussion of the organic matter is complete without its consideration.

Representatives of both animals and plants are abundant in the soil. Some of the organisms are large while others are very small. The whole gamut from the larger rodents, worms, and insects to the tiniest bacteria commonly occurs in the normal soil.

These organisms vary so much both in numbers and amounts as to make definite statements impossible. For example, the number of bacteria alone in a gram of soil may range from 100,000 to several billion, depending on conditions. The total weight of living matter, including plant roots, in an acre-furrow-slice of a representative mineral soil may be placed at 5000 pounds at least, while 10,000 or even 20,000 pounds may be more nearly correct for many soils. In any case the quantity of living organic matter is sufficient to influence the physical and chemical trend of soil changes. Indeed it can even be said that practically all natural soil reactions are directly or indirectly biochemical in nature.

Of the larger organisms, the influence of the earthworms is perhaps in general the most important (Fig. 16). Besides translocating and mixing the soil, these animals pass large quantities through their bodies. The earth is thus subjected to certain digestive processes, which must have considerable influence on its physical and chemical nature. The organic matter, which furnishes the earthworms with energy and with most of their tissue-building materials, is changed in greater degree by the enzymic processes of digestion than are the mineral substances present.

Other and perhaps better examples of the biological influences brought to bear on the soil, especially upon its organic constituents, may be obtained by turning to the fungi and bacteria. (See Fig. 18.) These forms, more perhaps than any others, determine the rate and character of organic synthesis and simplification. They govern by their enzymic activity the nature of the humus and control the volume of carbon dioxide produced. The appearance of ammonium compounds in the soil is due mainly to their action. Moreover, certain bacteria govern the production of nitrates and sulfates, indispensable sources respectively of nitrogen and sulfur for higher plants. In brief, without such microorganic activity, little simplification of any kind would occur, the solvent capacity of the soil water would not in any degree be augmented by carbon dioxide, and essential elements would not so readily become available to higher plants.

12. *The active portion of the soil*

It is now quite obvious that all normal soils are dynamic and that the markedly active constituents either are in a finely dispersed condition or are in contact with materials already in this state. In other words most soil reactions, physical, chemical, and biological, depend in large degree on the colloidicity of certain major constituents, both living and nonliving.

Clay and humus, more or less intimately mixed, constitute most of the colloidal matter found in soils. This finely divided fraction not only promotes activity catalytically, but also may participate intensively in the changes that occur. This is especially true of both clay and humus. In fact, the latter may react and be reacted upon to the extent of losing its colloidal character in the production of simple compounds. Adsorption, plasticity, cohesion, and certain chemical exchanges are all controlled by substances in the colloidal state. Very few reactions occur in the soil that are not connected in some way with matter in this condition. While the humic colloids are the more active, pound for pound, the presence usually of a larger amount of viscous, gelatinous, and more stable clayey matter preserves a balance in their relative importance. The two, existing in the soil in the most intimate contact, function with surprising intensity and rapidity and with an extraordinary degree of delicacy and precision.

13. *The colloido-biological concept*

In any study of the soil, the importance of the colloidal state of matter obviously cannot be ignored. Nor can one escape certain conclusions regarding the significance of the soil organisms. In fact, a colloido-biological approach must be made to most soil problems whether technical or practical in nature.

Enlarging on such a conception, the soil may be visualized as possessing a framework of mineral matter — in part noncolloidal and inert; in part colloidal and extremely active. In mineral soils clayey materials make up much of this latter fraction. But mixed with this viscous, gelatinous mineral matter, and partially adsorbed thereby, is a certain amount of humus, notably colloidal and unstable. These adsorptive, catalytic, and dynamic gels practically dominate the situation in a physical and chemical way.

Clinging to the surfaces of this organomineral filling and imbedded in its gelatinous, porous depths live a vigorous fauna and flora, profuse, diverse, and persistent. This life, multiplying and dying, active and dormant by turn, draws most of its energy from the soil organic matter and brings about changes and reactions, not inherent in lifeless colloidal matter. Through and over this activated mineral and organic mass circulate the air and water of the soil, augmenting or retarding the vital phenomena as the case may be.

The presence of higher plants on the soil markedly strengthens this colloido-biological conception. As the rootlets penetrate the soil, forcing their way into the pore spaces and through the gelatinous fillings, the contact between the root hairs and the soil colloidal matter becomes very close. In fact, so intimate are the colloidal contacts that the plant really becomes a part of the soil system. Such a relationship predicates direct interaction between the absorbing surfaces of the plant and the more active portions of the soil.

Simple as is this generalization, an inquiry into the details of such a complicated system is fraught with difficulties. The complexity of the various components of the soil, both organic and inorganic, the instability of the humic constituents, and the bewildering succession of life with its enzymic complications make analysis difficult, interpretation uncertain, and complete control impossible. Even a sample of the soil solution, simple though it may be, cannot be removed unchanged from its colloidal environment.

Chapter II. The Supply and Availability of Plant Nutrients in Mineral Soils

The edaphological feature that attracts especial attention is the capacity of soils to supply higher plants with certain essential constituents. This is a fundamental problem in crop production. Hence any sound concept of the interrelationships of soils and living organisms presupposes at the outset some knowledge of the essential elements as they exist and function in soils. Later three aspects of the subject, with some important details, will be presented in this chapter as follows: (1) the total supply in the soil, (2) the modes of transfer to the soil solution and (3) the forms and manner in which the essential elements are presented to the absorbing surfaces of microorganisms and higher plants.

14. *Factors controlling the growth of higher plants* [1]

The growth and development of higher plants depend on two sets of factors, the internal and the external. The latter group, of special interest from the soil standpoint, may be enumerated as follows: (1) light, (2) mechanical support, (3) heat, (4) air, (5) water, and (6) nutrients. With the exception of light, the soil is an agent in supplying, either wholly or in part, these essential conditions. [2]

Mechanical support is a function entirely of the soil. The comparatively loose and friable condition of most soils presents ample space for the ramifying roots. In some cases, however, the presence of a compact layer or a lack of adequate drainage may interfere with

[1] For an excellent discussion of these factors, see Russell, E. J., *Soil Conditions and Plant Growth*, Longmans, Green and Company, New York, 1937, Chap. II, pp. 32–57.

[2] Absence of disease and lack of serious insect pests are often mentioned as negative factors in this connection.

17

the root spread.   Although temperature depends almost wholly on weather relationships, the transfer of heat through the soil is of vital importance to activities of all kinds (see page 230).   Unfortunately, temperature control under field conditions is rather limited.

Air and water are usually supplied rather easily because of the open condition of the soil.   Oxygen and carbon dioxide function as chemical and biochemical agents, while water is a source of hydrogen and oxygen, as well as an efficient solvent.   By its circulation, it promotes an interchange and interaction of constituents and not only brings nutrients in contact with the absorbing surfaces of roots and microorganisms but also facilitates their penetration.   The two prime functions of the soil are thus realized through the coordination of the factors mentioned above — mechanical support and, under favorable conditions, a sufficient supply of certain essential elements.   For the present, the consideration of the first of these — the physical nature of the soil — will be passed over in order to present certain fundamentals regarding plant nutrition.

15. *The essential elements* [1]

For the normal growth of both higher and lower plants in or on the soil, two conditions of the nutrients are necessary.   First, certain elements must be present and available for the use of the plant; and second, the actual and proportionate supply of these nutrients must be adjusted properly.   The presence of too large an amount of one element may be as detrimental as an actual lack of this same constituent. Again the failure of the plant to utilize properly one element may be due to an over- or undersupply of another.[2]   Not only must nutrients be available but they should be physiologically balanced.[3]   This is one of the important problems of fertilizer practice.

Certain elements are, therefore, considered as especially desirable for successful crop growth.   If they are lacking or improperly bal-

[1] For a rather extended discussion of the nutrient elements, see Russell, E. J., *Soil Conditions and Plant Growth*, Longmans, Green and Company, New York, 1937, pp. 61–124.

[2] Too much nitrogen, for example, in proportion to the phosphorus available to plants, may encourage undesirable, if not abnormal, physiological conditions.   Also too much calcium may interfere with phosphorus and boron nutrition or may encourage chlorosis due to a reduction in the availability of the soil iron, zinc, or manganese.   An undersupply of calcium may retard both nitrogen and phosphorus availability.

[3] The importance of a balanced nutrient ration in the soil and the difficulties of its attainment in practice are dealt with on page 404.

anced, normal development does not occur. Ten such elements have been so recognized for a number of years, since their necessity can easily be demonstrated. More recent investigations have positively added four others to the list. These four are manganese, boron, copper, and zinc. Small amounts, often mere traces, of these latter elements usually suffice, while larger doses may be highly toxic[1]. Hence care must be observed in their use. In the following table will be found a list of the elements now definitely recognized as essential. They are classified according to sources — whether primarily from air and water or from soil solids — and whether used by plants in relatively large or small amounts.

Table I. Essential Nutrient Elements and Their Sources

Essential Elements Used in Relatively Large Amounts			Essential Elements Used in Relatively Small Amounts [a]	
Mostly from Air and Water	From Soil Solids		From Soil Solids	
Carbon	Nitrogen	Calcium	Iron	Copper
Hydrogen	Phosphorus	Magnesium	Manganese	Zinc
Oxygen	Potassium	Sulfur	Boron	

[a] The data in respect to other elements are rather confusing, some investigators claiming that certain ones are essential, while other workers fail to corroborate such findings.

Sodium, while apparently nonessential itself, seems at least partially to replace potassium as a plant nutrient. Sodium salts may, therefore, be used with some effect whenever a deficiency of potassium occurs. Several authors report marked increases in the growth of certain crops from the application of sodium salts. — See: Lehr, J. J., "The Importance of Sodium for Plant Nutrition: II. Effect on Beets of the Secondary Ions in Nitrate Fertilizers," Soil Sci., LII:373–379, 1941, and Harmer, Paul M., The Muck Soils of Michigan, Special Bulletin 314, Mich. State Agr. Exp. Sta., 1941.

Silicon, iodine, chlorine, fluorine, cobalt, strontium, and barium do not seem to be essential in any quantity, yet under certain conditions, they may increase crop yield. Their presence in plant tissue, often in appreciable amounts, thus may not be wholly without significance. Other elements may possess like relationships.

Two excellent reviews of the literature bearing on the subject are as follows:

Russell, E. J., Soil Conditions and Plant Growth, Longmans, Green and Company, New York, 1937, Chap. II, pp. 99–123.

Young, R. S., Certain Rarer Elements in Soils and Fertilizers, Memoir 174, Cornell Univ. Agr. Exp. Sta., 1935.

For a bibliography, see Willis, L. G., Bibliography of References to the Literature on the Minor Elements and Their Relation to the Science of Plant Nutrition, Chilean Nitrate Educational Bureau, Inc., New York, 1935. Also, First Supplement, 1940, Second Supplement, 1941, and Third Supplement, 1942.

[1] Even under natural conditions these elements sometimes occur in toxic amounts as is the case of manganese in some Hawaiian soils and zinc in New York peats. Zinc from smelter smoke is a good example of commercial contamination.

16. *Essential elements from air and water*

Higher plants obtain most of their carbon and oxygen directly from the air as photosynthesis and respiration proceed.[1] And their hydrogen is derived, either directly or indirectly, from the water of the soil. All of the other essential elements, except certain supplies of nitrogen acquired from the soil air indirectly by legumes,[2] are obtained from the soil solids.

It must not be inferred from this that the bulk of the plant tissue is synthesized from the soil nutrients. Quite the reverse is true. Ordinarily from 96 to 99.5 per cent of fresh plant tissue is made up of carbon, hydrogen, and oxygen, and only from 0.5 to perhaps 4.0 per cent is ash. In spite of this, it is the mineral elements of nutrition that usually limit crop development. Plant growth, except in cases of drought, cold weather, poor drainage, or disease, is not seriously retarded by a lack of carbon, hydrogen, and oxygen.[3] Hence the nutritional emphasis that is placed on the soil and the mineral elements that it supplies.

17. *Essential elements from the soil*

While all of the nutrient elements supplied by the soil must be present and available that plants may grow normally, six have received and are still receiving, except in certain cases,[4] the major

[1] In the process of photosynthesis, energy from the sun is able, in the presence of chlorophyll, to synthesize sugar from CO_2 and water, the former entering the plant through the stomata, the latter being absorbed from the soil. Formaldehyde and oxygen are thought to be intermediate products, the former probably being polymerized into hexose sugar. The synthesis may be indicated chemically as follows:

$$CO_2 + H_2O = H_2CO_3$$
$$H_2CO_3 + \text{energy (in presence of chlorophyll)} \rightarrow CH_2O + O_2$$
$$6\ CH_2O \rightarrow C_6H_{12}O_6$$

In respiration, synthesized food products are oxidized with the liberation of carbon dioxide and energy. In a very general way, this process is the reverse of photosynthesis.

$$C_6H_{12}O_6 + 6\ O_2 = 6\ CO_2 + 6\ H_2O + \text{energy}$$

[2] See page 384 for an explanation of this phase of nutrient acquisition.

[3] It is well to remember, however, that a serious lack of oxygen for roots may occur in heavy soils, especially if drainage is poor. This is an important factor in respect to the location of orchards, and is more critical than generally supposed.

[4] In some places the *trace* elements are temporarily critical but once the deficiency is met. the major fertilizer emphasis swings back again to the *primary* nutrients.

attention. They are *nitrogen, phosphorus, potassium, calcium, magnesium,* and *sulfur*. Because they are used by plants in relatively large amounts and because they are so commonly applied in commercial fertilizers, farm manure, and lime, they are sometimes designated for convenience as the *primary* elements. These elements may retard plant growth because they are actually lacking in the soil or because they become available too slowly. Often both limitations are operative. This is especially true in respect to phosphorus.

When nitrogen, phosphorus, and potassium are artificially supplied to the soil, they are usually added as farm manure or as commercial fertilizers. Therefore, they are often called *fertilizer* elements. In the same way calcium and magnesium are commonly applied as lime and are styled *lime* elements. Sulfur, other than that present in rain water, usually goes into the soil as an incidental ingredient of such fertilizers as farm manure, superphosphate, sulfate of ammonia, and sulfate of potash. Its addition, nevertheless, is very important in any scheme of fertility management. In special cases, sulfur is applied alone and in quantity as flowers of sulfur, either to correct nutritional deficiencies or to adjust the reaction of the soil.[1]

The other nutrient elements (iron, manganese, boron, copper, and zinc) are used by higher plants in but small amounts and as a consequence are sometimes called *trace* elements.[2] Such a designation does not mean that they are less essential than the so-called primary elements. In fact, such elements are fundamentally just as important. At present, some fertilizer manufacturers are placing small amounts of these elements in ordinary commercial fertilizers as an insurance against their possible lack or unavailability in the soil. This method, however, is too haphazard and random. If there is any serious deficiency, it usually is advisable to apply a salt of the limiting element separately to the soil as the amount necessary is generally greater than can be afforded in a commercial fertilizer designed essentially to supply nitrogen, phosphorus, and potassium.

[1] For instance, certain areas in eastern Washington and Oregon are notably deficient in sulfur if alfalfa is to be grown successfully. Sulfur, when it undergoes biological oxidation, develops sulfuric acid. This transformation is taken advantage of in the correction of alkali soils and in intensifying the acidity in soils for the growth of such plants as azaleas and rhododendrons that require a low pH.

[2] The terms *secondary, minor, micro,* and *rarer* are also used in referring to the elements used in such small amounts by plants.

Except for iron, trace elements are found sparingly in most soils.[1] Consequently, even though the removal by plants is small for any given season, the cumulative effects of crop production over a period of years is fast reducing the limited stores originally present. The so-called minor elements have become a major problem on many of the soils of the United States and deficiency symptoms once ascribed to other causes are now definitely known to be due to a lack of one or more of the trace elements.[2]

The probability of an actual nutrient deficiency, especially of the primary elements, occurring in a soil and the tendency for certain nutrients to be very slowly available, naturally raises three questions of great importance: (1) the amounts of the various primary elements present in mineral soils, (2) their forms of combination, and (3) the processes by which availability normally becomes possible. These phases will be considered in order.

18. *Amounts of the primary nutrient elements present in mineral soils*

Although soils vary greatly in chemical composition, it is possible to indicate the percentage range within which the primary nutrients are ordinarily found when a number of surface soils is considered (Table II).

Also, for the sake of brevity, an analysis may even be ventured for a

---

[1] The amounts of these trace elements in two New York soils are reported by Young as follows:

	Honeoye Silt Loam	Merrimac Coarse Sandy Loam
Manganese	0.0480%	0.0270%
Copper	0.0031	0.0008
Zinc	0.0010	Absent
Boron	Trace	Trace

Young, R. S., *Certain Rarer Elements in Soils and Fertilizers, and Their Role in Plant Growth,* Memoir 174, Cornell Univ. Agr. Exp. Sta., 1935.

Additional data as to manganese as well as figures regarding iron will be found on page 23.

[2] Copper, manganese, and zinc deficiencies are now of common occurrence in the citrus areas both in Florida and California. And with other crops growing on mineral soils, the lack of these nutrients, as well as of boron, is becoming more and more noticeable. A boron deficiency for apple trees, alfalfa, and cauliflower in eastern United States are cases in point. The situation on peat soils is just as urgent. Certain low moor soils of Florida respond to copper, manganese, and zinc, while a copper deficiency for lettuce and onions is common in New York peats.

For deficiency symptoms, see the following books: *Hunger Signs in Crops,* American Society of Agronomy, and the National Fertilizer Association, Washington, D. C., 1941. And *If They Could Speak,* Chilean Nitrate Educational Bureau, New York, 1941.

Table II. Amounts of the Important Constituents Present in Mineral Surface Soils

Constituents	Ranges in Percentages that Ordinarily May Be Expected	Representative Analyses			
		Humid Region Soil		Brown Aridic Soil	
		Percentage	Lb. to Acre Furrow-Slice	Percentage	Lb. to Acre Furrow-Slice [a]
Organic matter	0.40–10.00	4.00	80,000	3.25	65,000
Nitrogen (N₂)	0.02– 0.50	.15	3,000	.12	2,400
Phosphoric acid (P₂O₅)	0.02– 0.40	.10	2,000	.15	3,000
Potash (K₂O)	0.20– 4.00	2.00	40,000	2.40	48,000
Lime (CaO)	0.10– 5.00	.60	12,000	1.50	30,000
Magnesia (MgO)	0.20– 2.50	.50	10,000	1.00	20,000
Sulfur trioxide (SO₃)	0.02– 0.50	.10	2,000	.20	4,000

[a] The furrow-slice of a representative mineral soil is considered to contain approximately 2,000,000 pounds of dry earth to the acre.

representative humid temperate-region surface soil and for a brown aridic respectively. It must be remembered, however, that such figures do not belong to any particular soil, but present a very rough average of the data available. It is to be noted that aridic soils are in general higher in all-important constituents except organic matter and nitrogen. An exception, even to this, is found in the black earth soils (chernozems) of semiarid regions (see page 281).

It is evident that most surface soils [1] contain a considerable amount

[1] Below will be found complete analyses, expressed in percentage, of certain representative surface soils as presented by C. F. Marbut. For the complete set, see "Soils of the United States," *Atlas of American Agriculture*, Part III, U. S. Dept. of Agriculture, 1935.

Note the variations in composition, especially in respect to the lime. Only one sample, that from Nevada, contains carbonates. The ignition figure is not to be taken as an accurate measure of organic matter. It is usually too high.

Constituents	Norfolk Fine Sand, Florida	Sassafras Sandy Loam, Virginia	Ontario Loam, New York	Loam from Ely, Nevada	Hagerstown Silt Loam, Tennessee	Cascade Silt Loam, Oregon	Marshall Silt Loam, Iowa	Summit Clay from Kansas
SiO₂	91.49	85.96	76.54	61.69	73.11	70.40	72.63	71.60
TiO₂	0.50	0.59	0.64	0.47	1.05	1.08	0.63	0.81
Fe₂O₃	1.75	1.74	3.43	3.87	6.12	3.90	3.14	3.56
Al₂O₃	4.51	6.26	9.38	13.77	8.30	13.14	12.03	11.45
MnO	0.007	0.04	0.08	0.12	0.44	0.07	0.10	0.06
CaO	0.01	0.40	0.80	5.48	0.37	1.78	0.79	0.97
MgO	0.02	0.36	0.75	2.60	0.45	0.97	0.82	0.86
K₂O	0.16	1.54	1.95	2.90	0.91	2.11	2.23	2.42
Na₂O	Trace	0.58	1.04	1.47	0.20	1.98	1.36	1.04
P₂O₅	0.05	0.02	0.10	0.18	0.16	0.16	0.12	0.09
SO₃	0.05	0.07	0.08	0.12	0.07	0.21	0.12	0.11
Ignition	1.83	1.91	5.30	7.62	8.82	4.25	6.01	6.60
N	0.02	0.02	0.16	0.10	0.27	0.08	0.17	0.09

of organic matter. Yet this constituent is usually a critical factor due to its rapid oxidation and ready disappearance. Its inactivity is seldom serious except in very acid, very wet, or very dry soils. Nitrogen and especially phosphoric acid are always present in comparatively small amounts. While the nitrogen is generally rather readily

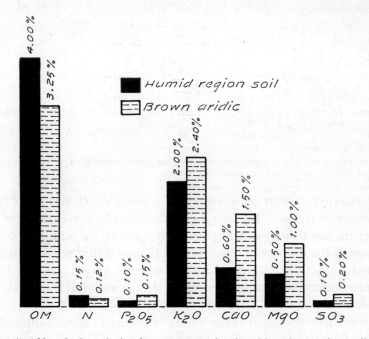

FIG. 4. Chemical analysis of a representative humid region surface soil and a brown aridic surface respectively. Note the relatively large amounts of organic matter and potash, the low percentages of nitrogen, phosphoric acid and sulfur, and the intermediate rating of the lime and magnesia. Typical aridic soils, other than chernozems, seem in general to be higher in all of the constituents mentioned except organic matter and nitrogen.

available since it is carried by the organic matter, the phosphoric acid is more or less insoluble and as a result is doubly critical as a nutrient element. In fact, when commercial fertilizers become necessary, phosphorus is generally the first element to be added. There are very few soils that are not somewhat deficient in this constituent.

Potash, in marked contrast to the phosphoric acid, is usually plentiful except in sandy lands. The main problem is one of availability. Lime shows great variations but it is generally present in lesser amounts than is potash. When it is lacking, soils tend to become acid. It is, therefore, generally added to correct this condition although the direct nutrient influence of calcium cannot be disregarded. Magnesium, besides its importance as a nutrient, functions in the soil much as does calcium. Although its deficiency in some soils has long been suspected, it has not, until recently, been considered especially critical since it is carried by most limestone and where liming is practiced, its lack often is automatically rectified. Now, however, it is considered as a major problem in certain areas in eastern United States.[1]

Sulfur, while usually no more plentiful than phosphoric acid, is more readily available since it is carried in large part by the organic matter. It becomes critical only under certain conditions. As already suggested the addition of sulfur in farm manure, rain water, and in fertilizers, tends in an automatic way to relieve a possible deficiency.

The above discussion seems to indicate that four constituents are likely to be critical especially in a humid region soil. Three — *organic matter, nitrogen,* and *calcium* — merit particular attention because of the comparatively small amounts present in and the ready loss from the average soil while one — *phosphorus* — faces a double handicap: an exceptionally small amount and a surprisingly low availability to higher plants. Even when phosphorus is added to the soil in a soluble condition, it becomes sluggish and slowly available because of certain complex reversions and adsorptions that tend to occur. It is not to be inferred from such generalizations, however, that potassium, magnesium, and sulfur may not be lacking in certain soils or that the problem of their supply may not at times be critical. The ever-increasing use of potash fertilizers, the demand for dolomitic limestone, and the emphasis placed on sulfur additions of various kinds are evidence of this.

19. *Forms in which the primary nutrient elements occur in soils*

An examination of a representative soil will soon reveal that in a general way the nutrient elements exist in two conditions: (1) complex and rather insoluble forms, and (2) simple compounds usually soluble

[1] Magnesium deficiency is especially prevalent in the citrus areas of Florida and its lack has been observed throughout the Atlantic seaboard trucking districts from Florida to Maine. Nor are deficiency symptoms absent on such crops as corn and small grains over much of eastern and central United States. Since magnesium is carried by the chlorophyll molecule, any lack is immediately registered by a characteristic chlorosis of the foliage of plants.

in the soil water and rather readily available to higher plants. Due to the chemical and biochemical processes at work in the soil, the general trend and the final disposition of the elements is, in part at least, from the complex to the simpler forms (see Table III). Thus the nutritional wants of higher plants are served as soil evolution progresses.

This does not mean, as a person might hastily assume, that the reverse process, that of synthesis and increased complexity, does not normally occur in soils. In fact, such reactions are continually taking place and in many cases are of tremendous practical importance. The building of elemental nitrogen, nitrates, and ammonium compounds into amino acids and proteins by microorganisms, the reversion of soluble phosphates to complex and insoluble forms, and the tying-up of iron, manganese, and zinc by a change in soil reaction are ample illustrations of such reversibility.

Since the simpler and more soluble constituents of soils, especially those of a humid region, readily disappear in drainage or are synthesized by microorganisms and higher plants, the greater proportion of each nutrient exists in the soil at any one time in a complex condition. From thence they gradually become available through various processes of simplification. The complex groups are thus a repository, the fertility of the soil depending not only on the total amounts of the various nutrients present but also on the ease with which transfer is made to simple and available forms. Such a situation indicates why a chemical analysis is likely to be of uncertain value in deciding what the fertilizer needs of a soil may be. The total amount of a nutrient may be determined with great accuracy but such a figure indicates little as to availability, the critical factor.

Usually the rapid decomposition of the soil organic matter allows nutrients held in this complex form to be released easily and made available for the use of higher plants. Practically all of the nitrogen and in some soils, a large proportion of the phosphorus [1] are held in organic combinations (see Table III). Since phosphorus in complex mineral forms is very slowly available, the advantage of the organic association is obvious. One of the important influences of the organic matter of the soil is to facilitate such rearrangements.

[1] Pearson and Simonson in a study of seven representative Iowa soils found that the proportion of the phosphorus in organic form ranged from 27 to 72 per cent of the total present. Pearson, R. W. and R. W. Simonson, "Organic Phosphorus in Seven Iowa Soil Profiles: Distribution and Amount as Compared to Organic Carbon and Nitrogen," *Proc. Soil Sci. Soc. Amer.*, IV:162–167, 1939.

Table III. Forms in Which the Primary Nutrient Elements Occur in Mineral Soils

I	II
The More Complex and Less Active Forms	*Some of the Simpler and More Available Forms and Their Ionic State*
Nitrogen	
Organic combinations; proteins, amino acids, and similar forms; colloidal and rather easily decomposed	Ammonium salts . . . . . NH_4^+ Nitrite salts . . . . . NO_2^- Nitrate salts . . . . . NO_3^-
Phosphorus	
Apatite, an original source Secondary Ca, Fe, Al phosphates Organic combinations	Phosphate of Ca, K, etc. . . $\left\{\begin{array}{l}PO_4^=\\ HPO_4^=\\ H_2PO_4^-\end{array}\right.$ Soluble organic forms
Potassium	
Original minerals such as feldspars and mica Complex secondary aluminum silicates Adsorbed by colloidal complex	Potassium salts, such as sulfates, carbonates, etc. . . . . . . K^+
Calcium	
Original minerals such as feldspars, hornblende, and calcite Secondary aluminum silicates Adsorbed by colloidal complex	A great variety of calcium salts . . Ca^{++}
Magnesium	
Minerals such as mica, hornblende, dolomite, and serpentine Secondary aluminum silicates Adsorbed by colloidal complex	Numerous salts of magnesium . . Mg^{++}
Sulfur	
Mineral combinations such as pyrite and especially as gypsum Organic forms; colloidal and rather easily decomposed	Various sulfates . . . . $SO_4^=$ and sulfites . . . . $SO_3^=$ of Ca, K, Mg, etc.

Most of the potassium and calcium exists in the soil in strictly mineral forms but with an important difference. A much larger amount, both actually and proportionately,[1] of the calcium is held in an easily replaceable condition by the colloidal complexes, both mineral and organic. As a result, the calcium is active in larger amounts and, therefore, is more readily available. It is, in fact, the most freely active metal in the soil. The potassium, on the other hand,

[1] In humid-region mineral soils, the amount of calcium in an exchangeable form is usually six or eight times greater than the potassium and three or four times greater than the magnesium. Moreover, as much as 40 per cent of the total calcium may be exchangeable while 2 per cent ordinarily is a high figure for potash and 10 per cent for magnesium. See page 73.

responds more slowly to processes of simple replacement. These relationships are reflected in the total amounts of these constituents in soil (see Table II) and in the frequent need of land for lime, due to the ready, and sometimes almost total loss of calcium in drainage. Thus the potash problem usually is that of slow availability; that of lime, actual deficiency.

While much of the magnesium exists in the soil in such a condition as to limit its rate of transfer to the soil solution, it is more mobile than the potassium. This is partially due to the greater proportion held as a replaceable ion by the colloidal complexes. In some degree, therefore, it functions as does the calcium but less freely.

While sulfur is held in both mineral and organic forms (see Table III), the latter combinations tend to predominate in humid-region soils, especially if the soil organic matter is properly maintained. Sulfur thus becomes available rather readily as the organic matter decomposes. Its transfer, when present in such soils in sufficient quantity, seldom, if ever, gives trouble. In aridic soils considerable sulfur may occur in the sulfate form as well as in organic combination. Such inorganic sulfur is usually present as gypsum.

20. *The transfer of plant nutrients to available forms*

The soil is such a complex body that it is impossible, at least at this point, to picture in any detail the various changes that normally occur. The discussion that follows can only indicate in a very general way some of the more important transformations, especially as they affect the availability of the elements that may be limiting factors in plant growth. The productivity of the soil, of course, depends on the trend of these reactions.

Since the soil nitrogen is an essential constituent of the organic matter, the decomposition of the latter must take place in order that the former may appear in simple forms. This decomposition is a biochemical process, very complex, especially in its early stages, and is accompanied by the evolution of much carbon dioxide. The nitrogen finally emerges as an ammonium compound and, if conditions are favorable, it is oxidized to the nitrite and finally to the nitrate form (see Table III). The two latter changes are spoken of as nitrification and are brought about by two special-purpose bacteria. Since much of the nitrogen utilized by higher plants is absorbed in the nitrate and ammonium forms, the importance of these processes is obvious. The transformations [1] may be outlined in a simple way as follows:

Organic nitrogen → Ammonium → Nitrite → Nitrate
(proteins, amino-   Salts   Salts   Salts
acid, etc.) NH_4^+ NO_2^- NO_3^-

$\underbrace{}$ $\underbrace{}$
Decomposition and   Nitrification
ammonification

Since the above transformations are largely due to the activity of bacteria and fungi, they are influenced profoundly by soil conditions. When the soil is cold or waterlogged, these biochemical changes do not progress rapidly. Again the lack of active lime, allowing the soil to become acid, retards the processes. The nitrifying organisms are especially susceptible to both conditions.

When organic matter with a large amount of carbon in proportion to the nitrogen present is added to a soil, the above process is not only retarded but may readily be reversed temporarily. The soil micro-organisms having large amounts of energy-producing materials at their disposal, multiply rapidly and use the nitrogen themselves, thus interfering with its simplification and appearance as ammonium and nitrates. In such cases, the soil flora is competing directly with the higher plants.[2] It must be concluded, therefore, that the simplifica-tion of the nitrogen is not always easy, rapid, or in proportion to the amounts present. This must, of course, be taken into consideration in the practical management of any soil.

When the phosphorus is held in organic combination, decay will greatly encourage its simplification. The mineral phosphorus, how-ever, presents a much more difficult problem. The various soil phos-phates are usually rather insoluble,[3] and even when the normal solvent agent, carbon dioxide, is supplied in large amounts, the rate of solu-tion is slow. The situation is made still more difficult by the small amounts of the element present. A simple example illustrative of the influence of carbon dioxide and water is given below, tricalcium phos-phate [4] tentatively representing the insoluble soil phosphates:

[1] Further information regarding decomposition, ammonification, and nitrification will be found on pages 371–380.

[2] A full discussion of the nitrogen-carbon ratio and its practical significance will be found on pages 133–136.

[3] For a statement regarding the various soil phosphates and their relative availability, see page 302.

[4] It is questionable whether the simple tricalcium phosphate ($Ca_3(PO_4)_2$) actually exists in soils. It is used here merely in an illustrative way.

$$Ca_3(PO_4)_2 + 4\,H_2O + 4\,CO_2 = CaH_4(PO_4)_2 + 2\,Ca(HCO_3)_2$$

Insoluble phosphate   Water-soluble phosphate   Soluble calcium bicarbonate

Plant rootlets by their contact and possibly by means of certain exudates seem to encourage the transfer illustrated above. They may force a solution and availability that might otherwise be almost negligible. Thus a soil may be able to supply a crop with appreciable quantities of phosphorus, and yet when uncropped its solution and drainage water may contain very small amounts of this element.

It should also be emphasized that this transfer, like that of the nitrogen, is reversible. Microorganisms may appropriate simple and soluble phosphorus compounds and build them up into complex organic forms. Again the addition to soil of such soluble compounds as $CaH_4(PO_4)_2$ and $NH_4H_2PO_4$ is usually attended by adsorption or a reversion to insoluble calcium phosphates or to the equally complex and insoluble iron and aluminum combinations.

The potassium and calcium, held largely in mineral forms, must also succumb to the solvent action of water charged with carbon dioxide if they are to be reduced to simple compounds. There is this difference, however. Much of the former is released from a molecular combination with the soil minerals. A large proportion of the calcium, on the other hand, is freed from the adsorptive colloidal surfaces by simple exchange. The reactions that follow illustrate the processes, a potash feldspar representing the complex groups of which the potassium is an integral part. The colloidal and easily replaceable combinations of the calcium are indicated by a generalized formula that symbolizes the adsorbed condition in which much of it exists in soils.

$$2\,KAlSi_3O_8 + CO_2 + 2\,H_2O = H_4Al_2Si_2O_9 + K_2CO_3 + 4\,SiO_2$$

Microcline feldspar   Hydrated silicate   Soluble carbonate

$$Ca\left(\begin{array}{c}\text{Colloidal}\\\text{surface}\end{array}\right) + 2\,H_2CO_3 = H_2\left(\begin{array}{c}\text{Colloidal}\\\text{surface}\end{array}\right) + Ca(HCO_3)_2$$

Replaceable calcium   Carbonic acid   Hydrogen colloid   Soluble bicarbonate

The transfer of much of the potassium is one of solution after water and carbon dioxide have produced soluble potassium compounds. A great deal of the calcium becomes mobile, however, by a simple exchange of hydrogen ions for those of calcium. This replacement, or *ionic exchange* as it is called, takes place with surprising ease and rapidity and undoubtedly is one of the most important types of reactions occurring in soils.[1] Because of this situation, soils, although containing in general considerably more potassium than calcium (see Table II), liberate the latter element much more lavishly. This has a direct bearing on calcium nutrition, soil acidity, liming, and other practical questions.[2]

Since magnesium is held in the soil in much the same condition as is calcium, the exchange reaction cited for the latter shows how the magnesium, at least in part, is released to the soil solution. However, some of the magnesium no doubt comes directly from the soil minerals by hydrolysis, just as does the potassium. Hence the illustrations cited for the transfer of potassium and calcium will serve for magnesium also. It is only necessary to visualize the formation and solution of magnesium bicarbonate by hydrolysis and carbonation in one case and by ionic exchange in the other. As to activity, magnesium seems to rival potassium but is much less mobile than is calcium.

As in the case of the nitrogen, the sulfur transformations are largely biological. They go on readily in most soils and while probably subject to marked retardation at times, such influences are apparently not serious practically as in the case of the nitrogen. The transformations may be indicated in a general way as follows:

Organic sulfur $\longrightarrow$ Decay products $\longrightarrow$ Sulfites $\longrightarrow$ Sulfates
Proteins and   Of which H_2S $SO_3^=$ $SO_4^=$
other organic   and S_2 are
combinations   simple forms

$\underbrace{\hspace{4cm}}$ $\underbrace{\hspace{4cm}}$
Decomposition of organic matter   Sulfur oxidation

The last stage, sulfur oxidation,[3] is, like nitrification, brought about largely by certain types of bacteria. The sulfate compounds that result (see Table III) are the source of most of the sulfur acquired by higher plants.

[1] For a more detailed consideration of ionic exchange, see page 78.

[2] It should be mentioned at this point that the colloidal complex of the soil carries other cations besides calcium and hydrogen in a replaceable condition. Magnesium, potassium, ammonium, sodium, and other ions are present in minor amounts. Consequently, potassium probably becomes available in some degree by ionic exchange. Conversely, considerable calcium is present in forms other than those recognized as exchangeable. Appreciable hydrolysis and carbonation of the lime thus held is inevitable. Hence the distinctions drawn above in respect to the transfer of calcium and potassium are by no means clean-cut.

[3] More information regarding sulfur oxidation may be found on page 127.

Just as in the case of nitrogen and phosphorus, the processes resulting in the simplification of potassium, calcium, magnesium, and sulfur compounds are easily reversible. Thus when soluble compounds of potassium, calcium, or magnesium are added to a soil, the colloidal matter adsorbs and withdraws from solution large quantities of such metallic ions. Again, soil organisms, especially bacteria and fungi, utilize sulfur as well as the metals already mentioned. Their synthetic activities are excellent examples of a practical reversal of the simplifying processes. Such transpositions while they temporarily compete with higher plants, tend to conserve nutrients by reducing the loss of valuable constituents in drainage water.

21. *More about the soil solution — its pH*

It has already been emphasized (see section 9) that the soil solution exists in a state of minute subdivision and dispersion. Moreover, it is differentially adsorbed by the colloidal surfaces, part being held tightly and having little movement, while some suffers but slight restraint and circulates more or less freely. Again the soil solution is exceedingly changeable, varying as to the gross amount present in any soil, as to total concentration of dissolved salts, as well as to the amount and proportion of specific constituents.

If the moisture fluctuation in a humid-region mineral soil is of sufficient range, a variation from a few parts per million, say 100, to possibly 30,000 parts a million in the concentration of the soil solution seems quite possible in certain cases. But because of the heterogeneity of the solution and its constant fluctuation, it is impossible to suggest an average or normal concentration. Perhaps under ordinary conditions the acre-furrow-slice of an arable humid-region mineral soil contains from 1000 to 2000 pounds of soluble salts.

In arid and semiarid regions, the soil solution is usually much more concentrated than where the rainfall is heavier, so much so as to interfere at times with the growth of plants. An excess of soluble salts is called *alkali*. The presence of even 0.5 per cent of total soluble salts is considered serious. This would mean about 10,000 pounds to the acre-furrow-slice.

Another point of importance in respect to the soil solution is its reaction — that is, whether it is *acid, neutral,* or *alkaline.* Without considering at this time the conditions controlling soil reaction (see page

290), it suffices to say that some soil solutions possess a preponderance of H over OH ions and, therefore, are acid. Some, on the other hand, show the reverse and are alkaline, while others having an equal concentration of H and OH ions, are neutral. The exact relationship in any particular case is usually evaluated in terms of H-ion concentration and expressed logarithmically in pH values. Soil acidity, therefore, is an H-ion concentration of the soil solution and the pH is less than 7. In contrast, soil alkalinity refers to an OH-ion concentration of the solution and is at a pH above 7.[1]

In expressing the reaction of a soil solution in terms of H-ion concentration, that is as pH, two things should not be overlooked. First, only a part of the soil water functions as a true soil solution. Some (the hygroscopic) is held so tightly at the solid-liquid interfaces that it is largely in an inactive condition (see page 157). On the other hand, some (the gravitational) is subject ordinarily to rapid removal by drainage. Consequently pH has to do only with that part of the soil water existing in a liquid condition and yet retained strongly enough to resist removal by gravity flow (see page 158).

Second, it is not to be inferred that we are dealing with a homogeneous distribution of the H and OH ions. It has already been emphasized (page 12) that the soil solution is heterogeneous as to its

---

[1] If the reader is not definitely familiar with pH values, it would be well to consult a good textbook on chemistry rather than grope through this and subsequent discussions with but a vague idea as to the real significance of this much-used terminology.

Since the pH value of a solution is the logarithm of the reciprocal of the H-ion concentration, it may be stated conveniently as follows:

$$pH = \log \frac{1}{[H^+]}$$

The small p indicates that the values are logarithmic while the capital H is a reminder that the hydrogen ion concentration is being measured.

It should always be remembered that pH values are logarithmic and that several disadvantages are encountered in their use as follows:

1. As the H-ion concentration increases, the pH values decrease and vice versa.

2. The change in H-ion concentration is geometric and not arithmetic since there are 9 acid units between pH 6 and 7, 90 between pH 5 and 6, and 900 between pH 4 and 5, and so on.

3. Alkalinity is expressed in terms of H-ion concentration, a pH greater than 7 indicating an alkaline reaction.

4. The system conflicts with our mental habits since most thinking is usually along the lines of arithmetic rather than geometric progression.

In spite of these objections, the use of the pH values is highly desirable because of their linear relationships to the voltage readings of the potentiometer, because they afford a simple figure indicative of the H-ion concentration, and because a tremendous range in H-ion concentration may be expressed within logarithmic limits that admit of easy diagrammatic representation.

solutes. And since H ions usually are adsorbed by soils to a greater degree than are the OH ions, a similar heterogeneity is bound to exist. Therefore, one is prepared to visualize the H ions as being especially concentrated at and near the colloidal interfaces and as becoming less numerous as the outer portions of the films are approached. Since the OH ions vary in numbers inversely with the H ions, this makes for a higher pH in the outer zones. As a result, the

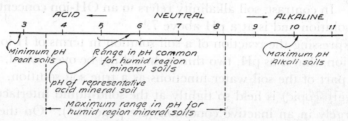

FIG. 5. Diagram showing the maximum range of pH of humid region mineral surface soils, the range commonly found, and the pH of the representative mineral surface soil of temperate humid regions. The maximum alkalinity for alkali soils is also indicated as well as the minimum pH likely to be encountered in acid surface peats.

drainage water from even a markedly acid soil may be only slightly acid or even neutral or alkaline due to this inverse heterogeneity in respect to H and OH ions. Such a situation has many nutritional consequences in respect both to microorganisms and higher plants.

From the practical standpoint, it is often necessary to interpret the pH of the soil solution in general and comparative terms. The following table will be found helpful, not only in this respect, but also in appreciating the range in pH that ordinarily can be expected in soils:

Very alkaline	above 8.0	Moderately acid	5.5–5.9
Alkaline	7.4–8.0	Strongly acid	5.0–5.4
Neutral or nearly so	6.6–7.3	Very strongly acid	4.3–4.9
Slightly acid	6.0–6.5	Extremely acid	below 4.3

When soils over wide areas are examined, the maximum range in pH is found to be rather great. The most acid mineral soils may show a pH, determined by the usual potentiometer method, as low as 3.5, although a pH of 4 is more usual. Some peats, however, may in extreme cases be as acid as pH 3. The maximum pH for both mineral and organic soils is generally somewhere near 8 or even considerably above in aridic soils especially if they contain sodium carbonate. However, the range in pH, within which most soils fall, is commonly considered to lie between 5 and 7.   The average pH value for representative mineral soils of humid-temperate regions probably is near 5.8.   (See Fig. 5.)

22. *The nutrient elements as solutes*

It now remains to follow the nutrient elements into this surprisingly dynamic biological medium, the soil solution.   Many of the salts projected into it by the processes already discussed are those of high ionization.[1]   As a consequence, the soil solution, especially that of a humid region, is definitely ionic, the degree depending in part on the concentration.   When the solution is dilute, a considerable proportion of the soluble constituents are present as ions.   As the solution becomes more concentrated, during a dry spell for example, the proportion of the soluble substances in molecular association tends to increase.   This same condition, but much accentuated, holds true for arid-region soils also.

The soil nutrients are thus presented to the plant both in ionic and molecular forms, the proportions depending on conditions.   In an arable soil, especially that of a humid region, the ionic intake is thought to predominate, not only because of the nature of the soil solution, but also probably because of the greater ease with which the ions penetrate the absorbing tissues.   Knowing the soluble salts that commonly enter the soil water, it is easy to list the nutrient ions that are brought in contact with the absorbing tissues of microorganisms and higher plants.   They may be tabulated as follows:

Nitrogen	NH_4^+, NO_2^-, NO_3^-	Calcium	Ca^{++}
Phosphorus	$PO_4^=$, $HPO_4^=$, $H_2PO_4^-$	Magnesium	Mg^{++}
Potassium	K^+	Sulfur	$SO_3^=$, $SO_4^=$
Iron	Fe^{++}, Fe^{+++}	Zinc	Zn^{++}
Manganese	Mn^{++}, Mn^{++++}	Boron	$BO_3^=$
Copper	Cu^+, Cu^{++}		
Carbon	$CO_3^=$, HCO_3^-	Water	H^+, OH^-

Certain explanations should be made regarding the use by plants of certain ions.   Those carrying nitrogen, phosphorus, and sulfur will

---

[1] According to the theory of electrolytic dissociation, many compounds when in solution break up into electrically charged portions called *ions*.   Ions may be single atoms or groups of atoms.   For instance, KCl dissociates into K^+ and Cl^- ions while $NaNO_3$ yields Na^+ and NO_3^-.   Many electrolytes when in dilute concentration ionize almost completely.   The degree of dissociation is in general greater for inorganic salts than for those organic.

be considered first. Most of the nitrogen apparently is absorbed in ammoniacal and nitrate forms, depending on the condition of the soil, the kind of plant, and its stage of growth. In general, the presence of both ions seems most favorable. When nitrification is active, nitrites are oxidized so readily to the nitrate form or are disposed of in other ways that little can accumulate. This is fortunate as any concentration of nitrite nitrogen is likely to be toxic. Here, then, is a very important ion but one that does not function to any extent directly as a nutrient.

The particular phosphate ion presented to higher plants seems to be determined to a considerable extent by the pH of the soil. When the latter is distinctly alkaline, the PO_4 ion apparently predominates in the soil solution. This form is utilized least readily by crops. As the pH is lowered and the soil becomes slightly to moderately acid, the HPO_4 and H_2PO_4 ions prevail, while at high acidities the phosphorus, if soluble at all, is present largely as H_2PO_4. These two forms are considered to be readily absorbed by higher plants. It is rather surprising that soluble organic forms of phosphorus, although they seem to predominate in many soil solutions,[1] cannot be used to any extent directly by higher plants but must undergo mineralization and appear in the ionic forms already indicated before appreciable utilization takes place.

The intake of sulfur by higher plants apparently is largely as the SO_4 ion. This is the final product and if sulfur oxidation is vigorous, little $SO_3^=$ can at any time accumulate. The situation in some respects resembles that already cited regarding nitrite nitrogen.

Little need be said at this point regarding potassium, calcium, magnesium, zinc, and boron as they occur in the soil solution mostly as a single ion, respectively. But iron, manganese, and copper are in a little different category. The oxidation-reduction condition of the soil is a factor here. If the soil is well aerated, the higher ion in each case tends to predominate. But if drainage is poor, reduction may dominate and the ionic condition of the soil solution in respect to the nutrients mentioned, changes.[2] Thus aeration, especially in the sub-

[1] Pierre, W. H., and F. W. Parker, "Soil Phosphorus Studies: II. The Concentration of Organic and Inorganic Phosphorus in the Soil Solution and Soil Extracts and the Availability of the Organic Phosphorus to Plants," *Soil Sci.*, XXIV: 119–128, 1927.

[2] Ignatieff conceives a dynamic equilibrium between ferric (Fe^{+++}) and ferrous (Fe^{++}) iron in the soil, with the former dominating when good aeration prevails. Under waterlogged conditions, the relationship is reversed. The ferrous iron probably enters the colloidal complex more readily than the ferric iron and apparently is more soluble and

soil, is of tremendous nutritive importance in an indirect way as well as through the direct influence of oxygen upon microorganisms and the roots of higher plants.

The carbon dioxide of the atmosphere in its photosynthetic role is the direct source of most of the carbon acquired by higher plants, but not of all. In the soil solution carbonates and bicarbonates occur in abundance, which, when dissociation occurs, develop CO_3 and HCO_3 ions. If these are absorbed by higher plants, and there seems no reason why they should not be, carbon might be thus acquired. In fact, at times a considerable amount of carbon probably enters the plant directly from the soil.[1]

While most of the water absorbed by higher plants goes to offset transpiration losses (see page 179), some is used to satisfy the nutritional needs for hydrogen and probably to a certain extent for oxygen also. Since water under all conditions is somewhat dissociated into H and OH ions, these are presented to the absorbing root surfaces along with the large molecules of water, although in infinitely lesser numbers. This bilateral situation is of great significance in its relationship to plant nutrition. Not only do H and OH ions penetrate the absorbing membranes of microorganisms and higher plants but they also, by their relative proportions one to the other, determine soil pH. In practice, soil reaction is deemed of such importance that the pH is usually one of the factors considered in making a soil fertility decision.

23. *The nutritional importance of soil pH*

To strengthen the inferences respecting the nutritional importance of soil pH illustrations are in order. H ions seem to have considerable influence not only upon (1) the solubility but also upon (2) the facility with which nutrients, even when readily soluble, are absorbed and used by plants. Iron, manganese, and zinc are excellent examples of the first relationship, as they tend to become less and less soluble as the pH rises towards 8. Almost all nutrients appear in the second category, their absorption and utilization, after they become

available. Ignatieff, V., "Determination and Behavior of Ferrous Iron in Soils," *Soil Sci.*, LI: 249–263, 1941.

[1] Livingston, B. E., and Ruth Beal, "The Soil as a Direct Source of Carbon Dioxide," *Plant Physiol.*, IX:237–259, 1934. These authors estimate that, under certain conditions, plants may obtain as much as 5 per cent of their carbon from the soil.

soluble, being in some degree conditioned by the H-ion concentration of the soil solution. The influence upon the utilization of nitrate and ammoniacal nitrogen by plants is an excellent illustration of this. At a pH above 6, ammonium salts are thought to be utilized the more readily. But in moderately to strongly acid soils, nitrates apparently are absorbed with greater ease.[1]

The case of phosphorus in respect to pH is especially interesting. While it is never readily soluble in the soil, it seems to be held with less tenacity in a pH range centering between 5.6 and 6.5 (see page 303). Here most plants seem to be able to extract it from the soil with least difficulty. Moreover, at this pH, as already suggested, the ions presented are mostly $H_2PO_4^-$ and $HPO_4^=$, which seem to be easily and readily utilized by plants. Since the illustrations cited are only a few of the ways in which H and OH ions function physiologically in soils, it is easy to see why so much importance is placed on pH in the diagnosis of fertility problems.

24. Soil and plant interrelations

It might hastily be assumed from what has been said regarding the transfer of nutrients that their solubility and availability are due entirely to a series of soil phenomena, the plant simply absorbing in a

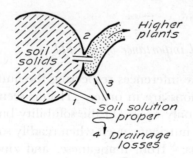

FIG. 6. Diagram suggestive of the (1) interchange between the soil solids (colloidal and non-colloidal) and the soil solution proper, (2) movements of constituents to and from the plant root surfaces within the zone of colloidal influence (contact zone), and (3) interchange between the free soil solution and the absorbing surfaces of plant root systems. The loss of nutrients in drainage (4) is from the freer portion of the soil solution.

[1] See Tiedjins, V. T., "Factors Affecting Accumulation of Ammonia and Nitrate Nitrogen, Particularly in Tomato and Apple," *Plant Physiol.*, IX: 31–57, 1934.

passive sort of way that which is presented. Such, however, is probably not the case. The rootlets and root hairs are in most instances in very intimate contact with the soil colloidal surfaces. In fact, the relationship is so close that nutrients are thought to pass from the soil solids to the plant without leaving the sphere of colloidal influence.[1] The nutrients thus appropriated are soluble but have not appeared in the soil solution as free, unadsorbed migrating ions or molecules (Fig. 6). By intimate contact, plants may acquire nutrients before they have a chance to enter the soil solution proper and suffer loss by drainage.[2] A solubility and availability may thus be encouraged that otherwise might not take place so readily.

This contact effect apparently is much accentuated by root exudates and by microbial activity in the immediate neighborhood of the absorbing surfaces. Plant roots not only give off large amounts of CO_2 but possibly other acids as well. These, functioning at the soil-plant interfaces, no doubt speed up interchange to a remarkable degree. Also organic matter is continually being sloughed off by plant roots, thus providing food and energy for microorganisms. The concentration of microbial activity within the rhizosphere is ample proof of this.[3] Such biochemical phenomena cannot fail to increase greatly the rate and ease of transfer of nutrients from soil to plant.

From this, it appears that the relationship between plant roots and the soil is very close — so close in fact that plants participate, directly and indirectly, in the transfer of nutrients from an unavailable to a soluble and available condition. Moreover, the flow of nutrients is

[1] See Jenny, H., and R. Overstreet, "Cation Interchange between Plant Roots and Soil Colloids," *Soil Sci.*, XLVII:257–272, 1939.

[2] This postulates two interdependent phases of the soil solution: (1) that of the contact zones, rather small in volume and (2) that external thereto. The latter is much greater in amount and its solutes are much less influenced by the colloidal complexes. A nutrient present in the contact zones is soluble but does not function as freely as though present in the soil solution proper. It is not subject to loss in drainage unless dislodged in some way. Chapman, H. D., "Absorption of Iron from Finely Ground Magnetite by Citrus Seedlings," *Soil Sci.*, XLVIII:309–313, 1939.

[3] Starkey, for instance, has clearly demonstrated the localization of microorganisms around rootlets and root hairs. While bacteria and actinomyces seem to dominate, fungi were also present in appreciable numbers. The organisms were by no means confined to dead roots but were very numerous on the surfaces of living ones as well, possibly because of excretions suitable as microbial food. Starkey, R. L., "Some Influence of the Development of Higher Plants upon the Micro-Organisms in the Soil, VI. Microscopic Examination of the Rhizosphere," *Soil Sci.*, XLV:207–227, 1938. See also Timonin, M. I., "The Interaction of Higher Plants and Soil Micro-organisms, I. Microbial Population of Rhizosphere of Seedlings of Certain Cultivated Plants," *Can. Jour. Res.* (c), XVIII:307–317, 1940.

not wholly in one direction. Just as constituents by precipitation and adsorption pass from a soluble to an insoluble condition within the soil itself, so nutrients are passing from plant roots back into the soil as well as in the opposite direction. These facts serve to emphasize the intricacy of the soil-plant relationship as well as to indicate clearly that a plant growing on a soil is an integral part, for the time being, of the complex biocolloidal system.

25. *Soil fertility inferences*

Certain practical conclusions are inescapable in respect to the plant nutrient relationships just presented. An adequate supply of each nutrient must be maintained in the soil. In addition, provision must be made for a rate of availability suitable to normal crop growth. This involves a more or less complex transfer to the soil solution and to the plant, the latter seeming to participate in ways other than those of mere absorption. Moreover, an adequate nutrient proportion is requisite, the total concentration of available nutrients being vital. Such a balance tends to ensure the desirable physiological conditions necessary for successful plant production. The pH of the soil solution, since it influences profoundly many of the important soil processes, plays a critical role in such an adjustment. Soil management, to be successful, must deal with all of these phases.

Chapter III. Some Important Physical Properties
of Mineral Soils

Physically, a mineral soil is a porous aggregate of inorganic particles with an admixture of decaying organic matter in varying amounts. The larger fragments are imbedded in and coated over with colloidal gels and other materials in a fine state of subdivision. In some cases large mineral particles predominate and a gravelly or sandy soil results. In other cases, the mineral colloidal gels are in such amounts as to give the soil clayey characteristics. All gradations between these extremes are found in nature. The colloidal organic matter, in proportion to its amount and activity, leavens the mass, imparting physical properties and biochemical attributes that have much to do with its capacity to support higher plants.

The mineral particles of a soil range in size from those easily discernible with the naked eye (stone, gravel, and sand) to those even below the range of the electron-microscope (colloidal complexes). As already indicated (see pages 9–10), they impart their properties to the soil mass and, according to their proportions, determine in large degree the physical nature of the soil. In discussing the size or sizes of these mineral particles, the term *texture* is commonly used. Thus the texture of a particular soil may be coarse, medium, fine, or very fine depending on the group or groups of particles that dominate.

In the time covered by a generation of man, the soil processes, while surprisingly active, do not alter appreciably the size of these mineral particles. Thus a sand remains a sand and a clay a clay. However, this does not prevent a change in the intensity of the physical properties of a soil or in the effectiveness of its biochemical activities. The addition of organic matter, for example, may have such an influence on the properties both of a sand and a clay as to alter profoundly their mechanical and nutrient relationships to higher plants. Again the downward movement of some of the clay particles,

41

especially from the surface layers into the subsoil, may noticeably modify the physical nature of the profile, especially in respect to the rapidity of drainage and the degree of aeration.

26. *Classification of soil particles and mechanical analysis*

In order that the mineral particles of a soil, which vary so widely in size, may be studied successfully, they must be separated into convenient groups. The various groups are spoken of as *separates*. While such a classification is arbitrary, it must meet certain requirements. It must be simple, short, and capable of throwing some light on the physical properties of the soil mass. Moreover, it must lend itself to an actual separation and percentage evaluation. This analytical procedure is called a *mechanical analysis*.

As might be expected, a number of different classifications have been devised, depending on the methods of separation employed and on the uses which the investigators desired to make of the results. Two of the most important will be cited, that established by the United States Department of Agriculture and that more recently advanced by the International Society of Soil Science. They will be found in Tables IV and V respectively with representative mechanical analyses.[1]

Table IV. The Classification of Soil Particles as Established by the United States Department of Agriculture.[2] The Mechanical Analyses of Three Soils Are also Given

Separate	Diameter Limits, mm.	Sandy Loam, Per Cent	Loam, Per Cent	Clay, Per Cent
1. Fine gravel	2–1	3.1	4.3	0.0
2. Coarse sand	1–0.5	10.5	6.0	0.3
3. Medium sand	0.50–0.25	8.2	4.5	0.4
4. Fine sand	0.25–0.10	25.3	11.7	3.0
5. Very fine sand	0.10–0.05	22.0	13.2	9.8
6. Silt [a]	0.05–0.002	21.1	43.2	38.0
7. Clay	below 0.002	9.8	17.1	48.5

[a] Previous to 1938 the silt range was .05–.005. This must be kept in mind in dealing with mechanical analyses made before that date.

[1] Shaw has compared the two methods, checking them especially with regard to their use in deciding the class names of soils. He finds it difficult to harmonize results obtained in the two ways. Shaw, C. F., "Field Textures and Physical Composition Determined by Two Methods of Mechanical Analysis," *Trans. Third Internat. Cong. Soil Sci.*, I: 42–46, Oxford, Eng., 1935.

[2] Briggs, L. J., et. al., *The Centrifugal Method of Soil Analysis*. Bulletin 24, Bureau of Soils, U. S. Dept. of Agriculture, 1904.

In the first column of each table are given the names of the various separates, and in the second the range in size of each group. Columns three, four, and five show the percentages of each separate in three very different specimen soils, a sandy loam, a loam, and a clay. In order to obtain such figures, a sample of the dry soil must actually be separated into the arbitrary groups and the percentage of each group in respect to the whole soil calculated from the dry weights

Table V. The Classification of Soil Particles as Established by the International Society of Soil Science.[1] The Mechanical Analysis of Three Soils Are also Given.[2]

Separate	Diameter Limits, mm.	Sandy Loam Shropshire, Per Cent	Loam Anglesey, Per Cent	Heavy Clay, Czechoslovakia, Per Cent
Coarse sand	2.00–0.20	66.6	27.1	0.9
Fine sand	0.20–0.02	17.8	30.3	7.1
Silt	0.02–0.002	5.6	20.2	21.4
Clay	below 0.002	8.5	19.3	65.8

obtained. This operation is the mechanical analysis already mentioned.[3]

Stone and large gravel, while they figure in the practical examination and evaluation of a field soil, do not enter into the analysis of the fine earth. Their amounts are usually rated separately. The organic matter, comparatively small in quantity, is distributed more or less proportionately through the groups. The percentage of total organic matter, however, is sometimes quoted with the mechanical analysis as it throws additional light on the physical nature of the soil in question. The percentage of calcium carbonate, if this salt is present, may also be given.

[1] Based on Atterberg. Atterberg, A., "Die Mechanische Bodenanalyse und die Klassifikation der Mineralboden Schwedens," *Internat. Mitt. für Bodenkunde*, II:312–342, 1912.

Schucht, F., "Uber die Sitzung der Internationalen Kommission für die Mechanische und Physikalische Bodenundersuchung in Berlin am 31, October, 1913," *Internat. Mitt. für Bodenkunde*, IV:1–31, 1914.

[2] Robinson, G. W., *Soils, Their Origin, Constitution, and Classification*, Thomas Murby & Co., London, 1936, p. 15.

[3] The principle involved in the method is simple. When soil particles are suspended in water, they tend to sink and the rapidity of settling is proportional to their size. The suspension of a sample of soil is, therefore, the first step; the second step is subsidence and the withdrawal by some means of successive grades; and the third step is the determination of the percentage of each group of particles based on the original sample.

The apparatus and technique are rather complicated. For methods used in the United States, see Fletcher, C. C. and H. Bryan, *Modifications of the Method of Soil Analysis*, Bulletin 84, Bureau of Soils, U. S. Dept. of Agriculture, 1912; Bouyoucos, G. J., "The Hydrometer Method for Studying Soils," *Soil Sci.*, XXV: 365–369, 1928; and Olmstead, L. B., L. T. Alexander, and H. E. Middleton, *A Pipette Method of Mechanical Analysis of Soils Based on Improved Dispersion Procedure*, Technical Bulletin 170, U. S. Dept. of Agriculture, 1930.

The gravel and sand, when dominant in a soil, give properties known to everyone as *sandy*, while if the soil is made up largely of silt and clay, its plasticity and stickiness indicate that it is clayey in nature. The characteristics of the soils of Tables IV and V may be inferred readily from their mechanical analyses.

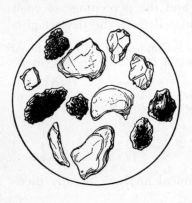

FIG. 7. Sand grains from soil. Note that the particles are irregular as to size and shape. While quartz usually predominates, other minerals may also occur. The particles are often iron stained or coated with organic material.

Not only is a mechanical analysis valuable in picturing in a general way the physical properties of a soil but it is also of use in deciding as to the textural name — that is, whether a soil is a sand, sandy loam, loam, etc. This phase is considered in section 29.

The classifications and separations, as outlined above, are open to one rather serious criticism. They do not indicate with any accuracy the amount or particularly the nature of the colloidal substances present. Since matter in this state of aggregation is the most active portion of the soil, both physically and chemically, the objection is well founded. An examination of the soil separates will soon show that not all of the colloidal matter is carried by the group designated as *clay*. Some is found in the silt group as the plasticity, cohesion, adsorption, and catalytic capacity of this separate testify. In fact, a silt particle in nature probably consists of a core of original or secondary mineral surrounded by a viscous and gelatinous coating.

27. *The physical nature of the soil separates* [1]

Stone, gravel, and sand, because of their sizes, function as separate particles. They are irregular in shape and often rounded, the continual rubbing that they have received being sufficient in many cases to have effaced their angularity. When free of clay and silt, they exhibit very low plasticity and cohesion, and as a consequence, are

---

[1] Mineralogically the sands are dominated by quartz, the silt by quartz and feldspars, while most humid temperate-region clays are composed of colloidal minerals of the kaolinite, mica, and montmorillonite groups. (*Continued on next page.*)

little influenced by changes in moisture content. Their water-holding capacity is low, and because of the large size of the spaces between each separate particle, the passage of percolating water is rapid. They, therefore, facilitate drainage and encourage good air movement. In all the grades of sand, the separate particles are visible to the naked eye, which is impossible with the silt and clay groups. Soils containing much sand or gravel, therefore, are of open character, possess good drainage and aeration, and are usually in a loose friable condition.

The clay particles are highly plastic and when kneaded with just the correct amount of water they become sticky and impervious. On drying, they shrink with the absorption of considerable energy. On wetting again, swelling occurs with the evolution of heat. This is called the *heat of wetting*. The adsorptive capacity of clay material for water, gases, and soluble salts is very high due

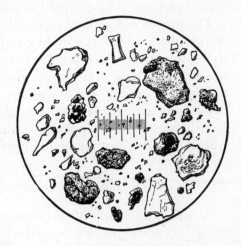

Fig. 8. Very fine sand and silt particles as they appear under an ordinary microscope. Particles below ten spaces in diameter are silt. Differences in the shapes of the various particles are striking. Quartz usually predominates both in sand and silt.

Chemically, larger amounts of the important mineral nutrients are usually found in the clay fraction. This is well shown in the following table:

Composition of Separates from Various United States Soils [a]

Soils	Number of Samples	Percentage of P_2O_5 in			Percentage of K_2O in			Percentage of CaO in		
		Sand	Silt	Clay	Sand	Silt	Clay	Sand	Silt	Clay
Crystalline residual	3	0.07	0.22	0.70	1.60	2.37	2.86	0.50	0.82	0.94
Limestone residual	3	0.28	0.23	0.37	1.46	1.83	2.62	12.26	10.96	9.92
Coastal plain	7	0.03	0.10	0.34	0.37	1.33	1.62	0.07	0.19	0.55
Glacial and loessial	10	0.15	0.23	0.86	1.72	2.30	3.07	1.28	1.30	2.69
Arid	2	0.19	0.24	0.45	3.05	4.15	5.06	4.09	9.22	8.03

[a] Failyer, G. H., and others, *The Mineral Composition of Soil Particles*, Bulletin 54, Bureau of Soils, U. S. Dept. of Agriculture, 1908.

to its colloidal state. Silt possesses some plasticity, cohesion, and adsorption but, of course, to a very much lesser degree than clay. In fact the influence of silt is such as to make it rather unsatisfactory unless supplemented by adequate amounts of sand and clay.

The presence of silt and especially clay in a soil imparts to it a fine texture, with a tendency to slow water and air movement even when well granulated. Such a soil is highly plastic, becoming sticky when too wet, and hard and cloddy when dry. The expansion and contraction on wetting and drying are very great. The water-holding capacity of a clayey or silty soil is high. Such soils are spoken of as *heavy* because of their difficult working qualities, markedly in contrast with the easily tilled sandy and gravelly soils.

28. *Soil class — the textural names of soils*

As soils are composed of particles varying greatly as to size and shape, general terms are needed which will not only give some idea of the textural make-up of soils but at the same time will afford some indication of their physical properties. For this, class names are used, such as sand, sandy loam, silt loam, and the like.

These class names have originated through years of agricultural observation, and gradually have been more or less standardized because of the necessity of definite distinctions. Four fundamental groups of soils are recognized: *gravels*, *sands*, *loams*, and *clays*. On the basis of these, additional class names have been devised.

A soil made up wholly of gravel does not often occur and is not important agriculturally because of its low fertility and unfavorable physical condition. Gravel as well as stone particles, however, are frequent in other soils and must be given consideration especially in tillage operations and in naming. The other three classes or modifications of them make up most of the arable lands.

The sand group includes all soils of which the silt and clay separates make up less than 20 per cent of the material by weight. Its properties are, therefore, characteristically sandy in contrast with the more open character of gravel and the stickier and more clayey nature of the heavier groups of soil.

A soil to be designated as a clay must carry at least 30 per cent of the clay separate. It may even have more silt than clay but as long as the percentage of clay is 30 or above, the characteristics of this separate are distinctly dominant and the class name is clay.

The loam class is more difficult to explain. In mechanical composition, it is more or less midway between sand and clay. A loam may be defined as such a mixture of sand, silt, and clay particles as to exhibit light and heavy properties in about equal proportions. It is a half-and-half mixture on the basis of properties, although the sum of the sands and the sum of the silt and clay are generally near 50 per cent, respectively. Because of the intermixture of coarse, medium, and fine particles, loams in most cases are soils of suitable physical character. Usually they possess the desirable qualities both of sand and clay without exhibiting those undesirable properties, such as extreme looseness and low water capacity on the one hand and stickiness, compactness, and very slow air and water movement on the other. Most soils of agricultural importance are some type of loam.

It is obvious that in the field various kinds of sandy, loamy, and clayey soils must occur. Moreover, these groups grade into each other, thus giving rise to a considerable number of field names. *Stony* and *gravelly* are in most cases qualifying terms that give added information as to the physical nature of the soil in question. Some of the more common class names are listed below:

Sandy Soils	*Loamy Soils*	*Clayey Soils*
Gravelly sands	Stony sandy loams	Stony clays
Coarse sands	Gravelly sandy loams	Gravelly clays
Medium sands	Coarse sandy loams	Sandy clays
Fine sands	Medium sandy loams	Silty clays
Very fine sands	Fine sandy loams	Clays
Loamy sands	Very fine sandy loams	
	Loams, gravelly loams, and stony loams	
	Silty loams and stony silt loams	
	Silty clay loams	
	Clay loams and stony clay loams	

From what has been said before, the meanings of these names should be clear except possibly those of the loam group. Loam, as already explained, refers to a soil possessing light and heavy properties in about equal proportions. If, however, this condition pertains but with one size of particles predominating to such an extent as to give noticeable character to the soils, the name of that particular separate is prefixed. Thus, a loam in which sand is dominant will be classified as a sandy loam of some kind; in the same way there may occur silt loams, silty clay loams, and clay loams. It is to be noted that the loams make up more than half of the class names. In fact, the greater proportion of the soils so far classified in the United States are loams, which is fortunate as, in general, they are more favorable for crop production than any of the other class groups.

29. *The determination of soil class*

The common method of class determination is that employed in the field. It consists in an estimation of organic content, and especially in a testing of the feel of the soil in order to decide as to the class

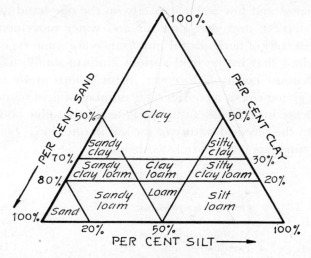

FIG. 9. Diagram by means of which the textural name of a soil may be determined from a mechanical analysis. In using the diagram, the points corresponding to the percentages of silt and clay present in the soil under consideration are located on the silt and clay lines respectively. Lines are then projected inward, parallel in the first case to the sand side of the triangle and in the second case parallel to the silt side. The name of the compartment in which the two lines intersect is the class name of the soil in question.

name. Probably as much can be judged as to the texture and class of a soil merely by rubbing it between the thumb and the fingers or in the palm of the hand as by any other superficial means. The sand particles are gritty, the silt has a floury or talcum-powder feel when dry, and is only moderately plastic when moist, while the clayey material is harsh when dry and very plastic and sticky when wet. The method really consists in sufficiently recognizing by feel the textural composition of a soil so that the proper class name may be applied. This method is used in all field operations, especially in soil survey, land classification, and the like. Accuracy in such a determination is of great practical value and depends largely on experience. Facility in class determination is one of the first things a field man should develop and it can only be acquired by the careful study and evaluation of known samples.

A more precise and accurate method has been devised by the United States Department of Agriculture for the naming of soils based on a mechanical analysis. This has been of great practical value in standardizing field identification, which, as already explained, is a generalized expression of the mechanical make-up of a soil. Now that the field identification is well established, the practical mission of the mechanical analysis, in this respect at least, is largely attained. And since the method is somewhat tedious and can be applied only to a rather limited number of samples, the decision as to class name directly from a mechanical analysis is not so often resorted to. The method of identification is shown diagrammatically in Fig. 9. The drawing reemphasizes that a soil is a mixture of different sizes of particles and that a close correlation exists between particle size and the properties of soils.

30. *The specific gravity of soils*

The weight of the soil particles themselves is expressed by specific gravity which indicates the number of times heavier the dry solid particles are than an equal volume of water. It is unaffected by soil condition, remaining the same whether the soil is loose or compact. Although considerable range is observed in the specific gravity of the individual soil minerals, the figures for purely mineral soils usually vary within the narrow limits of 2.6 and 2.7. This occurs because quartz, feldspar, and the colloidal silicates, with specific gravities near these figures, make up the bulk of mineral soils. The fineness of the particles seems to have little effect.

Only one condition, the amount of organic matter present, may markedly influence the specific gravity of a mineral soil. As a consequence, the specific gravity of surface soils usually is somewhat less than that of subsoils. Some highly organic mineral soils may drop as low as 2.0 in specific gravity. Nevertheless, for general calculations, the average arable surface soil may be considered as having a specific gravity of about 2.65.[1]

31. *The volume weight of soils*

The actual weight of dry soil in any given volume is generally expressed by volume weight, a figure indicating the number of times heavier the dry soil [2] is than the water that will occupy the same total soil volume. Thus, if the dry soil in a cubic foot of space weighs 87.4 pounds, the volume weight would be 87.40 ÷ 62.42 or 1.40.[3]

---

[1] The specific gravity of a soil is generally determined by means of a picnometer, a bottle fitted with a perforated ground-glass stopper and accurately calibrated. By comparing the weight of the total water held by the bottle, usually 50 cc., with the weight of the water when any given amount of dry soil, say 5 gms., is present in the bottle, the weight of the water displaced by the soil can be determined and the specific gravity calculated therefrom. A sample calculation follows:

Weight of picnometer	23.257 gms.
Volume of picnometer	50.000 cc.
Wt. of picnometer + 5 gms. abs. dry soil + X gms. water	76.357 gms.
Wt. of picnometer + 5 gms. abs. dry soil	28.257 gms.
Wt. of X gms. water	48.100 gms.
Water displaced (50 − 48.10)	1.900 gms.

$$\text{Specific gravity} = \frac{5.00}{1.90} = 2.63+$$

[2] In order to have a constant and comparable basis for calculation, almost all soil data are computed on dry soil. Consequently, unless something is said to the contrary, this should always be assumed. See note on page 151.

[3] In the field the volume weight of a soil may be estimated by driving a cylinder of known volume into the ground and obtaining thereby a core of natural soil. By weighing the soil and then determining the amount of water that it contains, the amount of absolutely dry soil may be ascertained. Dividing this by the weight of an equal volume of water gives the figure for volume weight.

The rubber-tube method has proved very convenient for the field determination of volume weight. A hole is bored in the soil to the required depth by a specially constructed auger, the soil being carefully removed and later oven-dried. A very thin-walled tubular rubber bag of the size of the auger hole is carefully inserted in the hole previously bored. The tubular bag is then filled with water flush with the surface of the soil. The water is measured and the volume of the soil removed is thus determined. Knowing the weight of the dry soil and its original volume, the volume weight may be calculated. The experimental error of the method is rather low. See Israelsen, O. W., "A New Method of Determining Volume Weight," *Jour. Agr. Res.*, XIII:28–35, April, 1918.

The paraffin-immersion method is valuable with heavy soils. Small pieces of soil are dried, weighed, and then coated very thinly with paraffin, just sufficiently to prevent the entrance of water, yet not enough to introduce serious experimental error. The weight of the water displaced by a number of such pieces may be determined easily by the use of a graduated cylinder. See Shaw, C. F., "A Method for Determining the Volume Weight of Soil in Field Condition," *Jour. Amer. Soc. Agron.*, IX:38–42, 1917. See also Trinka, R., "Eine Studie Über Einige Physikalischen Eigenschaften des Bodens," *Internat. Mitt. für Bodenkunde*, IV:363–380, 1914.

For other methods proposed, see:

Volume weight differs from specific gravity in that it compares the weight of the dry soil to the weight of water that will occupy the total soil volume — that is, the space usually filled by soil particles, soil air, and soil water. Specific gravity, however, compares the weight of the dry soil to that of water that only will occupy the same volume as the particles alone, taking no consideration of the normal pore space. It is consequently always the higher figure. As a soil is compacted, its volume weight increases due to the increased volume occupied by the soil particles and the corresponding decrease in pore space. If it were possible to compact a soil to a completely solid condition, its volume weight would approach its specific gravity as a limit. Specific gravity represents, therefore, 100 per cent soil. Volume weight in comparison may be used to indicate the proportion of space occupied by the soil particles.

The volume weight of any particular soil is determined by the specific gravity of the particles and by their arrangement — that is, their structural condition. Since the specific gravity of mineral soils, in general, shows no great variation, soil structure becomes the major factor in accounting for normal fluctuations in volume weight. And structural conditions in turn are determined in large degree by the interlocking influences of texture and the degree of aggregation, especially aggregation induced by organic matter.

The particles of sandy soils generally tend to lie in close contact, thus increasing the weight of soil in a given volume. The rather low organic matter of these soils further encourages this. The particles of finer soils, such as silt loams, clay loams, and clays, on the other hand, being smaller and lighter, ordinarily do not exist so close together. The weight of such soils thus tends to be less, especially as the organic content is in general higher than those of the coarser types and the tendency towards aggregation is greater.

Clay, clay loam, and silt loam surface soils may range from 1.00 to as high as 1.60 in volume weight depending on their condition, while a variation from 1.20 to 1.80 may be found in sands and sandy loams. Very compact subsoils regardless of texture may have volume weights in the neighborhood of 2.0. That great variations are to be expected in all horizons, even in soils of the same texture, is clearly shown by

Frear, W., and E. S. Erb, "Excavation Method for Determining the Apparent Specific Gravity of Soil," *Jour. Assoc. Agr. Chem.*, IV:103–105, 1921.

Frosterus, B., and H. Frauenfelder, "Apparatus for Soil Volume Determination," *Internat. Rev. Proc. and Sci. Agr.*, III:100–104, 1926.

data respecting Illinois silt loams presented by Harland and Smith (Table VI). Moreover, there is some tendency for the volume weight to rise as the profile is penetrated. This may be due to a lower content of organic matter, less aggregation, a compaction due to the weight of the overlying layers, and perhaps in certain cases to a downward movement of clay.

Table VI. Volume Weight Figures for Certain Illinois Silt Loams [1] to a Depth of 40 Inches. (The successive horizons beginning with A_1 were approximately 8, 9, 11, and 12 inches in thickness resp.)

Soil Type	Horizon			
	A_1	A_2	B_1	C_1
Muscatine silt loam (Henry Co.)	1.20	1.27	1.32	1.40
Edina silt loam	1.22	1.39	1.32	1.54
Muscatine silt loam (Champaign Co.)	1.28	1.28	1.36	1.35
Carrington silt loam	1.29	1.29	1.35	1.57
Yellowish gray silt loam on orange mottled tight clay	1.35	1.28	1.30	1.69
Clinton silt loam	1.46	1.48	1.46	1.48
Gray silt loam on tight clay	1.51	1.56	1.51	1.56
Yellow-gray silt loam on compact, medium plastic clay	1.62	1.53	1.49	1.76

Differences in the volume weight of surface soils may be accentuated by methods of farm management. The addition of farm manure in large amounts tends to lower the weight figure as does also a bluegrass sod. Intensive cultivation operates in the opposite direction. A Hagerstown loam (surface soil) on the Jordan plots at Pennsylvania State College held in bluegrass, showed a volume weight of 1.07 while the figure for a comparable plot cropped to a common rotation for almost sixty years was 1.25.[2] Swanson and Peterson [3] found that a Marshall silt loam near Cherokee, Iowa, after at least fifty years of cropping to corn, oats, and occasionally clover, had a specific gravity and volume weight of 2.59 and 1.13 respectively as compared to a virgin surface sample figure of 2.49 and 0.93.

[1] Harland, M. B. and R. S. Smith, "Volume Weight of Certain Field Soils," *Jour. Amer. Soc. Agron.*, XX:533–541, 1928.

[2] Alderfer, R. B. and F. G. Merkle, "The Measurement of Structural Stability and Permeability and the Influence of Soil Treatments upon These Properties," *Soil Sci.*, LI: 201–212, 1941.

[3] Swanson, C. L. W. and J. B. Peterson, "The Use of the Micrometric and Other Methods for the Evaluation of Soil Structure," *Soil Sci.*, LIII:173–185, 1942.

When the volume weight of a soil is known, its dry weight in pounds to the cubic foot may be found by multiplying by 62.42, the weight of a cubic foot of water. Clayey and silty surface soils may vary from 70 to 100 pounds to the cubic foot, while sands and sandy loams may show a variation of 80 to 110 pounds. The greater the organic content, the less is this weight. Very compact subsoils, regardless of texture, may weigh as much as 125 pounds per cubic foot. The figures quoted are for the absolutely dry soil and do not include the water present, which may be much or little, according to circumstances.

The actual weight of a soil also may be expressed in terms of an acre-foot, referring to a volume of soil 1 acre in extent and 1 foot deep. The weight of an acre-foot of surface mineral soil may vary from 3,000,000 to 4,800,000 pounds of dry substance. The figure most commonly used, however, is 2,000,000 or sometimes 2,500,000 pounds as the weight of average surface soil to a depth of 6 or 7 inches. This is considered as an *acre-furrow-slice*.

Volume weight, besides being an interesting and significant physical characteristic, is very important as a basis for certain computations. Weight figures, especially those for the furrow-slice, may be used to calculate the amounts of water, the amounts of organic matter, and the actual number of pounds of the mineral constituents that are present. Moreover, volume weight is necessary in the calculation of the total pore space present in soil. Such information affords a valuable means of judging and comparing soils.

32. *The pore space of mineral soils*

The pore space of soil is occupied by air and water in constantly varying proportions. The amount of this pore space is determined largely by structural conditions — that is, by the interrelated influences of texture, compaction, and aggregation.

As already emphasized, the volume weight of coarse surface soils is high due to the close contact of the particles, while finer soils are generally lighter due to the tendency of the small particles to resist compaction and the readiness with which granulation occurs, especially when sufficient decomposing organic matter is present. This means that surface sands and sandy loams usually contain somewhat less pore space than silt loam, clay loam, and clay surface soils.

The validity of the above generalizations may readily be substantiated by the use of a very simple formula [1] involving specific-gravity and volume-weight figures. A sandy soil having a volume weight of 1.50 and a specific gravity of 2.65 has, according to this formula, 43.4 per cent of pore space. A silt loam in which the above figures are 1.30 and 2.65 respectively, possesses 50.9 per cent of air and water space. This latter value is close to the pore capacity of a normally granulated loam, silt loam, or clay loam surface soil. (See Fig. 3.)

As might be expected, considerable difference in total pore space occurs depending upon conditions. Sandy surface soils show a range of from 35 to 50 per cent while heavy soils vary from 40 to 60 per cent or perhaps even more in cases of high organic matter and marked granulation. Pore space also varies with depth, some compact subsoils dropping as low as 25 or 30 per cent. This accounts in part for the inadequate aeration of such horizons. The handling of a soil exerts a marked influence upon the pore space of the furrow-slice. For instance, the continuous bluegrass sod of the Jordan plots, already referred to (page 52) had a total porosity of 57.2 per cent while the comparable rotation plot showed only 50 per cent. The figure for the virgin Marshall silt loam of Swanson and Peterson (page 52) was 62.7 per cent but the same soil under cultivation for 50 years dropped to 56.2 per cent of pore space.

Two types of individual pore spaces in general occur in soils — macro and micro. While no sharp line of demarcation occurs, the former characteristically allow the ready movement of air and percolating water. The equalization of gases in the latter type of pore is greatly impeded while water movement is restricted largely to slow capillary adjustment. Thus in a sandy soil, in spite of the low total porosity, the movement of air and water is surprisingly rapid due to the dominance of the macrointerstices. Heavy soils, on the other hand, allow slow gas and water adjustment in spite of the unusually large amount of total pore space. Here the dominating micropores readily maintain themselves full of water, and aeration, especially in

$$^1 \text{ \% pore space} = 100 - \left(\frac{\text{vol. wt.}}{\text{sp. gr.}} \times \frac{100}{1} \right)$$

It has already been explained (see page 51) that the specific gravity of a soil represents 100 per cent soil material or the weight of absolutely solid soil. Volume weight indicates in comparison thereto the soil material actually present. The ratio of the volume weight to the specific gravity when multiplied by 100 becomes the percentage of the soil volume occupied by the soil particles. Subtracting from 100 gives per cent pore space.

the subsoil, often is inadequate for satisfactory root development and desirable microbial activity. It seems to be the size of the individual pore spaces rather than their combined volume that, after all, is the important consideration. The loosening and granulating of heavy soils promote aeration, not so much by increasing the pore space in total but by influencing the proportion of the macro- and micro-interstices.

33. *The structure of mineral soils* [1]

While texture is of great importance in determining the general characteristics of a soil, it is evident that the arrangement as well as the size of the particles must exert considerable influence. The term *structure* is used to refer to the arrangement or grouping of the soil materials into aggregates. It is at once apparent that soil conditions — such, for example, as aeration, water movement, heat transfer, and similar properties — will be much affected by structure. As a matter of fact, the important physical changes wrought by the farmer in making his soil better suited as a foothold for plants are structural rather than textural.

Structural forms under virgin conditions apparently have arisen from one or both of two nonstructural states — *single grained* and *massive*. In the former, the single, solid particles function as individuals. Loose sand is a good example of this. In the latter case, the soil masses are very large, irregular, and featureless as far as characteristic aggregations are concerned. These two extremes are the theoretical boundaries of the four structural types commonly recognized in soil profiles. They are as follows: [2]

1. *Platy*. . . . In this structural type the aggregates are arranged in relatively thin horizontal plates, leaflets, or lenses. Such an aggregation usually is confined to the A horizon of humid-region soils.

2. *Prismatic*. . . . This type is characterized by vertically oriented aggregates or pillars. These elongated blocks vary in length with different soils and may reach a diameter of 6 inches. They commonly occur in the B

[1] For a consideration of all phases of soil structure, see Baver, L. D., *Soil Physics*, John Wiley & Sons, Inc., New York, 1940, Chap. V.

[2] Nikiforoff, C. C., "Morphological Classification of Soil Structure," *Soil Sci.*, LII:193–207, 1941. See also Russell, J. C., L. B. Olmstead, and B. H. Hendrickson, *Forms of Soil Structure*, Bulletin 10, Amer. Soil Survey Assoc., IX:120–133, 1929.

horizon of semiarid soils. When the tops are rounded, the term *columnar* is used.

3. *Blocky*. . . . In this case the aggregates are in the shape of irregular blocks with rather sharp edges. These blocks are firm and solid, and range in different soils from a fraction of an inch in diameter to 2 or 3 as a maximum. When small, the term *nut* structure is sometimes applied. The aggregates usually lie closely together and when wetted, the swelling may entirely close the intervening macropores. A blocky structure is common in the B horizons of many different soils.

4. *Granular*. . . . All rounded aggregates may be placed in this category although the term more properly refers to those not over $\frac{1}{2}$ inch in diameter. These rounded aggregates ordinarily lie loosely and are readily shaken apart. When wetted, the intervening spaces usually are not closed by the swelling as may be the case with a blocky structural condition. When the granules are especially porous, the term *crumb* is significantly applied. A granular structure is characteristic of many surface soils, especially those high in organic matter and is the physical condition of particular importance in land under cultivation.

Several of the structural conditions mentioned above usually occur in the same soil solum. In fact, all might be found in one virgin profile, although this would be rather unique. In humid temperate regions, a granular aggregation in the A horizon with a blocky type of some kind in the subsoil, is usual although granular B horizons are not uncommon. In aridic soils, the blocky type in the subsoil may be replaced in part or wholly by a prismatic arrangement. This is likely to be true especially with alkali soils.

The mechanics of structure genesis are rather obscure. Without a doubt the nature of the parent material and its origin are important factors, as well as the trend of the physical and biochemical processes of soil formation, especially those that result in the synthesis of clay and humus. Climate is, therefore, a consideration. Soluble salts surely play an important role, particularly in aridic soils. Nor should the migration of clay, of iron oxides, and of lime be overlooked. Undoubtedly, also, the accumulation of organic matter and its type of decay has much to do with the processes, especially the development of the crumb structure so common in the surface soils of grasslands. In fact the preservation and encouragement of this particular structural condition, since it occurs at the surface and since it is of such prime importance in respect to seedbed control, become one of our most important soil problems. Let us turn to this phase without further delay.

34. *Granulation and its promotion in arable soils* [1]

A soil granule is a rounded porous mass of mineral particles of varying sizes, heterogeneously interspersed with humus. The granule itself may be large or small and its stability weak or strong according to circumstances. Apparently its content of clay and humus is higher than that of the whole soil and its porosity is closely related to its organic content. Its stability seems to depend upon the amount and nature of the clay and humus present. The ease with which air and water penetrate the individual granule is as important as the magnitude of its pore space. And its internal surface is of tremendous significance in respect to the adsorptive capacity of the soil and its catalytic powers. In fact, most of the chemical and biochemical changes that occur in granular soils must take place within the tortuous and endless mazes of the crumbs.

Just what draws and holds the individual granule together once the proper contacts have been made and the aggregate is assembled, is most obscure. It is clearly evident, however, that the chemical and physical interrelations of clay, humus, and water play the principal roles. And, no doubt, the electrical condition of these components is fundamentally involved, as well as dehydration, precipitation, and cementing effects. Several theories have been advanced thereto. [2]

It suffices to say here, however, that granules probably develop from two distinct sources — (1) by accretion or build-up from smaller units and (2) by the disintegration of larger and less stable aggregates. In cultivated soils, the former origin probably is the more common. Several interrelated factors seem to account for granule genesis. [3] Of

[1] Below will be found a few of the important articles available on soil aggregation:

Alderfer, R. B. and F. G. Merkle, "The Comparative Physical Constitution of Water Stable Granules and of the Original Soil," *Soil Sci.*, LIII:105–113, 1942.

Retzer, John L. and M. B. Russell, "Differences in the Aggregation of a Prairie and Gray Brown Podsol," *Soil Sci.*, LII:47–58, 1941.

Elson, Jesse, "A Comparison of the Effect of Certain Cropping and Fertilizer and Manuring Practices on Soil Aggregation of Dunmore Silt Loam," *Soil Sci.*, L:339–353, 1940.

Rost, C. O. and Chas. A. Rowles, "A Study of Factors Affecting the Stability of Soil Aggregates," *Proc. Soil Sci. Soc. Amer.*, V:421–433, 1940.

[2] A review of these theories will be found in Baver, L. D., *Soil Physics*, John Wiley & Sons, Inc., New York, 1940, pp. 133–149.

[3] See Baver, L. D., *ibid.*, pp. 149–157.

these (1) wetting and drying, (2) freezing and thawing, (3) the physical activity of roots and soil animals, (4) the influence of decaying organic matter and of the slimes from the microorganisms and other forms of life that accomplish the decomposition, and (5) the modifying effects of adsorbed bases are most important. These factors in ever-changing intensity and coordination apparently encourage crumb-structure genesis to such an extent as to make the maintenance of suitable granulation possible even in intensively cultivated lands. In

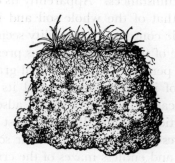

Fig. 10. A puddled soil (left) and a well-granulated soil (right). Plant roots and especially humus play the major role in soil granulation. For that reason a sod tends to restore the structural condition of cultivated land.

well-granulated surface soils, 70 or 80 per cent of the total mass may exhibit a crumb-structure type of aggregation, although 40 or 50 per cent is more usual.[1]

Obviously any action that will develop lines of weakness, shift the particles to and fro, and force contacts that otherwise might not occur, should encourage granulation if attractive and binding agencies, electrical or otherwise, are effective. Consequently, it is not surprising that the alternate contraction and expansion of water films, the segregative and distensive influences of freezing and thawing, the physical effects of root extension, and the mixing action of soil fauna tend, in many cases, to encourage crumb structure. The benefits of fall plowing on certain types of soil and the slaking of clods under the influence of a gentle rain have long been known and taken advantage of in seedbed preparation. And the granulating influences of earthworms and other soil organisms have not passed unnoticed (page 96).

[1] Baver, L. D., *ibid.*, p. 160.

The major agency, however, in the encouragement of granulation probably is organic matter, especially as it undergoes decay and is synthesized into humus. Not only does it bind but it lightens and expands, making possible the tremendous porosity so characteristic of individual soil crumbs. Plant roots probably promote granulation as much or more by the decay of the distributed organic matter as by the disruptive action of their ramifications. The electrochemical properties of the humus, no doubt, are fully effective in the organization and the later stabilization of the aggregates. Moreover, some investigators [1] maintain that at times slime and other viscous microbial products greatly encourage crumb development and exert a stabilizing influence as well. Granulation thus assumes a highly biological aspect.

At the same time organic matter promotes ready air and water movement and, not only does it lower the plasticity and cohesion of the soil mass, but it also localizes the influence of the clay, since this constituent seems to be concentrated in the newly formed aggregates. Moreover, the high adsorptive capacity of humus for water tends to intensify the disruptive effects of temperature changes and moisture fluctuations. In fact, the granulation of a clay soil cannot be promoted adequately without the presence of a certain amount of humus. The maintenance of organic matter, therefore, is of great practical concern, not only chemically and biologically but physically as well.

One of the outstanding characteristics of the colloidal complexes of the soil, both mineral and organic, is the ability to adsorb cations. As already stated, many different positive ions are held by the colloidal nuclei in a replaceable condition. Moreover, the domination or even partial domination of certain of these cations tends to develop more or less definite physical conditions. For instance, the adsorption of calcium and certain other ions promotes granulation by a phenomenon called *flocculation*. When this occurs, the colloidal matter, especially that of a highly viscous and gelatinous nature, is coagulated and a localization occurs. This disrupts the soil mass and tends to

---

[1] Martin, James P. and S. A. Waksman, "Influence of Microorganisms on Soil Aggregation and Erosion: II," *Soil Sci.*, LII:381–394, 1941.

Myers, H. E. and T. M. McCalla, "Changes in Soil Aggregation in Relation to Bacterial Numbers, H-ion Concentration and Length of Time Soil Was Kept Moist," *Soil Sci.*, LI:189–199, 1941.

Peele, T. C. and O. W. Beale, "Influence of Microbial Activity upon Aggregation and Erodibility of Lateritic Soils," *Proc. Soil Sci. Soc. Amer.*, V:33–35, 1940.

encourage the crumb structure which is so desirable. Flocculation in itself, however, is not granulation as it usually does not provide for the stabilization of the aggregates.

While most soils highly charged with native calcium exhibit granulation to a marked degree, it must not be inferred that this or any other adsorbed ion plays a major role in soil granulation. Exchangeable cations merely modify the influence of other factors especially the over-all effects of decaying organic matter. The addition of lime, therefore, is effective as a granulating agency largely through its influence on biotic forces.[1] Moreover, the amounts applied are too small to have much effect directly on structural conditions. Nevertheless, the consistent use of lime may tend to maintain, if not to increase, the granular condition of arable lands.

Some may be surprised that plowing and cultivation are not listed as major factors in the granulation of arable soils. It cannot be denied that the soil is loosened and aerated by tillage, that the organic matter is mixed thereby with the mineral constituents, and that conditions are made more favorable for the activity of the natural forces of granulation. Nevertheless, tillage in most cases seems only to make more noticeable the aggregation already attained. Other than this, it may even impair crumb structure by purely mechanical means. In fact, land long under cultivation usually shows a decrease in granulation partly because of a reduction in organic matter and partly, perhaps, because of the direct disruptive influence of tillage upon the soil aggregates. Soil-granulation maintenance seems to be determined not only by the effective control of organic matter through additions and a suitable crop rotation but also by the application of tillage in such a way as to reduce granule destruction to a minimum.

35. *The structural management of light and heavy soils*

The paucity of inorganic colloidal matter in sandy soils has certain obvious advantages. Looseness, friability, good aeration and drain-

[1] Metzger, W. H. and J. C. Hide, "Effect of Certain Crops and Soil Treatments on Soil Aggregation and the Distribution of Organic Carbon in Relation to Aggregate Size," *Jour. Amer. Soc. Agron.*, XXX:833–843, 1938.

Browning, G. M., "Changes in the Erodibility of Soils Brought About by the Application of Organic Matter," *Proc. Soil Sci. Soc. Amer.*, II:85–96, 1937.

Bradfield, R., *The Value and Limitations of Calcium in Soil Structure*, Bulletin 16, Amer. Soil Survey Assoc., 31–32, 1936.

Baver, L. D., "Aggregation of Soils and Calcium Ion Saturation," Bulletin 16, Amer. Soil Survey Assoc., 28–30, 1936.

age, and easy tillage are characteristics. On the other hand, such soils are often too loose and open, and lack the capacity to adsorb and hold sufficient moisture and nutrient materials. They are, as a consequence, likely to be droughty and lacking in fertility. There is only one method of improving in a practical field way the structure of such a soil — the addition of organic matter. Organic material, if it undergoes favorable decomposition when incorporated with the soil, will not only act as a binding material for the particles but will also increase the water capacity. It may be applied as crop residues or as farm or green manures. The maintenance of a soil in sod is recognized the world over as a highly effective means of promoting granulation.

The structural management of a silicate clayey soil is not such a simple problem as that of a sandy one. In the latter, the plasticity and cohesion are never great even after the addition of large amounts of organic materials. In clays and similar soils of temperate regions, however, the potential plasticity and cohesion are always high due to the presence of large amounts of complex hydrated aluminum silicates in a colloidal condition. The more plastic a soil becomes, the more likely it is to puddle,[1] especially if worked when wet. Moreover, a soil of high plasticity is prone to become hard and cloddy when dry, due to the cohesive tendencies of the small particles. Such soils must, therefore, be treated very carefully, especially in tillage operations. If plowed too wet, the aggregation of particles is broken down, and an unfavorable structure is sure to result. If plowed too dry, great clods are turned up which are difficult to work down into a good seedbed. In a sandy soil, no such difficulties usually are encountered.

Not only must tillage operations be carefully timed in a heavy soil but granulation must be encouraged to the fullest degree. As already emphasized, organic matter is a major concern. The methods of maintenance have been enumerated. In this respect sod crops should be utilized to the fullest extent and the rotation planned to attain their maximum benefits. It is needless to say that drainage as well as erosion control must also be considered. Unless a certain minimum of granulation is maintained in a heavy soil, its full cropping capacity cannot be realized.

[1] When a soil in a plastic condition has been worked until its pore space is much reduced, it becomes practically impervious to air and water, and is said to be *puddled*. The presence of gelatinous and viscous colloidal materials seems to be the controlling factor in such a condition, the pore spaces of a puddled soil being filled with such material. When a soil in this condition dries, it is hard and dense.

36. *Soil temperature* [1]

It is universally recognized that chemical and biological activities are an energy expression and that such changes, especially the latter, will not continue with adequate intensity unless certain temperatures are maintained. The temperature of the soil is thus a factor of vital concern. For instance, nitrification does not begin until the soil reaches a temperature of about 40° F., the most favorable limits being 80° to 90° F. Temperatures optimum for seed germination and plant growth, as might be expected, vary widely, being low for such crops as bluegrass and high for corn. The energy by means of which the soil maintains its normal activities comes, of course, directly or indirectly from the sun.

Insolation contingencies. The amount of solar insolation accorded any particular locality depends fundamentally upon climate. But the amount of energy entering the soil is, in addition, contingent largely upon (1) the color, (2) the slope, and (3) the vegetative cover of the site under consideration. It is well known that dark soils will absorb more energy than light-colored ones and that red and yellow soils will show a more rapid temperature rise than those that are white. [2] Observation has also shown that the nearer the angle of incidence of the sun's rays approaches the perpendicular, the greater will be the absorption. As an example, a southerly slope of 20 degrees, a level soil, and a northerly slope of 20 degrees receive energy on June 21 at the 42nd parallel, north, in the proportion of 106, 100, and 81, respectively.

Wollny [3] found near Munich that the temperature of southward slopes varied with the time of year. For example, the southeasterly inclination was warmest in the early season, the southerly slope during

---

[1] For a rather full edaphological discussion of soil heat, see Lyon, T. L. and H. O. Buckman, *Nature and Properties of Soils*, The Macmillan Company, New York, 1922, Chap. IX. See also Baver, L. D., *Soil Physics*, John Wiley & Sons, Inc., New York, 1940, Chap. VIII.

[2] Bouyoucos, G. J., *An Investigation of Soil Temperature*, Technical Bulletin 17, Mich. Agr. Exp. Sta., p. 30, 1913.

Lang, C., "Über Warme-absorption und Emission des Boden," *Forsch. a.d. Gebiete d. Agr.-Physik.*, I:379–407, 1878.

Wollny, E., "Untersuchung über den Einfluss der Farbe des Bodens auf dessen Erwärmung," *Forsch. a.d. Gebiete d. Agr.-Physik.*, IV:327–365, 1881.

[3] Wollny, E., "Untersuchungen über den Einfluss der Exposition auf die Erwärmung des Bodens," *Forsch. a.d. Gebiete d. Agr.-Physik.*, I:263–294, 1878. This publication contains a number of other papers on this subject by Wollny.

midseason, and the southwesterly slope in the fall. Although such a relationship will not hold universally, it indicates that slopes vary in their desirability depending on the crop to be grown. For instance, south or southeasterly slopes are often preferred by gardeners. While orchardists and foresters consider exposure an important factor not only in regard to the species or variety of tree to be grown but also in respect to sunscald and certain plant diseases.

Whether the soil is bare or covered with vegetation is another factor that markedly influences the amount of insolation received. The effect of a forest is universally recognized while even an ordinary field crop, such as bluegrass, has a very noticeable effect, especially upon temperature fluctuations. Bare soils warm up more quickly and cool off more rapidly than those covered with vegetation, or with artificial mulches, while during the winter, frost penetration is considerably greater in noninsulated land.

Equalizations of heat in soil. Before dealing with actual temperatures, let us follow the insolation into the surface layer of soil. In so doing, we immediately find that mineral soils not only vary in respect to the energy necessary to raise their temperature but also that this variation is largely in proportion to the amounts of water present. For instance, the dry weight *specific heat* [1] of mineral soils, in spite of variations in texture and organic matter, is about 0.20.[2] But if the moisture is advanced to 20 per cent, the specific heat of the wet mass becomes 0.33, while an increase to 30 per cent of moisture raises the wet weight specific heat to 0.38. Obviously, therefore, moisture is one of the major factors in respect to the heat capacity of a soil and, hence, has much to do with its rate both of warming up and cooling off.

Before considering the subsurface-soil horizons, it is well to empha-

---

[1] The specific heat of any material may be defined as its thermal capacity compared with that of water. It is expressed as a ratio of the quantity of heat required to raise the temperature of a given amount of a certain substance from 15° to 16° C.

[2] The following weight specific-heat figures from Lang, Patten, and Bouyoucos are interesting:

Lang [a]		Patten [b]		Bouyoucos [c]	
Coarse sand	0.198	Sand	0.185	Sand	0.193
Limestone soil	0.249	Sandy loam	0.183	Gravel	0.204
Organic soil	0.257	Loam	0.191	Clay	0.206
Garden soil	0.276	Loam	0.194	Loam	0.215
Peat	0.477	Clay	0.210	Peat	0.252

[a] Lang, C., "Über Wärme Capacität der Bodenconstituenten," *Forsch. a.d. Gebiete d. Agr.-Physik.*, I: 109–147, 1878.
[b] Patten, H. F., *Heat Transference in Soils*, Bulletin 59, Bureau of Soils, U. S. Dept. of Agriculture, p. 34, 1909.
[c] Bouyoucos, G. J., *An Investigation of Soil Temperature*, Technical Bulletin 17, Mich. Agr. Exp. Sta., p. 12, 1913

size that the surface layers, where energy is continually being received, are subject to sudden and often drastic fluctuations in temperature. This is due in part to variations in solar insolation and in part to the losses to the atmosphere. The latter consist in (1) *conduction* [1] to the atmosphere, (2) *radiation* [2] into space, and (3) to the cooling effects of moisture *evaporation*. While the contact equalization of heat between soil and air no doubt is of considerable importance, especially if the latter is in rapid movement, radiation probably accounts for a greater loss of energy. Terrestrial bodies are continually giving off energy waves into the atmosphere and since they are mostly of the infrared type and make no impression on the eye, they are often spoken of as *dark rays*. Suffice to say, their energy capacity is high and, as their emission is continuous, much heat is lost in this way. This accounts in part, especially during clear weather, for rapid changes in surface-soil temperatures. Now let us consider evaporation in this regard.

The vaporization of soil water is caused by an increased molecular activity and requires the expenditure of a certain amount of energy [3] which results in a cooling effect especially at the surface where most of the evaporation occurs. It requires 265.2 kilogram calories to evaporate 1 pound of water at 68° F. This is sufficient to lower the temperature of a cubic foot of a representative mineral soil at optimum moisture about 28° F., providing that all of the energy of evaporation comes from the soil and its water. Such a figure is, of course, empirical as only a part of the heat of vaporization comes from the soil itself. Nevertheless it indicates the tremendous cooling influence of evaporation.

The low temperature of a wet soil is due partially to evaporation and partially to high specific heat. King [4] found during April that an undrained soil in Wisconsin ranged from 2.5° F. to 12.5° F. lower than one of the same type well drained. Drained and undrained soils at

[1] A molecular transfer of energy from one body to another when they are in contact or from one part of a particular body to another. The energy is conceived as communicated progressively from molecule to molecule.

[2] A transfer of energy through space by means of waves or pulsations which are transformed into heat values when they encounter an obstructing body.

[3] It requires 536.6 gram calories to evaporate 1 gm. of water at 100° C., while 596.7 calories are necessary if evaporation takes place at 0° C. The calories (C) required to vaporize 1 gm. of water at any Centigrade temperature (t) may be calculated by the formula:

$$C = 596.74 - 0.601 \, t.$$

[4] King, F. H., *Physics of Agriculture*, pub. by author, Madison, Wis., 1910, p. 20.

Urbana, Illinois,[1] showed maximum differences of 13.7° F., 9.0° F., and 6.2° F. at depths of 1, 2, and 4 inches respectively. The influence upon the surface layers is, therefore, marked.

Not all of the solar insolation, however, is dissipated into the atmosphere. Some slowly penetrates the profile largely by *conduction*. While this type of movement is influenced by a number of factors, the most important is probably the moisture content of the soil layers. Heat passes from soil to water about 150 times easier than from soil to air. As the water increases in a soil, the air decreases and the transfer resistance is lowered decidedly. When sufficient water is present to join most of the soil particles, further additions will have little effect on heat conduction. Here again the major role of soil moisture comes to the fore.

The significance of conduction in respect to field temperatures is not difficult to grasp. It provides a means of temperature adjustment but, because it is slow, the subsoil changes tend to lag behind those to which the surface layers are subjected. More than this, the changes that do occur are always less. In temperate regions, we expect surface soils in general to be warmer in summer and cooler in winter than the subsoil, especially the lower horizons of the latter.

Soil temperature data. The temperature of the soil at any time depends on the ratio of the energy absorbed and that being lost. The constant change in this relationship is reflected in the seasonal, monthly, and daily temperatures. The accompanying data from Lincoln, Nebraska, (Table VII) are representative of average seasonal temperatures in temperate climates where the rainfall is moderate.

It is apparent from these figures that the seasonal variations of soil temperature are considerable even at the lower depths. The surface layers vary more or less in accord with the air temperature and, therefore, exhibit a greater fluctuation than the subsoil. On the average the surface 6-inch layer of soil is warmer than the air at every season of the year, while the subsoil is warmer in autumn and winter but cooler in spring and summer due to its protected position and the lag in conduction.

This lag in temperature change in the subsoil is especially noticeable when the monthly march of soil temperature at Lincoln, Ne-

[1] Mosier, J. G. and A. F. Gustafson, *Soil Physics and Management*, J. B. Lippincott Company, Philadelphia, 1917, p. 302.

Table VII.   Average Soil Temperature Readings Taken at Lincoln, Nebraska, 1890–1902.   Degrees Fahrenheit [1]

Season	Atm. Air	1″ Deep	3″ Deep	6″ Deep	12″ Deep	24″ Deep	36″ Deep
Winter	25.9	28.8	28.8	29.5	32.2	36.3	39.1
Spring	49.9	54.8	53.6	51.6	48.5	45.7	44.3
Summer	73.8	83.0	80.9	79.1	73.8	69.0	66.2
Autumn	53.9	56.4	57.6	57.1	57.5	59.3	60.3

braska is considered.   It is evident from the curves (Fig. 11) that the monthly range in temperature change in the surface soil is greater than that of the air.   The absolute range is, of course, greater for the air. It must be kept in mind that changes in soil temperature, except at the very surface, are gradual while the air may vary many degrees in a very short time.

The daily and hourly temperatures of the atmospheric air and the soil in temperate zones may show considerable agreement or marked divergence according to conditions.   Fluctuations are, of course, more

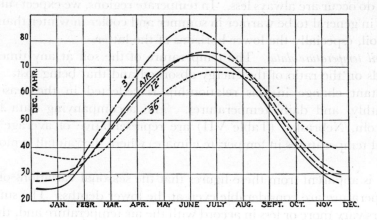

Fig. 11.   Monthly march of air and soil temperatures at Lincoln, Nebraska, average of twelve years.   Note that the three-inch soil layer is consistently warmer than the air above and that the thirty-six-inch soil horizon is cooler in spring and summer, but warmer in the fall and winter than the surface soil.

[1] Swezey, G. D., Soil Temperatures of Lincoln, Nebraska, 16th Annual Report, Neb. Agr. Exp. Sta., 95–102, 1903.
Further temperature data may be found as follows:
Baver, L. D., Soil Physics, John Wiley & Sons, Inc., New York, 1940, pp. 283–289.
Smith, Alfred, "Seasonal Subsoil Variations," Jour. Agr. Res., XLIV:421–428, 1932.
Gustafson, A. F., Soils and Soil Management, McGraw-Hill Book Company, Inc., New York, 1941, p. 50.

rapid in the case of air temperatures, and in temperate regions usually greater. It is well to remember, however, that the maximum temperature of a dry surface soil may definitely exceed that of the air, possibly approaching in some cases 125° or 130° F. But in winter even surface soils do not fall greatly below freezing. With a solar control and a clear sky, the air temperature rises from morning to a maximum at about two o'clock. The surface soil, however, does not reach its maximum until later in the afternoon due to the usual lag. This retardation is greater and the temperature change is less as the depth increases. The lower subsoil shows little daily or weekly fluctuation, the variation, as already emphasized, being a slow monthly or seasonal change.

Besides the fundamental temperature relations pointed out above, there is a corollary idea that must ever be kept in mind. This is the influence of moisture upon soil temperature and soil-temperature changes. Whether it is a question of acquisition of insolation, loss of energy to the atmosphere, or the movement of heat to and fro within the soil, the percentage of water present is always important. Water regulation seems to be the key to what little temperature control it is possible to exert on field soils.[1]

[1] For a further consideration of this phase, see page 230.

Chapter IV. Inorganic Soil Colloids. Their Nature and Practical Significance

It has already been emphasized that the most active part of the soil is in the colloidal state [1] and that the two distinct types of colloidal matter, mineral and organic, exist in intimate and heterogeneous intermixture.

Attention will be focused for the present on the inorganic colloidal matter, leaving that of organic origin largely for later consideration (pages 128 and 130). This clayey matter is the seat of such varied and vigorous changes that it deserves diligent study. In fact, most investigators feel that many problems, especially those relating to the genesis, the profile characteristics, and the normal functioning of this natural body we call the *soil*, will not be satisfactorily solved until we know more about the mineral colloidal matter.[2]

37. *The general constitution of silicate clays*

In a broad way, two types of clays are recognized — the *silicate clays* characteristic of temperate regions, and the iron and aluminum

[1] The colloidal state refers to a "two-phase system in which one material (or materials) in a very fine state of aggregation, approaching but not attaining a molecular subdivision, is heterogeneously dispersed through a second." Materials in this state are distinguished especially by three properties — (1) great effective surface or interface, (2) capacity to fix and hold solids, gases, salts, and ions, and (3) catalysis, the tendency to hasten or retard chemical reactions.

Because of the importance of surface exposure, the following definition is especially apt. "A colloidal system may be defined as a complex in which a tremendously large interface is attained by the very fine, heterogeneous dispersion of one (or more) substance in a second substance or material." Each of the two phases of a colloidal system may be a solid, liquid, or gas. A soil is in large degree a solid-liquid system and, as it exists in nature, it normally is in a gel condition.

Reference should be made to a standard text on colloidal chemistry if the above statements are not clear.

[2] The literature dealing with soil colloidal matter is exceedingly voluminous. Perhaps the best beginning can be made with Marshall, C. E., *Colloids in Agriculture*, Edward Arnold & Co., London, 1935.

hydroxide clays found in the tropics and semitropics. Our concern for the present will be with the former since the great agricultural regions of the world are dominated in a large degree by clays of a siliceous nature.

When a soil is analyzed mechanically, it is divided arbitrarily into fractions, the most finely comminuted of which is called *clay*. The maximum size limit of this separate usually is considered as 0.002 mm. or 2 microns (see page 42). It is generally conceded, however, that the upper limit in particle size of the mineral colloidal matter is not greater than 0.001 mm. (1 μ) and perhaps even less. Thus not quite all of the clay, as that term is ordinarily used, is strictly colloidal, and to so consider it is somewhat questionable. Nevertheless, in ordinary parlance such a use is permissible and will be so employed subject to the error pointed out.

Early students of clayey colloid matter visualized the individual particles as more or less spherical. However, it is now definitely established that the particles are laminated, and variable in respect to their lateral extension. Under the electron-microscope [1] they appear definitely as plates,[2] the size and shape depending on their particular mineralogical organization. Some are definitely hexagonal while others seem to be flat frayed fibers or lath-shaped blades. In all cases, the plates are infinitely thin. With some, the edges are clean-cut while others appear as fluffy clumps of exceedingly minute crystals. All clay particles are crystalline and not amorphous as was originally supposed.

Each clay particle regardless of its individual shape is made up of sheetlike molecules or units, held loosely together. Since these units may be disengaged or may, according to conditions, become associated again when brought closely together, clay particles show considerable variation in size. It is well to note, also, that the platelike molecules themselves have a lamellar organization, their sheets of

[1] Shaw, B. T. and R. P. Humbert, "Electron Micrographs of Clay Minerals," *Proc. Soil Sci. Soc. Amer.*, VI:146–149, 1941. Also, Marshall, C. E., R. P. Humbert, B. T. Shaw, and O. G. Caldwell, "Studies of Clay Particles with the Electron-Microscope: II. The Fractionation of Beidellite, Nontronite, Magnesium Bentonite, and Attapulgite," *Soil Sci.*, LIV:149–158, 1942.

[2] The micalike shape of clay particles can be demonstrated in this simple way. By rotating a suitable clay suspension, the particles in motion are oriented temporarily in the same direction. As a result, a reflection of light results that is quite different from that observed when the suspension is at rest and no orientation exists. A suspension of round particles will not show this phenomenon.

atoms being two or three in number. These units are quite definite, usually changing in size only by lateral extension. A clay particle might be visualized by comparing it with a piece of mica — the flakes of the latter representing the platelike molecules or units.

As can readily be seen, clay particles, merely because of their fineness of division, must expose a large amount of *external* surface. But this is by no means all. There are *internal* surfaces as well, the sum of which usually greatly exceeds that of a superficial character. This

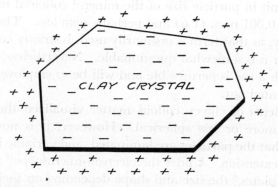

Fig. 12. Diagrammatic representation of a colloidal clay crystal with its lamellar nucleus or micelle, its innumerable negative charges, and its swarm of exchangeable cations. Under the influence of an electric current such a particle will move towards the positive electrode.

internal interface occurs between the platelike units that make up each particle and is particularly well developed in montmorillonite and hydrous mica clays (page 74). Thus the tremendous interface that characterizes clay is accounted for not only by fineness of division but by the platelike organization of the tiny particles. Just how great this surface in total may be cannot be said. But as a conservative estimate, it is suggested that the active interface due to clay in an acre-furrow-slice of representative mineral soil probably exceeds the land area of Illinois or Florida at least forty or fifty times.

The minute and heterogeneously dispersed clay particles are electrically active, ordinarily carrying a considerable electrical potential. This is due to an ionic double layer phenomenon. The inner layer is an immovable stratum of negatively charged ions (anions) that are an integral part of the surfaces, both external and internal, of the colloidal particles. The outer layer is made up of certain positive ions (cations) that are, at least in part, readily displaced. (See Fig. 12.) Thus as the clay particle moves through its dispersive medium, it is accompanied by a swarm of cations and the farther away the more active members of this pulsating throng maintain themselves, the greater is the electrical potential of the particle. Since the charges on the particle itself are normally negative, it functions much like a simple acid radical such as Cl^- or $SO_4^=$ and will

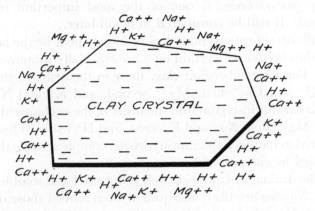

FIG. 13. Diagram of a clay crystal showing the various cations that usually occupy the exchange complex. Note that Ca and H ions are dominant, but that some K, Mg and Na ions are present. No attempt has been made to indicate the numerous adsorbed molecules of water.

migrate to the positive pole when subjected to an electrical current. For convenience in designation the individual particle is spoken of as an *acidoid*, a *micelle*, or a *nucleus*.

Associated with the layer of cations that throng the interfacial zones of clay particles is a large and indefinite amount of water. Part of the water molecules is carried by the swarm of cations since all are definitely hydrated.[1] In addition, water molecules apparently are packed in the interstices and channels between the plates that make up the loosely organized clayey micelle. Even the external faces of the particle may hold water molecules in considerable amounts.

[1] A familiar case of hydration is calcium sulfate or gypsum ($CaSO_4 \cdot 2H_2O$). Not only do molecules of many salts carry combined water but cations seem to have the same capacity. Na and K ions are heavily hydrated. Ca and Mg ions carry water molecules but not in the amounts that characterize the alkali ions.

According to Remy, the order for the monovalent ions in respect to hydration is Na > K > H. For the divalent ions Mg > Ca. See Gortner, R. A., W. F. Hoffman, and W. B. Sinclair, "Physico-Chemical Studies on Proteins, III. Protein and Lyotropic-Series," *Colloidal Symposium Monograph*, V:179–198, 1928.

It is now evident that the micalike clay particles are composed of two distinct parts, the inner, porous, and enormously larger insoluble acidoid, or micelle, and the outer and more or less dissociated swarm of cations with variable amounts of water of hydration. Since these adsorbed cations are usually rather easily displaced, they are spoken of as *exchangeable ions*. This replacement, called *ionic exchange*, or more commonly *base exchange*, is one of the most important of all soil phenomena. It will be considered in detail later.

While all sorts of cations may thus be loosely held by the adsorptive power of the clay nuclei, certain ones are especially prominent. (See Fig. 13.) For a humid-region clay, these in the order of their numbers are H^+ and Ca^{++} first, Mg^{++} second, and K^+ and Na^+ third. For well-drained arid-region soil, the order of the exchangeable ions is Ca^{++} and Mg^{++} first, Na^+ and K^+ next, and H^+ least. The first clay is considered as having a calcium-hydrogen complex, while the second is dominated by calcium and magnesium.[1]

When the drainage of an aridic soil is impeded and soluble salts accumulate, Na ions are likely to equal or even exceed those of the adsorbed Ca. Here then would be a sodium clay. By the same rule the displacement of the metallic cations by H ions would give a hydrogen or acid clay. Since the cation, or cations, preponderant in a colloidal clay has much to do with its physical and chemical properties and its relationship to plants, this phase of the subject is of tremendous practical importance.

The statements above indicate that calcium and magnesium are the adsorbed metallic cations held in largest amounts by the siliceous clays of most natural soils. And that exchangeable potassium is sparingly present. The following data (Table VIII) in corroboration are representative of the large amount of information available respecting this relationship.

Since adsorbed cations are replaceable and, therefore, available, we can explain, in light of the data of Table VIII, why calcium is so active in the soil and plays such a dominant role therein. The amount of adsorbed magnesium ordinarily is about one-third as much while the potassium is often exceedingly low. These relationships account for the contrast, already emphasized (page 27), between the calcium and potash problems of arable soils. Since so much of the total cal-

---

[1] Other exchangeable cations that may be present but usually in small amounts are those of iron, aluminum, copper, manganese, zinc, and ammonium.

cium is replaceable, its activity is assured. The main concern, therefore, is the amount present. Hence the practice of liming. With potash the total amount is often ample (page 23) but the proportion active is exceedingly small. Hence availability is a major consideration.

Table VIII. Relative Numbers of Adsorbed Cations Present in Clay of Soils from Widely Different Parts of the United States [1]

Soil	Metallic Cations, 100 Taken as Total			
	Ca	Mg	K	Na
Amarillo silty clay loam — Texas	66.2	27.0	5.8	1.0
Superior fine sandy loam — Wisconsin	64.5	16.9	6.4	12.2
Beckett loam — Massachusetts	57.6	24.2	6.7	11.5
Davidson clay loam — North Carolina	62.1	24.3	3.9	9.7

38. *The mineralogical nature of silicate clays* [2]

For many years, even after its colloidal nature was recognized, clay was thought to be an amorphous body. X-ray examinations, however, show definitely that in spite of their inconceivable smallness, the lamellar clay particles are crystalline.[3] According to Marshall,[4] two general types of atomic sheets constitute the individual units or molecules (see page 69) that built up the complicated clay particles. One is a silica sheet ($2SiO_2 \cdot H_2O$) and the other alumina ($Al_2O_3 \cdot 3H_2O$). These sheets probably are held together by an oxygen linkage to form the individual molecules. As might be suspected, various kinds of

[1] Calculated from Anderson, M. S. and H. G. Byers, *Character of the Colloidal Materials in the Profiles of Certain Major Soil Groups*, Technical Bulletin 228, U. S. Dept. of Agriculture, pp. 10–17, 1931.

[2] See Kelley, W. P., W. H. Dore, and J. B. Page, "The Colloidal Constituents of American Alkali Soils," *Soil Sci.*, LI:101–124, 1941.

Brown, I. C. and M. Drosdoff, "Chemical and Physical Properties of Soils and of Their Colloids Developed from Granitic Materials in the Mojave Desert," *Jour. Agr. Res.*, LXI:335–352, 1940.

Hendricks, S. B. and L. T. Alexander, "Minerals Present in Soil Colloids, I. Descriptions and Methods for Identification," *Soil Sci.*, XLVIII:257–268, 1939.

Kelley, W. P., W. H. Dore, A. O. Woodford, and S. M. Brown, "The Colloidal Constituents of California Soils," *Soil Sci.*, XLVIII:201–255, 1939.

[3] Kelley, W. P., "The Evidence as to the Crystallinity of Soil Colloids," *Trans. Third Internat. Cong. Soil Sci.*, III:88–91, 1935.

[4] Marshall, C. E., *Colloids in Agriculture*, Edward Arnold & Co., London, 1935, p. 76.

clay are possible because of differences in the number of these lattice sheets and also because of substitutions therein of metallic cations such as iron, magnesium, calcium, and the like. Under certain conditions, even aluminum and silicon may substitute each other. As a result clays may vary not only mineralogically and chemically but also in respect to such physical characteristics as size and shape of particles and the amount and effectiveness of the interfaces.

Two groups of clays are commonly recognized, (1) the *kaolin* and (2) the *montmorillonite*. The molecules of the former are thought to be composed of two sheets or plates, one of silica and one of alumina. Such clays, therefore, are said to have a 1 to 1 type of crystal lattice. Since the molecules apparently are held together rather tightly, the internal interface is much restricted. Moreover, the micelles are comparatively large and definite in outline. Consequently, the two important representatives of the kaolin group, kaolinite and halloysite, do not exhibit colloidal properties of an unusually high order.

The second general group of clays, the montmorillonite, apparently is composed molecularly of two silica sheets and one of alumina. It is, therefore, considered as having a 2 to 1 type of crystal lattice. Of the three common representatives of the group, montmorillonite, beidellite, and nontronite, the two first mentioned apparently are found in soils in largest amounts. The molecules of these clays are less firmly linked together than those of the kaolin group and, therefore, are usually farther apart. An unusually large amount of internal interface is thus exposed and molecules of water and the cations of various substances may force themselves between the sheetlike molecules. As a result, adsorption is more marked than in the case of the kaolin clays. And other colloidal properties such as plasticity, cohesion, and especially base exchange are greatly in evidence. In fact montmorillonite particles disperse so readily that the tilth of soils dominated by this clay is more difficult to maintain than though the soil clay were kaolinite.

Associated with the montmorillonite minerals is a rather indefinite group called the *hydrous micas*. They seem to be of an intermediate nature, arising from the weathering of the original micas. Since they resemble the montmorillonite clays in a number of important respects, they are here classed as of that group. Some authors, however, set them apart and recognize three groups of clays; namely, *kaolin, montmorillonite,* and *hydrous micas.*

In discussing the mineralogical [1] nature of silicate clay, it must not be forgotten that other minerals besides the ones mentioned are present, either as mere accessories or as an important part of the colloidal complex. Of these, the hydrated oxides of silicon, iron, and aluminum should be mentioned. While these probably occur but sparingly in temperate-region soils, the latter two are especially important in tropical and semitropical regions, giving rise to what are spoken of as *laterite soils*. Although the hydroxide clays will be considered later (page 86), it is well to note that, as progress is made from a humid temperate region to the humid tropics, the silicate clays often contain a larger and larger admixture of colloidal iron and aluminum oxides. The red and yellow soils of our southern states (page 276) are very good evidence of this transition.

Table IX.   Relative Amounts of Colloidal Minerals Present in Clays from Certain Representative Soils of the United States [2]
(Expressed as ratios)

Soils from which Clays Were Obtained	Ratio Relations		
	Kaolin	Hydrous mica	Montmorillonite
5 Red podzolic soils from southern states	9	1	0
8 Gray podzolic soils from eastern U. S.	5	3	0
1 Prairie soil, Iowa	4	4	1
1 Chernozem, N. Dak.	3	4	2
4 Desert soils, Calif.	2	7	

[1] The mineralogical compositions of sand and silt are markedly in contrast with that of clay. Quartz seems to predominate in sand, while feldspar and quartz are prominent in silt.

Below is given the mineralogical description of very fine sand and silt from a Marshall silt loam from Missouri.

Very fine sand — minerals other than quartz, 20 per cent. Orthoclase, 10 per cent. Muscovite, 2 per cent. Biotite, magnetite, epidote, albite, labradorite, oligoclase, tourmaline, zircon, garnet, and augite are also present.

Silt — minerals other than quartz, 34 per cent. Orthoclase, 4 per cent. Muscovite, 4 per cent. Biotite, magnetite, epidote, albite, labradorite, oligoclase, tourmaline, rutile, glaucophane, hornblende, and augite are also present.

From Robinson, W. O., *The Inorganic Composition of Some Important American Soils*, Bulletin 122, U. S. Dept. of Agriculture, 1914.

[2] From data presented by Alexander, L. T., S. B. Hendricks, and R. A. Nelson, "Minerals Present in Soil Colloids: II. Estimation in Some Representative Soils," *Soil Sci.*, XLVIII:273–279, 1939. The estimates, because of the nature of the original data, can be considered only as roughly comparative.

As one might well surmise, the clay of any particular soil is made up of a mixture of different colloidal minerals. This occurs because the kind of clay that develops depends not only upon climatic influences and profile conditions but also upon the nature of the parent material. The situation may be further complicated by the presence in the parent material itself of clay that was formed under a preceding and perhaps an entirely different type of climatic regime. Nevertheless, some general deductions seem possible as the preceding data (Table IX) intimate.

It would seem in general that the clay in our southern soils is likely to be markedly dominated by kaolin minerals. In the cool humid regions to the north, hydrous mica tends to become prominent, especially if potassium, which is characteristic of the minerals giving rise to this clay, is present in large amount. Nevertheless, the kaolins still are likely to dominate. Shifting to prairie soils where the rainfall is less effective, montmorillonite appears and with the hydrous micas equals or exceeds the kaolin. Chernozems with a definitely lower rainfall show less kaolin and more of the montmorillonite and hydrous mica, while in desert soils the two latter are definitely dominant. While these conclusions are more or less tentative, they suggest that clay mixtures vary with different soils and that the type of clay mineral predominating is controlled to a considerable degree by climate. Nevertheless it is yet to be shown just why a particular clay mineral occurs under any given condition.

39. *The chemical composition of silicate clays*

A mineralogical consideration of colloidal clay naturally leads to an inquiry as to its quantitative chemical composition. A considerable amount of data [1] is available but because of the mineralogical heterogeneity of the clayey complex, such figures throw little light on the exact composition of the minerals as individuals. The situation is

[1] See especially:

Robinson, W. O. and R. S. Holmes, *The Chemical Composition of Soil Colloids*, Bulletin 1311, U. S. Dept. of Agriculture, 1924.

Anderson, M. S. and H. G. Byers, *Character of the Colloidal Materials in the Profile of Certain Major Soil Groups*, Technical Bulletin 228, U. S. Dept. of Agriculture, 1931.

Robinson, G. W., *Soils, Their Origin, Constitution and Classification*, Thomas Murby & Co., London, 1936, p. 83.

Brown, I. C. and H. G. Byers, *The Chemical and Physical Properties of Dry-land Soils and of Their Colloids*, Technical Bulletin 502, U. S. Dept of Agriculture, 1935.

analogous to an attempt to determine the mineral nature of a whole soil from its total chemical analysis. Chemical analyses do indicate, however, (see Table X) that the five main constituents, silica, alumina, iron, organic matter, and combined water may make up from 90 to 97 per cent of colloidal clay. Also it will be found that the colloidal matter of a soil is higher in the important plant nutrients than the soil itself and hence than the noncolloidal fraction also. This is of important practical significance and partially accounts for the fact that soils of fine texture are considered as strong soils agriculturally.

Table X. Chemical Composition of Colloidal Clay Extracted from the Surface Soils Belonging to Three Very Different Series and Obtained in Various Parts of the United States [1]

Constituent	Miami Series from Indiana and Michigan	Chester Series from New Jersey, Pennsylvania, Virginia, and Maryland	Cecil Series from Virginia, North Carolina, Georgia, and Alabama
	Mean Percentage of 9 samples	Mean Percentage of 15 samples	Mean Percentage of 17 samples
SiO_2	49.78	36.47	37.50
Al_2O_3	25.34	31.68	36.39
Fe_2O_3	9.36	13.83	10.47
CaO	0.76	0.51	0.21
MgO	2.09	1.65	0.44
K_2O	2.67	1.02	0.71
Na_2O	0.23	0.12	0.05
TiO_2	0.75	0.71	0.94
P_2O_5	0.29	0.42	0.21
SO_3	0.20	0.28	0.13
MnO	0.20	0.33	0.12
Organic matter	5.95	7.11	5.11
Combined water	8.22	12.86	13.60

40. The salt-acidlike nature of clay

Clay particles, regardless of their mineralogical character, have the same general organization. That is, they are made up of a complex negative radical, the acidoid or micelle, and a miscellany of adsorbed cations, of which, in a humid region, those of calcium and hydrogen

[1] Holmes, R. S. and Glen Eddington, *Variations of the Colloidal Material Extracted from the Soils of the Miami, Chester, and Cecil Series*, Technical Bulletin 229, U. S. Dept. of Agriculture, 1930.

are by far the most numerous. Consequently, a clay complex may be represented in the following simple and convenient way:

$$x \text{ Ca r H (acidoid)}$$

The significance of the Ca and H are, of course, obvious since in a humid region these cations dominate the complex. The r stands for the small amounts of cationic Mg, K, Na, etc., that are usually present in the ionic outer layer. The x indicates that the number of micelles is indefinite.

It has already been emphasized that the acidoid is micalike as to shape, highly hydrated, possesses a tremendous interface, and carries a multitude of negative charges. The latter characteristic allows it to function as a true acid radical. Consequently the presence of such adsorbed cations as Ca or K or Mg forms just as true a salt as though $CaSO_4$ or KNO_3 were produced. In the same way if H ions are adsorbed, an acid results — insoluble and stable, but nevertheless as definitely an acid as H_2SO_4 or HNO_3.

The concept, therefore, is clear. Soil clay is not only a mixture of different minerals but, from the chemical standpoint, it also is a mixture of acids and the salts of these acids, or if looked at in the singular, a complex acid salt. This concept of the clayey colloidal matter and the simple formula method of expression recorded above make possible the explanation in a very simple way of colloidal transactions that undoubtedly are actually very complex. One of these, a reaction of tremendous importance — *base exchange* — will be considered forthwith.

41. *Base exchange* [1]

With the fundamental colloidal conceptions already presented as a background, base exchange may be accounted for very simply. The tendency of carbonic acid to force such a transfer will be taken as illustrative of this intrinsic colloidal phenomenon, since an exchange so motivated is perhaps one of the commonest and most important soil reactions.

Consider, to begin with, a representative humid-region mineral-

[1] The term *ionic exchange* is preferable to *base exchange*, as base here connotes metallic cations and this is not the usual meaning of the term. However, the term *base exchange* is too firmly embedded in the literature to be ignored.

surface soil, rather high in replaceable calcium, and functioning under optimum conditions of moisture and temperature. Naturally a considerable amount of CO_2 is evolved as the organic matter decomposes and an appreciable carbon dioxide pressure develops. The presence of carbonic acid (H_2CO_3) in the soil solution is inevitable. The ionic hydrogen thus generated is exceedingly active and will tend to replace the exchangeable calcium of the colloidal complex. This occurs not only because of mass action effect but also because ionic hydrogen is adsorbed more strongly than is the ionic calcium.[1] This reaction may be shown graphically as follows, only one ion of the adsorbed calcium for simplicity being represented in action:

$$\boxed{\text{Micelle}}\ Ca^{++} + 2\,H_2CO_3 \rightleftharpoons \boxed{\text{Micelle}}\begin{matrix}H^+\\H^+\end{matrix} + Ca(HCO_3)_2$$

| Clay high in replaceable Ca | Carbonic acid | Clay with an increase in H⁺ and decrease in Ca⁺⁺ | Soluble calcium bicarbonate |

The adjustment is very simple, almost instantaneous, and the interchange of calcium and hydrogen chemically equivalent. And if the soluble bicarbonate is removed by drainage, as commonly occurs in humid regions, the movement of the lime will be continuously outward. Because of this phenomenon, and the presence in most soils of relatively large amounts of adsorbed calcium, this element is active in larger amounts than any other soil metal and the metal most largely lost in drainage. Moreover, the continual assumption of H ions by the colloidal clay at the expense of the calcium tends by equilibrium to increase the H-ion concentration of the soil solution and the pH of the soil is gradually lowered. This illustration emphasizes not only the tremendous loss of lime that most soils are subject to (see page 356), but also indicates why humid-region soils tend to become acid. The phenomenon may now be expressed in a more exact and less cumbersome way as follows:

$$x\,CarH(acidoid) + y\,H_2CO_3 \rightleftharpoons x\,CarH(acidoid) + y\begin{cases}Ca(HCO_3)_2\\r\ carbonate\ or\\bicarbonate\end{cases}$$

[1] The strength of adsorption, that is replacing power, of the various cations is H > Ca > Mg > K > Na. Mass action, of course, is also a very important factor. This order seems to be related to the valency of the ions and their degree of hydration.

Weigner, G., "Some Physico-Chemical Properties of Clays, I. Base Exchange or Ionic Exchange," *Jour. Soc. Chem. Ind.*, L, No. 8: 61 T and 71 T, 1931.

As the above reaction indicates, the active hydrogen in nature replaces other cations as well as those of calcium. But because the exchangeable calcium ions are much more numerous, especially on the outer and more exposed surfaces of the micelle,[1] they are very easily released. Thus in almost every normal soil, calcium is replaced by the natural process explained above to a greater extent than any other cation.

The reversibility of any exchange reaction is, of course, highly probable. If lime is applied to an acid soil, that is, one in which the colloidal complex is definitely dominated by hydrogen, a replacement, the reverse of the one just cited, readily occurs. The active calcium ions by mass action replace the hydrogen and other cations, the latter, of course, to a lesser degree. As a result the clay becomes higher in exchangeable calcium, the pH is raised, and the whole physiological setup of the soil is modified. Liming, therefore, promotes, among other alterations, a temporary reversal in the direction of calcium movement. This phase is dealt with more fully on page 357.

One more illustration of ionic exchange will be offered. A soil fairly high in replaceable calcium is treated with a liberal application of potassium chloride, a common fertilizer salt. The exchange will tend to move as follows:

$$x \; CarH(acidoid) + y \; KCl \rightleftharpoons x \; CaKrH(acidoid) + y \begin{cases} CaCl_2 \\ HCl \\ r \; chlorides \end{cases}$$

The reaction is not difficult to interpret. Some of the added potassium pushes its way into the colloidal complex and forces out an equivalent number of calcium and other ions. These appear in the soil solution. And, although the fertilizer seems to encourage an increased loss of lime in drainage, field experiments indicate little tendency towards an increase in acidity. This probably is due to the fact that the calcium is replaced by another metal. The entrance of the added potassium into the exchange complex is considered to be of advantage to microorganisms and higher plants since a nutrient so held no doubt remains in a rather easily available condition. Hence base exchange

[1] While Ca ions are especially numerous on the outer surfaces of most clay particles, it is probable that the number of magnesium and perhaps potassium ions increase proportionately between the plates of the micelle. This is indicated by the fact that grinding markedly increases the replaceable magnesium. See Kelley, W. P., W. H. Dore, and S. M. Brown, "The Nature of the Base-Exchange Material of Bentonite Soils and Zeolites as Revealed by Chemical Investigations and X-Ray Analysis," *Soil Sci.*, XXXI:25–45, 1931.

is an important consideration not only in respect to nutrients naturally present in soils but also in relation to those applied in commercial fertilizers and in other ways.[1]

Marshall [2] states that, next to photosynthesis, base exchange "is the most important chemical reaction in the whole domain of agriculture." Considering the influence of ionic exchange on the physico-chemical condition of soils, on the availability of nutrients to microorganisms and higher plants, on the loss of soluble constituents in drainage, and on the effectiveness of lime and commercial fertilizers, the reason for such a statement is readily understood.

42. *Base-exchange capacity of clay* [3]

It is probable that higher plants, possibly by contact replacement, can make ready use of at least a part of the exchangeable constituents of soils. The nutritional importance of base exchange is, therefore, undoubted. To the inquiring mind, a question immediately arises. What is the magnitude of this all-important property or in technical terms, what is the *exchange capacity* of silicate clays?

Before dealing with base-exchange capacity, which is simply another term for the relative adsorptive power of a clay, the method of expressing its magnitude must be explained. The unit is a *milliequivalent*. And it is defined as "one milligram of hydrogen or the amount of any other ion that will combine with or displace it." Milliequivalents when applied to soils are usually expressed on the basis of 100 grams of dry substance.

Thus if a clay has a total exchange capacity of 1 milliequivalent, it is capable of adsorbing and holding 1 milligram of hydrogen or its equivalent [4] for every 100 grams of dry substance. This, of course, is 1 milligram to 100,000 milligrams of clay or 10 parts per million. In

[1] It should be noted that anionic adsorption and exchange takes place and in some cases assumes considerable importance. This is especially true in respect to the adsorption of phosphate ions. This phase is dealt with on page 303.

[2] Marshall, C. E., *Colloids in Agriculture*, Edward Arnold & Co., London, 1935, p. 79.

[3] A number of different methods are available for the determination of the base-exchange capacity of clay or soil. One of the common procedures is to displace the original adsorbed cations by treating the sample with an ammonium or barium acetate solution of a given pH. The capacity of the clay or soil to adsorb ammonium or barium ions under controlled conditions is taken as a measure of exchange capacity.

[4] Note well the term *equivalent*. This means that other ions may be expressed in milliequivalents by changing them over into their hydrogen equivalents. This phase will receive consideration later.

terms of percentage, it is 0.001 per cent. Or an acre-furrow-slice of pure clay weighing 2,000,000 pounds could adsorb for each milli-equivalent the equivalent of 20 pounds of exchangeable hydrogen. This method of expression is so convenient and is so commonly used that a person dealing with the literature of soil science must be perfectly familiar with it.

As might be expected, the exchange capacities of soil clays exhibit a wide range since a number of different clay minerals are always present and their proportionate amounts markedly vary with conditions of climate and soil material. As to the individual clay minerals, Russell and Haddock [1] decided from their study of clays extracted from Iowa soils, that the exchange capacities of montmorillonite, hydrous mica, and kaolin were in the order of 100, 30, and 10 milliequivalents respectively. It is thus easy to see why the clay complex of southern soils, dominated as they are by kaolin minerals (see Table IX), should have a low exchange capacity, ranging perhaps between 20 and 30 milliequivalents. On the other hand, the clays functioning in the soils of the Middle West, where hydrous mica and montmorillonite are prominent, have a much higher base-exchange capacity, ranging from 50 to possibly 100 milliequivalents depending on conditions.

The practical significance of the above statements is far-reaching. Clays differ markedly in their base-exchange properties. Hence soils also will differ widely in this all-important capacity, not only because they possess different amounts of clay but also because the clay complex is so variable. This heterogeneity of soil clay is a fertility factor of tremendous importance.

43. *Other properties of clay — plasticity, cohesion, and flocculation*

Without a doubt, the base-exchange property of clay is outstanding. Yet, from the practical as well as the technical standpoint, certain other characteristics also assume considerable importance. Those to receive attention here are three — *plasticity, cohesion,* and *flocculation.* As might be expected, they all are surface phenomena and their intensity depends upon the amount and nature of the interface presented by the clay.

[1] Russell, M. B. and J. L. Haddock, "The Identification of the Clay Minerals in Five Iowa Soils by the Thermal Method," *Proc. Soil Sci. Soc. Amer.*, V:90–94, 1940.

When a small amount of colloidal clay is dispersed in a much larger quantity of water, a condition designated by the colloidal chemist as a *sol* exists.   When this relationship is reversed and the relatively small quantity of water is present, a viscous condition results.   The colloidal mass is now called a *gel*.   Field soils, because of the limited amount of water usually present, are normally in the gel condition.[1]

Many gels, especially the siliceous clays of humid regions, exhibit plasticity, that is, pliability and the capacity of being molded.   This property is probably due to the platelike nature of the clay particles and the lubricating yet binding influence of the adsorbed water.   Thus the particles easily slide over each other much like panes of glass with films of water between them.   In a practical way, plasticity is extremely important as it is such a noticeable characteristic and allows a ready change in soil structure.   This must be considered in tillage operations.   As everyone knows, the cultivation of a heavy soil when it is too wet will, because of the ease with which the clay particles glide over each other, result in a puddled condition, inimical to suitable aeration and drainage.   With clayey soils, especially if low in humus, plasticity presents a real problem.

A second characteristic closely related to plasticity is *cohesion*.   As the water of a clay gel is reduced, shrinkage occurs and various structural forms develop depending on the nature of the soil involved. The shrinkage, which splits the soil mass into aggregates, is accompanied by a cohesion of the particles which makes structural developments not only possible but also more or less permanent.   This tendency of the clay particles to stick together probably is due at least in part to the mutual attraction of the water molecules carried by the replaceable cations.

Soils, because of alternate imbibition and shrinkage, accompanied, of course, by cohesion and influenced by soluble salts, develop characteristic profile structures.   These are important in field classification and description.   Such natural structural forms as *granular, massive, fragmentary, nut, shot, prismatic, platy,* and *columnar* are recognized by pedologists (see pages 55–56).   Of these, the granular structure is especially important in surface cultivated soils not only because it is extremely favorable for crop growth but also because it can be en-

---

[1] Clay matter of soil is called a *reversible colloid*, since it will readily assume a gel or a sol condition after losing its dispersion by drying.   From the standpoint of soil condition and plant growth this is a fortunate characteristic.

couraged and maintained by the proper handling of the land (see page 57). That organic matter is of vital importance in such control must not be forgotten.

Flocculation, a term applied to a coagulation of matter in the colloidal state, is an outstanding characteristic of most clayey soils. A very good example is afforded by treating a colloidal clay suspension with a little calcium hydroxide. The tiny clay particles almost immediately coalesce into floccules, that, because of their combined weight, sink to the bottom of the containing vessel, leaving the supernatant liquid clear. The phenomenon is called *flocculation* because of the peculiar appearance of the aggregates. The same action apparently takes place in the soil itself, but, of course, much less rapidly.

The coagulating capacity of the various cations is in the order of H and Ca > Mg > K > Na. This is fortunate as the colloidal complexes of humid-region soils are usually dominated by calcium and hydrogen. Therefore, such soils gradually tend to assume a coagulated condition in the field, which is of some consequence in respect to granulation. It is well to remark again (page 60) that flocculation is not granulation, since the latter is most satisfactorily attained only through the agency of organic matter. Flocculation really only sets the stage. Nor does lime, in the amounts ordinarily applied, particularly encourage granulation except through its influence on humus development.

Just why hydrogen and calcium cations are so effective as flocculative agents is difficult to say, although it is probably related to the electrical potential of the particles, their degree of hydration, and their migration velocities.[1] In contrast with these cations active potassium and especially sodium tend to work in the opposite direction. This accounts for the dispersed and sticky condition of certain alkali soils and for the undesirable physical effects of large applications of nitrate of soda as a fertilizer.

It is plain to be seen that plasticity, cohesion, and flocculation are important physical characteristics of soils especially from the standpoint of practical management. The field control of soil structure must definitely take them into account. With the colloidal viewpoint now provided, it might be worth while to review the discussion al-

---

[1] Wiegener, G., "Coagulation," *Jour. Soc. Chem. Ind.*, L, No. 7:55T–62T, 1931.
Russell, E. W., "The Present Position of the Theory of Coagulation of Dilute Clay Suspension," *Jour. Agr. Sci.*, XXII:165–199, 1932.

ready offered (pages 57 through 61) relating to the structural management of arable soils.

44. *The genesis of silicate clays*

The silicate clays seem to develop most readily from silicate minerals such as feldspar, mica, and the like. The process apparently begins with hydrolysis which is, in a sense, base exchange. The initial step may be illustrated as follows:

$$KAlSi_3O_8 + HOH = HAlSi_3O_8 + KOH$$

This simple replacement of the large potassium atoms by the much smaller hydrogen atoms initiates a long train of complicated reactions.[1] These are too complex and speculative for consideration here. Suffice to say the silicate crystal immediately becomes open and porous because of replacements and thus further and more drastic changes are encouraged. Gradually the minute and lamellar clayey nuclei, already described, are evolved, partly by dissolution and partly by subsequent synthesis. The plate shape of the molecules as well as their chemical nature seem to encourage the rapidity of the build-up. Under the acid weathering of temperate regions, part of the alumina and iron is removed with the more mobile metallic constituents, such as calcium, sodium, and potassium, and silicate clays result. The lateritic weathering of the tropics, however, is less acid. Here silica is diminished instead of the sesquioxides, and hydroxide clays develop (see next section).

The exchange complex of fully developed humid-region silicate clay, as has frequently been stated, is usually dominated by calcium and hydrogen ions. Why this occurs is an interesting speculation. In the early stages of clay formation the solution surrounding the decomposing silicates undoubtedly is high in active calcium, as this element is readily liberated by weathering. Since this cation is adsorbed more strongly than most of the other metals commonly present (the order is Ca > Mg > K > Na), the outer surfaces of the developing clay, and to some extent the inner faces of the laminated particles

[1] Byers, H. G., "Chemical Composition of the Colloids of the Great Soil Groups," *Trans, Third Internat. Cong. Soil Sci.*, I:76–79, Oxford, England, 1935.

Jenny, H., "Behavior of Potassium and Sodium during the Process of Soil Formation," Research Bulletin 162, *Missouri Agr. Exp. Sta.*, 1931.

also, are soon dominated by exchangeable calcium. Thus a calcium complex comes into being.

As organic matter gradually accumulates and soil processes are initiated, carbonic acid is generated and hydrogen ions, because they are so strongly adsorbed, gradually enter the cationic swarm by base exchange. The clay, as the replaced calcium is lost in drainage, becomes a calcium-hydrogen complex and acidity develops in rough proportion to the dominance of the replaceable hydrogen. Thus one can visualize in this simple way the genesis of a silicate clay, a process that no doubt is infinitely complex.

45. *Hydroxide clays*

The discussion so far has dealt only with silicate clays. However, hydroxide clays deserve attention, not only because they occur in temperate regions intermixed with silicate clays, but also because this type of colloidal matter is common in the tropics and semitropics. The red and yellow lateritic soils of these regions are dominated in large degree by hydrated iron and aluminum oxides.

The origin of these clays is closely related to the type of climate prevalent in equatorial regions. Although tropical weathering is exceedingly drastic, it is less acid than that of the cool temperate regions. This is because of the rapid oxidation of the soil organic matter and its decomposition products. Under such conditions silicon is readily removed leaving the iron and aluminum hydroxides in a highly colloidal state. Incidentally these clays, under comparable conditions, are less acid than the silicate clays already considered. The origin of hydroxide clays is more fully discussed under laterization (page 277).

An understanding of silicate colloids makes it possible to dispose of hydroxide clays briefly but clearly. In the first place, the general organization is the same as those of the silicate type — that is, a large insoluble nucleus, negatively charged and accompanied by a swarm of cations of which hydrogen and calcium are predominant. Hence the same generalized formula already specified — x CarH(acidoid) — may be used.

Hydroxide clays in general are yellow or red, if there has been adequate opportunity for the hydration and oxidation of some of the iron. Moreover, they are much lower in plasticity and cohesion than the silicate clays. As a consequence, soils dominated by them can be cultivated immediately after a heavy rain and do not erode seriously unless the slope is quite steep. Structural condition is not a serious problem in lateritic soils. Moreover, the base-exchange capacity of hydroxide clay is exceptionally low, hardly equal to that of the kaolin clays. This has a fertility bearing of no mean importance. Another fertility relationship is the large amount of active iron and aluminum present. These cations tend to render phosphorus, both native and added, particularly unavailable to plants (page 302).

All of the characteristics mentioned above are but a reflection of the nature of the micelle and serve to emphasize the physical and chemical differences that can be expected when a change is made from lateritic soils to those dominated by a silicate complex. A further consideration of laterites will be found on page 280.

46. *Organic colloids*

Since the clays of surface soils always carry an appreciable admixture of humus, a brief word is necessary at this point regarding organic colloids. Otherwise the soil significance of the colloidal state of matter cannot be fully visualized.

We shall not concern ourselves here with the origin of humus or with its chemical composition. Those phases are more appropriately considered under soil organic matter (page 128). Moreover, we shall merely mention in passing the color relations, the low plasticity, the low cohesion, and the high water capacity of the organic colloids. This will allow the emphasis for the present to be placed on two closely related phases (1) the general organization of the humic complex and (2) its base-exchange capacity.

The organization of the soil humus, in spite of its variable and complex chemical nature, is comparatively simple. To say that the same general formula — x CarH(acidoid) —, already employed for the clays, can be used to show the colloidal setup of humus appropriately covers the situation. If the ideas implied by the formula are clear, no further explanation should be necessary in this regard. Since the soil colloidal matter is a mixture of clay and humus, the possibility of expressing this heterogeneous complex with one simple formula is indeed fortunate. The base-exchange reactions already written for silicate clays (page 79) hold just as definitely not only for humus but also for the indefinite mixture of colloidal matter present in the normal soil.

In respect to base-exchange capacity, the contrast of humus with clay is striking. It has already been suggested that the colloidal silicate minerals vary in respect to their exchange capacity from 20 to perhaps 100 milliequivalents, depending on the particular mineral under consideration (page 82). On the other hand, the capacity of a well-developed humus from mineral soils may range from perhaps 200 to 300 milliequivalents. In general, 1 per cent of organic matter in a mineral soil means an exchange capacity in the neighborhood of 2 milliequivalents. One per cent of clay, in contrast, will affect the base-exchange capacity much less, perhaps only from 0.3 to 0.6 of a milliequivalent. Although the figures themselves are extremely tentative, the ideas that they convey are definite and extremely significant.

47. *Exchange capacity of soils — percentage base saturation*

Two ideas of a general nature stand out clearly from the preceding discussion: (1) that the colloidal situation within a normal soil is infinitely complicated and (2) practically every soil characteristic and activity has, in one way or another, a colloidal phase. The first idea needs little added emphasis. Soils are a mixture of noncolloidal and colloidal materials in all possible proportions. Both are complicated, especially the latter. The colloidal fraction,[1]

[1] A method for determining the amount of colloidal matter in soil, perfected in the United States Dept. of Agriculture, provides for the separation from the soil, after sufficient agitation, of a sample of colloidal matter by means of a high-powered centrifuge. When air-dried, the adsorptive power of this colloidal material for water vapor is determined by exposure over a 3.3 per cent water solution of sulfuric acid. At the same time the adsorptive capacity for water vapor is determined on an air-dried sample of the whole soil. The following calculation is then made:

$$\frac{\text{Adsorption per gram of whole soil}}{\text{Adsorption per gram of extracted colloid}} \times \frac{100}{1} = \% \text{ of colloidal matter in soil sample.}$$

Gile, P. L., N. E. Middleton, W. O. Robinson, W. H. Fry, and M. S. Anderson, *Estimation of Colloidal Material in Soils by Adsorption*, Bulletin 1193, U. S. Dept. of Agriculture, 1924.

A method of an entirely different type for estimating the amount of colloidal matter in soils has been devised by Bouyoucos. By means of a suitable stirring apparatus a soil suspension is obtained. Definite proportions of soil and water are, of course, used. After standing a given time in a cylinder, the suspension is tested with a suitably calibrated hydrometer and the percentage of colloidal matter read directly. Bouyoucos. G. J., "The Hydrometer as a New and Rapid Method of Determining the Colloidal Content of Soils," *Soil Sci.*, XXIII:319–330, 1927. Also, "A Sensitive Hydrometer for Determining Small Amounts of Clay or Colloids in Soils," *Soil Sci.*, XLIV:245–246, 1937.

made up as it is of a heterogeneous mixture of several different clays and humic bodies of variable composition, presents a situation with which, until recent years, scientists were unable to cope. Its secrets are now yielding to persistent research.

As to the second general idea, any chapter of this text offers ample illustration and confirmation. Since colloidal relationships are so numerous and varied, only one phase, particularly germane and applicable at this point, will be considered here — base-exchange capacity of soils and some correlated characteristics.

Since the phenomenon of base-exchange is so important in soils, the question of their exchange capacity is sure to arise. This may be answered by considering data from Pierre and Scarseth regarding a wide variety of soils. These are presented in Table XI.

Table XI. Total Exchange Capacity of a Wide Variety of Soils [1]

Soil Type	Exchange Capacity, m.e.
Norfolk sandy loam — Ala.	1.83
Greenville sandy loam — Ala.	2.33
Norfolk sandy loam — Ala.	3.00
Cecil clay — Ala.	4.00
Susquehanna fine sandy loam — Ala.	4.05
Cecil clay loam — Ala.	4.85
Cecil sandy loam — S. Car.	5.50
Greenville fine sandy loam — Ala.	6.97
Cory silt loam — Ill.	7.76
Delta light silt loam — Miss.	9.41
Miami silt loam — Wis.	9.79
Colby silt loam — Wis.	13.28
Aktibbeha clay — Ala.	19.36
Grundy silt loam — Ill.	26.33
Susquehanna clay — Ala.	34.25

In scanning the data one perhaps notices first of all the great range in the figures presented. This is to be expected since soils vary so tremendously in the amounts of clay and humus present. Also the various types of clay show wide contrasts in adsorptive capacity. This has already been emphasized in respect to kaolin and montmorillonite (page 82). Besides, humus developed in different climates or from diverse residues does not possess the same base-exchange capacities.

[1] Pierre, W. H. and G. D. Scarseth, "Determination of Percentage Base Saturation of Soils and Its Value in Different Soils at Definite pH Values," *Soil Sci.*, XXXI:99–114, 1931.

A more careful examination of the data will reveal a rough cor-relation between texture and exchange capacity, the latter in general increasing as soils become heavier. This relationship, however, is by no means consistent due to differences in the individual clay minerals and the humic complexes. As already suggested (page 82) southern soils, carrying clays of a kaolin nature, should show, under comparable conditions, a lower exchange capacity than northern Middle West soils whose clay complex contains more hydrous mica and montmoril-lonite.

Let us carry the consideration one step farther and inquire briefly as to the proportion of bases (that is, Ca, Mg, K, etc.) to hydrogen in the exchange complex. This relationship ordinarily is expressed in terms of *percentage base saturation*, that is the percentage extent to which the colloidal complex is occupied by exchangeable bases. Thus if the percentage base saturation is 80, four-fifths of the exchange capacity, expressed in milliequivalents, is held by bases and only one-fifth by hydrogen ions.

The percentage base-saturation data for different soils show wide variations, the colloidal complexes in arid-region soils being prac-tically saturated with bases while those of humid-region soils are likely to be comparatively low in metallic cations and correspondingly higher in adsorbed hydrogen. Such differences are extremely impor-tant not only from the fertility standpoint but also in respect to the H-ion concentration of the soil solution. In this regard it is sufficient to say, here, that a rather definite correlation exists between the per-centage base saturation of a soil and its pH. And as the former is reduced, due to the loss in drainage of lime and other metallic con-stituents, the pH also is lowered. This is in line with the common knowledge that leaching tends ordinarily to increase the acidity of humid-region soils. The mechanism by which colloids control soil pH will be considered later (page 290).

Since the differences that soils in general are likely to exhibit in respect to base-exchange capacity and percentage base saturation, are firmly in mind, it may not be too misleading to suggest more detailed figures of an average nature. A representative surface mineral soil from a humid temperate region and at an intermediate fertility level, will be considered. The data (Table XII) are merely tentative but it is felt that they afford a more tangible idea of base-exchange capacity and other related characteristics than has yet been offered.

These figures may be modified to suggest the exchange condition of a corresponding arid-region surface soil by lowering the adsorbed hydrogen and increasing the metallic cations proportionately until the percentage base saturation reaches 90 or even 100. The pH, of course, approaches 7 or may even exceed this figure if carbonates are present. These changes definitely indicate the differences that in

Table XII.   Suggested Exchange Data for a Representative Mineral Surface Soil
of a Humid Temperate Region

Exchangeable calcium	6 to 9 m.e. [a]
Other exchangeable bases	2 to 3 "
Exchangeable hydrogen	4 to 6 "
Total exchange capacity	12 to 18 m.e.
Percentage base saturation	66.6
Probable pH	5.3 to 5.6

[a] In order that the amounts of such exchangeable cations as Ca, Mg, K, etc. may be accurately compared with the amounts of adsorbed H, they must be reduced to milliequivalents. The conversion is easy.

Suppose, for example, that 40 mgs. of exchangeable Ca are present in 100 gms. of dry soil. Since one atom of Ca (atomic wt. 40) will replace two atoms of H (atomic wt. 1), the weight relation is 40:2 or 20:1. Hence the 40 mgs. of Ca is equivalent to 2 mgs. of H or to 2 milliequivalents.

One milliequivalent of any cation is equivalent on the basis of the acre-furrow-slice (2,000,000 lbs. of dry soil) to 20 lb. of hydrogen (page 82) or to 1000 lb. of CaCO₃. This is a convenient conversion relation to remember.

Applying this conversion to the maximum figures quoted in Table XII, we find that the total exchange capacity of the soil in question is equivalent to 18,000 lb. of CaCO₃ an acre-furrow-slice and that the actual amount of exchangeable calcium present is equal to 4½ tons of CaCO₃. These figures provide a definite idea as to the magnitude of the exchange capacity of soils and as to the amount of replaceable calcium that might be present.

general can be expected when representative humid and arid temperate-region soils are compared in respect to their exchange characteristics, percentage base saturation, and pH.

48. *Ionic exchange and the availability of nutrients*

It is generally assumed that adsorbed nutrients are rather readily available both to higher plants and to microorganisms. And experimental results unquestionably bear this out. But just how is the transfer from soil colloid to soil organism effected? We have in base exchange the mechanism that undoubtedly facilitates the availability of nutrients held in this way.

Apparently base exchange functions under two more or less distinct conditions as far as plant roots and microorganisms are concerned.

In one case the nutrients dislodged by the H ions, which effect most of the interchange, find their way into the outer and freer portion of the soil solution. There they may ultimately contact the absorptive surfaces of root hairs and microorganisms or react again with the soil solids or be removed in drainage water. The large amounts of calcium, magnesium, and potassium lost by leaching indicate that many ions escape biological absorption in this manner.

On the other hand, if the contact of the root hairs and microorganisms with the colloidal surfaces of the soil complex is close, and apparently this is the case, there may be a definite overlapping or integration of interfaces. (See Fig. 6.) Under such a condition the H ions, generated at the surfaces of the root hairs and the microorganisms, might effect an interchange with the nutrient cation without either of the ions emerging from the interfacial zones. Under such conditions nutrients might be acquired by higher plants and microorganisms with great ease and facility and at the same time there would be little chance of loss in drainage. This contact absorption has been mentioned before (page 38) and undoubtedly is of great importance as it enables plants to easily acquire nutrients that might later escape in drainage or even might not otherwise be readily exchangeable at all.

The availability of adsorbed nutrients is not always so easy and copious as the explanation above might lead one to surmise. The proportion of the total exchange capacity occupied by a given nutrient is a very important factor. For instance, if the percentage base saturation of a soil is high, calcium and magnesium presumably are present in relatively large amounts and their displacement easy and rapid. Other cations, such as potassium, must, like calcium and magnesium, occupy a certain proportion of the total exchange capacity before they are easily dislodged. The availability of an adsorbed cation, therefore, is not entirely a question of milliequivalents present. The interface concentration is a factor. Hence 6 milliequivalents of an exchangeable cation in a soil whose total exchange capacity is 8 probably would mean ready availability. But 2 milliequivalents when the total exchange capacity is 20 might present quite the opposite condition. Ionic exchange, therefore, is a fertility factor of important, yet variable, intensity.

Chapter V. The Organisms of the Soil

A consideration of clay is logically followed by a discussion of the organic matter of the soil. The colloidal concept would be incomplete without it. First, however, another phase, most intimately related claims our attention. Humus, like clay, is a product of dissolution and of synthesis. And the agency is the organic population of the soil. Before a proper understanding of the various organic transformations and products can be acquired, some attention, even though brief, must be accorded the fauna and flora, the living colloidal fraction, of the soil.[1]

A vast number of organisms live in the soil. By far the greater number of these belong to plant life and are the forms most important in promoting the final changes in structure and composition which contribute to soil productiveness. Yet animals are not to be minimized, especially in respect to the early stages of organic decomposition. Most soil organisms are so minute as to be seen, if at all, only by the aid of the microscope, while a much smaller number range from this size to that of the larger rodents.

49. *Macroanimals* [2]

The larger animals of the soil are chiefly (1) rodents and insectivora, (2) insects, (3) millipedes, (4) sowbugs (woodlice), (5) mites, (6) slugs and snails, (7) centipedes, (8) spiders, and (9) earthworms.

The burrowing habits of rodents, of which the ground squirrel,

[1] One of the better comprehensive treatises on the subject of soil organisms is Waksman, Selman A., *Principles of Soil Microbiology*, The Williams & Wilkins Company, Baltimore, 1932. A more popular consideration by Waksman, Selman A., and Robert L. Starkey, is *The Soil and the Microbe*, John Wiley & Sons, Inc., New York, 1931. See also, Russell, E. John, *Soil Conditions and Plant Growth*, Longmans, Green and Company, New York, 1937.

[2] For data concerning the animal life of the forest soils of northeastern United States see Eaton, Theodore H., Jr., and Robert F. Chandler, Jr., *The Fauna of Forest Humus Layers*, Memoir 247, Cornell Univ. Agr. Expt. Sta., 1942.

pocket gopher, woodchuck, Kangaroo rat, and prairie dog are familiar examples, depending upon the region, result in the pulverization and transfer of very considerable quantities of soil. Insect-eating animals, especially moles, are equally important in many cases. While their activities are usually unfavorable to agricultural operations, the effect on the character of the soil is beneficial and analogous to that of tillage. Not only do these animals incorporate much organic matter in soils but also their burrows serve to aerate and drain the land.

A great variety of insects are found in soils, some of which have very little influence on the organic matter, while others, such as ants, beetles, springtails, etc., appreciably affect the humic constituents, either by translocation or by digestion. In some regions, the work of

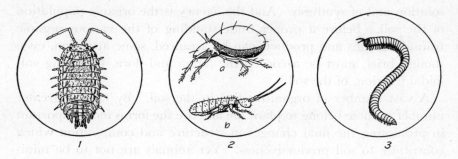

Fig. 14. Four animals having much to do with the digestion of the organic matter especially of forest soils. *1*, Sow-bug (*Trachelifus rathkei*); *2a*, mite (*Oribata Sp.*); *2b*, Spring-tail (*Tomocerus Sp.*); *3*, millipede (*Parajulus Sp.*).

ants is often especially noticeable. In association with these insects are millipedes, sowbugs, mites, slugs, and snails, organisms that use more or less undecomposed plant tissue as food. In fact, some humus is synthesized quite largely from their feces. They thus serve to initiate the decomposition processes that are continued by bacteria and fungi. In some peat soils, the millipedes not only have much to do with the digestion of the organic matter but markedly influence, by forming casts, the structure of the horizons in which they are active. Centipedes and spiders, being in large degree predatory, are of minor importance as far as the processes of humus synthesis are concerned.

While many of the animals just mentioned are rather unimportant in organic transfers as individual groups, in mass they become highly significant even if they do nothing more than contribute at death to the accumulation of decomposable tissue. A number of these organisms are, perhaps, of more concern as plant or animal pests and are

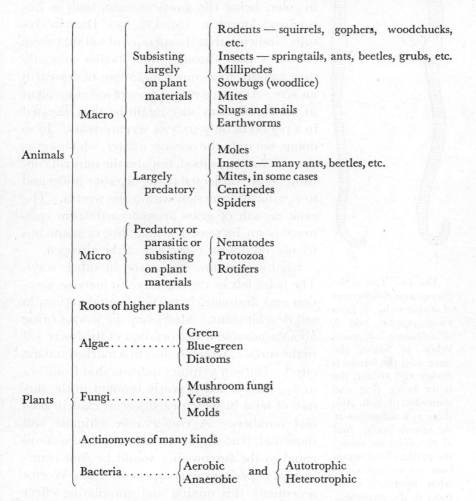

Animals
- Macro
  - Subsisting largely on plant materials
    - Rodents — squirrels, gophers, woodchucks, etc.
    - Insects — springtails, ants, beetles, grubs, etc.
    - Millipedes
    - Sowbugs (woodlice)
    - Mites
    - Slugs and snails
    - Earthworms
  - Largely predatory
    - Moles
    - Insects — many ants, beetles, etc.
    - Mites, in some cases
    - Centipedes
    - Spiders
- Micro
  - Predatory or parasitic or subsisting on plant materials
    - Nematodes
    - Protozoa
    - Rotifers

Plants
- Roots of higher plants
- Algae..........
  - Green
  - Blue-green
  - Diatoms
- Fungi..........
  - Mushroom fungi
  - Yeasts
  - Molds
- Actinomyces of many kinds
- Bacteria.........
  - Aerobic
  - Anaerobic
  and
  - Autotrophic
  - Heterotrophic

Fig. 15. Chart showing the more important groups of organisms that commonly are present in soils.

thus of greater interest to the pathologist and entomologist than to the student of soil science. In any case, however, they are a part of perhaps the most intricate biological cycle in the world.

One of the most important of the macroanimals of the soil is the

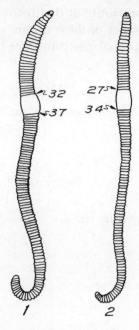

ordinary earthworm,[1] of which there are a number of species,[2] *Lumbricus terrestris*, a reddish organism, and *Allolobophora caliginosa*, pale pinkish in color, being the most common, both in Europe and America. (See Fig. 16.) Darwin's results [3] indicate that the amount of soil that these creatures pass through their bodies annually may amount to as much as 15 tons of dry earth an acre. At such a rate, a mass of soil equivalent to the acre-furrow-slice might be thus digested in a period of only sixty or seventy years. In so doing, not only the organic matter, which serves the earthworm as food, but also the mineral constituents are subjected to the digestive juices and to a triturating action within the worms. The rank growth of grass around earthworm casts suggests an increased availability of plant nutrients, no doubt, especially of the nitrogen.

FIG. 16. Two of the commonest earthworms of arable soils. *1, Lumbricus terrestris* and *2, Allolobophora caliginosa*. While of about the same size, the former is darker and redder, the latter being pale and somewhat pinkish. Also there is a difference in the mouth parts. And as the diagram shows, the girdles of the organisms are located somewhat differently in respect to the segments.

Earthworms are important in other ways. The holes left in the soil serve to increase aeration and drainage, important considerations in soil development. Moreover, the worms bring about a notable transportation of the lower soil to the surface, which results in a marked mixing effect. Darwin's studies indicate that from $\frac{1}{10}$ to $\frac{2}{10}$ inch of soil is yearly brought to the surface of land in which earthworms exist in normal numbers. A conservative estimate will show that, if no duplication occurs, a mass of soil equal to the furrow-slice would be thus translocated in perhaps sixty or seventy years. Worms accentuate this mixing and granulating effect by dragging into their burrows quantities of un-

[1] Walton, W. R., *Earthworms as Pests and Otherwise*, Farmers' Bulletin, 1569, U. S. Dept. of Agriculture, 1928.

[2] Gates, G. E., "The Earthworm Fauna of the United States," *Science*, LXX:266–267, 1929.

Eaton, T. H., Jr., "Earthworms of the Northeastern United States: A Key with Distribution Records," *Jour. Wash. Acad. Sci.*, XXXII:242–249, 1942.

[3] Darwin, Charles, *The Formation of Vegetable Mold*, D. Appleton-Century Company, Inc., New York, 1885.

decomposed organic matter, such as leaves and grass, to serve as food and as a protection. In some cases, the accumulation is surprisingly large. In uncultivated soils, this is more important than in plowed land where organic matter is turned under in quantity. Certain forests and grassland soils owe the marked admixture of organic matter with the *A* horizon (called a *mull layer*) to this type of earthworm activity. Such is particularly true of the gray-brown forest soils of eastern United States and the prairie lands of the Middle West.

Earthworms prefer a moist habitat and, therefore, are found mostly in medium to heavy soils whose moisture capacity is high, rather than in those of a sandy, droughty nature. Moreover, they must have organic matter and thrive best in land where this constituent is plentiful. It seems, also, that earthworm nutrition depends on certain lime-secreting glands. Perhaps because of this, they are not found abundantly in soils that are low in replaceable calcium and acid in any marked degree. It is quite surprising to find how suddenly the earthworm population will change as to vigor, numbers, and even species within very short distances.

Russell [1] found that the numbers of earthworms were markedly affected by the application of farm manure, an influence that, from their dependence upon organic matter and their response to fertility level, might well be expected. He quotes them as ranging from 13,000 an acre in a soil receiving no farm manure to over 1,000,000 an acre on land to which farm manure in quantity was applied. Assuming each worm to weigh on the average ½ gram, the live weight would range from approximately 15 pounds to the acre in the one case to over 1100 pounds in the other. Due to conditions presented by different soils and to variations in the size and species of worms present, these figures should be applied with caution. They are merely suggestive, but they do indicate what range may be expected as to earthworm population in arable soils.

The influence of earthworms on soil fertility and productivity has been subject to much speculation, but authentic data thereon are meagre. Over fifty years ago, Wollny conducted experiments with soil, in one case containing earthworms, and in another, destitute of them. Although there was much variation in his results, they were

[1] Russell, E. J., *Soil Conditions and Plant Growth*, Longmans, Green and Company, New York, 1932, p. 414.

in every case in favor of the soil containing the worms. Recently Puh [1] conducted a similar experiment in China. The soil with the worms contained more organic matter at the end of the test period, the base-exchange capacity was higher, and the availability of the phosphorus and potash was increased. Moreover, the castings always had a higher pH than the original soil, a rather significant sidelight on the digestive influence of the worms.

50. *Microanimals*

Of the abundant microscopic animal life in soils, two groups are particularly important — nematodes and protozoa. A third — the rotifers — at least deserves mention. They will be considered in order. (See Fig. 17.)

Nematodes, threadworms, or eelworms as they are commonly called, are found in almost all soils, often in surprisingly large numbers. A maximum of 50 to the gram of dry soil would mean about 45 billions to the acre-furrow-slice. They are round or spindle-shaped in form, one end usually being acutely pointed. Thus, they distinctly differ from the segmented earthworm both in size and external characteristics. In size, they are almost wholly microscopic, seldom being large enough to be seen at all readily with the naked eye. When quiescent in the soil water, they are often coiled in simple shapes. By a sudden straightening out or by a less vigorous undulatory movement, they may effect a rather aimless change in position.

Three groups of nematodes may be distinguished on the basis of their food demands: (1) those that live on decaying organic matter, (2) those that are predatory [2] on other nematodes, small earthworms, and the like, and (3) those that are parasitic, attacking the roots of higher plants, passing at least a part of their life cycle imbedded in such tissue. The first group is by far the most numerous in the average soil and most varied. The last group, however, especially those of the genus Heterodera [3] is the most important to the plant specialist. Due to their pointed form they find it easy to penetrate plant tissue. The roots of practically all plants are infested, and the damage done is

[1] Puh, Y. C., "Beneficial Influence of Earthworms on Some Chemical Properties of the Soil," *Sci. Soc. China*, Biol. Lab. Contrib., Zool. Ser., XV, No. 9:147–155, 1941.

[2] Cobb, N. A., "The Mononchs, A Genus of Free-Living Predatory Nematodes," *Soil Sci.*, III:431–486, 1917.

[3] *Root-Infecting Eel Worms of the Genus Heterodera; A Bibliography and Host List*, Imp. Bur. Agr. Parasitology, St. Albans, 1931.

often very great, especially to vegetable crops grown in southern United States. Even in greenhouses, they may become a serious pest unless care is taken to avoid infestation. Their control [1] is very difficult in spite of their many enemies, which include fungal parasites, predacious mites, and nema-trapping fungi.

While nematodes, rotifers, and similar organisms are no doubt present in soil in great numbers, the protozoa are the most varied and numerous of the microanimal population. As many as 250 species have been isolated, sometimes as many as 40 or 50 occurring in a single sample of soil. The presence of protozoa has been reported in soils from most of the countries of Europe, the United States, and many other regions. Most of these organisms are highly adaptable and occur in habitats other than that of the soil.

Protozoa [2] are probably the simplest form of animal life. They are all one-celled organisms, considerably larger than bacteria and of a distinctly higher organization. Some are merely masses of naked protoplasm, amoeba, while others exhibit a much higher development and are even, in some cases, protected with siliceous or chitinous coverings. For convenience of study, soil protozoa are divided into three groups: (1) amoeba, (2) ciliates or infusoria, and (3) flagellates. The presence of numerous cilia or hairs and of flagella, long whiplike appendages of protoplasm, are the bases for the two latter subdivisions. (See Fig. 17.) The flagellates are usually most numerous in soil followed in order by the amoeba and the ciliates. Testaceous forms are especially common in acid peat soils but practically absent from neutral or alkaline cultivated mineral lands.

The nutritional habits of protozoa are not well known. No doubt, most of those in the soil depend on nonliving organic matter as a source of food. There are some indications, however, that certain groups may ingest bacteria and thus, in an indirect way, may interfere with higher plants, especially if the microorganisms preyed on are at all important in the production of available plant nutrients. Thus, any marked check in ammonification or nitrification might be of serious concern.

[1] Godfrey, G. H., *Root-Knot: Its Cause and Control*, Farmers' Bulletin 1345, U. S. Dept. of Agriculture, 1923. Also Linford, M. B., Francis Yap, and J. M. Oliveira, "Reduction of Soil Populations of the Root-Knot Nematode during the Decomposition of Organic Matter," *Soil Sci.*, XLV:127–140, 1938.

[2] Sandon, H., *The Composition and Distribution of the Protozoan Fauna of the Soil*, Oliver and Boyd, Edinburgh, 1927.

The numbers of protozoa in the soil are subject to extreme fluctuation, even when conditions apparently are continuously favorable. Aeration, as well as the available food supply, is probably a very important factor. Most of the organisms are thus confined to the surface horizons. Usually, the numbers are highest in the spring and autumn. Perhaps 1,000,000 protozoa of all kinds to the gram of dry soil might be considered a maximum for the representative soil. This might amount to a live weight of 100 or 200 pounds to the acre.

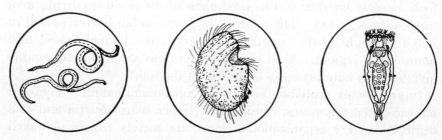

FIG. 17.   Parasitic nematodes (left), a ciliated protozoan (center) and a common rotifer (right).   (First two after Waksman.)

That rotifers occur in the soil is well known and under moist conditions, especially in swampy land, their numbers may be great. As many as fifty different species have been found under such environs. These animals are mostly microscopic in size, their anterior being modified into a retractile disk bearing circles of cilia which, in motion, give the appearance of moving wheels. Hence the name. These hairs sweep floating food materials into the animal. The posterior end tapers to a tail or foot by which the rotifer can attach itself to chosen objects. (See Fig. 17.) Just how important in the soil rotifers are is unknown, but no doubt they enter into the cycle of organic dissolution in a more or less important way, especially in wet places.

51. *Plant life of the soil*

The organisms of a plant nature are numerous and, from some standpoints, are more important than are the animal forms, especially in respect to the final stages of organic matter dissolution and the production of compounds simple enough for the direct nutrition of higher plants. It must be remembered, however, that, especially in forest soils, the initial digestion is very often due to animals such as millipedes and springtails greatly assisted by earthworms if the lime content and other conditions of the residues are favorable.

The plant life of the soil will be considered under five heads as follows: (1) roots of higher plants, (2) algae, (3) fungi, (4) actinomyces, and (5) bacteria. (See Fig. 18.)

52. *Roots of higher plants*

As a source of organic matter, the roots of higher plants are of supreme importance since they supply much more original tissue than all of the other organisms combined. In fact, the life of the soil might, not inaptly, be divided into two opposite and, in some respects, opposing groups — (1) those that supply organic residues, and (2) those that are engaged primarily in tearing them down. Plant roots are, of course, the all-important representative of the first group, while millipedes, springtails, earthworms, bacteria, molds, and actinomyces are principals in the second type of activity.

A good crop of oats will produce perhaps 4000 pounds of dry matter to the acre in its aboveground parts, while the figure for corn on the same basis is about 6000 pounds. If the roots left in the soil when such crops are harvested amount to even half these weights, the added organic residues are, by no means, inconsiderable. They are much greater than could accrue from any other natural source. The accumulation of organic matter under pasture land and meadow, and the surprisingly slow reduction of humus in a land cropped to a well-balanced rotation are thus accounted for. In fact, and this is a situation seldom appreciated by farmers, the maintenance of organic matter in arable soils is possible in large degree because of root residues added in this automatic way.

The roots of higher plants also function in a more intimate manner than as a source of dead tissue. When alive, they not only influence the equilibrium of the soil solution by the simple withdrawal of soluble nutrients, but they also have something to do in a direct way with this availability. The contact between the colloidal surfaces of the absorbing root hairs and the interface of the soil colloids is unavoidably close. So intimate, in fact, that ionic exchange, or something analogous to it, no doubt occurs and constituents, both anionic and cationic, that otherwise might remain in the soil interface, are readily removed (see page 38).

Moreover, root exudates, such as carbon dioxide, probably become better solvents at the zones of contact than otherwise would be the case. Again certain excretions, aided by the sloughing of root tissue undoubtedly locally stimulate the microflora to an intensity of action not attained in other parts of the soil. This means that the adsorptive surfaces of the rhizosphere become the seat of unusual nutrient availability. This has already been explained (page 92) and indicates in part why the roots of higher plants are classified as soil organisms. They not only force a transfer of nutrients but also an availability that, under other conditions, might be very slow.

53. *Algae* [1]

Most algae are chlorophyll-bearing organisms and, as such, must live at or very near the surface of the soil, if they are to survive in a habitat of this nature. However, certain forms seem able to obtain their energy from organic matter and, with such a capacity may exist within and below the surface horizon. The number of these, however, is not large. Thus, some algae live and function much like higher plants, while others in their nutritional habits are typical soil microorganisms. Over sixty species have been isolated from soils, those most prominent being the same the world over. Soil algae are divided into three general groups: (1) blue-green, (2) green, and (3) diatoms.

Naturally, algae in vegetative form are most numerous in the surface layers, especially in the upper inch of arable soils. In subsoils, most algae are present as resting spores or cysts. Grassland seems especially favorable for the blue-green forms, while in old gardens, diatoms are often numerous. All of the ordinary types of algae are greatly stimulated by the application of farm manure. Both the green and the blue-green algae outnumber the diatoms, 100,000 to a gram of dry surface soil being an estimated minimum under favorable conditions for each in Rothamsted soils.[2] In certain Utah soils,

[1] A good summary is presented by Bristol-Roach, B. M., "The Present Position of Our Knowledge of the Distribution and Function of Algae in the Soil," *Proc. and Papers, First Internat. Cong. Soil Sci.*, III:30–38, Washington, 1928. See also Waksman, S. A., *Principles of Soil Microbiology*, The Williams and Wilkins Company, Baltimore, 1932.

[2] Russell, E. J., *Soil Conditions and Plant Growth*, Longmans, Green and Company, New York, 1937, p. 420.

Martin [1] reports the total algal population as reaching a maximum of 800,000 to a gram of dry soil.

Since algae are present in most soils in rather large volume, they surely must facilitate some changes of importance. But just what these are cannot be stated with any certainty. Algae, no doubt, contribute to the organic content of the soil and may be valuable as a storage of energy during unfavorable periods due to their great vitality and powers of recovery. They are thought by some authors to encourage the fixation of nitrogen by Azotobacter. But if this should be true, it probably is of little importance.[2] The blue-green algae themselves undoubtedly fix some atmospheric nitrogen [3] but, by no means, to the extent effected by bacteria. It would seem, therefore, that the most important role of algae, in general, is the aid they give to bacteria and fungi in the decomposition of plant tissue, the liberation of nutrients, and the synthesis of humus.

54. *Fungi* [4]

It is only within comparatively recent years that the importance of the role played by fungi in the soil has been recognized. While their influence is still by no means well understood, it is now known that they play a very important part in the transformations of the soil constituents. A large number of species have been identified. Like the bacteria and actinomyces, fungi contain no chlorophyll and must depend for their energy and carbon on the organic matter of the soil.

The superficial characteristic that distinguishes fungi is the filamentous nature of their vegetative forms. Their mycelial threads may be simple and restricted or profusely branched and of such dimensions as to attract even casual attention. More than this, the special spore-forming or fruiting bodies often attain, with some groups, macroscopic sizes. Fungal organisms may thus vary from the

---

[1] Martin, Thomas L., "The Occurrence of Algae in Some Virgin Utah Soils," *Proc. Soil Sci. Soc. Amer.*, IV:249, 1939.

[2] Stokes, J. L., "The Role of Algae in the Nitrogen Cycle of the Soil," *Soil Sci.*, XLIX:265–275, 1940.

[3] Allison, F. E., and H. J. Morris, "Nitrogen Fixation by Blue-Green Algae," *Science*, LXXI, No. 1834:221–223, 1930.

[4] Jensen, H. L., "The Fungus Flora of the Soil," *Soil Sci.*, XXXI:123–158, 1931.
Gilman, J. C., and E. V. Abbott, "A Summary of Soil Fungi," *Iowa Jour. of Sci.*, I:225–343, 1927.

simple microscopic yeasts to mushroom and bracket fungi of extraordinary dimensions.

For convenience of discussion, fungi may be divided into three groups as follows: (1) yeasts, (2) molds, and (3) mushroom fungi. Of these, only the last two are important in soils, as yeasts occur to a very limited extent in such a habitat. They, therefore, need not receive further consideration here.

The distinctly filamentous, microscopic, or semimacroscopic fungi are commonly spoken of as *molds*. (See Fig. 18.) In soils, they play a role infinitely more important than the mushroom fungi, approaching or even excelling the influence of bacteria. They respond especially to soil aeration, their numbers and activities diminishing as air movement is retarded. Molds will develop vigorously in acid, neutral, or alkaline soils, some being favored, rather than otherwise, by a lowered pH. Consequently, they are noticeably abundant in acid soils, where bacteria and actinomyces offer milder competition. Were it not for fungi, there would be little decomposition and digestion of the organic residues in acid forest soils other than that effected by millipedes, springtails, mites, and other animals.

Molds are found in all horizons of the soil profile, the greatest numbers being, of course, in the A layers where organic matter is plentiful and aeration adequate. Many species have been isolated, some of the more common being Penicillium, Mucor, Fusarium, Aspergillus, and Rhizopus. All of the common species occur in most soils, conditions determining which shall dominate. Their numbers fluctuate greatly with soil conditions, perhaps 1,000,000 individuals to the gram of dry soil representing a more or less normal population.[1] This might well amount to 1000 or 1200 pounds of living organisms to the acre. Perhaps the most important factor relating to the activity of fungi is food supply. The addition of almost any kind of decomposable organic matter to the soil, especially farm manure, has a surprising effect on mycelial development. Even commercial fertilizers increase the number of molds present. When conditions are unfavorable, the vegetative tissue diminishes, and spores are formed which have great powers of resistance. Molds are an important part of the general-purpose, heterotrophic group of soil organisms that fluctuate so greatly in most soils (see page 109).

---

[1] Brierley, W. B., S. T. Jewson, and M. Brierley, "The Quantitative Study of Soil Fungi," *Proc. and Papers, First Internat. Cong. Soil Sci.*, III:48–71, 1928.

It is hardly necessary to state that molds are of paramount importance in soils. In their ability to decompose organic residues they are the most versatile and perhaps the most persistent of any group. Cellulose, starch, gums, lignin, as well as the more easily affected proteins and sugars, readily succumb to their attack. In humus formation, molds are perhaps more important than bacteria. This is certainly true in acid forest soils. Moreover, they function more economically than bacteria in that they transform into their tissues a larger proportion of the carbon and nitrogen of the compounds attacked and give off as by-products less carbon dioxide and ammonia. As much as 50 per cent of the substances decomposed by molds may become fungal tissue. However, they cannot oxidize ammonium compounds to nitrates as do certain bacteria, nor can they fix atmospheric nitrogen. Soil fertility depends greatly on molds, since they keep the decomposition processes going when bacteria and actinomyces alone would not suffice.

Numerous varieties of mushroom fungi, producing such fruiting bodies as mushrooms, toadstools, and puffballs, are found in forests, often in great profusion. The mycelia of certain members of this general group often infest the roots of trees giving an association called *mycorrhiza*. This apparently is of advantage both to the host and the parasite. The latter seems to digest and, in some way, pass on to the trees certain nutrient constituents that perhaps the host might not obtain so readily alone. In acid soils, which are so prevalent under many forests, and in which nitrification is often negligible, the associated fungus may enable the trees to make use of complex nitrogenous forms that otherwise would remain unavailable. Under such conditions, they are much more important than the ordinary types of fungi.[1]

55. *Actinomyces* [2]

Actinomyces resemble molds in that they are filamentous, often profusely branched, and produce fruiting bodies in much the same way. Their mycelial threads are smaller, however, than those of

[1] For a review of recent research, see Rayner, M. C., "The Mycorrhizal Habit in Relation to Forestry," *Chron. Bot.*, VI:12–13, 1940.

[2] Waksman, S. A., *Principles of Soil Microbiology*, The Williams and Wilkins Company, Baltimore, 1932, Chap. XII.

Russell, E. J., *Soil Conditions and Crop Growth*, Longmans, Green and Company, New York, 1937, pp. 428–429.

fungi. Actinomyces are similar to bacteria in that they are unicellular and of about the same diameter. When they break up into spores, they resemble bacteria often rather closely. Like them, they are sensitive to acids, growing best in the presence of appreciable amounts of active calcium. On the basis of organization, actinomyces occupy a position between true molds and bacteria. They are sometimes called *thread bacteria*. (See Fig. 18.)

Actinomyces develop best in moist, well-aerated soil. But in times of drought, they remain active to a degree not exhibited by either bacteria or molds. They are very sensitive to acid soil conditions,

 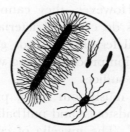 

FIG. 18. The three most important plant microorganisms of the soil, from left to right—Fungal mycelium, various types of bacterial cells, and actinomyces threads. The bacteria and actinomyces are much more highly magnified than the fungi.

their growth being practically prohibited at a pH of 5.0 or below. Their optimum development lies between 6.0 and 7.5 pH. This marked relationship to soil reaction is sometimes taken advantage of in practice, especially in respect to potato scab, a disease of wide distribution. It is often possible to effect a reduction in pH by the use of sulfur sufficient to keep the disease under control (see page 310).

Certain species of actinomyces, particularly in artificial culture, produce pigments of many colors: red, yellow, green, brown, and black being very common. Whether this is so marked in the soil is uncertain. Also on artificial media, actinomyces develop peculiar hard masses of tangled threads, often with spore-bearing hyphae. Whether they occur thus in soils is a question. No doubt, their mycelia are much less localized under natural conditions. The aroma of freshly plowed land, that is so noticeable at certain times of the year, is probably due to actinomyces, at least in part.

Except for bacteria, no other microorganisms are so numerous in the soil as actinomyces, their numbers sometimes reaching 15 millions or perhaps 20 millions to a gram of dry soil. In actual live weight, they excel bacteria but, by no means, equal the amount of fungal tissue normally present. Under especially favorable conditions, perhaps 600 to 800 pounds of actinomyces threads might be present in an acre-furrow-slice. These organisms are especially numerous in soils high in humus, such as old meadows or pastures where the acidity is not too great. There they exceed in numbers all other microscopic forms of life. The addition of farm manure markedly stimulates their activities.

Actinomyces undoubtedly are of great importance in respect to the dissolution of soil organic matter and the liberation of nutrients therefrom. Apparently, they reduce, rapidly and successfully, all sorts of compounds to simpler forms, even the lignins, the most resistant of all. The presence of actinomyces in such abundance in soils long under sod is some indication of this latter capacity. The simplification of humus is important, especially in respect to nitrogen. Considerable amounts of this element are tied up in complex humic forms and might long remain unavailable to higher plants. The actinomyces apparently are able to put it in circulation again. This one service alone ranks the actinomyces with fungi and bacteria as fertility agents in the average arable soil.

56. *Bacteria*

A better knowledge has been gained of bacteria than of any of the other microorganisms common in soils. And as a result, they have been considered, until recent years, the most important class. But as more becomes known of the other forms of life, scientists are beginning to question whether some of these, particularly the fungi and certain of the animals, may not, at times, equal or even outrank them.

Bacteria are single-cell organisms, the simplest and smallest forms of life known. They multiply by elongating and dividing into half. They are therefore often called *fission* fungi. The process is comparatively simple and, under favorable conditions, surprisingly rapid. A new organism may develop in twenty or thirty minutes with ease. This almost unlimited capacity to increase in numbers is extremely important in soils, since it allows certain groups quickly to assume their normal functions under favorable conditions, even though their numbers were originally small.[1] Bacteria may thus be considered as a force of tremendous magnitude in the soil, held more or less in check by conditions, but ever ready to exert an influence of profound importance. They, with the fungi and actinomyces, make up, in large degree, that general-purpose group of microorganisms, already mentioned, that fluctuates so markedly in response to soil conditions.

Bacteria are very small, the larger individuals seldom exceeding 4 or 5 microns (0.004 to 0.005 mm.) in diameter. Many soil bacteria are equipped with extremely delicate vibrating hairs called *flagella* which enable the organisms, on occasion, to swim through the soil water. This probably occurs sparingly, however, as the cells are held by the viscous surfaces of the soil colloidal matter or are imbedded in its gelatinous depths. The shape of bacteria is varied in that they may be nearly round, rodlike, or spiral. In the soil, the rod-shaped organisms seem to predominate. (See Fig. 18.) Because of their minute size and their chemical make-up, bacteria, as well as other soil microorganisms, are highly colloidal. This has much to do with their remarkable biochemical activity.[2]

In the soil, bacteria exist as mats, clumps, and filaments, called *colonies*, on and around the soil particles wherever food and other conditions are favorable. The jellylike mixture of mineral and organic colloidal matter makes an almost ideal medium for their development. While natural and artificial forces tend to distribute the organisms through the soil, the colonies, in most cases, enlarge, function, and die out in more or less their original position. Their existence depends on soil conditions, particularly food supply. Thus, there is a constant and rapid fluctuation — multiplication and death, often by starvation. Many of the soil bacteria are able to produce spores or similar resistant bodies, thus presenting both a vegetative and a resting stage. This latter capacity is important as it allows the organisms to survive unfavorable conditions of many kinds.

The numbers of bacteria present in soil are variable, as many conditions markedly affect their growth. In general, the greatest popu-

[1] If a single bacterium and every subsequent organism produced subdivided every hour, the offspring from the original cell would be about 17,000,000 in twenty-four hours. In six days, the organisms would greatly surpass the earth in volume. Under actual conditions, such multiplication would never occur, due to lack of food and other limitations.

[2] The surface exposed by soil bacteria, not considering that of the other microorganisms, is remarkable. Assuming that a single bacterium is, on the average, 1u long × 0.5 u thick and that one billion are present to 1 gm. of soil, the external surface exposed would amount to about 10 sq. ft. to the pound of dry soil, or about 460 acres to the acre-furrow-slice.

lation is in the surface horizon, since conditions of temperature, moisture, aeration, and food are here more favorable. The methods of determining the actual numbers present are quite inaccurate, since many organisms will not grow in the artificial media commonly used. Moreover, it is almost impossible to break up the clumps or colonies in such a way as to determine the number of individuals actually present. It is fairly certain, however, that the numbers of bacteria in soil are very large, possibly ranging as high as three or four billions [1] to a gram of soil. Four or five hundred pounds of live weight bacterial tissue to the acre-furrow-slice is probably a modest estimate.[2] Good soils seem, in general, to carry the greatest numbers. The bacterial flora, as well as the other soil organisms, fluctuates markedly with season, the numbers usually being the greatest in early summer and in the autumn.

Soil bacteria may be classified under two heads, *autotrophic* and *heterotrophic*. The former obtain their energy from the oxidation of mineral constituents, such as ammonium, sulfur, and iron, and most of their carbon from carbon dioxide. In numbers, they are insignificant, but since they include the organisms that support nitrification and sulfur oxidation, they are tremendously important in the sustenance of higher plants. Most soil bacteria, however, are heterotrophic, that is, their energy and carbon come directly from the soil organic matter. The general-purpose decay and ammonifying bacteria, as well as fungi and actinomyces, belong to this group.

57. *Conditions affecting the growth of bacteria*

Many conditions of the soil affect the growth of bacteria. Among the most important of these are the supply of oxygen and moisture, the soil temperature, the presence of organic matter, and the H-ion concentration of the soil solution.[3]

Oxygen. All soil bacteria require for their growth a certain amount

[1] Thornton, H. G. and P. H. Gray, "The Numbers of Bacterial Cells in Field Soils, as Estimated by the Ratio Method," *Proc. Roy. Soc. London*, Ser. B, CXV: 522–543, 1934.

[2] Thornton estimates the bacterial substance, both dead and alive, in the furrow-slice of the Barnfield soil, Rothamsted Experiment Station, as ranging from 1500 to 5600 pounds. This estimate is based on his improved method of determining numbers, which indicates that bacteria are more numerous in the soil than once supposed. See Russell, E. J., *Soil Conditions and Plant Growth*, Longmans, Green and Company, New York, 1932, p. 397.

[3] Useful supplementary reading on these factors will be found in Russell, E. J., *Soil Conditions and Plant Growth*, Longmans, Green and Co., New York, 1937, Chap. VII.

of oxygen. Some, however, can continue their activities with much less free oxygen than can others. Those requiring an abundant supply are called *aerobic* bacteria, while those able to function with but little are designated as *anaerobic.* This is an important distinction, because these groups bring about different types of transformations. No doubt, the aerobic and anaerobic organisms function in the soil at the same time, since certain parts, even of a well-aerated soil, are always highly charged with carbon dioxide. Moreover, some organisms may be deeply imbedded in the viscous and gelatinous colloidal matter, their air supply being thereby cut off. It is not improbable, also, that there exists a more or less beneficial interrelation between the two general groups. Besides, some are *facultative*, growing well regardless of the amount of free oxygen supplied.

Moisture. Bacteria require moisture for their growth, optimum water for higher plants seemingly being satisfactory for their best development. With a decrease of moisture, the soil becomes well aerated, while an excessive water supply tends to encourage anaerobic conditions. A fluctuation, not only in type of bacteria present, but also in microbial activity may thereby be forced.

Temperature. Soil bacteria, like other plants, continue life and growth under a considerable range of temperature. Freezing, while rendering bacteria dormant, does not necessarily kill them, and growth begins slightly above that point. From 70° to 100° F., their activity is greatest, and it diminishes perceptibly below or above these points. Only in some desert soils does the natural temperature reach a point sufficiently high actually to destroy bacteria, and there only near the surface.

Organic matter. The presence of a certain amount of organic matter is essential to the growth of most, but not all, forms of soil bacteria — autotrophic organisms being the exception. The organic matter of the soil, consisting as it does of the remains of a large variety of substances, furnishes a suitable food supply for a great number of different forms. The action of one set of bacteria on the cellular matter of plants produces compounds suited for other forms, and so, from one stage of decomposition to another, this constantly changing material affords sustenance to the bacterial flora, the extent and variety of which it is difficult to conceive. Moreover, the dead cells of one generation serve as sustenance for the oncoming group. A soil low in organic matter usually has a lower bacterial content than one containing a large amount and, under favorable conditions, the numbers increase with the content of organic residues. The addition of farm manure will usually increase bacterial counts tremendously.

pH level. It has already been remarked that molds will thrive in soils of high acidity and low lime. The response of most bacteria is quite the reverse, although there are several exceptions. At a pH much below 5.5, the average mineral soil is too low in active calcium to support vigorous bacterial action. Nitrifying and nitrogen-fixing organisms are especially sensitive to such a physiological condition. The marked increase in the concentration of carbon dioxide in the air and of nitrates in the solution of an acid soil after being limed is very good evidence of the stimulation of the bacteria by an increase in the percentage base saturation.[1]

It is hardly necessary to emphasize further the biochemical significance of soil bacteria. They participate in all of the more common transformations, besides supporting certain special changes. *Nitrogen fixation, nitrification,* and *sulfur oxidation* are essentially bacterial monopolies. These alone would justify the attention bestowed on these organisms — the simplest and most numerous of soil life.

58. *Injurious effects of soil organisms on higher plants*

It has already been suggested that certain of the soil fauna are injurious to higher plants. For instance, rodents and moles may, in certain cases, greatly damage crops. Snails and slugs in some climates are important pests, while the activity of ants, especially as to their transfer and care of aphis, must be sedulously combatted. Also, most plant roots are infested with eelworms, sometimes so seriously as to make the successful growth of certain crops both difficult and expensive. Protozoa, even though their effect may be indirect, also can exert an adverse influence on higher plants.

However, it is the plant forms of soil life that, in general, exert the most devastating effect on higher plants. All three groups — bacteria, fungi, and actinomyces — contribute their quota of plant diseases. They may be entirely parasitic in their habits or only partially so, and they may injure higher plants by attacking the roots or even the tops. Those that infest parts of the plant other than the roots are not strictly soil organisms, as they pass only a part of their life cycle

[1] Bizzell, J. A., and T. L. Lyon, "The Effects of Certain Factors on the Carbon-Dioxide Content of Soil Air," *Jour. Amer. Soc. Agron.,* X:97–112, 1918.

Lyon, T. L., and J. A. Bizzell, *Lysimeter Experiments, II,* Memoir 41, Cornell Univ. Agr. Exp. Sta., 51–93, 1921.

in the environs of the soil. Some of the more common diseases produced by soil flora are: wilts, damping off, root rots, clubroot of cabbage and similar crops, and the actinomyces scab of potatoes. These occur in great variety, induced by many different organisms.

Injurious organisms live for variable periods in the soil. Some of them will disappear within a few years if their host plants are not grown, but others are able to maintain existence on almost any organic substance. Once a soil is infested, it is likely to remain so for a long time or, indeed, indefinitely. Infection easily occurs. Organisms from infested fields may be carried on implements, plants, or rubbish of any kind, or even in stable manure containing infected plants or in the feces resulting from the feeding of such plants to animals. Erosion, if soil is washed from one field to another, may be a means of transfer.

Prevention is the best defense from diseases produced by such soil organisms. Once a disease has procured a foothold, it is often very difficult to eradicate it. Rotation of crops is effective for some diseases, but the entire absence of the host plant is often necessary. The regulation of the pH is effective to a certain extent with potato scab and the clubroot of cabbage. If the pH is held somewhat below 5.3 or 5.5, the former disease, which is due to an actinomyces, is much retarded. With clubroot, the addition of hydroxide of lime until the pH of the soil is somewhat above 7.0 seems effective but is objectionable with certain types of rotation. Steam sterilization is a practical method of treating greenhouse soils for a number of diseases. The breeding of plants immune to particular diseases has been successful in the case of the cowpea, cotton, and a number of crops.

Another way in which soil organisms, especially bacteria, fungi, and actinomyces, may be harmful to higher plants, at least temporarily, is by competition for available nutrients. This is a source of trouble recognized only in recent years. Nitrogen is the element usually most vigorously contested for, although organisms may utilize appreciable quantities of phosphorus, potash, and lime to the exclusion of the crops growing on the land.[1] Competition for trace elements may even be serious.

[1] Assuming that microbial tissue contains on the dry basis an average of 2.50 per cent P_2O_5, 10 per cent N, 0.60 per cent K_2O, and 0.60 per cent CaO, the synthesis of 500 lb. of such material dry (equal to approximately 1 ton of live-weight organisms) would require the equivalent of about 80 lb. of 16 per cent superphosphate, 312 lb. of commercial nitrate of soda, and 6 lb. each of commercial muriate of potash and ground limestone. Obviously, the feeding of the soil microflora is a problem in itself.

If a soil containing adequate nitrates is treated with organic matter high in easily decomposable carbohydrates, such as strawy farm manure or a nonleguminous green manure, tremendous biological activity is initiated. The general-purpose soil organisms, especially the fungi and bacteria, having a plentiful source of energy at their command, multiply rapidly. And as they must have nitrogen for the synthesis of new protoplasm, they use that which otherwise would go to the crop occupying the land. Nitrate and ammoniacal nitrogen disappear and, until the decay organisms decompose the added organic matter and diminish in numbers, the higher plant faces a serious nutritional situation.

59. *Activities of soil organisms beneficial to higher plants* [1]

In their influence on crop production, soil organisms are of vastly greater help than hindrance to the farmer. Not only do these organisms, especially the animal forms, influence the soil physically, but they are the main driving forces which convert the insoluble and unavailable nutrients into forms which the plant may use. All of the waste material which, by nature or by man, becomes a part of the soil is gradually resolved into simple products and humus. (See Fig. 20.) This humus, although the most resistant part of the organic residues, is itself finally destroyed. All forms of soil organisms, both animal and plant, have something to do with these processes of dissolution, simplification, and synthesis.

Besides the synthesis of humus (see page 128), so important as a structural agent in soils, certain simple compounds are produced in

[1] Apropos to the influence of soil organisms on higher plants is the capacity, enzymic or otherwise, that certain soil bacteria, fungi, and actinomyces possess of inhibiting the growth of other microorganisms, especially those not commonly found in soils. The failure of many disease organisms to survive in moist earth may, in part, be accounted for in this way. So also may be the sanitary capacity that soil has long been known to possess. Not only can bacteriostatic and bactericidal substances be extracted from normal soils, but also it may be possible to prepare valuable chemotherapeutic agents from cultures of antagonistic soil organisms. See:

Waksman, S. A., "Antagonistic Interrelationships among Microorganisms," *Chron. Botanica*, VI, No. 7:145–148, 1940.

Waksman, S. A., and H. B. Woodruff, "Actinomyces Antibioticus, a New Soil Organism Antagonistic to Pathogenic and Non-Pathogenic Bacteria," *Jour. Bact.*, XLII:231–249, 1941.

Waksman, Selman A., and H. Boyd Woodruff, "The Occurrence of Bacteriostatic and Bactericidal Substances in the Soil," *Soil Sci.*, LIII:233–239, 1942.

varying abundance.   Some of the most noteworthy are carbon dioxide, ammonium compounds, nitrates, and sulfates.

Carbon dioxide has already been specified as producing that all-important acid, H_2CO_3, as a source of carbonates and bicarbonates, as influencing the aeration of the soil, and as supplying carbon for autotrophic soil microorganisms and for higher plants.   The presence of this gas is not an indication merely of organic matter dissolution but of energy transfer and utilization by the flora and fauna of the soil.

The appearance in the soil of ammonium compounds and nitrates is the result of a long series of biochemical changes beginning with proteins and related compounds.   These steps are of vital importance to higher plants, since the latter obtain most of their nitrogen from ammoniacal and nitrate salts.   Thus, the various forms of by-product nitrogen resulting from microorganic synthesis serve as nutrients for plants of higher organization.

The production of sulfates is roughly analogous to the biological simplification of the nitrogen.   Here again a complicated chain of enzymic activities culminates in a simple soluble product — in this case the sulfate, the only important form in which sulfur may enter higher plants.

One other outstanding relationship that must not go unmentioned is the fixation of elemental nitrogen.   Such nitrogen, so plentiful in the atmospheric air, cannot be used directly by higher plants.   It must be in combined form before it can satisfy their nutritional needs. Two groups of bacteria participate in the capture of this nitrogen: the nodule organisms, especially of legumes, and free-fixing bacteria of several kinds.   The legume bacteria, using the carbohydrates of their hosts as an energy source, fix the nitrogen and pass part on to the infected host.   Some is left in the root tissue and in the sloughed nodules.   This is likely to appear later in ammoniacal and nitrate forms.   The free-fixing bacteria acquire their energy from the soil organic matter, fix the nitrogen, and make it a part of their own tissue.   When they die, decay, ammonification, and nitrification will render at least a part of this air nitrogen available to higher plants.

In enumerating the benefits accruing to higher plants from the activity of soil organisms, it must be clearly understood that the former develop in the face of and, in part, because of keen competition.   The organisms of the soil need energy and food. In obtaining them from the soil, they aid in the production of humus and, incidentally, leave behind soluble compounds which are useful to higher plants. It is an interesting example of natural economy and coordination and of the varied relationships upon which agriculture is based.

Chapter VI. The Organic Matter of Mineral Soils

In soil formation, the presence of decomposing organic matter is a sign that the synthetic processes are well begun and that biochemical activities are supplementing and augmenting those of a purely chemical nature. Under suitable climatic conditions, life, both plant and animal, soon gains a foothold on the weathering soil materials and, as generations pass, organic residues are left to decay and mix with the decomposing mineral mass. This relationship becomes more and more intimate as time goes on, and the soil, as a natural body, exhibits its most characteristic traits only when organic matter has become an integral part of its surface layers and has influenced the *B* horizons as well.

60. *The sources of soil organic matter*

The original source of the soil organic matter is plant and animal tissue, the former furnishing the initial and the major supply. Nevertheless, animals, as they work over the original plant tissues, not only contribute waste products but also donate their own bodies as their life cycles are consummated. Hence, organic residues on the surface of a virgin soil initially have accumulated from the aboveground parts of higher plants. Dead grass and the litter from forest trees are examples of this type of addition. Such materials, as they are decomposed and digested by soil organisms of many kinds, later become a part of the underlying *A* horizon by infiltration or by actual physical incorporation. Earthworms, centipedes, ants, and other forms of animal life play an important role in the latter translocation.

However, some of the organic matter of soils initially originates within the *A* horizon itself. Much of this is from the roots of such plants as trees, shrubs, grasses, and the like. These residues are the primary source of a large proportion of the soil organic matter, not only while the land is virgin but also after it has been placed under cultivation. The plowing of a virgin soil thoroughly mixes, and continues to mix, the organic residues from the two general sources cited. The organic layering, so characteristic of virgin profiles, thus ceases to exist. (See Fig. 47, page 264.) In fact, many persons are unaware of the distinctness with which not only the source but also the sequence of organic additions are shown in many undisturbed soil sections. In recent years, the study of the various layers of organic matter in representative virgin soils has added much to our knowledge of soil genesis.

61. *The composition of plant tissue*

About 75 per cent, or even more, of average green plant tissue is water. The dry substance is made up of carbon, oxygen, hydrogen, nitrogen, and mineral matter. (See Fig. 19.) Although over 90 per cent of the dry matter is carbon, oxygen, and hydrogen, the other elements, even though they may be present in minute amounts, play a vital role in plant nutrition and are important additions to the soil when the organic residues become a part thereof. Nitrogen, sulfur, phosphorus, and calcium from organic sources are particularly important as well as many others added in lesser amounts. A very large proportion of the soil nitrogen originally became a part of the solum as a constituent of the tissue of plants.

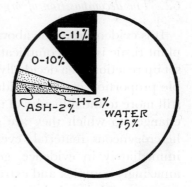

Fig. 19. Diagram showing the generalized composition of green plant tissue. The nitrogen is included in the ash. Plant tissue is made up largely of carbon, hydrogen and oxygen. (After Stoddard.)

The actual compounds in plant tissue are many and varied. (See Fig. 20.) For convenience, they may be classified very simply under four heads: (1) carbohydrates, (2) oils, waxes, and resins, (3) organic acids and their salts, and (4) nitrogenous compounds. The mineral materials, or plant ash, exist quite largely as a part of the compounds listed, becoming evident when the organic matter is ignited.

The carbohydrates include such readily decomposable compounds as starch and sugars and more stable substances, such as the various celluloses and lignins. The fats are represented by the glycerides of butyrin, stearin, olein, and the like, while oils and resins of many kinds, simple and complex, are associated with them. All plants contain organic acids and their salts, often in considerable amounts.

Of the various groups, however, the nitrogenous materials are probably the most complicated as they carry not only carbon, hydrogen, oxygen, and nitrogen, but such elements as sulfur, iron, phosphorus, and others in lesser amounts. They are compounds of high molecular weight and many are of unknown constitution. Simple and conjugated proteides, of which may be mentioned albumin, globulin, nucleoprotein, and phosphoprotein, are present in plants, besides such derived compounds as proteoses and peptones of many kinds. In addition, there are the complex and varied peptides, amino acids, and alkaloids.[1]

62. *The decomposition of organic tissue and the products of decay*[2]

It is evident from the above statements that the chemical nature of plant tissue is very complicated. Hence, its addition to the soil must set up reactions of a decidedly complex order. Moreover, a considerable proportion of these residues is in the colloidal state, which adds still more to the difficulty of their study, especially as to the successive changes to which they are subject in the soil. The decay of this heterogeneous material, even though some simple compounds are immediately in evidence, generally gives rise, at first, to residues amazingly complex and extremely dynamic. Hence, identification is uncertain. It is only later in the process that simple compounds other than carbon dioxide are produced in abundance. (See Fig. 20.)

Regardless of the complexity of the original tissues, something may be said in respect to the relative resistance of their various organic

[1] Waksman, S. A., (*Humus*, The Williams & Wilkins Company, Baltimore, 1938, p. 95.) gives the general composition of representative mature and dry plant tissue as:

Cellulose	20–50 per cent
Hemicellulose	10–28 per cent
Lignins	10–30 per cent
Tannins, fats, waxes, etc.	1–8 per cent
Proteins	1–15 per cent

[2] Schreiner, O., and P. R. Dawson, "The Chemistry of Humus Formation," *Proc. and Papers, First Internat. Cong. Soil Sci.*, III:255–268, 1927.

Russell, E. j., *Soil Conditions and Plant Growth*, Longmans, Green and Company, New York, 1937, Chap. V.

Waksman, S. A., *Principles of Soil Microbiology*, The Williams & Wilkins Company, Baltimore, 1932, Chaps. XVI and XVII.

groups — a phase of great practical significance. The starches, sugars, and water-soluble proteins are acted on first by the various soil organisms, decomposition and digestion being rapid. Crude protein is next in order, followed by the pentosans and hemicelluloses. True cellulose, while more resistant than hemicellulose, yields much more rapidly to enzymic action than do the oils, fats, and lignins. These with the waxes and resins are very persistent and are present as a residue when the decay processes begin to slow up. It is from such materials that humus, that all-important organic residue, is in part built up. In fact, they are the real basis of humus synthesis. Without these resistant groups, organic matter would quickly disappear from most soils.

While the rate of decomposition of the different carbohydrates varies greatly, their intermediate and especially their end products are much the same. When oxygen is plentiful and other conditions are favorable for enzymic action, carbon dioxide and water are likely to be the important products. In the case of the lignins, it must always be remembered, however, that decomposition is slow. Hence, their importance in respect to humus build-up. The oils, fats, waxes, and resins resemble the carbohydrates in their decomposition products and, like the lignins, they contribute greatly to the synthesis of humus. (See Fig. 20.)

Plant proteins and related nitrogenous compounds in the soil seem to break down into amino acids [1] of various kinds, the rate depending on conditions. Bacteria, fungi, actinomyces, and other soil organisms, both plant and animal, engage in the transformations, appropriating some of the nitrogen for their own use. Part of the protein, however, combines with lignin and other resistant compounds and becomes a part of the soil humus. It is thus protected, at least for a time, from enzymic decomposition. Once amino acids are formed, they may be hydrolyzed readily to carbon dioxide, ammonium compounds, and other products. Ammonium, by the process of nitrification, may, if

---

[1] Amino acids are produced by replacing one of the alkyl hydrogens with NH_2. Acetic acid (CH_3COOH) thereby becomes aminoacetic acid or glycocoll (CH_2NH_2COOH). Amides or acid amides are formed from organic acids by replacing the hydroxyl of the carboxyl group with NH_2. Acetic acid (CH_3COOH) thus becomes acetamide (CH_3CONH_2). Protein simplification probably progresses as follows:

Proteins → Proteoses → Peptones ⟨ Acid amides / Amino acids

conditions are favorable, be changed to nitrates, the form in which higher plants take up a large proportion of their nitrogen.

This mass of plant tissue, as it is worked over by the microorganisms, is a mixture of partially decayed products, living and dead microbial cells, and resistant compounds, such as waxes, resins, and lignin, that readily combine with proteins and similar nitrogenous materials. Indeed, the microbial tissue may even, at times, be preponderant, since the bacteria, actinomyces, and fungi in the presence of food multiply rapidly, and great quantities of complex tissue are synthesized. Since these organisms live only a short time, their bodies are soon subject to decay, and the compounds present are speedily on the road to simplification. Carbon dioxide is given off continually from the very beginning and is a rough measure of the intensity of the decay processes. Other simple products, especially the nitrates, are not present in large amounts until the more intense decomposition activities are somewhat abated. (See Fig. 20.)

As the intermediate compounds become simpler and are present in smaller and smaller amount, the microorganic activity lessens, and the living microbial tissue, as a result, becomes much reduced. Naturally, the more resistant organic compounds, such as the lignins, waxes, resins, combined or uncombined with protein or other nitrogenous compounds, now dominate the soil organic matter. Some readily reactive substances containing nitrogen, carbon, and sulfur are no doubt associated with them. This dark, incoherent, and heterogeneous colloidal mass, variable as to its resistance to microbial attack, is called *humus*. To it are to be ascribed many of the physical and chemical properties characteristic of soils. This persistence of certain portions of the soil organic matter is just as important as the ready decomposition of other parts. Both are vital.

Let us review the process briefly by first assuming that the decomposition of the soil organic matter is more or less complete and that, as a result, microbial activity has sunk to a minimum. Consequently, living soil organisms, especially bacteria and fungi, are much reduced in numbers, and the organic matter has been resolved largely to humus. Now, under favorable conditions, let us introduce an abundance of fresh, decomposable tissue. A tremendous change immediately occurs. In the presence of readily available energy and nutrients, the multiplication of soil microorganisms, hitherto so sluggish, suddenly increases manyfold, and microbial activity is soon at its peak, as is shown by the rapid liberation of energy and the tremendous evolution of carbon dioxide. That great group of general-purpose decay organisms, whose numbers fluctuate so tremendously with conditions, is soon in full control, and decomposition, as well as synthesis, goes on apace.

The soil organic matter at this stage contains a great variety of substances — intermediate products of all kinds, microbial cells, both living and dead, and stable bodies, such as waxes and lignin, which already are associated with the proteins, protecting them from decomposition, at least for the present. And, of course, carbon dioxide is being produced in volume. Finally, as the readily available energy is used up, microbial activity gradually lessens, and the soil organisms sink back again into comparative quiescence, which allows the presence in more or less abundance of simple products, such as nitrates and sulfates. And the organic matter that still remains is largely in the form of humus. In short, we are back again to the condition first postulated after a complex cycle of decay, representative of the biochemical pulsations to which the soil is subjected, again and again, as the organic matter is continually renewed.

It is well to emphasize that the decomposition of the original organic tissue of the soil and of the concurrent microbial tissue is nothing more than a process of enzymic digestion. It is just as truly a digestion as though the plant materials entered the stomach of a domestic animal. The products of these enzymic activities, although numerous and tremendously varied, may be listed for convenience under three heads: (1) energy appropriated by the microorganisms or liberated as heat, (2) simple end products, and (3) humus.

63. *The energy of the soil organic matter and its transfer* [1]

The microorganisms of the soil, as they grow and multiply, must not only have substance for their tissue synthesis but energy as well. Both of these are obtained in very large degree, not entirely,[2] however,

---

[1] For a discussion of these phases see:

Waksman, S. A., *Principles of Soil Microbiology*, The Williams & Wilkins Company, Baltimore, 1932.

Buchanan, R. E., and E. I. Fulmer, *Physiology and Biochemistry of Bacteria*, The Williams & Wilkins Company, Baltimore, 1928.

[2] Autotrophic organisms obtain their energy, at least in part, from inorganic sources, while some of the tissue-building materials come from the mineral portion of the soil. Moreover, nitrogen-fixing bacteria draw large quantities of this element from the soil air.

from the soil organic matter. All manner of compounds are utilized as energy sources, some freely, others slowly and indifferently.

As might be expected, organic matter contains considerable potential energy, a large proportion of which is readily transferable to other latent forms or is liberated as heat. Plant tissue, such as that entering the soil, has a heat value of 4 to 5 kilocalories to the gram of air-dry substance. The application of 10 tons of farm manure, for example, containing 5000 pounds of dry matter, would mean an addition of 9,000,000 to 11,000,000 kilocalories of latent energy. A soil containing 4 per cent of organic matter possesses about 80,000 pounds of dry organic substance to the acre-furrow-slice (2,000,000 pounds). This amount of organic residue carries from 150,000,000 to 180,000,000 calories of potential energy, equivalent in heat value to 20 or 25 tons of anthracite coal.

I. Compounds characteristic of fresh plant tissue.

Decomposed with difficulty	*Decomposed easily*
Lignin	Cellulose
Oils	Starches
Fats	Sugars
Resins, etc.	Proteins, etc.

II. Complex Intermediate Products of Decay.

Resistant compounds	*Decomposition compounds*
Resins	Amino acids
Waxes	Amides
Oils and fats	Alcohols
Lignin, etc.	Aldehydes, etc.

III. Final Products of Soil-decomposition Processes.

Complex	*Simple*
Humus — A colloidal complex in which the lignoproteinate is considered especially important	Carbon dioxide
	Nitrates
	Sulfates
	Phosphates
	Ca compounds, etc.

Fig. 20. An outline showing, in a general way, the changes that the organic compounds of plant tissue undergo in the soil. The process is one of enzymic digestion which results in the synthesis of humus, the release of energy, and the formation of simple products.

Of this large amount of relatively accessible energy carried by the soil, only a part is used by soil organisms, the remainder being left in the residues and dissipated as heat. This heat loss of energy is the final stage and represents a large and continual removal from the soil. The evolution of carbon dioxide is not only a rough measure of this but also an indication of the rate of the disappearance of the organic matter.

A rather interesting phase of the subject is the rate at which energy is dissipated from soils. This should correlate closely with the activity of bacteria and fungi and with the evolution of carbon dioxide. To a certain extent, also, there should be a very rough correlation between energy loss and soil productivity. Certain estimates made at the Rothamsted Experiment Station,[1] England, on two plats of the Broadbalk field, are rather suggestive. It was calculated that 1 million kilocalories an acre were lost annually from the untreated soil, while 15 million kilocalories were dissipated from the soil receiving liberal supplies of farm manure. The magnitude of this loss is obvious. Assuming, as already suggested, that the average soil contains 150 million kilocalories of total organic energy to the acre and that the annual dissipation is 10 million, one-fifteenth must be the yearly loss, a surprisingly rapid turnover of the organic matter. Such figures, estimates though they are, emphasize the amount of food necessary for the support of the soil organisms and the difficulty that is usually encountered in maintaining a suitable amount of active organic matter in arable soils.

The maintenance of soil organic matter is urged in practice not merely, as many persons suppose, to influence the physical condition of the soil and supply nutrients, but also to place energy in the land and facilitate its turnover once it is there. This turnover represents biochemical activity and, while it is very costly and results in an exorbitant waste of organic matter, it is an absolute necessity. Otherwise, the soil would not function adequately either as a mechanical medium or as a source of nutrients for microorganisms and higher plants.

64. *Simple products of organic matter decomposition*

As the enzymic changes of the soil organic matter proceed and humus is gradually built up, simple products begin to manifest themselves. Some of these, especially carbon dioxide, which is given off

[1] Russell, E. J., *Soil Conditions and Plant Growth*, Longmans, Green and Company, London, 1937, p. 459.

in large volume, appear immediately, while others, such as nitrate nitrogen, accumulate only after the peak of the vigorous decomposition is over and the general-purpose decay organisms have diminished in numbers. Since these simple end products are readily lost, they sink to a minimum, unless fresh tissue is added at frequent intervals.

The simple products that result from the activity of the microorganisms may be listed conveniently according to the principal elements involved:

Carbon	CO_2, $CO_3^=$, HCO_3^-, CH_4, elemental carbon
Nitrogen	NH_4^+, NO_2^-, NO_3^-, elemental nitrogen
Sulfur	S, H_2S, $SO_3^=$, $SO_4^=$, CS_2
Miscellaneous	O_2, H_2, H_2O, K^+, Mg^{++}, Ca^{++}, $PO_4^{\equiv}$, $HPO_4^=$, $H_2PO_4^-$, H^+, OH^-, etc.

Some of the significant relationships of each of the four groups are presented in order in the following sections.

65. *Carbon compounds — the carbon cycle*

Carbon, regardless of the various other elements that may be present, is the characteristic and omnipresent constituent of all organic matter. As a consequence, its movements during the microbial digestion of plant tissue are extremely significant. Most of the energy acquired by the fauna and flora within the soil comes from the oxidation of carbon and, as a result, its oxide is evolved continuously and in large amounts. The various changes that this element undergoes within and without the soil are called the *carbon cycle* and are shown graphically in Fig. 21.

In all soil, higher plants furnish most of the various carbonaceous materials for microbial dissolution. As these are digested, carbon dioxide is given off. This is the main soil source of this gas, although small amounts are excreted by plant roots and are brought down in rain water. The carbon dioxide of the soil, evolved both in summer and winter, escapes in large degree to the atmosphere, where it may be used by plants and thus completes the cycle.

A lesser amount of carbon dioxide, and this is just as important a feature as the atmospheric loss, reacts in the soil, producing carbonic acid, and the carbonates and bicarbonates of calcium, potassium, magnesium, and other elements. These salts are readily soluble and may be lost in drainage or be used by higher plants. Thus, not only are Ca, Mg, and K ions presented to the absorbing surfaces of micro-organisms and higher plants, but CO_3 and HCO_3 ions are made available as well. Small amounts of carbon may, therefore, enter plants in this way (see note on page 37). Most of the carbon, how-ever, is acquired by photosynthesis.

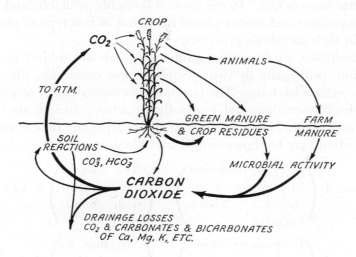

FIG. 21. Diagrammatic representation of the transformations of carbon, commonly spoken of as the *carbon cycle*. Note the stress placed on carbon dioxide both within and without the soil.

Besides carbon dioxide, carbonates, and bicarbonates, the simplifi-cation of organic matter results in other carbon products. Elemental carbon is found in soils to a certain extent and, while not especially important, its presence is significant. Under certain conditions, methane (CH_4) and carbon bisulfide (CS_2) may be produced in small amounts. But of all the simple carbon products, carbon dioxide is by far the most abundant.

66. *Ammonium, nitrites, nitrates, and elemental nitrogen*

While carbon dioxide may result from the decomposition of any organic substance, ammonium salts are formed only when nitrogenous bodies are involved. They are the first really simple nitrogen com-pounds that appear as the process of microbial digestion goes on. Amino acids and similar nitrogenous materials readily yield ammonium compounds by enzymic hydrolysis.   The transformation is usually spoken of as *ammonification* and may be brought about by a large number of heterotrophic organisms — bacteria, fungi, and actinomyces.   The ammonium ion, as it appears in the soil solution, commonly associates itself with carbonate or bicarbonate anions, so abundant in most soils.   In this form, it is readily available, and many microorganisms and higher plants make use of this type of nitrogen freely in their metabolic processes.

If conditions are favorable, ammonium ions are subject to ready oxidation, principally by two special-purpose organisms, the nitrite and the nitrate bacteria.   The enzymic processes are very sensitive to temperature, aeration, and especially to active calcium, the transformations taking place most readily when adequate lime is present. Nitrification may be shown simply and diagrammatically as follows:

$$NH_4 \text{ ions} + \begin{pmatrix} \text{Enzymic oxidation} \\ \text{in presence of ac-} \\ \text{tive Ca.   Nitrite} \\ \text{bacteria.} \end{pmatrix} = \begin{pmatrix} NO_2 \text{ ions in} \\ \text{association} \\ \text{with   bases,} \\ \text{esp.   Ca} \end{pmatrix} + CO_2 + E$$

$$NO_2 \text{ ions} + \begin{pmatrix} \text{Enzymic oxidation} \\ \text{in presence of ac-} \\ \text{tive Ca.   Nitrate} \\ \text{bacteria.} \end{pmatrix} = \begin{pmatrix} NO_3 \text{ ions in} \\ \text{association} \\ \text{with   bases,} \\ \text{esp.   Ca} \end{pmatrix} + CO_2 + E$$

The organisms, autotrophic in this case, obtain energy by the transfer, liberate some carbon dioxide, and incidentally leave, as a byproduct, nitrogen in the nitrate form.   The second reaction usually follows so closely on the first as to prevent any accumulation of nitrites.[1]   The nitrate salt presents NO_3 ions for absorption by higher plants.   Nitrates are a form of nitrogen that many plants must have for their growth.   And it is in this combination that most of the loss of nitrogen in drainage occurs.   Such removal is often so large as to seriously deplete soils of their nitrogen supply (see page 211).

One more end product awaits consideration — elemental nitrogen. Under certain conditions, the reduction of nitrates, nitrites, ammonium, and even some of the simpler amino compounds takes place in soils, and free nitrogen may be evolved.   This transfer is considered most likely to occur in poorly drained and aerated soils or in acid soils

[1] Some authorities hold that, in certain cases, the oxidation occurs as one set of reactions, no nitrites being detectable.

containing nitrites. The process is most obscure and apparently may be chemical as well as biochemical. In any case, however, the reduction is serious if the amount of nitrogen evolved is large, since elemental nitrogen ordinarily is extremely inert and is recombined with difficulty into compounds useful to higher plants. Some authorities feel that soils lose considerable nitrogen in this way (see page 381).

67. Sulfites, sulfates, and other sulfur products

Many organic compounds, especially those of a nitrogenous nature, carry sulfur, which appears in simple forms as decay progresses. General-purpose heterotrophic types of organisms apparently are first involved, but ultimately the sulfur is subjected to oxidation by special bacteria, active calcium being of great aid in facilitating the transaction. The enzymic process of sulfur oxidation may be shown as follows:

$$\text{Combined or elemental sulfur} + \begin{pmatrix} \text{Enzymic oxidation} \\ \text{in presence of active Ca} \end{pmatrix} = \begin{pmatrix} SO_3 \text{ ions in} \\ \text{assoc. with} \\ \text{bases, esp. Ca} \end{pmatrix} + CO_2 + E$$

$$SO_3 \text{ ions} + \begin{pmatrix} \text{Enzymic oxidation} \\ \text{in presence of active Ca} \end{pmatrix} = \begin{pmatrix} SO_4 \text{ ions in} \\ \text{assoc. with} \\ \text{bases, esp. Ca} \end{pmatrix} + CO_2 + E$$

The organisms obtain energy by the transfer, give off some carbon dioxide, and leave the excess of sulfur as the sulfate, the second reaction taking place so readily as to prevent any amount of sulfite sulfur from accumulating. As a matter of fact, the oxidation possibly occurs as one continuous reaction. Thus the sulfur, originally present in complicated combinations, emerges as a simple by-product and is available as the SO_4 ion, the form in which higher plants absorb practically all of their sulfur. Considerable amounts of sulfate are lost in drainage, a phase that deserves some attention from the standpoint of fertility maintenance (see page 211).

68. Miscellaneous simple products of organic decay

A number of simple products, such as water, elemental hydrogen and oxygen, and hydroxyl ions, need hardly more than simple enumeration.   Of greater significance in respect to the dissolution of soil organic matter, however, are soluble phosphates.   Much of the soil phosphorus is carried in organic form (see page 26).   And under the influence of microorganisms, this is rather readily simplified and mineralized, appearing in the soil solution in an ionic and available condition.   Since the small amount of phosphorus in mineral combination in soils usually is available only with difficulty, the organic sources thrown open by microbial decay become especially important.

One feature of the carbon cycle that has been emphasized again and again is the copious production of carbon dioxide and the development therefrom of carbonic acid.   Although very weak, carbonic acid develops enough active hydrogen to influence markedly the trend of numberless soil transactions.   In fact, most of the active hydrogen of the soil solution and the adsorbed hydrogen of the colloidal complexes can be traced back to the carbon dioxide evolved from decomposing organic matter.   Hence, the hydrogen-ion concentration of the soil solution fundamentally is an organic manifestation, as is also the constant displacement and loss of calcium and other bases from the colloidal complexes.

Because of its high adsorptive capacity, it is not surprising that soil organic matter usually carries considerable amounts of ionic potassium, calcium, magnesium, and other bases.   Naturally, they are readily liberated either by base exchange or by the microbial dissolution of the organic matter.   Also, some of these same bases are present as integral constituents of the organic material itself.   Hence, the addition to and the turnover in soils of organic residues cannot help but enhance the store of bases and, at the same time, markedly increase their mobility and usefulness.

69. *Humus — genesis and definition*

The formation of humus, although an exceedingly complicated biochemical process, may be described in general terms rather simply. Organic tissue, as it goes into the soil, is immediately and voraciously attacked, if conditions are favorable, by a host of different organisms, mostly bacteria, fungi, and actinomyces, although, at times, animals play an important role.   The easily decomposed compounds quickly succumb, first yielding complex intermediate substances and finally the simple, soluble products already enumerated.   However, the oils, fats, resins, and especially the lignins [1] are more resistant and tend to persist, either in their original or in a modified condition. This modification is of especial concern, since it seems to be due, at least in part, to a tendency of lignin and the other resistant materials to unite with proteins and allied nitrogenous compounds. An indefinite complex results that, for want of a better name, will be designated as a *lignoproteinate* because of the supposed prominence of lignin in the synthetic process. [2]

Just how the lignins and proteins are associated is wholly conjectural. But the resistance to microbial dissolution of the nitrogen compounds of the humus justifies the assumption of some type of combination. Whether the union results from the synthetic activity of the microorganisms or is a direct chemical reaction or both, cannot as yet be asserted. The net result, however, is clean-cut. Not only is humus persistent enough to influence soil character definitely but also, due to the protection of the proteins from microbial dissolution, the resultant mass carries considerable amounts of nitrogen, sulfur, phosphorus, and other nutrients. These certainly would not be present if the lignins, waxes, and resins, made up wholly of carbon, hydrogen, and oxygen, merely persisted in their original forms. [3]

Specifically, humus may be defined as a complex and rather resistant mixture of brown or dark brown amorphous and colloidal substances that develop synthetically as the original organic tissues suffer enzymic dissolution by the various soil organisms. It is a natural body and, though exceedingly variable and heterogenous, it possesses properties that distinguish it sharply from other natural organic aggregates. [4]

[1] Lignin is a waxy or resinous material that impregnates the cell walls of plants as they increase in age. It is a carbohydrate, exceedingly complex, and varies with different plants and with different tissues of the same plant. The chemical formula of lignin is in doubt. See Waksman, S. A., *Humus*, The Williams & Wilkins Company, Baltimore, 1938, pp. 99–101.

[2] See Waksman, S. A., *Humus*, The Williams & Wilkins Company, Baltimore, 1938, Chap. V.

[3] It seems that clay may also have the capacity of associating itself with proteins in such a way as to exert a protective action. This relationship should aid to a certain extent in the upkeep of nitrogen, sulfur, and phosphorus in mineral soils. See Ensminger, L. E., and J. E. Gieseking, "Resistance of Clay-Adsorbed Proteins to Proteolytic Hydrolysis," *Soil Sci.*, LIII: 205–209, 1942.

[4] There is no satisfactory method of determining the amount of humus in soils. Since the organic matter, when the vigorous digestive processes are complete, is resolved almost entirely to humus, it seems best for analytical and interpretative purposes to determine the total organic content of soils.

70. *Humus — nature and characteristics*

Humus, as has already been emphasized, is highly colloidal but unlike the mineral colloids of the soil, it is amorphous and not crystalline. Moreover, its surface exposure, its adsorption, and its catalysis are, comparatively, far in excess of those exhibited by clay. For instance, the base-exchange capacity of Montmorillonite clay commonly ranges from 80 to 100 milliequivalents. Well-developed humus from mineral soils, in sharp contrast, may show a total adsorptive power of from 200 to 300. In general, the presence of 1 per cent of humus in a mineral soil means an increase in exchange capacity of perhaps 2 milliequivalents. One per cent of clay, on the other hand, affects the adsorptive power only to the extent of possibly 0.3 to 0.6 of a milliequivalent, depending on the types of clay present and their proportionate mixtures. In respect to adsorbed water, the contrast is of the same order. The fully synthesized humus of a mineral soil will adsorb from a saturated atmosphere perhaps 80 or 90 per cent of water. Clay, on the other hand, may be able to thus acquire possibly only 15 or 20 per cent. The significance of these figures in respect to soil properties is obvious.

The low plasticity and cohesion of humus is a significant practical feature, since its maintenance in heavy field soils cannot help but alleviate unfavorable structural characteristics induced by large amounts of clay. A small increase in humus has physical effects far in excess of its proportionate amount. This is due to a considerable extent to granulation which is so markedly encouraged thereby. The nature and mechanics of granulation have already been adequately explained (page 57), and the importance thereof, in respect to drainage and aeration, needs only to be reemphasized here.

Another character that is of outstanding interest is the color imparted to soils by humus. It is well to note definitely that the development of a black pigment in humus varies with climate.[1] In chernozem soils, occurring in northern semi-arid regions with an annual rainfall around 20 inches, the pigment is very dark and abundant. The alternation of cold winters and hot, dry summers, with much of the rainfall coming in the spring, may, in part, account for this. Besides, the high lime content of the soil also may be a factor.

[1] Gillam, W. S., "The Geographical Distribution of Soil Black Pigment," *Jour. Amer. Soc. Agron.*, XXXI: 371–387, 1939.

In humid-temperate zones, the pigmentation is less intense, while the least coloration is found in the humus of the tropics and semitropics. Color thus becomes an expression of climate. This is a point well worth remembering, as it indicates that organic pigmentation, or depth of color in mineral soils, cannot be used satisfactorily as a comparative measure of the amount of organic matter present.

Soil humus, as a colloidal complex, is organized in much the same way as clay. The lignoproteinates, and no doubt other constituents as well, function as complex acidoids or micelles. Under ordinary conditions, these carry innumerable negative charges and usually migrate under the influence of an electric current to the anode. But instead of being made up principally of Si, O, Al, and Fe, as are the silicate clayey acidoids, the humic micelles are composed of C, H, O, N, S, P, and other elements.

The humic micelles, like the lamellar particles of clay, exhibit the double-layer phenomenon and carry a swarm of adsorbed cations in exactly the same way. The same exchangeable cations (Ca^{++}, H^+, Mg^{++}, K^+, Na^+, etc.) are found in the outer layers, and base-exchange properties of a markedly higher order occur. An understanding of the general organization of clay (page 77) supplies a basis for a conception of the colloidal setup and chemical functioning of humus, especially in respect to ionic-exchange phenomena. For this reason, humus, colloidally, may be represented by the same structural formula used for clay (namely, CarH(acidoid)), and the same reactions will serve to illustrate base exchange in both (page 79).

Before referring to the colloidal coordination of humus and clay in mineral soils, there is one more characteristic of the former that merits particular attention — the capacity of humus to increase the activity of certain nutrient bases, such as calcium, potassium, and magnesium. It seems that an H-humus, as is the case with an H-clay, acts much like an ordinary acid and can react with minerals in such a way as to extract their bases. This is important, but more important still is the unusual capacity of an acid humus to effect such a transfer. Once the exchange is made, the bases so affected are held in a loosely adsorbed condition and, hence, are easily available to higher plants or readily appear in the soil solution. This capacity to mobilize nutrients is rated as one of the outstanding characteristics of humic colloids functioning in mineral soils.[1]

[1] Albrecht, William A., "Soil Organic Matter and Ion Availability for Plants," *Soil Sci.* LI: 487–494, 1941.

In representing the colloidal matter of a humid, temperate-region mineral soil by the general formula, CarH(acidoid), and in considering base exchange as a combined function of the mineral and organic colloids, it must always be remembered that one is dealing with a heterogeneous mixture of two very different groups, each within itself remarkably diversified. In detail, a person should not forget the nature of the acidoid radicals in the two cases, one an iron aluminum-silicate and the other complexly organic, dominated by C, H, O, N, S, and P. The clayey nucleus, crystalline and lamellar, is markedly stable under ordinary conditions and is active almost wholly by base exchange. The organic acidoid, on the other hand, amorphous and of no definite form, is susceptible to microorganic attack and has a twofold activity — ionic exchange and marked energy liberation. With the aid of such fundamental details, the conceptions regarding the clayey and humic substances may be combined to expand still further the biocolloidal concept of soils.

71. *Direct influence of organic compounds on higher plants*

One of the early beliefs in regard to plant nutrition was that organic matter, as such, is directly absorbed by higher plants. This opinion, afterwards, was definitely discarded. More recently, Hutchinson and Miller,[1] as well as other investigators, carefully studied the question of the assimilation of nitrogenous organic compounds by higher plants. The results, in general, indicate that certain of these can be absorbed by higher plants, often rather readily. That such substances ordinarily do not satisfy their need for nitrogen is indicated by the ready response that most plants make to an application of nitrates.

Viewed in the light of such findings, it may be concluded that the soil organic matter may, to some extent, serve as a direct source of plant nutrients, providing not only nitrogen and sulfur but also carbon, oxygen, and hydrogen, elements usually considered as coming from air and water. Since these ingredients are absorbed in a complex molecular condition, a great saving of energy is effected, as

[1] Hutchinson, H. B., and N. H. J. Miller, "The Direct Assimilation of Inorganic and Organic Forms of Nitrogen by Higher Plants," *Jour. Agr. Sci.*, IV, Part 3:282–302, 1912.
Schreiner, O., and J. J. Skinner, *Nitrogenous Soil Constituents and Their Bearing upon Soil Fertility*, Bulletin 87, Bureau of Soils, U. S. Dept. of Agriculture, 1912. Also Schreiner, O., and others, *A Beneficial Organic Constituent of Soils; Creatinine*, Bulletin 83, Bureau of Soils. U. S. Dept. of Agriculture, 1911.

they probably become a part of the cell contents with less synthetic activity than would be the case with simpler nutrients. However, even under the most favorable conditions, such intakes undoubtedly are too small to be of practical significance from the nutrient stand-point.

However, the beneficial effects of an exceedingly small absorption of organic compounds might be accounted for by postulating the presence of growth-promoting substances. In fact, it is quite possible that vitaminlike compounds are developed as organic decay progresses in soils. If this be the case, the direct effect of humic substances upon higher plants might be much more important than hitherto has been suspected.

On the other hand, some soil organic compounds no doubt may be harmful.[1] As an example, dihydroxystearic acid may be mentioned, as this was one of the first to be so studied. This compound was isolated from soil and identified in the United States Department of Agriculture and is very toxic. Other compounds of a harmful nature were also isolated by the same investigators.

While twenty soils, out of a group of sixty taken in eleven states, were found to contain dihydroxystearic acid, this does not necessarily mean that this or similar injurious compounds are serious detrimental factors. It is very probable that such compounds are merely products of improper soil conditions and are not the direct cause of depressed crop yield. When such conditions are righted, the so-called toxic matter will disappear. Good drainage and tillage, lime, and fertilizers are so efficacious that organic toxicity need never be a factor in soils rationally managed.

72. *The nitrogen-carbon ratio*[2]

While some investigators have attempted the isolation and identifi-cation of the organic compounds of the soil, others have pursued a

[1] Schreiner, O., and E. C. Shorey, *The Isolation of Harmful Organic Substances from Soils,* Bulletin 53, Bureau of Soils, U. S. Dept. of Agriculture, 1909.

Schreiner, O., and J. J. Skinner, *Nitrogenous Soil Constituents and Their Bearing upon Soil Fertility,* Bulletin 87, Bureau of Soils, U. S. Dept. of Agriculture, 1912.

[2] Sievers, F. J., and H. F. Holtz, "The Significance of Nitrogen in Soil Organic Rela-tionships," *Proc. and Papers, First Internat. Cong. Soil Sci.,* III:423–436, 1927.

Jensen, H. L., "On the Influence of Carbon-Nitrogen Ratios of Organic Material on Mineralization of Nitrogen," *Jour. Agr. Sci.,* XIX:71–82, 1929.

McLean, W. B., "The Carbon-Nitrogen Ratio of Soil Organic Matter," *Jour. Agr. Sci.,* XX:348–354, 1930.   (Continued on next page.)

different attack, the determination of the elemental composition of the soil organic matter. In this respect, carbon and nitrogen have received particular attention because of the energy relations of the former and the nutrient importance of the latter. Determinations of the amounts of organic carbon and total soil nitrogen are, therefore, commonly made.[1] While such figures are valuable in a number of different ways, the proportion of the total soil nitrogen to the carbon in the organic matter is of especial interest. This relationship is commonly spoken of as the *nitrogen-carbon ratio.*

The original plant tissue as it goes into the soil is, as already indicated, variable, the ratio of nitrogen to carbon ranging from 1 to 20 or 30 in legumes and farm manure to as high as 1 to 70, or even more, in certain strawy residues. All gradations between these extremes are found. The nitrogen-carbon ratio of the bodies of microorganisms, on the other hand, is not only more constant but much narrower, ordinarily falling between 1:4 and 1:9. Bacterial tissue is somewhat richer in protein than that of fungi.

As the process of decomposition goes on in the soil, the organic residues are thoroughly worked over by the organisms present. The rapid synthesis that takes place, coordinate with the multiplication of the microorganisms, requires large amounts of energy. This results in the dissipation of great quantities of carbon as carbon dioxide and a rapid reduction in organic matter. Nitrogen, being in great demand and in the minimum, is rapidly synthesized by the bacteria and fungi and is held as a part of the microbial tissue. At the same time, considerable protein is associated with and protected by lignins and similar compounds. This results in a further conservation of nitrogen. As a result, the proportion of carbon lessens rapidly as the process goes

---

Leighty, W. R., and E. C. Shorey, "Some Carbon-Nitrogen Relations in Soils," *Soil Sci.*, XXX:257–266, 1930.

Salter, F. J., "The Carbon-Nitrogen Ratio in Relation to the Accumulation of Organic Matter in Soils," *Soil Sci.*, XXXI:413–430, 1931.

Holtz, H. F., and S. C. Vandecaveye, "Organic Residues and Nitrogen Fertilizers in Relation to the Productivity and Humus Content of Palouse Silt Loam," *Soil Sci.*, XLV: 143–163, 1938.

Waksman, S. L., *Humus*, The Williams & Wilkins Company, Baltimore, 1938, pp. 178–183.

[1] The amount of organic carbon in the soil may be determined by the classical dry-combustion method or more easily by wet combustion, preferably using chromic acid. The total nitrogen of the soil is usually found by means of the modified Kjeldahl method. See *Official and Tentative Methods of Analysis of the Assoc. of Official Agr. Chemists*, 5th ed., Official Agriculture Chemists, Washington, 1940.

on, and the nitrogen-carbon ratio, of necessity, becomes much narrower.

When the soil organic matter has been reduced largely to humus, the marked activity of the general-purpose soil organisms having, of course, subsided, the nitrogen-carbon ratio will be found to have approached that of the bacterial and fungal tissue. This is to be expected, as the soil humus now consists of a colloidal adsorptive complex, of which decaying microbial tissue makes up no mean proportion. Most soils, especially if under similar climatic conditions, and unless they have recently received large amounts of original tissue, tend to have about the same nitrogen-carbon ratio. This ratio, somewhat above that of microorganic tissue, ranges, for surface soils, from 1:8 to 1:18, the median being between 9 and 12.[1] The variations seem to be correlated closely with climatic conditions, especially temperature and the amount and distribution of rainfall.[2] For instance, it is rather well established that the nitrogen carbon ratio tends to be lower in aridic soils than in those of humid regions when temperatures are comparable, and lower in warmer regions than those cooler, providing the rainfalls are of about the same magnitude. Also the ratio is narrower for subsoils, in general, than for the corresponding surface layers.

A pertinent question might be raised at this point. Why does the nitrogen-carbon ratio in any particular soil sink to a certain level and remain more or less constant, unless fresh tissue is added or a radical change in soil environment, external or internal, takes place? The answer seems to be this. As carbon dioxide is lost and the nitrogen-carbon ratio, as already explained, becomes narrower, the amount of available carbon grows smaller, and the activities of the general-purpose heterotrophic organisms are much curtailed. The microbial demand for nitrogen, therefore, markedly diminishes and, as a result, by-product ammonium begins to appear. Nitrification may now take place, if other conditions are favorable, and nitrate nitrogen, which hitherto has been absent, becomes evident. This form of nitrogen is subject to loss in drainage and also may be readily removed from the soil, together with the ammonium forms, by higher plants.

As decomposition processes go further, both carbon and nitrogen

[1] See Anderson, M. S., and H. G. Byers, "The Carbon-Nitrogen Ratio in Relation to Soil Classification," *Soil Sci.*, XXXVIII:121–138, 1934.

[2] See Jenny, H., *A Study on the Influence of Climate upon the Nitrogen and Organic Matter Content of the Soil*, Research Bulletin 152, Missouri Agr. Exp. Sta., 1930.

are now subject to loss, and it is only a question of time until their relative rate of disappearance from the soil becomes constant, 9 or 10 parts of carbon being oxidized to 1 part of nitrogen changed to the nitrate. The nitrogen-carbon ratio, as a result, becomes more or less constant, always being somewhat greater than the ratios that characterize microbial tissue. This is because humus, due to the basic lignin and other carbonaceous materials, can never carry so much nitrogen as does the proteinaceous complex of microorganisms.

73. *The significance of the nitrogen-carbon ratio*

The nitrogen-carbon ratio of soils is an important factor in a number of ways, only two of which will be mentioned here. In the first place, as long as the nitrogen-carbon ratio of the soil organic matter is wide, the activity of the general-purpose decay organisms will be intense and the demand for nitrogen great.[1] Little ammoniacal nitrogen will be available for nitrification, and nitrates will appear but sparingly, if at all. Higher plants growing on such a soil may, therefore, suffer from a lack of available nitrogen. A wide nitrogen-carbon ratio thus means severe competition between the various microorganisms of the soil as well as between the soil organisms and higher plants. The addition of straw or similar carbonaceous material to a soil will initiate such a contention. However, this is not always undesirable. In fact, it is often highly advantageous, as nitrogen is thus held in complex combinations that are not susceptible to loss in drainage. Thus, nature provides a method of nitrogen control and conservation that is highly efficacious.[2]

When, however, the activity of the heterotrophic bacteria and of the fungi has somewhat abated, and the N:C ratio has become narrower, the microbial demand for nitrogen will be less. Ammoniacal nitrogen now becomes available for nitrification, and nitrate accumulation can take place. The nitrogen needs of higher plants may now be satisfied. The manipulation of the soil in such a way as to favor one or the other of these conditions is a part of good soil management and is constantly practiced.

[1] Hutchings, I. J. and T. L. Martin, "Influence of the Carbon-Nitrogen Ratios of Organic Matter on Rate of Decomposition in the Soil," *Jour. Amer. Soc. Agron.*, XXVI:333–341, 1934.

[2] Waksman, S. A., and I. J. Hutchings, "The Role of Plant Constituents in the Preservation of Nitrogen in the Soil," *Soil Sci.*, XL:487–497, 1935.

A second important phase of the nitrogen-carbon ratio relates to the maintenance of soil humus. Since the nitrogen, during the rapid dissolution of the soil organic matter, is held tightly in the soil by microorganisms, lignin, and clay, and the carbon is reduced to a more or less definite level with it, the amount of soil nitrogen really determines the amount of organic carbon finally present. Thus, the greater the amount of nitrogen present in the original tissue, the greater will be the accumulation of organic carbon. And since a rather definite ratio (1:1.724) exists between the organic carbon and the soil organic matter, the amount of organic matter that can be maintained in any soil is, like the organic carbon, contingent upon the amount of nitrogen present.[1] This microbial relationship of the soil nitrogen to the maintenance of the soil organic matter is surprisingly powerful and consistent. Both features of the nitrogen-carbon ratio referred to will be expanded later, as they are of tremendous importance in the practical management of soils.

74. *Amounts of organic matter and nitrogen in soils*

The amounts of organic matter in mineral soils vary so widely that it is difficult to present representative figures. Mineral surface soil, corresponding roughly to the furrow-slice, may contain from a trace to 12 or 15 per cent of organic matter. The percentage figures for the gray-brown soils of West Virginia and certain Russian chernozems are indicative of the variations that are encountered:

	Range	Average
West Virginia soils [a]	0.73–15.14%	2.88%
Russian chernozems [b]	3.45–16.72%	8.07%

[a] Salter, R. M., and C. F. Wells, *Analyses of West Virginia Soils*, Bulletin 168, W. Va. Agr. Exp. Sta., 1918.
[b] Kossowitsch, P., "Die Schwarzerde," *Internat. Mitt. für Bodenkunde*, I:316, 1912.

The following data (Table XIII) are suggestive of the average amounts of organic matter that may be expected in representative soils from various parts of the United States. The subsoils, of course, run much lower in every case.

[1] Millar, H. C., F. B. Smith, and P. E. Brown, "The Rate of Decomposition of Various Plant Materials in Soils," *Jour. Amer. Soc. Agron.*, XXVIII:914–923, 1936.

Table XIII. Percentages of Organic Matter (C × 1.724) in Certain Representative Soils of the United States [1]

Description	Surface	Subsoil
8 Residual soils — Robinson [a]	1.76	0.64
3 Glacial and loessial soils — Robinson [a]	4.59	1.44
2 Kansas till soils — Call [b]	2.86	1.98
6 Nebraska loess soils — Alway and McDole [c]	3.83	1.96
30 Minnesota till soils — Rost and Alway [d]	7.46	1.88
95 N. Y. glacial soils — Bizzell [e]	4.43	
240 Maryland soils — Bartlett, et al. [f]	1.56	
21 Southern Great Plains, upland — Daniel, et al. [g]	1.55	.95

[a] Robinson, W. O., *The Inorganic Composition of Some Important American Soils*, Bulletin 122, U. S. Dept. of Agriculture, 1914.

[b] Call, L. E., et al., *Soil Survey of Shawnee County, Kansas*, Bulletin 200, Kans. Agr. Exp. Sta., 1914.

[c] Alway, F. J., and G. R. McDole, "The Loess Soils of the Nebraska Portion of the Transition Region: I. Hygroscopicity, Nitrogen and Organic Carbon," *Soil Sci.*, I: 197–238, 1916.

[d] Rost, C. O., and F. J. Alway, "Minnesota Glacial Soil Studies: I. A Comparison of the Soils of the Late Wisconsin and Iowan Drifts," *Soil Sci.*, XI:161–200, 1921.

[e] Bizzell, J. A., Unpublished analyses, Dept. of Agronomy, Cornell Univ. Agr. Exp. Sta.

[f] Bartlett, J. B., R. W. Ruble, and R. P. Thomas, "The Influence of Hydrogen Peroxide Treatments on the Exchange Capacity of Maryland Soils," *Soil Sci.*, XLIV:123–138, 1937.

[g] Daniel, Harley A., and Wright H. Langham, "Some Physical and Chemical Properties and the Kind of Organic Matter Affection Color in Randall Clay and Upland Soils of the Southern Great Plains," *Soil Sci.*, XLV:369–383, 1938.

As the nitrogen, especially in humid-region soils, is carried almost wholly by the organic matter, its further consideration at this point is opportune. Since soil nitrogen is so closely related to the organic matter, it, like the humic content, shows great variations. The following percentage data, respecting the range and average amounts of nitrogen, are most significant from the fertility standpoint.

	Range	Average
West Virginia surface soils [a]	0.043–0.539%	0.147%
Louisiana surface soils [b]	0.001–0.109%	0.049%
New York surface soils [c]	0.010–0.406%	0.212%

[a] Salter, R. M., and C. F. Wells, *Analyses of West Virginia Soils*, Bulletin 168, W. Va. Agr. Exp. Sta., 1918.

[b] Walker, S. S., *Chemical Composition of Some Louisiana Soils as to Series and Texture*, Bulletin 177, La. Agr. Exp. Sta., 1920.

[c] Bizzell, J. A., *The Chemical Composition of New York Soils*, Bulletin 513, Cornell Univ. Agr. Exp. Sta., 1930.

[1] There is no satisfactory method of determining directly the exact quantity of organic matter in soil. The usual procedure is to find first the amount of organic carbon. This figure multiplied by the factor 1.724 will give the approximate amount of organic matter present.

The following figures (Table XIV) show the average percentages of nitrogen that may be expected in certain representative soils of the United States and also throw further light on the comparative amounts of organic matter usually present.

Table XIV.   Percentages of Nitrogen and Approximate Percentages of Organic Matter (N × 20) in Certain Representative Soils of the United States [1]

Description	Nitrogen		Organic Matter	
	Soil	Subsoil	Soil	Subsoil
71 Cecil soils of North Carolina [a]	0.048	0.024	0.96	0.48
165 Norfolk soils of North Carolina [b]	0.039	0.020	0.78	0.40
16 Loess soils of Central U. S. [c]	0.154	0.083	3.08	1.66
381 Kentucky soils [d]	0.120	0.070	2.40	1.40
30 Minnesota till soils [e]	0.338	0.092	6.76	1.84
100 New York Soils [f]	0.212	0.085	4.24	1.70

[a] Williams, C. B., et al., *Report on the Piedmont Soils, Particularly with Reference to Their Nature, Plant-Food Requirements, and Adaptability for Different Crops*, Bulletin, N. Car. Dept. Agr., XXXVI, No. 2, 1915.

[b] Williams, C. B., et al., *Report on Coastal Plain Soils, Particularly with Reference to Their Nature, Plant-Food Requirements, and Suitability for Different Crops,"* Bulletin, N. Car. Dept. Agr., XXXIX, No. 5, 1918.

[c] Robinson, W. O., et al., *Variation in the Chemical Composition of Soils*, Bulletin 551, U. S. Dept. of Agriculture, 1917.   Alway, F. J., and G. R. McDole, "The Loess Soils of the Nebraska Portion of the Transition Region: I. Hygroscopicity, Nitrogen and Organic Carbon," *Soil Sci.*, I: 197–238, 1916.   Also Bennett, H. H., *Soils and Agriculture of the Southern States*, The Macmillan Company, New York, 1921, pp. 332–353.

[d] Averitt, S. D., *The Soils of Kentucky*, Bulletin 193, Ky. Agr. Exp. Sta., 1915.

[e] Rost, C. O., and F. J. Alway, "Minnesota Glacial Soil Studies: I. A Comparison of the Soils of the Late Wisconsin and the Iowan Drifts," *Soil Sci.*, XI: 161–200, 1921.

[f] Bizzell, J. A., *The Chemical Composition of New York Soils*, Bulletin 513, Cornell Univ. Agr. Exp. Sta., 1930.

75. *Variations in soil organic matter and nitrogen — correlations*

In scanning the data just presented, one cannot but be impressed by the variability in organic matter and nitrogen contents of representative mineral soils.   Wide differences are evident, not only between soils of different physiographic provinces but also between closely contiguous areas in any particular locality.   Heterogeneity seems to be the rule.   This is expected by pedologists.   Let us consider the broader aspects first.

[1] The percentage of organic matter in a single sample of soil, when calculated from the percentage of total nitrogen by the usual factor (N × 20), is an extremely untrustworthy figure.   But when the factor is applied to the average percentage of nitrogen in a large number of soils, it gives a comparatively accurate group figure, especially for arable soils.

Climatic conditions,[1] especially temperature and rainfall, exert an important influence on the amounts of nitrogen and organic matter found in soils. As progress is made from a warmer to a cooler climate, even though the rainfall may not be exactly the same as to amount and distribution, the organic matter and nitrogen of soils tend to increase. At the same time, the nitrogen-carbon ratio widens. In general, the decomposition of organic matter is accelerated in warm climates while an accumulation is favored in cool regions. Within belts of uniform moisture conditions and comparable vegetation, the average total organic matter and nitrogen increase from two to three times for each 10° C fall in mean annual temperature. The situation is well illustrated by conditions in the Mississippi Valley region. Here, the northern prairie soils and chernozems contain considerably greater amounts of total organic matter and nitrogen than those that lie to the southward. When the amount of original tissue yearly added to the soil is taken into consideration, the tropics, where plants grow so luxuriantly, afford an even better example of the influence of temperature on the rapidity of decay and disappearance of organic materials.

Rainfall also seems to exert a control upon the accumulation of organic matter and nitrogen in soils as definite, in many respects, as that of temperature. In general, under comparable conditions, the nitrogen and organic matter increase as the effective moisture becomes greater. At the same time, the nitrogen-carbon ratio becomes wider. This is especially true for the grasslands. The explanation lies not only in the rapid microbial action in areas of moderate to low rainfall but also in the scantier vegetation of these regions. In arriving at the rainfall correlation such as advanced above, it must not be forgotten that the organic situation in any one soil is in large degree an expression of both temperature and precipitation. Climatic influences never work singly.

Besides the broader aspects discussed above, there are numerous local relationships that should be mentioned. In the first place, the texture of the soil, other factors being constant, seems to influence the

[1] Jenny is perhaps the best single author to consult on this phase. Jenny, H., "Relation of Climatic Factors to the Amount of Nitrogen in Soils," *Jour. Amer. Soc. Agron.*, XX:900–912, 1928. And *A Study of the Influence of Climate upon the Nitrogen and Organic Matter Content of Soil*, Research Bulletin 152, Missouri Agr. Exp. Sta., 1930. Also *Factors of Soil Formation*, McGraw-Hill Book Company, Inc., New York, 1941.

Jenny's conclusions are confirmed by Vanderford, H. B., and W. A. Albrecht, *The Development of Loessial Soils in Central United States as It Reflects Differences in Climate*, Research Bulletin 345, Missouri Agr. Exp. Sta., 1942.

percentage of humus and nitrogen present. A sandy soil, for example, usually carries less organic matter and nitrogen than one of a heavier nature. This is probably due to the lower moisture content and to the more ready oxidation that occurs in the lighter soils. Again, the soils lying along streams, because of their moisture relations and to the wash that they receive, are generally much higher in organic residues and nitrogen than their upland equivalents. The lime content of a soil, its drainage and erosion, its vegetative cover, and the vagaries of weather are other factors that may exert an influence upon the accumulation and the activity of the soil organic matter and its nitrogen.

While such conditions are somewhat indefinite, they are very important practically. They indicate that every soil, depending on a number of complexly interlocked factors, has more or less definite organic matter and nitrogen levels. These levels, it is well to emphasize, differ markedly with the handling of the soil and its vegetative cover. A virgin soil and its cultivated equivalent will differ radically. In practice, therefore, it is hardly worth while to attempt a maintenance of the soil nitrogen and organic matter above certain percentages, providing good crops can be grown under these conditions.

76. *Influence of soil organic matter*

Before discussing the practical maintenance of soil organic matter, it might be well to indicate very briefly what is expected from this all-important constituent. The most obvious soil influence — the darkening in color — will be mentioned first. The grays, browns, and blacks in various shades and tints are, in most cases, due to humus. Granulation, under favorable conditions, is a concomitant influence and is, of course, especially to be encouraged in heavy soils where drainage and aeration are so vital. In most cases, tilth is never satisfactory unless the organic matter is up to a certain level. Moreover, an increase in water-holding power as well as in total exchange capacity is sure to result as the humus content of a soil is raised. Perhaps one-third of the total exchange capacity of a representative mineral surface soil is due to organic matter.[1] While with some cases,

---

[1] See Bartlett, J. B., R. W. Ruble, and R. P. Thomas, "The Influence of Hydrogen Peroxide Treatments on the Exchange Capacity of Maryland Soils," *Soil Sci.*, XLIV: 123–138, 1937, and Olson, L. C., and R. H. Bray, "The Determination of the Organic Base-Exchange Capacity of Soils," *Soil Sci.*, XLV: 483–496, 1938.

such as the Florida sands and the Portsmouth series of the Atlantic Coast, 80 or 90 per cent of the adsorptive power is ascribed to the humic fraction.

In addition, an increase in organic matter not only means a greater percentage of total nitrogen and sulfur but a greater activity as well. Nor is this activity limited to the two constituents mentioned. The evolution of carbon dioxide is a case in point. The high proportion of the soil phosphorus carried by the organic matter is also significant. Moreover, due to the capacity of humus, both directly and indirectly, to react with the soil minerals, nutrients, that otherwise might remain dormant, are rendered available. Beyond a doubt, the soil organic matter is a great mobilizer (page 131). Again, there are the biological influences, not only in respect to energy supply, but also as regards nutrients. These complex biochemical interrelations are really the basis of much of the influence that makes humus an indispensable constituent of soils.

77. *Maintenance of soil organic matter*

The maintenance of a proper supply of organic matter in arable soils is a question of great practical importance, as productive capacity is governed, to a great extent, by such material. This maintenance is rendered more urgent by the rapid turnover of the organic residues, especially in cultivated land, and the large proportion that is dissipated each year. The subject may be considered under three heads: (1) the source of supply, (2) the promotion of proper soil conditions in order that the organic matter may perform its legitimate functions, and (3) the economy of humus maintenance. They will be considered in order.

Source of supply. The organic matter of a cultivated soil may be increased more or less naturally by the plowing under of green crops. This is called *green-manuring* and is a very satisfactory practice when it can be accommodated to the rotation. Such crops as rye, buckwheat, oats, peas, soybeans, vetch, as well as others lend themselves to this method of soil improvement. Not only do these crops increase the actual organic content of a soil, but in the case of legumes, at least a part of the nitrogen may be drawn from the air, if the nodule bacteria are present and active.

Farm manure, while it contains a large amount of organic matter, is valuable also because of its nitrogen supply. This nitrogen functions as a nutrient and, in this way, increases the residues from crops. Again the nitrogen, due to its control of the organic carbon (see page 137), makes possible a higher level of organic maintenance. Its use, in general, favors the upkeep of the organic matter of the soil.

Crop residues and roots form no inconsiderable portion of the organic matter added each year to the land. Such materials are perhaps the most important source in arable soils. Without them, the maintenance of organic matter would be impossible. In this respect, sod crops are especially valuable, being looked upon as humus builders, in contrast with cultivated crops that encourage humus reduction. The heavier crop yield after a sod can thus be explained in part. By the same reasoning, a rotation should be properly balanced in respect to its cultivated crops, small grains, and hay. With soils so handled and, at the same time, adequately limed and fertilized, the maintenance of the soil organic matter at a suitable level should be possible, especially if farm manure is applied.

Proper soil condition. In order that organic materials added to any soil may produce the proper decomposition products and perform their normal functions, soil conditions, in general, should be of the best. This means careful and opportune tillage and cultivation. Tile drainage should be installed, if necessary, in order to promote satisfactory aeration and granulation. Lime should be added if basic materials are lacking, for it promotes bacterial activity as well as plant growth. The addition of fertilizers will often be a benefit, as will also the establishment of a suitable rotation. The increased crop growth should make possible a larger addition of organic matter, especially through crop residues and farm manures.

Economy in humus maintenance. Since the rate at which carbon is lost from the soil increases very rapidly as the organic content is raised, the maintenance of the humus at a high level is not only difficult but also expensive. It is, therefore, unwise to hold the organic matter above a level consistent with crop yields that pay best.[1] Just what this level should be will depend on climatic conditions, soil type, and the crops grown. Obviously, it should be higher in the chernozem region of North Dakota than in central Kansas where the temperature is higher or in northern Montana where the effective rainfall is lower. In any

[1] Russell, J. C., "Organic Matter Requirements of Soils under Various Climatic Conditions," *Jour. Amer. Soc. Agron.*, XIX: 380–388, 1927.

event, always maintain the soil organic matter at an economic minimum, consistent with a suitable physical condition, satisfactory biochemical activity, an adequate availability of nutrients, and paying crop yields.

The second economy phase has to do with the control that nitrogen exerts upon humus accumulation. It has already been shown that the greater the amount of nitrogen present in the organic matter added to a soil, the greater, conditions being comparable, will be the retention of organic carbon (page 137). It would seem wise, therefore, to utilize, wherever possible, residues with low nitrogen-carbon ratios such as farm manure and legumes. The maintenance of organic matter, therefore, assumes a decided fertilizer aspect. Obviously, the addition merely of carbonaceous residues would not only be most uneconomic but also would fail to solve the humus problem.

Good soil management, therefore, seeks to adjust the addition of organic residues, the physical and chemical conditions of the soil, and the losses through biological activity in such a way that paying crops may be harvested without reducing the humus supply of the soil below a definite level. Any system of agriculture that tends permanently to lower the organic matter of the land below a point where successful crops can be produced is improvident and unscientific.

Chapter VII. Forms of Soil Water. Energy Relations and Classification

A soil, in order to function as a medium for plant growth, must contain a certain amount of water. This moisture promotes the innumerable chemical, physical, and biological activities of the soil, acts as a solvent and carrier of nutrients, and in addition functions as a nutrient itself. The manner in which moisture is held in the soil, how it moves, its relationship to plants, and to what extent its translocations and amounts may be controlled must be reckoned with in any study of soil and plant relationships. As an introduction to these fundamental questions, let us consider first the nature of the pore spaces that make the presence of water in soils possible.

78. *Size, shape, and arrangement of soil pores*

It is common observation that the profile of a normal mineral soil is made up of a series of horizons, each a porous mass of particles variable in size, shape, arrangement, and degree of compaction. Between these particles lies an intricate network of openings, just as heterogeneous as to size and shape as the solid fraction itself. Some of these pores, especially if the soil is sandy or well granulated, are likely to be large enough to facilitate a rapid downward movement of water by gravity. Others, in marked contrast, are so minute as to impede, if not entirely prevent, the liquid flow of water. Naturally innumerable interstices of intermediate sizes occur, giving a continuous range of no mean magnitude.

The pores of macrosize lie between the larger soil grains and granules and usually are connected by interstices and passages much smaller in diameter. Their arrangement is by no means regular although they often tend to occur in vertical strings (Fig. 28, page 170). And, as might be expected, their outline and connections are tortuous

145

beyond description. When large and continuous passages do occur, they usually are due to the vertical cracking of the soil during dry spells, to holes formed by earthworms and other soil fauna, and to channels developed by the decay of plant roots. The tendency of trees and such field crops as alfalfa and sweet clover to develop the latter type of fissure is well known.

The smaller pores usually possess diameters that render them capable, if not wholly clogged with colloidal matter, of a marked capillary conduction of water. It must not be inferred, however, that the adjustment through them is necessarily rapid. Indeed, when the capillaries are very small and highly hydrated or when plugged with colloidal matter, they may allow but a very sluggish movement. In picturing the network of soil pores, such constrictions must always be kept in mind, since the movement of air and water through soils is in a large degree determined by their size and condition. Thus the flow of water from one large pore to another may be slow or rapid according to the nature of the connecting channels. Moreover, the size of the microinterstices that ramify an individual soil granule will determine in part the rate at which water may penetrate or be withdrawn from such an aggregate.

79. *The adjustment of water in the soil pores*

When water is applied to the surface of an air-dry field soil in good physical condition, it tends to penetrate due to the combined action of gravity and capillarity. As it enters the labyrinth of soil pores, its downward moving front forces a part of the soil air ahead of it. The remaining gases, often large in volume, are entrapped in the capillary interstices, especially those of the granules. This ensures some free air in spite of the downward flood of water. At the same time moisture is being absorbed by the smaller pores and imbibed by the colloidal matter. Downward movement is, of course, greatly influenced by the size of the connecting channels. If these interstices contain colloidal matter, the swelling of such material may not only reduce the size of these passages but may render them incapable of gravity conduction of water.

When enough water has entered the soil to satisfy the adsorptive capacity of the surface layer, the excess usually sinks into the lower horizons. In the case of heavy and prolonged rains this drainage water, if not too much impeded, penetrates farther and farther into the subsoil until it joins a temporary or permanent water table or escapes into ditches or streams through natural or artificial channels. Even if the water-holding capacity of the furrow-slice is not satisfied, a slow downward adjustment will continue to take place through the smaller as well as the larger interstices until equilibrium with the layers below is attained.

In the meantime, if we are dealing with normal conditions, the evaporation of water probably has begun at the surface of the now moist soil. This loss increases the curvature of the films in the exposed interstices and promotes an adjustment called *capillarity*. This phenomenon, which will be discussed later in more detail (page 163), is well exemplified by the upward movement of oil in a wick. Under its influence water flows slowly upward through the capillary pores until surface evaporation may be so markedly enhanced as seriously to deplete the soil of water that might otherwise be used by plants. During this time internal vaporization occurs and the diffusion of this water vapor, even though slight, normally is sufficient to maintain the soil air near saturation.

This survey, brief as it is, suggests three things of great practical importance. First, the soil has the capacity, not only of admitting water, but also of adsorbing and holding at least a part of it more or less tenaciously within its labyrinth of pores. Second, much of the water that finds its way into a soil later exhibits some type of movement, the nature depending on the conditions to which it is subjected. And third, most of the water present in a soil sooner or later is lost as the natural cycle of events rolls around. In short, water is an extremely variable and dynamic soil constituent. This implies energy exchange. In fact, energy exchanges are so obvious in every soil-moisture phenomenon that this approach to the subject will be adopted without further delay. It is hoped, thereby, that the intricate problems of soil water may be presented more clearly and accurately.

80. *The retention of water by soil*

When water is adsorbed by a soil, or by any other porous medium, energy as heat is liberated. This is easily demonstrated by moistening a dry soil under controlled conditions. Therefore, it is logical to suppose that, if the process is reversed and water is torn away, the removal will require a certain amount of work. This latter phenomenon will be used to introduce some of the simpler energy concepts relating to soil water.

Two forces account for the temporary fixation of water in soil. One is the attraction of the soil surfaces for water molecules. This establishes a thin layer of water, very tightly held at the solid-liquid interfaces. If sufficient moisture is present, this layer is immediately augmented by the action of a second force — the attraction of the water molecules for each other. This latter force not only can maintain in the macropores films that are comparatively thick but also usually holds the small interstices — the capillaries — entirely full of water if entrapped air does not prevent.

The attractive force of water molecules for each other is manifest at all liquid-air interfaces by a phenomenon called *surface tension*. This well-understood stress, which is evidenced by the tendency of the film to contract, reduces the water-air interface in any particular case to the least possible area and in so doing develops a negative pressure.[1] Moreover, it is well known that this pressure, produced by surface tension, varies directly with the curvature of the film. Hence the greater the curvature of the water-air surfaces within a soil, the greater will be the negative pressure and the greater must be the work required to remove a unit mass of water so retained.[2]

One idea, implied in this simple statement of facts, deserves amplification — soil moisture, depending on its position, is held with

[1] Surface tension may be more precisely defined as that property, existing in the surface films of all liquids, which tends to reduce the contained volume to the form exposing the least amount of superficial area. Naturally this surface film is very thin since it represents the greatest distance through which two particles will exert mutual cohesion. Particles lying in the liquid but below this film are equally attracted on all sides and are, therefore, in equilibrium. But those within the film itself are attracted inward to a greater degree than outward and a surface stress or tension results.

Since this film is under stress it tends to contract and, if possible, it will reduce the liquid body to a globular shape — the form that exposes the least amount of surface. Also the stress — that is, the tendency of the film to contract — develops an inward pressure that must be overcome before the liquid can be disrupted or its shape distorted.

[2] The pressure (P) developed by surface tension in dynes per centimeter (T) is commonly expressed by the following formula in which r is the radius in centimeters of the drop of liquid under study:

$$P = \frac{2\,T}{r}.$$

As the drop becomes smaller, its radius (r) diminishes and the pressure (P) developed by surface tension becomes greater. Since the curvature of the film increases as the drop becomes smaller, it is obvious that the greater the curvature of the film, other conditions remaining constant, the greater will be the pressure developed by surface tension.

different degrees of tenacity by the two forces that temporarily retain water in soil. That adsorbed at the interfaces is fixed most tightly — in fact, it is held so closely as to be largely in a nonliquid condition. But as progress is made outward, each succeeding layer of molecules added is subject to less and less tension until the retaining force is that developed by surface tension alone. And when the liquid-air interface of a thick film with little curvature is considered, the water located at its surface may be just able to maintain itself against gravity. Obviously then, when the soil is near saturation, it should be easy to remove a small increment of water, but as the moisture becomes less and less in a soil, the greater and greater will be the force necessary to tear away a unit amount.

This dynamic concept is especially important for several reasons. It furnishes a thoroughly scientific basis for a classification of soil moisture. As a result the movement of soil water can be expressed with greater precision, its availability to plants can be accurately designated, and its practical control more satisfactorily explained.

81. *Determination and expression of energy values*

Without going into details, it may be stated that it is quite possible by the use of certain methods to measure, under controlled conditions, the force necessary to remove successive increments of water from soil.[1] Thus a soil may be saturated with water and by measuring the force required to remove each successive portion, an evaluation in energy units may be obtained for practically all of the moisture of any particular soil, including even that adsorbed with such tremendous rigidity at the solid-liquid interfaces.

Accepting the validity of such determinations, it is necessary, before investigating actual energy values, that a person understand the method employed in designating the magnitude of the surface forces with which soil retains its water. The force in any particular case is expressed in terms of the height in centimeters of a unit water column, whose weight just equals the force under consideration. The greater the centimeter height, the greater, of course, is the force measured. We thus may express the tenacity with which water is held by soils in

---

[1] For further information consult Schofield, R. K., "The pF of the Water in Soil," *Trans. 3rd Internat. Cong. of Soil Science*, II: 37–48, 1935. Also, Baver, L. D., *Soil Physics*, John Wiley & Sons, Inc., New York, 1940, pp. 204–207.

simple gravity units or, in other words, we may evaluate concisely the force necessary to remove a unit increment of moisture from a soil.

One complication, however, arises. While some of the soil water is held very loosely, some, as already intimated, is retained with such tremendous tenacity that the suction or pull necessary to remove it, if expressed directly in centimeter heights of water, gives awkwardly large figures. For instance, certain increments of the colloidally adsorbed moisture require for their removal a force more than equivalent to the weight of a column of water 1,000,000 centimeters in height. This exceeds by several thousand feet the elevation of our loftiest mountains. In order to avoid such cumbersome figures and to make the plotting of curves possible, energy values may be expressed, not in centimeter heights of unit water columns, but as the logarithm of such figures. This is called, for convenience, the *pF*. Thus the force equivalent to the weight of 100 centimeters of water corresponds to a pF of 2; that of 1000 centimeters to a pF of 3; and so on until the extreme force with which water is held by soils is reached. This is approximately 10,000,000 centimeters, or a pF of 7.

In further explanation it may be said that the expression pF is somewhat analogous to pH. The symbol p indicates that the value is logarithmic while the capital F suggests force or energy. Thus pF is a simple expression of the energy necessary to produce a given pull or suction, in terms of the logarithm of the height in centimeters of a unit column of water. It may be remarked further that 1 atmosphere of pressure (about 14.7 pounds per square inch) has a pF value slightly over 3, while 10 atmospheres are equivalent to a pF of just over 4. An understanding of the pF method of energy expression is desirable if the physics of soil moisture are to be clearly understood.[1]

[1] A Table of pF Equivalents

pF Values	Height of a Unit Column of Water in Centimeters	Approximate Atmospheres of Pressure [a]	
0	1	1/1000	(.0009)
1	10	1/100	(.0096)
2	100	1/10	(.0968)
2.7	501	1/2	(.485)
3	1,000	1	(.968)
4	10,000	10	(9.68)
4.2	15,849	15	(15.3)
4.5	31,623	31	(30.6)
5	100,000	100	(96.8)
6	1,000,000	1,000	(968.0)
7	10,000,000	10,000	(9680.0)

[a] The actual atmospheric equivalents are given in brackets.

82. *pF graphs for mineral soils*

By the determination of pF values at various moisture contents for particular soils, graphs may be constructed indicative of their moisture-energy relationships. In order to point out the significance of such curves, generalized graphs are presented representative of three texturally different soils — a sand, a sandy loam, and a silt loam. (See Fig. 22.) It is to be first noted that pF values are plotted against percentages of soil moisture (based on dry soil) [1] and that equivalent atmospheric pressures [2] are shown at the right of the graph.

It is clearly apparent from the curves that some of the water in soil is held under tremendous negative pressures, approaching 10,000 atmospheres. This has already been suggested. On the other hand when a soil is well supplied with water, a very slight suction is sufficient to withdraw a unit amount. Moreover, the pF curves show all gradations between these extremes thus indicating an energy continuity. Obviously moisture distinctions fundamentally are those of degree and not of kind. And with a total lack of lines of demarcation, it will be difficult to establish a clear cut classification of soil water even on the basis of energy units.

It is obvious also that the water held most tenaciously is subject to the direct attraction of the solid surfaces — that is, adsorbed at the solid-liquid interfaces, and that those increments held very loosely are maintained almost wholly by surface tensional forces. This indicates that the particular characteristics exhibited by water in different parts of a soil are in large degree an expression of the pressure magnitudes to which such moisture is being subjected. It must always be borne in mind, however, that pF values express only the tension of water at the

[1] The usual method of expressing the amount of water present in a soil is in terms of percentage based on dry soil. Thus if 100 gms. of moist soil (soil + water) when dried lose 20 gms. of water, the 80 gms. of dry matter are used as a basis for the percentage calculation. Therefore, $(20 \div 80) \times 100 = 25\%$. The weight of the wet soil is undesirable as a basis for calculation since it changes with every moisture fluctuation.

A moisture determination on a sample of soil is generally carried out as follows: 100 gms. of the sample, after thorough mixing, is weighed into a suitable dish and air-dried. The sample is then placed in an oven and heated at 100° or 110° C. for seven or eight hours. It is then cooled in a desiccator and weighed. The loss in weight is water. The moisture is then calculated as a percentage based on the dry matter of the soil.

[2] The average pressure of the atmosphere at sea level is about 14.7 lb. per sq. in. This is equivalent to 76 cm. of mercury or about 1033 cm. of water. The pF of this pressure (Log 1033) is 3.014.

liquid-air interfaces — that is, moisture at the surface of the film. Thus a thin film might possess a pF of 4.2 but, if thickened by additions, the water occupying the position of the original film will be subject to considerably less tension and will move much more freely than before. This must not be forgotten in the use of pF values, otherwise a serious misconception is entertained.

Further examination of the pF curves will show that they vary characteristically with soil texture. Not only do the heavier soils

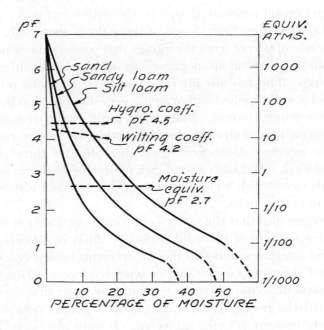

Fig. 22. The *pF* curves for three representative mineral soils. At right will be found the corresponding atmospheric pressures. Note the rapid drop in tension as the amount of soil moisture increases. The water is expressed in percentage based on dry matter.

retain a greater percentage of moisture in total but the ascendancy is also evident through the entire energy range. This is to be expected as the heavier soils, because of their smaller particles, their greater percentage of total colloidal matter, and their commonly superior organic content, usually present not only a greater total porosity but a porosity labyrinth with a higher proportion of capillary interstices and a much greater adsorptive surface.

83. *The hygroscopic coefficient, the moisture equivalent, and pF 0*

Certain critical points may be established with considerable accuracy on the pF curve of any soil. Three are of especial significance — the *hygroscopic coefficient* and the *moisture equivalent* and *pF* 0. They will be considered in order.

When any dry porous substance, such as a soil sample, is exposed to water vapor, it will take up a certain amount of moisture depending on the nature and magnitude of the surface presented, the temperature, and the degree of humidity. The amount of water thus adsorbed on the particle surfaces from an atmosphere of known relative humidity and at a standard temperature is designated as the *hygroscopic coefficient*. Naturally when the air saturation is at or near 100 per cent, the maximum amount of such moisture, for any given set of conditions, will be acquired. As determined,[1] the hygroscopic coefficient usually approaches this amount and is conveniently expressed in percentage based on dry soil. As used hereafter in this text, the term *hygroscopic coefficient* refers to maximum hygroscopicity.

It will be noted by reference to the pF curves (Fig. 22) that the maximum hygroscopic coefficient for mineral soils falls at or near a pF of 4.5, equivalent to a pressure of about 31 (30.6) atmospheres. Hence it may be used as a measure of the soil water that is held at very high tensions, so high in fact as to render most of it almost wholly inactive biologically. The forces effective at and above the hygroscopic coefficient are due mostly to the attraction of the soil surfaces for water molecules. As might be expected the hygroscopic coefficient, when expressed in percentage, is larger for the soils of heavier texture due to their greater content of colloidal matter. Organic substances tend also to magnify the hygroscopic coefficient.

[1] The method of determining the hygroscopicity of a soil at any given vapor pressure is simple in outline. Air-dry soil in thin layer is exposed to an atmosphere of definite humidity under conditions of constant temperature. When equilibrium is reached, the moisture content of the sample is determined. As might be expected, technical difficulties are encountered which detract from the accuracy of the results.

Different degrees of air saturation or vapor pressure develop different pF values for the moisture adsorbed. At 50 per cent air saturation the corresponding pF is about 6, at 75 per cent it is about 5.6, at 94.3 per cent about 5, and at 98.2 per cent it is pF 4.5. Naturally if the hygroscopic coefficient is to represent a maximum adsorption, an atmosphere nearly saturated should be employed. For this reason many investigators favor the use of a 3.3 per cent solution of sulfuric acid which gives a relative humidity at laboratory temperature of 98.2 per cent and a pF of 4.5. See Baver, L. D., *Soil Physics*, John Wiley & Sons, Inc., New York, 1940, pp. 68–75 and 236–237.

It must always be kept in mind that the point designated as the hygroscopic coefficient is more or less arbitrary as there is no sharp line of demarcation between the moisture above and below it — only a pressure difference. Nevertheless, such a designation is of considerable value, as it indicates the amount of water that, for the time being, is almost immobile. Since the magnitude of the hygroscopic coefficient is a direct function, more or less, of the colloidal surfaces that control moisture adsorption, it may be used comparatively and even analytically [1] as a measure of the amount of matter present in the colloidal state. These considerations justify the determination of such a factor, arbitrary though it may be.

The moisture equivalent is another arbitrary point on the pF curve obtained by subjecting a sample of wet soil, held in a vessel of specified dimensions, to a centrifugal force of 1000 times gravity.[2] The average film tension of the water remaining in the soil after this operation is equivalent to about ½ atmosphere of pressure or a pF of approximately 2.7.[3] As with the hygroscopic coefficient, the moisture equivalent is wholly arbitrary. Nevertheless it has considerable practical significance. This is because it happens to coincide more or less closely with the moisture content at which the capillary adjustment of soil water becomes somewhat sluggish and little interchange takes place unless moisture films with appreciably lower pF values are in close proximity.[4] The importance of this in relation to the acquisition of moisture by plant roots will be considered in some detail later. (See page 181.)

A pF of 0 is a much less arbitrary moisture-energy designation than

---

[1] For this method see note at bottom of page 88.

[2] Briggs, L. J. and J. W. McLane, *The Moisture Equivalent of Soils*, Bulletin 45, Bureau of Soils, U. S. Dept. of Agriculture, 1907.

For some of the technicalities relating to the moisture equivalent, see Veihmeyer, F. J., J. Oskenkowsky, and K. B. Tester, "Some Factors Affecting the Moisture Equivalent of Soils," *Proc. First Internat. Cong. Soil Sci.*, I: 512–534, 1927.

Due to the conditions to which the short column of soil is subject as the pressure is applied, the average tension is equivalent to a pull on a free column of only 500 times the force of gravity. Hence the moisture equivalent corresponds to a pF of 2.7 or about ½ atmosphere.

[3] The moisture of a soil, especially one of medium to heavy texture, may be adjusted to this energy level as follows. Water is added to a moderately compact column of air-dry soil in amount that will allow a penetration only part way through the column. When adjustment, undisturbed by surface evaporation has taken place, the water films in the moist part of the column will be under a tension of about pF 2.7.

[4] Moore, R. E., "Water Conduction from Shallow Water Tables," *Hilgardia*, XII: 383–426, 1939.

is either the hygroscopic coefficient or the moisture equivalent. Since the log of 1 is zero, a pF of 0 represents a force just equal to the pull of gravity on a water column only 1 centimeter high.[1] It is, therefore, obvious that at this tension water will leave the soil in response to a

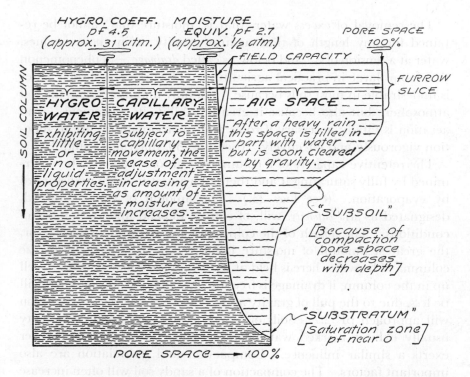

FIG. 23. Diagrammatic representation of the moisture distribution in a soil column of uniform texture saturated at the bottom but well drained at the surface. Three forms of water are commonly recognized in soils — *hygroscopic, capillary,* and *drainage* or *free*. The latter when present occupies the volume designated in the diagram as *air-space*. The tension ranges are shown in *pF*. The exact quantity of moisture present at any particular *pF* will, of course, vary with the soil under consideration and its physical condition.

very slight suction. This does not mean, however, that water with a tension greater than pF 0 will not move downward in the soil in response to gravity. In fact, due to the weight of the water columns, moisture with tensions up to somewhat above pF 2.7 in heavy soils and somewhat below in lighter ones will, if no obstructions exist, move

[1] This is so slight that for all practical purposes pF 0 may be considered as zero tension.

readily to lower levels.[1] Consequently a pF of 2.7, in addition to the significance already ascribed to it, designates in a general way the zone of transition between water that moves by capillarity alone and that susceptible to both capillary and gravity movements. (See Fig. 23.)

The removal of excess water, that is, moisture that cannot be retained for any length of time against gravity or in energy values, water at a tension of 2.7 and below, is called *drainage* — a phenomenon that looms large in practical agriculture. The presence of such water is undesirable in most soils because it not only unduly reduces the soil atmosphere but also because it greatly inhibits its movement. And aeration is vitally necessary if roots and microorganisms are to function vigorously and effectively. (See Fig. 30, diagrams 1 and 2.)

The retentive capacity of a column of soil for water may be determined by fully saturating it and then allowing it to drain undisturbed by evaporation. (See Fig. 23.) The amount of water retained, designated as *field capacity*, will, of course, depend upon a number of conditions. The length of the column of soil is an important factor, the greatest amount of moisture being retained at the base of the column. The water here is held at a pF of approximately zero. Well up in the column, if drainage is free, the amount of water retained will be less, due to the pull of gravity and, as already suggested, its tension will approach pF 2.7. Soils of heavy texture and high colloidicity usually exhibit marked water-holding capacities. Organic matter exerts a similar influence. Compaction and granulation are also important factors. The compaction of a sandy soil will often increase its water-holding powers, while the effect is likely to be just the opposite with a soil of a heavy nature. Granulation in most cases, especially with the finer textured soils, tends to enhance the amount of moisture retained against gravity.

84. *The classification of soil moisture*

On the basis of the three energy factors established on the pF curve, it is possible to classify the water more or less temporarily retained by

---

[1] Veihmeyer, F. J. and A. H. Hendrickson, "The Moisture Equivalent as a Measure of the Field Capacity of Soils," *Soil Sci.*, XXXII:181–193, 1931. Also Browning, G. M., "Relation of Field Capacity to Moisture Equivalent in Soils of West Virginia," *Soil Sci.*, LII:445–450, 1941.

soils very simply under three heads — *hygroscopic*, *capillary*, and *gravita-tional*. The first includes the moisture held with a tension of pF 4.5 and above. The second term comprehends the moisture of the soil that exhibits the fluid adjustment commonly spoken of as capillarity. It is extremely variable in amounts. When at a minimum its pF is approximately 4.5, at field capacity the pF is near 2.7. (See Fig. 23.) The water that moves out of the soil due to the pull of gravity is distinguished by the term *gravitational* or *drainage*. In well-drained soils it soon ceases to be an important factor. It must be remembered, however, that such a classification implies no lines of demarcation or clear-cut distinctions, in fact considerable overlapping occurs. The terms are merely used as a convenient way of referring to soil water within certain energy ranges and possessing certain types of move-ment. And the differences, so often considered as definitely char-acteristic, vary gradually and progressively.

85. *Hygroscopic water*

The hygroscopic water which is held so tenaciously by the soil exists as a very thin film at the solid-liquid interfaces. This film, thought to be made up of not over fifteen or twenty layers of water molecules, has a maximum thickness that probably does not exceed 4 or 5 millimicrons. Because of the tremendous pressures exerted upon them, approaching 10,000 atmospheres at the interface, the molecules are closely packed and most of the layer is nonliquid. It must be remembered, however, that in the neighborhood of the hy-groscopic coefficient the pressure is so much less, approximately 31 atmospheres or pF 4.5, that a transition to the liquid state is gradually taking place.

Not only is much of the hygroscopic water in a nonliquid state, but as such it is immovable and probably participates but to a slight de-gree in the biological activities of soil. However, when a hygro-scopically saturated soil is exposed to a partially saturated air, hygro-scopic water will be lost due to vapor-pressure adjustments. The drier the air, the lower will this form of water tend to become. For convenience of determination, it is generally assumed that all but a small portion of the hygroscopic water that happens to be present will be driven from an air-dry soil by heating for eight or ten hours at a temperature of 100° or 110° C.

As already intimated, the maximum hygroscopic coefficient is considered of especial significance respecting the water held at high-energy levels. That its amount varies from soil to soil is a foregone conclusion. For a sandy loam, containing little organic matter, the hygroscopic coefficient may be as low as 1 or 2 per cent by weight, while in a heavy clay, with 4 or 5 per cent of organic matter, it may rise as high as 12 or 15 per cent. This is because of the tremendous interface presented. With peat soils the quantity is still greater, in some cases reaching 60 or 70 per cent. This relatively inactive water thus is surprisingly large in some soils.

86. *Capillary water*

The water in the so-called capillary zone, as already emphasized, shows a considerable range in energy values. These different energy levels are reflected in movement differences in spite of the fact that all of the capillary water is in a fluid state. At the higher tensions, say between pF 4.2 and 4.5, capillary adjustment is very sluggish and comparatively ready movement does not occur until pressures in the neighborhood of 2.7 (moisture equivalent) are reached. The mechanics of this capillary adjustment will be considered later (page 163).

An idea of supreme importance should not be lost sight of. As a result of its energy relations, the capillary water is the only fluid water bearing solutes that remains in the soil for any length of time if drainage is satisfactory. Consequently, it functions, chemically and physically, in such ways as to justify the designation of *soil solution*. The hygroscopic water is largely nonliquid, while the gravitational water, although it acts as a solvent, usually is too transient to be considered as an integral part of the soil. The soil solution is coincident, therefore, with that part of the liquid water that remains in the soil after free drainage has taken place. Hence it exhibits an energy range from pF 4.5 to roughly pF 2.7. (See Fig. 23.)

The conditions that influence the maximum amount of capillary water that soils will hold are numerous and variable and their interrelationship complex. Four of the most important in a practical way will be briefly considered — (1) texture, (2) structure, (3) organic matter, and (4) position in the soil column.

The finer the texture of a mineral soil, the greater is likely to be its capillary capacity. The validity of this statement is clearly substantiated by the pF curves of Fig. 22 (page 152). This is due to the porous colloidal materials and to the great number of minute interstices and angles that carry water films.

As soils become more granular, especially if organic matter is one of the granulating agents, the interstitial spaces of microscopic size are likely to be enlarged and their water capacity greatly increased. And since much of the capillary water is lodged in such pores, an increase in capillary retention tends to occur. The compaction of heavy soils by reducing their porosity is also sure to reduce their capacity to hold capillary water, but with sands or sandy loams the opposite effect is likely to result. This is because the compaction, while reducing the total pore space, may increase the number of pores of capillary sizes.

Humus is regarded as having a very high capillary capacity, far exceeding the mineral portion of soil in this respect. Not only is the porosity of such material very high but interstices of microscopic size make up a large proportion of the total pore space. It is no wonder that the practical man is insistent upon granulation and a granulation that is encouraged by the maintenance of an adequate supply of organic matter. He realizes the biological importance of the soil water held at the lower tensions and that one of the problems of water control is the enlargement of such soil capacity.

As already explained (page 156), the maximum amount of capillary water that may be held by a soil varies with the length of the column, the pull of gravity causing water to collect at its base especially in the last few centimeters if the column is free. Consequently, in arriving at the *maximum retentive capacity* of a soil sample, Hilgard's procedure [1] (or a modification thereof) usually is followed and the amount of water retained by a very short column (5 to 10 millimeters in length) against gravity is determined. This corresponds to a tension in the neighborhood of pF 0. At the upper end of a long column of soil, however, the pull of gravity is much greater, the maximum amount of capillary water retained somewhat less, and the tention notably higher. In a well-granulated surface soil, the pF, as complete drainage is attained, approximates 2.7. This energy level already has been designated as *field capacity*. All this is clearly shown in Fig. 23.

In order to provide a more tangible idea as to the maximum amounts of hygroscopic and capillary water that soils may retain and

[1] Hilgard, E. W., *Soils*, The Macmillan Company, New York, 1911, p. 209.

the influence of texture and organic matter thereon, figures are offered from Alway and McDole, and also from Russell (Table XV). Data for the moisture equivalent (approximate field capacity), the energy level where capillary adjustment first shows signs of sluggishness, are included. While these moisture values are expressed as percentages based on dry soil, their energy equivalents should be constantly kept in mind.

Table XV. Hygroscopic Coefficients and Capillary Capacities of Various Soils (Alway and McDole, and Russell)

Soils	Organic Matter, Per Cent	Hygroscopic Coefficient (pF 4.5), Per Cent	Moisture Equivalent (Field Capacity) (pF 2.7), Per Cent	Maximum Retentive Capacity (near pF 0) Per Cent
Alway and McDole: [a]				
Sandy soil (Nebr.)	1.22	3.3	7.9	34.2
Red loam (N. Mex.)	1.07	10.0	19.2	49.0
Silt loam (Nebr.)	4.93	10.2	27.8	60.9
Black adobe (Ariz.)	2.22	12.9	25.8	60.3
Russell: [b]				
Dickinson fine sand	2.13	3.41	7.6	44.5
Clarion sandy loam	3.01	6.93	15.5	58.0
Marshall silt loam	3.58	10.40	24.0	76.5
Wabash silty clay	5.91	16.10	30.4	87.0

[a] Alway, F. J. and G. R. McDole, "The Relation of Movement of Water in a Soil to Its Hygroscopicity and Initial Moisture," *Jour. Agr. Res.*, X:391–428, 1917.

[b] Russell, M. B., "Soil Moisture Sorption Curves for Four Iowa Soils," *Proc. Soil Sci. Soc. Amer.*, IV:51–54, 1939.

87. Gravitational water

The energy relations of this type of moisture have already been clearly defined so that it is necessary only to briefly emphasize why gravitational water, even though it is superfluous or excess in nature, receives so much attention. Two outstanding reasons are evident — (1) the necessity of adequate drainage, and (2) the loss of plant nutrients that its removal entails.

Since the gravitational water occupies the larger pore spaces of the soil, it excludes air and interferes with oxidation. (See Fig. 30, page 184.) A poorly drained soil is soon unsatisfactory for the production of most crops. The normal soil processes, both chemical and biological, are slowed down and favorable physical relations are weakened. In fact, the whole cycle of events on which most higher plants depend is thrown out of adjustment.

Most persons know that the removal of the gravitational water, so important in soil sanitation, entails the loss of considerable amounts of nutrient materials, and that this greatly augments the difficulty of maintaining the fertility of soils. The magnitude of this loss is, however, seldom realized nor its seriousness fully appreciated. At Cornell University the removal of nitrogen, potassium, and calcium in drainage was measured for a term of ten years. The average annual losses are given below (Table XVI) in terms of their commercial equivalents in order that their full significance may be evident. The soil is the Dunkirk silty clay loam and was managed in three different ways.

Table XVI. Average Annual Drainage Losses in Pounds an Acre of Nitrogen, Potassium, and Calcium in Terms of Their Commercial Equivalents. Cornell University Lysimeters. Average of Ten Years [1]

Commercial Equivalents	Soils Bare Continuously, Pounds	Soils Cropped to a Rotation, Pounds	Soils in Grass Continuously, Pounds
Nitrate of soda	431	48	15
Muriate of potash	173	138	149
Ground limestone	1213	726	824

It is obvious that the losses of nitrogen, potassium, and calcium by leaching are large where ever percolation is appreciable. Moreover, it is noticeable that cropping tends definitely to reduce these removals, especially as regards nitrogen. In the case of sod this loss is hardly 3 per cent of what it was from bare land. Apparently one way to conserve soil fertility in humid regions is to keep crops on the land, especially at times when percolation may be active. Nevertheless the large loss of calcium even under the best cropping control cannot fail to attract attention. Undoubtedly this element is extremely mobile.

[1] Bizzell, J. A. and T. L. Lyon, "Composition of Drainage Water from Lysimeters at Cornell University," *Proc. and Papers, First Internat. Cong. Soil Sci.*, II:342–357, 1927.

Chapter VIII. Movements of Soil Water
and Plant Relationships

In discussing the energy values of soil moisture and the characteristics that are exhibited at different energy levels, adjustment and movement have been stressed again and again. And rightly so, as water is a notably dynamic soil constituent. Three types of movement are recognized — *capillary adjustment*, *percolation*, and *vapor equalizations*. So important, both theoretically and practically, are these changes in position that they merit individually more than passing references. Their examination in the following sections will be climaxed by a consideration of their plant relations, a particularly significant phase.

Before an explanation of the first type of water movement — capillary adjustment — can adequately be made, certain fundamentals should be clearly in mind. They will be considered forthwith.

88. *Capillary fundamentals*

Two especially important types of interface exist in soils — *liquid-solid* and *liquid-air*. At the former interface adsorption not only of water but also of other constituents takes place. Here lies the high-energy hygroscopic water. In the moisture films of the latter interface, surface tension develops an inward pressure. This phenomenon has already been mentioned (page 148). Also it has been emphasized that the force developed by surface tension varies directly with the curvature of the moisture film — the greater the curvature, the greater is the pressure. In addition, it should be kept in mind that the direction in which the force is exerted depends on the nature of the curvature. If the latter is convex, the force is inward. If, on the other hand, the film is concave, the force is effective outward.

162

Now consider an ideal case. If a glass tube of capillary dimension is introduced into water, the liquid, due to the attraction of the capillary surfaces, rises around the edges on the inside, producing a concave surface. This concave film, as already stated, exerts an outward, therefore, an upward pressure in this case, and water rises in the tube until its weight is just equal to the force developed by the contracting concave film (Fig. 25 a). Since a small capillary tube maintains a film of greater curvature than a larger one, a greater pull per unit cross section is exerted and water will rise higher in the smaller capillary.[1] This is a commonplace observation and is an excellent example of the pressure exerted by a concave film. Also it emphasizes again that the greater the curvature of a film, the greater is the lift. While the adjustment is upward in the illustration cited, in the soil it may be in any direction depending on the position of the film in respect to the mass of water of which it is a part.

With these fundamental ideas as a background, capillarity as it influences the adjustment of soil moisture may be described with some assurance. The water subject to such a movement covers a tension range from about pF 4.5 to perhaps pF 1.6.[2]

89. *Capillary adjustment as it most commonly occurs in soils*

When a soil is wetted at the surface by rain or irrigation water, the stage is set for a downward adjustment analogous to the movement of moisture in a simple capillary tube. The adsorption of water fills the surface interstices, even the larger ones, and liquid-air interfaces are instantly established. Since most of these initial interstitial films are concave, a pull away from the liquid mass occurs, in this case largely downward, and movement takes place in this direction, modi-

---

[1] The height (h) to which water rises in a capillary tube is expressed by the formula:

$$h = \frac{2\,T}{r\,d\,g}$$

where T is surface tension in dynes per centimeter, r, the radius of the tube in centimeters, d, the density of the liquid, and g, gravity in dynes per centimeter. It is obvious from the formula that the smaller the radius of the tube, the higher will be the rise of the liquid in it.

[2] In a rough way pF 1.6 represents the transition from capillary to noncapillary pores — the moisture below pF 1.6 moving largely by gravity. Between pF 2.7 and 1.6 water may be affected definitely by both capillarity and gravity, but above pF 2.7 the adjustment is almost entirely of a capillary nature. See Nelson, W. R. and L. D. Baver, "Movement of Water through Soils in Relation to the Nature of the Pores," *Proc. Soil Sci. Soc. Amer.*, V: 69–76, 1940. Also, Browning, G. M., "Relation of Field Capacity to Moisture Equivalent in Soils of West Virginia," *Soil Sci.*, LII: 445–450, 1941.

fied, of course, by some lateral capillarity. Moreover, the pull of gravity is of some assistance. In addition, if the amount of water added at the surface is large enough to temporarily fill the macropores in this vicinity, the rate of capillary movement is greatly encouraged by the bridging effect.

When a large amount of water is received at the surface, capillary adjustment, aided by gravity flow through the larger interstices, will

Fig. 24. A body of water, not connected with a water-table, at momentary equilibrium in the soil. The film curvatures are exerting a tension of approximately 2.7 pF at all fronts. An increase curvature at any point in the system will increase the tension and encourage an adjustment in that direction.

ultimately moisten the whole profile unless an impervious layer is encountered. But if the addition is limited, as is very often the case under natural conditions, the downward adjustment will soon become wholly capillary and the penetration will be halted at some point in the soil profile. With a light rain this may be only a few inches below the soil surface. The tension of the water front when equilibrium occurs is approximately a pF of 2.7. (See page 156.)

This halt in downward movement takes place, not because the downward pull has become less, but because this tension is counterbalanced by an upward pull in the water mass, especially at its upper surfaces. Since little gravitational water now is present, liquid-air interfaces of a capillary nature have appeared in the interstices at and near the soil surface. They are concave to the air above and exert a pull in that direction. And as surface evaporation takes place the concavity, and hence the tension, of these films increases rapidly. When this tension equals that of the downward-moving water front, the latter comes to a standstill. (See Fig. 24.) And should evaporation or some other phenomenon further increase the concavity of the upper films, capillarity adjustment may be reversed and the flow directed upward.

The phenomenon of capillary adjustment back and forth according to film tension, when little or no gravitational water is present, is of prime importance as it represents the capillary setup commonly operating in soils. The movement may be downward, upward, or lateral depending on the curvature of the water films at the periphery and in the interior of a given mass of soil water. And what is especially important, the removal of water from any given interstice, whether through evaporation or plant action, by increasing the film curvature and hence the tension at this point, initiates a movement in this direction.

The rate of adjustment under a given tension is influenced by the size and continuity of the pore spaces and by the moisture content of the soil mass invaded by the capillary water front. Large capillary pore spaces, such as are likely to be present in sandy soils, encourage, due to low friction, a comparatively rapid adjustment but the presence of macrointerstices provides discontinuities which may greatly impede such movement. The capillary channels in heavy soils, although more likely to be continuous, often are so small or may be so clogged with colloidal matter as to make adjustment slow. It is to be expected that the granulation of heavy soils will reduce the friction and tend to increase the rate of capillary adjustment. In most cases the movement is more rapid with all types of soils if the mass invaded already contains some capillary water as an air-dry soil resists wetting, oftentimes to a surprising degree.

Capillary water at its maximum extension in the soil, whether moving upward, downward, or laterally from a capillary-saturated center, possesses at its front an energy capacity, as already stated (page 164), of approximately pF 2.7 and this amount of force must be exerted in order to facilitate a further outward adjustment.

90. *Upward capillary movement from a soil water table*

Under field conditions the wetting of the soil particles and granules at a water table develops a curvature of films and capillary forces become operative in the manner already described. But the upward movement proceeds very irregularly and spasmodically and the advancing front is greatly distorted and deformed. The swelling of the soil colloids due to imbibition and the presence of entrapped air impede the rate of movement while many of the large interstices cannot be bridged at all. As a result, the adjustment becomes slower and slower until the water front halts at a comparatively short distance above the water table. At the capillary front the pores are almost completely filled but the soil layers above are still at or near their original moisture content. The line of demarcation is surprisingly sharp and the tension at the water front is probably in the neighborhood of pF 2.7. (See Fig. 25 b.)

Were the conducting capillaries continuous, uniform in size, and unobstructed by entrapped air and viscous colloidal substances, capillarity upward from a water table would be very effective. It would be possible to calculate the probable height of rise and its rate.[1] But

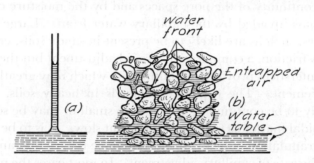

Fig. 25. The upward capillary movement from a water-table, (a) in a suitable capillary tube and (b) in a soil column. While the mechanism is the same in both cases, the adjustment is extremely irregular in the soil due to the tortuous nature of the channels, their variability in size, their discontinuities and the presence of entrapped air.

soils in nature present a complicated labyrinth of pores, tortuous, variable in size and shape, clogged with colloidal matter of various kinds and partially filled with air, some of which is very difficult to dislodge. (See Fig. 25 b.) And more than this, many of the interstices are so large as to be capillarily noneffective. Consequently a break in the water column is almost sure to occur. This alone presents a most serious obstruction as no upward capillary movement occurs unless the interstitial cross section is held full of water. As a result, the adjustment under field conditions is likely to be rather uncertain both as to height and rate of rise.

Usually the height of capillary rise is greater with the heavier soils, if sufficient time is allowed and the interstices are not too small. This is readily explained on the basis of the size and continuity of the capillaries. Moreover, the proportion of the pore space made up of very large interstices is comparatively low. With sandy soils the adjust-

[1] Puri maintains, however, that the laws of surface tension and capillarity can be applied with some precision if the pores are kept full of water and no obstructions occur. Puri, A. N., "Physical Characteristics of Soils, V. The Capillary Tube Hypothesis of Soil Moisture," *Soil Sci.*, XLVIII:505–520, 1939.

ment is rapid but so many of the pores are practically noncapillary that the height of rise cannot be great.

The situation in any particular case is sure to be greatly modified by the particular structural condition involved. Compacting a sandy soil and thereby adjusting the size of the capillaries and increasing their number may increase the water rise. But with a heavy soil

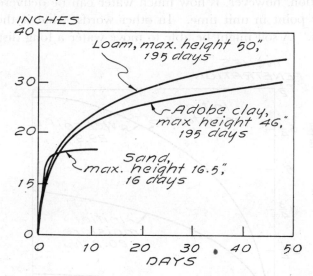

FIG. 26. Upward movement of moisture from a water-table through soils of different textures and structures. (Drawn from data presented by Loughridge.) Note the rapid rise in the sand, but the moderate height attained. Apparently the interstices of the loam are favorable both for a rapid rise and a maximum height. However, the important consideration is the amount of water that can be delivered to a certain point in a unit period of time.

compaction as well as the infiltration of clay are likely to impede capillarity greatly. Hence, granulation, especially with a soil of fine texture usually tends to increase the rate of adjustment if not the height of rise. In all cases the original moisture content of the soil is extremely important, since a dry soil resists wetting, sometimes to a marked degree. Consequently a moist soil encourages not only a higher but also a faster rise. More tangible ideas as to the influence of texture on the height and rate of water rise through soil from a water table may be obtained by consulting Fig. 26 drawn from data presented by Loughridge of California.[1]

[1] Loughridge, R. H., "Investigations in Soil Physics; the Capillary Rise of Water in Soils," *Annual Report, 1892–1894*, Calif. Agr. Exp. Sta., pp. 91–100.

91. *The capillary conductivity of soils*

In discussing the mechanics of capillary movement frequent reference has been made to the distances through which the adjustment may take place. While distance undoubtedly is important, the prime consideration, however, is how much water can be delivered at any particular point in unit time. In other words, what is the *capillary conductivity?* A soil might be able to move water a long distance but

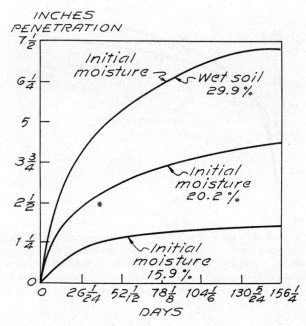

FIG. 27. Curves showing the movement of water from a moist soil to a drier one. (After Gardner.) The higher the water content of the moist soil, the greater will be the tension gradient and the more rapid will be the delivery. Water adjustment between two slightly moist soils at about the same water content will be exceedingly slow.

if the amount finally delivered is insignificant, the phenomenon lacks practical import.

While the texture and structure of soils markedly influence the conduction [1] or efficiency of capillary flow, the fundamental control in any particular case is the difference in tension per unit distance.

[1] Richards, L. A., "Capillary Conductivity Data for Three Soils," *J. Amer. Soc. Agron.*, XXVIII:297–300. 1936.

This may be referred to as the *tension gradient*. If it is high, that is, if the difference in tension between two points a unit distance apart is great, water will adjust toward the higher tension with comparative rapidity. Under comparable conditions, on the other hand, a low gradient means a slower adjustment and consequently a lower delivery. This influence of tension gradient is well illustrated by moisture curves drawn from Gardner and Widtsoe [1] (Fig. 27). Here the rate of water movement from a moist soil into a drier one is shown. The higher the percentage of water in the moist soil, the greater is the tension gradient and the more rapid is the delivery. In this case capillary conductivity obviously is a function of the tension gradient.

But a high-tension gradient is not necessarily enough in itself to ensure adequate capillary conductivity. A soil must possess a continuity of capillary pores of high-conduction efficiency containing enough water to ensure rapid liquid flow. When the capillary water is low in amount, it is held within the soil interstices at very high energy levels and adjustments even under the urge of high-tension gradients are likely to be sluggish. Such seems to be the case when the pF of the soil water is somewhat greater than 2.7. This means that a considerable proportion of the so-called capillary water may become more or less immobile, thus imposing a special significance upon the soil water held at tensions extending from somewhat above pF 2.7 down to about 1.6. Effective capillary conductivity can be expected only from water within this energy range. The practical significance of capillary conductivity will become more apparent when the evaporation losses of water from soils and the acquisition of moisture by plants are considered.

92. *Gravity flow of water through soils*

The soil pores already have been tentatively classified under two heads — *micropores* and *macropores*. The former usually are small enough to create a viscous friction of such magnitude as to greatly retard the downward flow of gravitational water unless subjected to considerable pressure. But if the interstices are not too small, the weight of water accumulating above or below may be sufficient to force a passage. The macropores on the other hand, are large enough

[1] Gardner, W. and J. A. Widtsoe, "The Movement of Soil Moisture," *Soil Sci.*, XI:230, 1921.

to facilitate a very ready movement of fluid water in response to gravity unless impeded or obstructed in some way.

Were these large pores more or less vertical and continuous and were they numerous enough to ensure a large carrying capacity, the percolation of water through soils would be very rapid. Such is not the case except in very sandy soils. In many respects this is fortunate. Water would be removed, especially from the root zone, before the

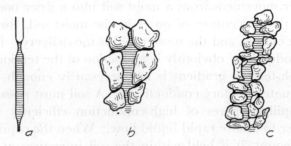

a   b   c

Fig. 28. Obviously the gravity flow of water through a glass tube *a* will be markedly influenced by the constrictions, which might be small enough to prevent ready movement. In *b* an attempt is made to picture the corresponding situation in a soil. In *c* a string of soil macro-pores are shown with their connecting channels. The large interstices cannot drain until the resistance at the constrictions is overcome.

soil mass could adsorb sufficient moisture to attain its field capacity. This would result in the loss of water useful to plants, that otherwise would be retained if drainage were slower.

From what has been said in respect to soil porosity, the probable situation in respect to the drainage system of a representative mineral soil may be tentatively postulated. Except for cracks, wormholes, and root passages, the larger pores are separated by channels and interstices of capillary size. An individual setup is probably analogous to a glass tube with a constriction near the top and at the bottom. If the tube is filled with water, the rate at which it can be emptied will be controlled in part by the size of the constrictions. And no movement by gravity will occur unless the weight of the water in the tube is sufficient to overcome the resistance at the constrictions (Fig. 28, *a* and *b*). For the furrow-slice of cultivated soils such a structural concept is of some value, since cultivation is thought in general to promote such a pore arrangement. In virgin soils this type of a structure is modified by cracks, wormholes, and root passages. This also is true of many subsoils although the greater compaction and higher clay contents characteristic of the lower horizons usually tend to reduce the number and size of the macropores.

Since percolation, except in soils permeated by very large and continuous channels, is a question of overcoming the film tension and friction in a series of restrictions of variable sizes and shapes, drainage undoubtedly is a phenomenon of considerable complexity. A large pore must partially or wholly fill with water before the weight of the accumulated liquid is sufficient to overcome the resistance in the capillaries above and force a discharge into the interstice below. Since the macropores are probably connected in indefinite vertical series and since the resistance of the whole series must be overcome before much movement can take place, drainage probably occurs intermittently along irregular and ever-changing vertical courses, depending on the nature of the constrictions. (See Fig. 28 c.) The large interstices, therefore, empty only when the weight of the accumulated water in the string is greater than the resistance at the constrictions. Before this can occur, however, the series must be connected with the outer air in such a way as to allow a ready equalization of pressure. Under such circumstances it is obvious that the rate of percolation through any particular string of pores is conditioned in large degree by the sizes of the connecting interstices. And the total discharge from a soil is determined by the number of such strings — or, in other words, by the magnitude of the porosity of the macropores.[1]

Other factors further complicate the percolation of water through soils. First, the colloidal matter may clog not only the macropores but especially the smaller connecting channels, thus increasing the pressure necessary to ensure complete drainage. However, such colloidal matter may offer little obstruction for a time but as it swells, due to the imbibition of water, it may ultimately close the pores that at first afforded a ready passage for gravitational water. Thus heavy soils that crack during dry weather at first allow rapid percolation of rain water. Later, however, these cracks may swell shut thus reducing percolation to a minimum. Second, the constrictions may be clogged somewhat by adsorbed water molecules — a hydration of the pores. Third, entrapped air, which is sure to be abundantly present in such a complicated system, may also seriously impede the rate of

[1] See Baver, L. D., "Soil Permeability in Relation to Non-Capillary Porosity," *Proc. Soil Sci. Soc. Amer.*, III:52–56, 1938.

percolation. And finally the whole situation is modified by the ir-regular occurrence not only of cracks but of wormholes, insect bur-rows, and decayed root passages. In short the nature and configura-tion of the drainage channels, their individual magnitudes, and the total noncapillary space that they present determine the rate at which soils are relieved of their excess water.

In general the finer the texture of the soil, the slower will be the rate of gravitational water flow, providing other conditions are more or less comparable. In sandy soils the pores are large, the amount of colloidal matter low, and conduction is easy. In heavy soils the pore spaces are small and clogged with colloidal materials and the con-strictions are many. Unless granulation is encouraged by organic matter and other means, drainage will be slow and ineffective. In fact, unless a clayey farm soil possesses considerable granulation, it will not drain rapidly enough to permit agricultural operations suffi-ciently early in the spring or soon enough after a heavy rain later in the season.

The two outstanding effects of sufficiently rapid percolation — the loss of plant nutrients and the promotion of aeration — have already been mentioned (page 160). Yet the latter is so vital to satisfactory crop growth that further consideration is well worth while. Diagrams 1 and 2 of Fig. 30 show graphically the change in the moisture-air ratio that may be expected as drainage is consummated in a well-granulated soil. When the furrow-slice finally is freed of its excess water, air occupies perhaps 50 per cent of the total pore space and even the subsoil, unless it is heavy and compact, is rather well aerated. The water table, if such exists, has been relegated to the substratum. Note also that the capillary moisture is left at *field capacity* with a tension in the neighborhood of pF 2.7.

93. *Vapor movement of soil water*

Water vaporization as it relates to soils may be distinguished for convenience of discussion as *internal* and *external*. In the one case the change from the liquid to the vapor state takes place within the soil, that is, in the interstices, mostly those of macro- and semimicro-size. In the second case the phenomenon occurs at the land surface and the resulting vapor is lost to the atmosphere by diffusion and convection. But first some preliminary considerations.

Where a free water surface is in contact with air, equalization tends to occur, water molecules moving from the liquid to the air and from the air back to the liquid. As long as the air is unsaturated and temperature differences do not interfere, the movement in the former direction is the faster, and the liquid phase is reduced. This is called *evaporation* and exerts a cooling effect.

However, if the phenomenon is confined in a closed vessel, the movements in the two directions soon become equal and a state of dynamic equilibrium is established. Under this condition the air becomes saturated, that is, the relative humidity is 100 per cent. Since the liquid phase is not now subject to reduction, evaporation is said to have ceased and the temperature of the system is no longer affected by the interchange that is still going on. The system is in dynamic equilibrium.

If the temperature of the system should now be raised, the capacity of the air for water vapor would increase and evaporation with its cooling effect would again occur. But if the temperature of the system should be lowered, the capacity of the air for vapor would be decreased and condensation, that is, a faster return of molecules to the liquid than the outgo therefrom, would take place. This would have a warming effect in contrast with the cooling influence of evaporation. There are thus three possibilities in respect to the interrelations of a liquid and its vapor.

The water vapor maintained in the air by the interchanges just referred to exerts a pressure called *vapor pressure* or aqueous tension. At any given temperature it is at a maximum when the air is saturated and declines as the relative humidity grows less. Also the vapor pressure of a liquid varies with temperature, the pressure rising with the temperature of the system. This is due to the increasing ease with which molecules leave the liquid surface.

94. *Internal vapor movement*

Within the soil the interstitial air, due to the equalization already explained, is held at or very near the saturation point as long as the moisture content is not below that of the hygroscopic coefficient. At this tension (pF 4.5) and less, water seems to be free enough molecularly to maintain the air at approximately 100 relative humidity. But when the soil moisture drops below the hygroscopic coefficient, and consequently is held with a greater tenacity than pF 4.5, water vaporizes with greater and greater difficulty and its vapor pressure becomes lower and lower. At pF 7 the aqueous tension is practically zero. Hence when the soil water is less than the hygroscopic coefficient, the soil air is unsaturated and very markedly so if the pF lies near 6 or 7. But with larger quantities of water, that is, at pF values lower than 4.5, a saturated atmosphere can be expected. This maintenance of the soil air at, or very near, a relative humidity of 100 per cent throughout ordinary soil moisture ranges is of tremendous importance especially in respect to biological activities. Nevertheless the actual amount of water present in the vapor form in a soil at optimum moisture is surprisingly small being, at any one time, perhaps not over 10 pounds to the acre-furrow-slice.

A movement of this water vapor, produced by internal vaporization, tends to occur because of differences in vapor pressure, the move-

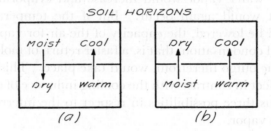

Fig. 29. Diagram indicating the vapor movement tendencies that may be expected between soil horizons differing as to temperature and moisture. In *a* the tendencies more or less negate each other; but in *b* they are coordinated and considerable vapor transfer may be possible.

ment being from points of high aqueous tension to those that are lower. Thus if a moist soil where the vapor pressure is high is in contact with an air-dry layer where the aqueous tension is lower, a diffusion into the drier area will occur. Likewise, if the temperature of one part of a homogeneously moist soil mass is lowered, water vapor will tend to move in this direction due to the lowered vapor pressure. Heating will have the opposite effect.

The two soil conditions mentioned above seem to determine in large degree the movement of water vapor under ordinary field conditions. However, they may work at cross purposes and reduce vapor transfer to a minimum or they may be so coordinated as to raise it to a maximum. The possible situation is set forth in Fig. 29. In the first case (*a*) the movement tendencies more or less negate each other. But in the second case (*b*) differences in the temperature and moisture of the two soil layers are such as to maintain marked vapor-pressure differences and hence appreciable vapor transfers can be expected.

While some vapor transfer, especially under the favorable conditions suggested above, undoubtedly does occur, the extent of the movement from one horizon to another or in and out of the soil, has not been widely investigated. Some very significant data, however, are presented by Lebedeff [1] from Odessa, Russia, where the annual rainfall is low (16 to 18 inches). His investigations indicate that the surface layer of a Chernozem soil was able to acquire an appreciable amount of moisture from the atmosphere by condensation when the temperature of the air-dry soil was lower than that of the air. Also moisture was shown to have distilled upward from the lower soil layers when they were warmer than the surface horizon. The acquisition of moisture by the surface layer in the latter manner was equivalent for a year to 5.3 inches of rain. How universal a transfer of water vapor of the magnitude reported may be is unknown. Nevertheless, considerable condensation from the atmospheric air is quite possible and during the late fall and winter, when the surface soil may be cooler and drier than the subsoil, appreciable upward distillation might well occur. In the spring and early summer this vapor movement would tend to be in the opposite direction. Whether such transfers are great enough to be of widespread field significance is still in doubt.[2]

95. *External vapor movement — evaporation*

While the extent to which water vapor translocates within the soil is open to question, the removal of water by surface vaporization un-

[1] Lebedeff, A. F., "The Movement of Ground and Soil Waters," *Proc. Internat. Congress Soil Sci.*, I:459–494, 1927.

[2] W. O. Smith, working with soil under laboratory conditions, and carefully controlled as to temperature and moisture, found a considerable transfer of water from areas of higher to areas of lower temperatures even though the temperature gradient was not great. The moisture range of the samples studied extended from about pF 5.6 to about pF 2.7. Whether the transfer, which Smith considered to be due largely to distillation, would be equally significant at higher moistures (lower pF values) was not indicated by this research. Smith, W. O., "Thermal Conductivities in Moist Soils," *Proc. Soil Sci. Soc. Amer.*, IV:32–40, 1939.

doubtedly is very large and of great practical concern. Several factors by their joint influence upon the vapor-pressure gradient [1] account for this wholesale loss of water by evaporation. The principal conditions are (1) the relative humidity of the atmosphere, (2) the amount of water at the soil surface and especially its rate of replacement, (3) the temperature difference of the two moisture phases, and (4) wind action.

Relative humidity. If the moisture content of a soil and the temperature of both air and moist soil be considered momentarily constant, changes in the vapor-pressure gradient and hence in the rate of evaporation will be determined by fluctuations in the relative humidity of the atmosphere. The lower the relative humidity the more pronounced will be the vaporization. But atmospheric air is not always at a low relative humidity. Sometimes it approaches 100 per cent saturation and under this condition evaporation might not only cease but condensation could be induced. Since relative humidity fluctuates rather widely from time to time, it cannot but exert a variable yet important influence upon the loss of water from soil by evaporation.

Capillarity. However, a vapor-pressure gradient essential for rapid evaporation cannot be maintained any length of time unless the water lost from the soil surface is continually replaced. Rain may temporarily wet the surface but for such moisture to be especially effective a phenomenon already discussed must be active; namely, capillarity. Were it not for this pumping action, the loss of water by surface vaporization would be of little practical significance. Since the mechanics of capillary movement have already been explained (page 163), it is sufficient at this point to say that if the soil layers contiguous to the surface are wet and their capillary conductivity high enough to maintain such a state, considerable moisture will be moved to the surface and dissipated by evaporation.

In evaluating the practical importance of this upward movement in respect to evaporation, two things should be considered: (1) the type of water influenced and (2) the depth to which the soil may suffer moisture losses in this way. As to the former, it is already known that only the soil water held at the lower tensions can readily respond to

[1] A vapor-pressure gradient is simply the difference in vapor pressure of two points a unit distance apart. The greater this difference, the more rapid diffusion tends to become and the greater is the transfer of vapor water during a unit period.

capillarity. This is the moisture at an energy level in the neighborhood of pF 2.7. Since low-energy values render this moisture easily available to plants, its loss by evaporation, even in regions of high rainfall, is likely to be serious. (See diagram 3, Fig. 30.)

In respect to the depth to which soils may be depleted by this evapo-capillary pumping, soil physicists are agreed that the distance is far short of the 10, 12, or even more feet previously postulated.[1] The conditions that impede and interrupt the flow are such as to allow it to deliver important amounts of water to the surface only through comparatively short distances. Some investigators think that the rate of evaporation is often so rapid as to cause the moisture column to break relatively near the surface, and that this is one of the major inhibitions. But whatever the explanation, a 24-inch depth is probably a maximum range and in many cases only the water of the furrow-slice suffers appreciable diminution by surface evaporation.[2]

Temperature. Temperature differences, especially as occasioned by sunshine, play a particularly important part in influencing the vapor-pressure gradient at the surface of soils. In direct sunlight the soil and its water often have temperatures several degrees above that of the atmospheric air. This increases the vapor pressure and so markedly steepens the gradient that evaporation is greatly encouraged. In fact this temperature effect on vaporization is usually much more important than that resulting from a lowering of the relative humidity of the air. For instance, raising the temperature of the water only 5° C. above that of the atmospheric air (say from 20° to 25° C.) is equivalent, in its effect on the vapor-pressure gradient, to lowering the relative humidity about 35 per cent.[3] Hence temperature difference is a major control of the vapor-pressure gradient and, therefore, of the evaporation of water from soils.

Wind. At the same time, if a wind is stirring, the air directly above

[1] See Cameron, F. K., *The Soil Solution*, The Chemical Publishing Co., Easton, Pa., 1911, p. 23.

McGee, W. J., *Field Records Relating to Subsoil Water*, Bulletin 93, Bureau of Soils, U. S. Dept. of Agriculture, 31–32, 1913.

[2] Leather, J. W., *The Loss of Water from Soil during Dry Weather*, Mem. Dept. Agr., Agr. Res. Inst., Pusa, India, Chem. Series I, 79–116, 1908.

Alway, F. J. and G. R. McDole, "Relation of the Water-Retaining Capacity of a Soil to its Hygroscopic Coefficient," *Jour. Agr. Res.*, IX:27–71, 1917.

Veihmeyer, F. J., "Some Factors Affecting the Irrigation Requirements of Deciduous Orchards," *Hilgardia* II:125–291, 1926–27.

[3] Curtis, O. F., "Comparative Effects of Altering Leaf Temperatures and Air Humidities on Vapor Pressure Gradients," *Plant Physiol.*, XI:595–603, 1936.

the soil is continually replaced. And as the accumulated vapor is swept away, the vapor-pressure gradient is maintained. The drying effect of even a gentle wind is noticeable although the air in motion may not be at a particularly low relative humidity. Hence the capacity of a heavy wind operating under a steep vapor-pressure gradient to enhance evaporation both from soil and plants is tremendous. Farmers of the Great Plains dread the *hot winds* characteristic of that region. A general idea as to the changes that are likely to occur in a cropped soil during a prolonged dry spell may be obtained by comparing diagrams 2 and 3 of Fig. 30. Note especially that the available water has practically disappeared from the root zone.

96. *Magnitude of evaporation*

In spite of the fact that evaporation, as we are using the term, is subject to several variable controls and that only the upper and comparatively shallow layer of soil is subject to such loss, the moisture removal in the aggregate is surprisingly large. This is because all of the water as it enters the soil must pass through this critical zone and of necessity must pay an evaporation toll, large or small, according to soil and climatic conditions. As an example, the evaporation from a bare soil in the Rothamsted lysimeters [1] averaged 14.7 inches annually and showed little variation from year to year in spite of a considerable range in precipitation. The average rainfall for the period of the experimentation was 28.8 inches. On this basis about 50 per cent of the rain received was lost as thermal water. Even though cropping should reduce this direct loss, perhaps by one-half, evaporation would still be a factor of major importance. Naturally figures from different localities vary with the climate, the soil under study, and the land-cover and its management but they usually show that an appreciable proportion of the effective rainfall is lost by surface evaporation.

97. *Functions of water to higher plants*

Water acts as a solvent, forming in the soil a solution (see page 158) which continually bathes the absorptive surfaces of the rootlets. It thus may function as a medium for the transfer of nutrients from soil

[1] Hall, A. D., *The Book of the Rothamsted Experiments*, E. P. Dutton & Company, Inc., New York, 1917, p. 2.

to plant. Even when the root hairs are imbedded in the colloidal gel of the soil and an intensely intimate contact is established between the soil and plant surfaces, the intake of nutrients is still facilitated by this water.

After water enters the plant, it may be utilized in the production of new compounds or may engage in cell activities without molecular change. By maintaining turgor and by facilitating quick shifts of nutrients and food from one part of the plant to another, water makes possible the intricate metabolic processes that are known to take place.

Because of the readiness with which moisture passes from plants into the atmosphere, large quantities must be taken from the soil in order that the plant may maintain its proper turgor and function in a normal manner. This loss, called *transpiration*, is of such magnitude as often to make the maintenance of adequate moisture in the soil a difficult problem. In fact, the farmers' main concern during the growing season is likely to be that of insufficient moisture.

98. *Transpiration losses of water*

As might be expected, the pounds of water transpired for every pound of aboveground dry matter produced in the crop is very large. This figure, called the *transpiration ratio*,[1] ranges from 200 to 500 for crops in humid regions, and almost twice as much for those of arid climates. The following data (Table XVII) drawn from various investigators give some idea of the water transpired by different crops.

Much of the variation observed in the ratios already quoted arises from differences in climatic conditions.[2] As a rule, the less the rainfall, the lower is the humidity and the greater is the relative transpi-

---

[1] A brief discussion of the various methods used in determining the transpiration ratio will be found as follows:

Montgomery, E. G., "Methods of Determining the Water Requirements of Crops," *Proc. Amer. Soc. Agron.*, III:261–283, 1911.

Also, Briggs, L. J. and H. L. Schantz, *The Water Requirement of Plants*, Bulletin 285, Bureau of Plant Industry, U. S. Dept. of Agriculture, 1913.

As these citations indicate, the term *water requirement* is often used instead of *transpiration ratio*. The latter term, however, seems to be the more desirable as it is yet to be shown that transpiration is absolutely necessary for the normal growth of plants. Apparently it is a lavish loss of water instead of an actual requirement.

[2] Briggs, L. J. and H. L. Schantz, "Daily Transpiration During the Normal Growth Period and Its Correlation with the Weather," *Jour. Agr. Res.*, VII:155–212, 1916.

Kiesselbach, T. A., *Transpiration as a Factor in Crop Production*, Research Bulletin 6, Nebr. Agr. Exp. Sta., 1916.

ration. This accounts for the high figures obtained in arid and semi-arid regions. In general, temperature, sunshine, and wind vary together in their effect on transpiration. That is, the more intense the sunshine, the higher is the temperature, the lower is the humidity, and the greater is likely to be the wind velocity. All this would tend to raise the transpiration ratio.

Table XVII. Transpiration Ratios of Plants as Determined by Different Investigators

Crop	Lawes,[a] Harpenden, England 1850	Wollny,[b] Munich, Germany 1876	Hellriegel,[c] Dahme, Germany 1883	King,[d] Madison, Wisconsin 1895	Leather,[e] Pusa, India 1911	Briggs and Schantz,[f] Akron, Colorado 1911–1913
Barley	258	774	310	464	468	534
Beans	209	...	282	...	...	736
Buckwheat	...	646	363	...	...	578
Clover	269	...	310	576	...	797
Maize	...	233	...	271	337	368
Millet	...	447	...	...	...	310
Oats	...	665	376	503	469	597
Peas	259	416	273	477	563	788
Potatoes	...	...	...	385	...	636
Rape	...	912	...	...	...	441
Rye	...	...	353	...	.,.	685
Wheat	247	...	338	...	544	513

[a] Lawes, J. B., "Experimental Investigation into the Amount of Water Given Off by Plants During Their Growth," *Jour. Hort. Soc., London*, V:38–63, 1850.

[b] Wollny, E., *Der Einfluss der Pflanzendecke und Beschattung auf die Physikalischen Eigenschaften und die Fruchtbarkeit des Bodens*, Wiegandt, Hempel and Parey, Berlin, 1877, p. 125.

[c] Hellriegel, H., *Beiträge zur den Naturwissenschaftlichen Grundlage des Ackerbaus*, Friedrich Vieweg and Sohn, Brunswick, Germany, 1883, p. 663.

[d] King, F. H., *Physics of Agriculture*, published by author, Madison, Wis., 1910, p. 139. Also, *The Number of Inches of Water Required for a Ton of Dry Matter in Wisconsin*, 11th Annual Report, Wis. Agr. Exp. Sta., 240–248, 1894; and *The Importance of the Right Amount and Right Distribution of Water in Crop Production*, 14th Annual Report, Wis. Agr. Exp. Sta., 217–231, 1897.

[e] Leather, J. W., *Water Requirements of Crops in India*, Memoirs, Dept. Agr., India, Chem. Series, I, No. 8:133–184, 1910, and No. 10:205–281, 1911.

[f] Briggs, L. J. and H. L. Schantz, "Relative Water Requirements of Plants," *Jour. Agr. Res.*, III:1–63, 1914. Also, "The Water Requirements of Plants," Bulletin 284, Bureau of Plant Industry, U. S. Dept. of Agriculture, 1913.

The factors inherent in the soil itself are of special interest as regards transpiration, since they can be controlled to a certain extent under field conditions. In general, an increase in the moisture content of a soil above optimum results in an increased transpiration ratio. This has been established by a number of investigators.[1]

Moreover, the amount of available nutrients and their balanced condition are also concerned in the economic utilization of water. The data available show that the more productive the soil, the lower is the transpiration ratio [2] provided the water supply is held at optimum. Therefore, a farmer in raising the productivity of his soil by drainage, lime, good tillage, farm manure, and fertilizers provides at the same time for a greater amount of plant production for every unit of water utilized. The total quantity of water taken from the soil, however, will probably be larger.

Although it may be seen from the transpiration ratios quoted that the amount of water necessary to mature the average crop is very large, a concrete example under humid conditions may be cited to advantage. Assuming that a representative crop of oats produces 4000 pounds of dry matter an acre and has a transpiration ratio of 500, the amount of water withdrawn from the soil during the growing season would be equivalent to almost 9 inches of rain. The corresponding figure for corn, assuming the dry matter as 6000 pounds and the transpiration ratio as 350, would be over 9 inches. These figures do not include runoff, drainage, and evaporation, nor the interception of rain by the aboveground parts of plants. These losses for the year usually greatly exceed the removal by crops but for the growing season the latter exerts the major moisture draft on soils. The possibility of moisture being a critical, if not the most critical, factor in crop production, is thus obvious.

99. *How plants are supplied with water — capillarity and root extension*

At any one time only a small proportion of the soil water lies at or is even in the immediate neighborhood of the adsorptive surfaces of plant root systems. Consequently a query arises as to how the im-

[1] Hellriegel, H., *Beiträge zur den Naturwissenschaftlichen Grundlage des Ackerbaus*, Friedrich Vieweg and Sohn, Brunswick, Germany, 1883, p. 628.

Montgomery, E. G., "Methods of Determining the Water Requirements of Crops," *Proc. Amer. Soc. Agron.*, III:276, 1911.

[2] Montgomery, E. G., *Water Requirements of Corn*, 25th Annual Report, Neb. Agr. Exp. Sta., 1912, p. XI. Also, Singh, B. N. and B. K. Mehta, "Water Requirement of Wheat as Influenced by the Fertility of the Soil," *Jour. Amer. Soc. Agron.*, XXX:395–398, 1938.

mense amount of water necessary to offset transpiration is so readily and steadily acquired by vigorously growing crops. Two phenomena seem to make adequate and continuous contact possible if the soil is in good condition for plant growth: (1) the capillary adjustment of the soil water and (2) the extension of the root system of plants, especially when the elongation is rapid.

As soon as the plant rootlets begin to absorb water at any particular point or locality in an optimum watered soil the interstitial films at the capillary fronts are thinned and their curvatures increased. This increases the pull in this direction and water tends to move toward the points of plant absorption, the rate depending on the magnitude of the tension gradients developed and the conductivity of the soil interstices. With some soils, depending on their structural condition, the adjustment will be fairly rapid and the flow appreciable; in others, especially heavy and poorly granulated clays, the movement will be sluggish and the amount of water delivered meagre. Thus a root hair, by absorbing some of the moisture with which it is in contact, automatically creates a tension gradient and a more or less effective flow of water is maintained toward its active interfaces. For many years capillarity has been considered an important factor in supplying plants with moisture.

Many of the early investigators, however, greatly overestimated the distances through which capillarity may be effective in satisfactorily supplying plants since they did not realize that the rate of water supply is the essential factor. Plants must have large amounts of water regularly and rapidly delivered. Therefore, capillarity, although it may act through a distance of several feet, if time be given, may actually be of importance through only a few centimeters as far as the hour by hour needs of plants are concerned. Under such conditions capillary adjustment is thought to be of immediate practical concern only in a restricted zone, perhaps a centimeter or two, around the absorbing surfaces of plant roots.[1] This must not be taken

[1] Burr, W. W., *The Storage and Use of Soil Moisture*, Research Bulletin 5, Neb. Agr. Exp. Sta., 1914.

Miller, E. C., "Comparative Study of the Root System and Leaf Areas of Corn and Sorghums," *Jour. Agr. Res.*, VI:311–331, 1916.

Keen, B. A., "The Limited Role of Capillarity in Supplying Water to Plant Roots," *Proc. and Papers, First Internat. Cong. Soil Sci.*, I:504–511, 1927.

Kramer, P. J. and T. S. Coile, "An Estimation of the Volume of Water Made Available by Root Extension," *Plant Physiol.*, XV:743–747, 1940.

to mean that the slower and long-ranged capillary adjustments are in the aggregate not important. They are important but in a broader and more seasonal way. Nor are gravitational and vapor transfers to be ignored entirely even in this hour-by-hour watering of plants.

This limited capacity of capillarity in respect to water supply directs the attention that much more forcibly to the rate of root extension and here early workers made an underestimate. They failed to recognize the celerity with which root systems expand and the extent to which new contacts are constantly established. In fact, during the early and midseason growing periods, roots elongate so rapidly and shift their feeding zones so constantly that satisfactory moisture contacts might well be maintained, even with a lessening water supply, without any great aid from capillarity. The mat of roots, rootlets, and root hairs in a meadow, between corn or potato rows, or under oats or wheat is ample evidence of the minutiae of the ramifications.[1]

The rate of root extension is surprising even to those engaged in plant production. Dittmer [2] estimates that a single rye plant under favorable conditions may develop, as a seasonal total, a root surface, including root hairs, of 6875 square feet and a total root length of 387 miles, carrying 6603 miles of root hairs. The average daily increase in root lengths alone was rated at 3.1 miles, with an elongation of considerably more than this during the period of most vigorous growth. Even though this figure may be somewhat too high, root extension obviously is surprisingly rapid. The rate of elongation calculated by Dittmer is considered by Kramer and Coile [3] to be great enough to take care of practically all of the water needs of a plant growing in a soil at optimum moisture, thus making the plant under this condition more or less independent of capillary adjustment for its immediate water supply.

---

[1] Dittmer, H. J., "A Comparative Study of the Subterranean Members of Three Field Grasses," *Science*, N. S., LXXXVIII:482, 1938.

Dittmer reports as follows regarding the roots and root hairs in 1 cu. in. of soil:

Plant	Number of Roots	Number of Root Hairs	Combined Length, Feet	Combined surface, Square Inches
Oats	110	150,000	630	15
Rye	150	300,000	1,300	30
Kentucky bluegrass	2,000	1,000,000	4,000	65

[2] Dittmer, H. J., "A Quantitative Study of the Roots and Root Hairs of a Winter Rye Plant," *Amer. Jour. Bot.*, XXIV:417–420, 1927.

[3] Kramer, P. J. and T. S. Coile, "An Estimation of the Volume of Water Made Available by Root Extension," *Plant Physiol.*, XV:743–747, 1940.

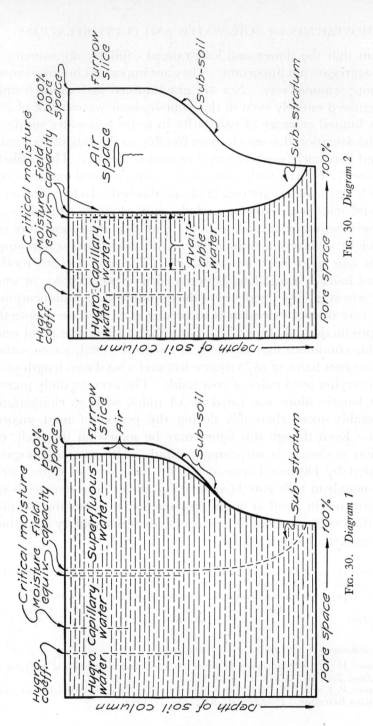

Fig. 30. *Diagram 2*

Fig. 30. *Diagram 1*

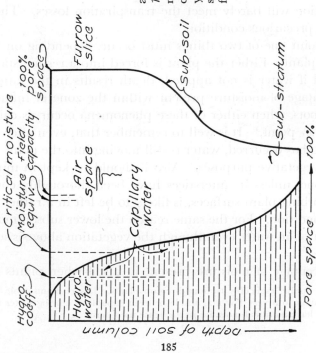

Fig. 30. The three diagrams show changes in the *moisture-air ratio* in a soil profile of uniform texture as the water is progressively reduced; 1 and 2 as drainage takes place, 2 and 3 as the profile at optimum moisture is depleted by evaporation and plant absorption. Note in diagram 2 that the furrow-slice and upper subsoil are well aerated and yet they contain a large amount of available water. In diagram 3 the surface few inches are very dry and no available water remains in furrow-slice.

Fig. 30. Diagram 3

185

100. *Critical moisture*

As long as the energy level of soil water is comparatively low, that is, somewhat less than pF 2.7, a vigorously growing plant should have little difficulty in obtaining water rapidly enough to offset transpiration. Its roots are ever pushing into moisture loosely held and absorption should be easy. In addition, capillarity conductivity is active and should bring in considerable low-energy water from contiguous zones.

But, if the root zone receives no new supply of water, a different condition soon develops. As the moisture of the soil is gradually reduced, surface evaporation, as well as plant action, usually participating in the withdrawal, the water remaining is held with ever-increasing tenacity. Absorption becomes more and more difficult against the higher and higher tensions, especially after a pF of 2.7 is reached. Moreover, above this energy range capillarity becomes appreciably sluggish and the movement of water towards the absorbing surfaces is so slow as to be of little moment. At first the plant is able to adjust to the diminished intake but soon the tension is such that the absorption will barely meet the transpiration losses. The plant is now in a precarious condition.

At this point one of two things must occur, depending on the nature of the plant. Either the plant is forced into a resting stage or it wilts. And if water is not applied, death results in the latter case. The percentage of moisture present within the zone of influence of the plant roots, when either of these phenomena occur, is called the *critical moisture* point.[1] It is well to remember that, even after permanent wilting has occurred, water is still moving into the plant but too slowly for vegetative purposes. Also it should be kept in mind that the root zone, unless its interstices have been thoroughly contacted by the absorbing plant surfaces, is likely to be left in a rather diverse moisture condition. For the same reason the lower subsoil may show little reduction in water even though the vegetation above is suffering badly.

The percentage of moisture present in a soil when plants perma-

[1] This term applies especially to humid-region plants. Desert plants, able to reduce their transpiration to a very low magnitude or even capable of storing water in special tissues, do not have a critical moisture in the sense used here.

nently wilt is called the *wilting coefficient* which can be determined with fair accuracy for seedlings.[1]   The extended work of Briggs and Schantz [2] indicates that the permanent wilting point is practically the same for all plants growing on the same soil.[3]   While this conclusion is open to certain criticisms,[4] it nevertheless seems more or less accurate.   If such is the case, the phenomenon can be accounted for only by the fact that the soil forces, in their effect on the entrance of water, are so powerful as to override any distinguishing characteristics that plants may possess in respect to moisture absorption, or at least to reduce such differences within the error of actual experimentation.

For want of a better procedure the critical moisture point of a soil is considered the same as its wilting coefficient.   In so doing not only is it assumed that the wilting coefficient is the same for a seedling as for a mature plant but also it is considered that at this moisture condition the shoot growth of different types of plants are all affected in much the same way.

Since the wilting of a plant is determined in large degree by the tenacity with which the soil water is held, it is to be expected that this phenomenon will occur at about the same pF for every normal soil.

[1] Briggs and Schantz, in their investigations, devised a satisfactory method for making determinations of the wilting point.   Glass tumblers holding about 250 cc. of soil in an optimum condition were used.   The seeds were placed in this soil, after which soft paraffin was poured over the surface in order to stop evaporation, thus removing this disturbing factor in the capillary equilibrium of the moisture.   The seedlings on germination were able to push through this paraffin.

While the plants were developing, the tumblers were kept standing in a constant-temperature vat of water in order to prevent condensation of moisture on the inside of the glass. The vegetative room was under temperature control.   When definite wilting occurred as determined in a saturated atmosphere, a moisture determination was made on the soil. The resulting figure, expressed as percentage of moisture based on dry soil, represents the wilting coefficient for the soil used.

Briggs, L. J. and H. L. Schantz, *The Wilting Coefficient for Different Plants and Its Indirect Determination*, Bulletin 230, Bureau of Plant Industry, U. S. Dept. of Agriculture, 26–33, 1912.

[2] Briggs, L. J. and H. L. Schantz, *ibid.*

[3] It must not be inferred from this conclusion that all plants have the same drought resistance.   With humid-region plants, root spread is by far the most important factor in this regard.   Plants with the more extended root systems are, of course, able to draw on a greater amount of water and better withstand a drought period.   Moreover, some plants can reduce their transpiration to a surprising degree, thus satisfactorily meeting the lessened intake of water.   Desert species are good examples.

[4] Caldwell, J. S., "The Relation of Environmental Conditions to the Phenomena of Permanent Wilting in Plants," *Physiological Researches*, U. S. Dept. of Agriculture, Vol. I, No. 1, 1913.

Experimental results show this to be at about pF 4.2, the figure ranging a little higher for sandy soils than for those of a heavy texture.[1] This means that humid-region plants cannot absorb water freely enough against such a pressure to offset transpiration losses. Since a pF of 4.2 is equivalent to about 15 atmospheres, the critical moisture point so expressed is located between the hygroscopic coefficient (approximately 31 atmospheres) and the moisture equivalent (about ½ atmosphere) and is definitely in the zone of very sluggish capillarity. (See Figs. 22 and 31.) When these three factors, the *hygroscopic coefficient*, *critical moisture*, and the *moisture equivalent* are expressed in percentage based on dry soil, their ratios are roughly 1:1.5:2.7.[2]

It is evident that the critical moisture point will be influenced by a number of soil conditions. Important among these are soil texture and the percentage of organic matter present. Their influence is best shown when moisture is expressed in percentage. In general the critical moisture will range from 2 to 3 per cent in the case of a sand to as high as 15 or 20 per cent with a heavy clay containing a large amount of humus. Peat soils with an organic content of 80 per cent will often show a critical moisture approaching 100 per cent.

101. *Biological classification of soil-water*

From the discussions already presented regarding the energy values of soil moisture and the different movements exhibited, it is evident that not all moisture present is available or suitable for the rapid vegetative growth of a plant. Three tentative divisions of the soil water may be made on this basis: *unavailable*, *desirably available*, and *superfluous*. (See Fig. 31.)

It is obvious that all of the water below the critical moisture point is out of reach of plants as far as rapid vegetative growth is concerned. For this reason it is termed unavailable although it is, in fact, not

[1] Russell, M. B., "Soil Moisture Sorption Curves for Four Iowa Soils," *Proc. Soil Sci. Soc., Amer.*, IV:51–54, 1939.

[2] After studying the relationships of the wilting coefficient to other soil conditions, Briggs and Schantz suggested the following formulae for the calculation of the wilting coefficient:

$$\text{Wilting coeff.} = \frac{\text{Hygro. coeff.}}{.68}$$

$$\text{Wilting coeff.} = \frac{\text{Moisture equiv.}}{1.84}$$

Briggs, L. J. and H. L. Schantz, *The Wilting Coefficient for Different Plants and Its Indirect Determination*, Bulletin 230, Bureau of Plant Industry, U. S. Dept. of Agriculture, 65, 1912.

entirely so. Such water includes all of the hygroscopic and that part of the capillary which is so tightly held as to show little or no fluid movement.

In rating the exceedingly sluggish capillary water as unavailable, some reservations should be made. Under certain conditions plants, especially those adapted to arid regions, are thought by some to reduce the soil water almost to the hygroscopic coefficient.[1] Roots imbedded in the soil colloidal matter probably make some use of such

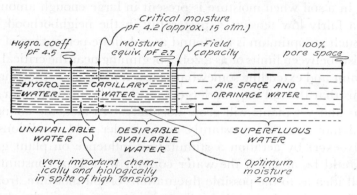

Fig. 31. Diagram showing the relationship of the various forms of soil moisture to higher plants. By the introduction of the *critical moisture* factor, the physical classification of soil water is converted into a *biological* classification and the plant significance of moisture tensions and adjustments are evidenced.

capillary water. Again bacteria and fungi growing on the viscous colloidal complexes probably use such moisture advantageously. Moreover, plants in a dormant condition on a dry soil may find this slowly adjusting moisture of some value.

Advancing from the critical moisture point of a soil, the capillary water, extending well below pF 2.7, is ordinarily considered as desirably available for the vegetative use of the plant. However, when free water is present, conditions detrimental to growth are encouraged, the situation becoming more adverse as the saturation point is approached. Much of the gravitational water is, therefore, designated as superfluous. The unfavorable effects of such moisture on the plant arise largely from the poor aeration. Not only are the roots deprived of their oxygen, but favorable bacterial activities, such as nitrification, nitrogen fixation, and ammonification, are much re-

[1] Alway, F. J., *Studies on the Relation of the Non-Available Water of the Soil to the Hygroscopic Coefficient*, Research Bulletin 3, Neb. Agr. Exp. Sta., 1913.

tarded. Moreover, adverse biochemical changes may be encouraged. The various forms of water in the soil and their availability to the plant are illustrated diagrammatically in Fig. 31.

102. *Optimum moisture for plant growth*

It is very evident that the most favorable moisture condition for the growth of higher plants, and also for most microorganisms as well, occurs in a soil when moisture is present in large enough amounts to be at a fairly low tension — preferably in the neighborhood of pF 2.7. Such an optimum is not found at a definite percentage of water but exists between limits or as a zone, beginning near the critical moisture point and extending somewhat below a pF of 2.7. (See Fig. 31.) It seems that the soil may undergo considerable fluctuation in water content and yet plants will grow normally. In fact, the changes in the soil moisture that constantly occur under field conditions may possibly exert by aeration a stimulating influence on plant growth that would be absent if the water content were kept constant. An over-all idea as to the possible fluctuations of soil moisture, from soil saturation to drouth, and their effect upon aeration, may be obtained by consulting Fig. 30.

Granulation has considerable influence on the extent of the optimum moisture zone, since the better the granulation, the better able is the plant to accommodate itself to changes in water content without a disturbance of normal growth. Drainage, liming, addition of organic matter, and tillage, by leading up to such a condition, increase the effectiveness and economy of soil-moisture utilization.

One of the important problems, therefore, is to keep the moisture of the soil somewhere within the optimum zone. After excessive rainfall, especially during the growing season, conditions should be such as to allow the presence of gravitational water in the soil for only a brief time. This means adequate underdrainage to remove quickly the excess water. It also includes arrangements whereby surface runoff may be disposed of with little erosion damage. The maintenance of optimum water also demands conservation methods in so far as they are effective, supplemented in arid and semiarid regions by irrigation. Thus the success of all fertility treatments depends in the end on the proper management of the water of the soil. The various phases thereof will be considered in the following chapters.

Chapter IX. Soil Moisture Control and Related Phases. Runoff, Erosion, and Percolation

While the ultimate objective in the field control of soil water is the maintenance of an optimum moisture condition for plants, there are many factors and phases involved. In order to obtain a clear insight into the situation, it is advisable first to consider how precipitation is received and utilized and the extent to which deflections and later losses occur. In practice the methods that are employed in moisture control depend directly on these losses and their magnitude. Moreover, certain influences, such as erosion, leaching, aeration, and temperature changes, concomitant to the dispersal of the soil water, swing into action and their regulation often becomes even more vital than the water requirements of crops.

103. *Types of precipitation loss*

The various ways in which precipitation is lost not only as it reaches the soil but also after it has effected an entrance, are five in number: (1) interception and evaporation from the leaves and stems of plants, (2) runoff over the soil surface, (3) percolation through the soil, (4) transpiration from the leaves of plants, and (5) evaporation from the soil surface. Figure 32 shows the situation diagrammatically.

Because of the complexities involved, each form of loss, its significance, and to some extent its control will be considered separately. Other phases relating to the crop utilization of soil moisture will be discussed as occasion arises. Finally the major ideas relative to soil moisture control will be drawn together in order that the general concept, which to many perhaps is the most important, may not be lost in the maze of detail.

191

104. *Interception by plants*

Rainfall data are often dealt with as though precipitation ordinarily reaches the soil in its entirety.   Such is far from the case as a person must realize when he considers the intercepting capacity of the vegetative cover, especially that presented by a dense forest.   The degree to which rain is thus caught and returned to the air by evaporation is surprisingly large.   But before considering data thereto it is well to remember that the losses of precipitation in this way are not

Table XVIII.   Seasonal Interception of Rainfall by Crops at Bethany, Missouri, and Sussex, New Jersey.   Average of Three Years' Records for Alfalfa and Corn and One Year for Soybeans.[2]
(The percentages are in terms of the total seasonal rainfall for each crop.)

Stems	Alfalfa, Per Cent	Corn, Per Cent	Soybeans, Per Cent
Canopy penetration	64.7	70.3	65.0
Ran down stem	13.7	22.8	20.4
Total into soil	78.4	93.1	85.4
Lost to atmosphere	21.6	6.9	14.6

only difficult to determine accurately but also extremely variable in amount.   The climate in general, the amount, intensity, and duration of the rainfall, the season during which the records are made, the kind of plant and its maturity and vigor are some of the more important vitiating factors.

In general the lower the rainfall the greater is the percentage diversion by the vegetative cover.   And as might be expected, the proportionate loss is markedly higher when the rain is received in light showers.   Such precipitation is often lost in its entirety.   Forests in humid temperate regions divert on the average perhaps 25 per cent of the yearly precipitation, allowing less than 5 per cent to run down the limbs and trunks into the soil.[1]   Surprisingly enough the influence of field crops, during the season that they occupy the soil, may approach that of forests in many cases.   The yearly interception is, of course, much less.   The above figures (Table XVIII) from Haynes are most significant.

[1] See Horton, R. E., "Rain Interception," *Monthly Weather Review*, XLVII:603–623, 1919.   Also, Zon, Raphael, "Forests and Water in the Light of Scientific Investigation," Reprinted with revised bibliography, 1927, from *Appendix V* of the *Final Report of the National Waterways Commission*, 1912 and Wicht, C. L., "An Approach to the Study of Rainfall Interception by Forest Canopies," *Jour. S. African Forestry Assoc.*, VI:54–70, 1941.

[2] Haynes, J. L., "Ground Rainfall Under Vegetative Canopy of Crops," *Jour. Amer. Soc. Agron.*, XXXII:176–184, 1940.

Although the data of Haynes cover such short periods and are subject to high experimental errors, they indicate something as to the magnitude of rainfall interception by field crops. In general it may be safe to conclude that from 5 to perhaps 20 per cent of the seasonal rainfall of humid temperate regions will be caught and returned to the atmosphere by ordinary field crops, the magnitude in any particular case depending in part on the kind, vigor, and stage of maturity of the crop occupying the land. Of a seasonal rainfall of 15 inches, for instance, only 12 to 14 inches might finally reach the soil, to say nothing of the diversity of the distribution therein due to the passage down the stems of a considerable proportion, perhaps 10 to 25 per cent, of the water actually reaching the soil.

105. *Runoff and its seriousness — soil erosion*

In regions of torrential rains and even in areas of moderate rainfall, especially where the land is sloping or rather impervious to water, a considerable amount of the moisture received is likely to be lost by running away over the surface. Under such conditions two considerations are important: (1) the loss of water that might otherwise be of use to plants, and (2) the removal of soil that usually occurs when much water escapes in this manner. This transfer of soil is spoken of as *erosion*.[1]

In some regions loss by runoff may rise as high as 50 or 60 per cent of the rainfall, while in arid sections it is usually low, unless the rainfall is of the torrential type as in the arid Southwest. While the loss of the water itself is critical, the erosion that accompanies it is often more serious, especially from the standpoint of soil-fertility maintenance. The surface soil is gradually taken away, which means not only a loss of the natural fertility but also of the nutrients that have been artificially added. Also it is the finer portion of this soil that is always removed first and this fraction, as already emphasized (note on page 45), is highest in fertility. Thus the objectives of any scheme of soil management, however good, are negated. More than this, the furrow-slice is forced down into the less fertile subsoil and the difficulty of maintaining a satisfactory physical condition greatly en-

[1] For a complete and detailed discussion of erosion in all its phases, see: Bennett, H. H., *Soil Conservation*, McGraw-Hill Book Company, Inc., New York, 1939.

hanced.   Many farmers today are cultivating subsoils unaware that the surface soils have been stolen from under their feet.

While everyone is familiar with the importance of water in the formation of alluvial and marine deposits, the concurrent destructive

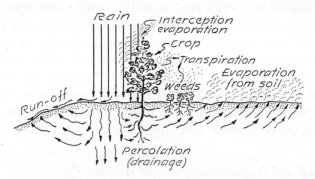

FIG. 32.   Diagram illustrating the various ways by which water may be lost from soils.

action that is going on in the uplands and the equally deplorable deposition in the lowlands have, in general, been disregarded.   This is partly due to the fact that erosion has been considered as more or less uncontrollable, an ill that cannot be avoided.   The major factor, however, has been a lack of observation — a failure to appreciate or measure the magnitude of the insidious removal.   An effect much more easy to appreciate, however, is the silting up of reservoirs which in many places is seriously reducing storage capacity and adding greatly to the expense of upkeep.[1]

The publicity that erosion losses are now receiving makes the quotation of extensive figures unnecessary.   Davis [2] estimates that 870 million tons of suspended material are carried yearly into the ocean by the streams of the United States — enough to cover a square mile 800 feet deep with sediment.   And this is only a part of the soil brought down from the uplands.   Much more is deposited on the way, to the detriment of the lower lands.   Bennett [3] estimates that

[1] Eakin, Henry M., *Silting of Reservoirs*, Technical Bulletin 524, U. S. Dept. of Agriculture, 1936.   This author states that few reservoirs in the United States have a life of two hundred years, while most will completely silt up, unless periodically cleaned, in from fifty to one hundred years.

[2] Davis, R. O. E., "Economic Waste from Soil Erosion," Year Book for 1913, U. S. Dept. of Agriculture, p. 213.

[3] Bennett, H. H., "The Problem of Soil Erosion in the United States," *Proc. and Papers, First Internat. Cong. Soil Sci.*, IV:748–757, 1939.   See also *Soil Erosion a National Menace*, Circular 33, U. S. Dept. of Agriculture, 1928.

63,000,000 tons of plant nutrients are annually swept from the cultivated fields and pastures of the farms of the United States. This is
twenty times the loss due to crop removal. The money value of such
an erosion loss is probably well over $2,000,000,000 yearly and repre-
sents crop reduction values running into millions of dollars.

Later estimates by Bennett [1] indicate that upward to 50 million

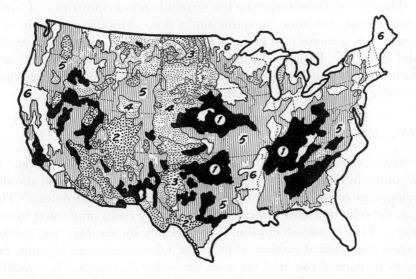

FIG. 33. Erosion map of the United States. *1*, severe sheets and gully erosion; *2*,
moderate to severe erosion of mesas and mountains; *3*, moderate to severe wind erosion with some gullying; *4*, moderate sheet and gully erosion with some wind action;
5, moderate sheet and gully erosion serious locally; *6*, erosion rather unimportant.
(After U. S. Soil Conservation Service.)

acres of cropland have been practically ruined in continental United
States, another 50 million reduced to a marginal state of productivity,
while erosion has seriously affected or is making rapid progress on 200
million acres more. Excluding the 100 million acres practically
ruined, erosion is a serious threat to perhaps one-half of the currently
arable land in this country. (See Fig. 33.) The figures for individual
states are equally striking. For instance, it is estimated that perhaps
83 per cent of Alabama shows some erosion, with approximately 29
per cent severely affected. The corresponding figures for Iowa are
58 per cent and 18 per cent. Although 34 per cent of New York is

[1] Bennett, H. H., *Soil Conservation*, McGraw-Hill Book Company, Inc., New York, 1939,
pp. 57–59.

said to exhibit some erosion, only about 2 per cent is greatly influenced.[1] The seriousness of the situation is such that a soil erosion service was instituted in 1933 and now as a bureau (Soil Conservation Service) in the United States Department of Agriculture it is actively combatting, in cooperation with various state agencies, the erosion menace.

The effects of erosion are no less serious in other countries — China, India, Syria, Palestine, to name but a few. Moreover, erosion evidently was a menace in ancient times, in Greece, in Italy, in Syria, and in Persia. Perhaps the fall of empires, such as that of Rome, was hastened by the exhausting influence on agriculture of the unchecked washing away of fertile surface soils.[2]

106. *Accelerated erosion — its causes*

Water erosion is one of the commonest of geologic phenomena. It accounts in large part for the leveling of our mountains and the development of plains, plateaus, valleys, river flats, and deltas. The vast deposits that now appear as sedimentary rocks originated in this way. This is *normal* erosion. It operates inexorably, yet slowly. When this natural erosion, due to the mismanagement of man, exceeds its normal rate and becomes unusually destructive, it is spoken of as *accelerated*. This is the water action that especially concerns agriculture.

One of the outstanding causes of accelerated water erosion in the United States as well as in other countries is unwise deforestation and the subsequent neglect of such lands. A well-established forest not only intercepts the rain water by its foliage (see page 192) but also develops a soil cover of organic matter. This humus layer, often quite deep, has a great absorptive capacity and tends to retard the rate of runoff as well as to reduce it greatly in magnitude. Again the tree roots hold the soil in place and thus prevent erosion even when the runoff is great. Since much woodland is steep, the removal of the forest cover usually results in very rapid erosion. Even on fairly smooth uplands, the surface layer of soil may be removed before the stumps are rotted away.

[1] "Reconnaissance Erosion Survey Data," Soil Conservation Service, U. S. Dept. of Agriculture, 1935.

[2] Bennett, H. H., *Soil Conservation*, McGraw-Hill Book Company, Inc., 1939, Chap. II.

A cause of serious erosion on arable land is the use of too many crops that either do not check erosion themselves or whose management and tillage greatly encourage washing. For instance buckwheat, although it completely covers the land, is notorious in its incapacity to prevent erosion. And intertilled crops, such as corn and potatoes, especially if the rows run with the slope, tremendously augment the removal of top soil. Moreover, the loss of water that might otherwise enter the root zone is of no mean consideration. Years of unwitting neglect and mismanagement as to rotation sequence and cultivation has brought the B horizon to the surface, forcing each year the undesirable addition of more and more infertile subsoil to the furrow-slice.

The rate of erosion depends on a number of factors. Those of importance are: (1) the amount and intensity of rainfall, (2) the slope of the land and its general topography, (3) the size and shape of the watershed, (4) the absence or presence of channels of concentration, (5) the type of vegetative covering, and finally, (6) the nature of the soil and subsoil. Acting together they determine how much water enters the soil, and not only how much runs off but also, and this is of the greatest moment, the manner and rate of its removal.

Of the two phases, amount of total rainfall and its intensity, the latter is usually the more important. A heavy annual precipitation received gently may cause little erosion, while a lower yearly rainfall descending torrentially may result in tremendous damage. This accounts for the marked erosion often recorded in semiarid regions.

Next in order is the degree of slope. The greater the slope, other conditions remaining constant, the greater the erosion due to increased velocity of water flow. Theoretically, a doubling of the velocity enables water to move particles sixty-four times larger, allows it to carry thirty-two times more material in suspension, and makes the erosive power in total four times greater. Moreover the length of the slope is of prime importance since the greater the extension of the inclined area, the greater is the concentration of the flooding water. This influence of slope is, of course, greatly modified by the size and general topography of the drainage area. Another modifying factor is the presence of channels, not only in the eroded area itself but in the watershed. The development of such channels controls the intensity of water concentration.

The type of vegetation is also a factor of vital importance in respect to the amount of erosion that occurs. Forests and grass are the best natural protective agencies known and are about equal in their effectiveness. But their influence varies. For instance, a forest with a heavy ground cover of humus and with a dense undergrowth is markedly superior to open woods with little organic accumulation. Again the kind of grass, the thickness of the stand, and the vigor of its growth greatly affect erosiveness and are of great importance in control measures. Field crops also vary in their influence; some, such as wheat and oats, offer considerable obstruction to surface wash; while others, especially intertilled crops, tend to encourage erosion.

Finally, there is the nature of the soil itself. Those of lateritic origin, even when clayey, are not especially susceptible to erosion because of their porous nature. In the tropics and semitropics, great areas of such soils occur and while some of them receive as high as 80 inches or more of rainfall annually, erosion is not serious. On the other hand, the siliceous silty and clayey soils, which are common in continental United States, are greatly affected by runoff water. Heavy surface soils underlain by impervious subsoils are especially susceptible. However, such erosion is less serious than that which takes place when the lower horizons of the soil are loose and sandy. Once erosion channels have cut through the upper layers, the caving-in that occurs makes this form of wash especially destructive. The coastal plain soils of the southern states often exhibit this type of erosion.

107. *Control of water erosion*[1]

Three more or less distinct types of water erosion are generally recognized: *sheet, rill,* and *gully.* In the former, soil is removed more

[1] A voluminous literature in regard to water erosion has developed in the last few years, of which a rather complete list may be obtained by writing to the Soil Conservation Service, U. S. Dept. of Agriculture, Washington, D. C. Consequently, only a few references will be given here.

Bennett, H. H., *Soil Conservation*, McGraw-Hill Book Company, Inc., New York, 1939.

Gustafson, A. F., *Conservation of the Soil*, McGraw-Hill Book Company, Inc., New York, 1937.

Ayres, Q. C., *Soil Erosion and Its Control*, McGraw-Hill Book Company, Inc., New York, 1936.

Roe, H. B., and J. H. Neal, *Soil Erosion Control in Farm Operations*, Special Bulletin 170, Minn. Agr. Exp. Sta., 1935.

Baver, L. D., *Soil Erosion in Missouri*, Bulletin 349, Mo. Agr. Exp. Sta., 1935.

Duley, F. L. and F. G. Ackerman, "Run-Off and Erosion from Plots of Different Lengths," *Jour. Agr. Res.*, XLVIII, No. 6:505–510, 1934.

Weir, W. W., *Soil Erosion in California, Its Prevention, and Control*, Bulletin 538, Calif. Agr. Exp. Sta., 1932.

or less uniformly from every part of the slope. However, this type is often accompanied, especially on bare land newly planted or in fallow, by tiny gullies irregularly dispersed. This is *rill* erosion. But where the volume of water is concentrated, the formation of small ravines by undermining and downward cutting occurs. This is called *gully* erosion. While all are serious, the losses due to sheet and rill erosion, although less noticeable, are probably greatest.

A number of different methods for the reduction and control of sheet and rill erosion may be utilized. Anything that will increase the adsorptive capacity of the soil, such as deep plowing, surface tillage, and more organic matter, will lessen the runoff over the surface. The nature of the crop grown is also an important factor. Intertilled crops such as corn or potatoes may actually encourage erosion, especially if the rows possess much slope. Small grains tend to impede such loss. Of all field crops, grasses are perhaps the most efficacious in this respect. This is so well recognized that a sod is almost always recommended in places where erosion is likely to take place. The following data from Missouri (Table XIX) indicate that sod is extremely effective on moderated slopes. The experiment cited has been continued for fourteen years on a 3.7 per cent slope and under a rainfall of about 40 inches.

Table XIX.   Losses from Erosion.   Missouri Agricultural Experiment Station.[1]
Average of Fourteen Years

Treatment	Runoff, Per Cent of Rainfall	Tons of Soil Lost an Acre a Year	Relative Erosion, Bluegrass as 1	No. Yrs. to Erode 7 in. of Soil
No crop, plowed 4 inches deep, cultivated regularly	30.7	41.64	122	24
Corn grown continuously	29.4	19.72	58	50
Wheat grown continuously	23.3	10.10	30	100
Rotation; corn, wheat, and clover	13.8	2.78	8	368
Bluegrass sod continuously	12.0	0.34	1	3043

In scanning these data, it is well first to note the large amount of soil lost especially from the bare plat and that cropped to corn. In the first case, the surface soil would disappear in only one generation; while in the other, two generations would suffice to bring the furrow-slice entirely into the subsoil.

The influence of the different crops is just as definite. Corn is least

[1] Miller, M. F. and H. H. Krusekopf, *The Influence of Systems of Cropping and Methods of Culture on Surface Run-Off and Soil Erosion*, Research Bulletin 177, Mo. Agr. Exp. Sta., 1932.

effective, with wheat next. While a good rotation exerts an appreciable control, grass, as is to be expected, is most efficacious. The
erosion loss here is negligible. A well-managed forest is of the same
order of efficiency as grass. Since a vigorous sod is more effective
than one in a less healthy condition, the fertilization and management
of pastures and meadows have become an important feature of practical erosion control.

Considering the Missouri experiments still further it is interesting
to note the amount of some of the important nutrients swept away by
erosion. These losses are likely to be greater than one might expect
since the finer particles of mineral matter, much higher in fertility
than the whole soil (page 193), are sorted out and carried away. Also
the humus, unless the soil is well granulated, is subject to this selective
removal. This means accelerated loss of all of the fertility elements.
For comparison, tentative figures as to the nutrients withdrawn from
the soil by the average crop of a standard rotation may also be quoted.
The data, in round numbers, are shown in Table XX.

Table XX. Nutrients Removed Annually [1] in Pounds to the Acre in the Missouri
Erosion Experiment Compared to the Yearly Draft of an Average Field Crop

Condition	N	P_2O_5	K_2O	CaO	MgO	SO_3
Erosion removal						
Corn grown continuously	66	41	729	309	145	42
Rotation; corn, wheat, and clover	26	18	258	120	48	15
Crop removal						
Average for standard rotation	60	25	50	30	20	20

While such data are not of universal application, certain conclusions
may be drawn. Erosion losses, even on a 4 per cent slope, may easily
exceed the removal of nutrients by crops occupying the land. Moreover, large savings can be expected by procedures that everyone recog-
nizes as merely applications of sound soil management principles.
Care in selecting the rotation sequence and the judicious use of sod
crops are a matter of course.

In cultivating corn and similar crops, it is important that the cultivation be across the slope rather than with it. This is called *contour
tillage*. On long slopes subject to sheet and rill erosion, the fields may
be laid out in narrow strips across the incline, alternating the tilled
crops, such as corn and potatoes with hay and grain. Water cannot
attain much velocity on the narrow strips of cultivated land, while

[1] These data are for two years only.

the hay and grain tend to markedly check the runoff flow. Such a layout is called *strip cropping* and is the basis of much of the erosion control now advocated.

When the cross strips are laid out rather definitely on the contours, the system is called *contour strip cropping*. The width of the strips will depend primarily upon the degree of slope and upon the permeability of the land and its erodibility. Table XXI from Gustafson gives some idea as to the practicable widths. Contour strip cropping often is guarded by diversion ditches and waterways between fields. When their grade is high, they should be grass covered. This precaution is a number one rule in most erosion control. However, when slopes are subject to very serious erosion, they should either be reforested or kept in permanent pasture, guarding always against incipient gullying. Even in permanent pastures and in young plantations *contour furrowing* at suitable intervals often is practicable as it not only aids in stabilizing the soil but also provides more water for the crop. This is especially important on droughty slopes.

Table XXI. Suggested Strip Widths in Feet for Contour Strip Cropping [1]

Slope Per Cent	Soil Conditions		
	Well-drained, Erodibility Low	Medium Drainage, Erodibility Moderate	Poor Drainage, Erodibility High
5	125	100	75
10	100	75	50
15	75	50	..

When the simpler methods of checking sheet erosion on cultivated lands become ineffective, it is often advisable to resort to terraces constructed across the slope. These catch the water and conduct it away at a gentle grade. The Mangum terrace and its modification are now largely in vogue. Such a terrace is generally a broad bank of earth with gently sloping sides, contouring the field at a grade from 6 to 8 inches to 100 feet. It is usually formed by backfurrowing and scraping. The interval between the successive embankments depends on the slope and erodibility of the land. Since the terrace is low and broad, it may be cropped without difficulty and offers no obstacle

[1] Gustafson, A. F., *Soils and Soil Management*, McGraw-Hill Book Company, Inc., New York, 1941, p. 207.

to cultivating and harvesting machinery. It wastes no land, and is effective if properly maintained. Where necessary, waterways are sodded. Such terracing is really a more or less elaborate type of contour strip cropping.[1]

Small gullies, while at first insignificant, soon enlarge into unsightly ditches or ravines. Moreover, they quickly extend into the land above, exposing the subsoil and increasing the sheet and rill erosion, already undesirably active. If small enough, such gullies may be plowed in and seeded down, using a nurse crop such as oats, barley, or wheat, which will check the runoff until the grass obtains a start. Once the sod is established, it may entirely stop the erosion.

When the gully erosion is too active to be thus checked and the ditch is still small, dams of rotted manure or straw at intervals of 15 or 20 feet are very effective. Such dams may be made more secure by placing stakes and boards or strips of wire netting below them. After a time the ditch may be plowed in and the site of the gully seeded and kept in sod permanently. It thus becomes a *grassed waterway*, an important feature of almost all successful erosion projects.

With larger gullies, dams of various kinds may be utilized. These are built at intervals along the channel. If brush is used, it is piled in the gully at the desired location with the butt ends upstream. Stakes are then driven through the brush into the soil below. If the stakes are wired together before finally being driven down, the brush will be compressed and held firmly in place. Straw thrown above the dam will make it more effective in catching the eroded soil. Dams just as effective may be constructed from woven wire properly staked and secured. These are just a few of the details relating to this phase of water control.[2]

With very large gullies, dams of earth, concrete, or stone are often installed with success. Most of the sediment is deposited above the

[1] For further information see:

Bennett, H. H., *Soil Conservation*, McGraw-Hill Book Company, Inc., New York, 1939.

Ayres, Quincy C., *Soil Erosion and Its Control*, McGraw-Hill Book Company, Inc., New York, 1936.

Gustafson, A. F., *Conservation of the Soil*, McGraw-Hill Book Company, Inc., New York, 1937.

Huff, Warren C. and Paul R. Hoff, *Diversion Terraces and Contour Strip-Cropping*, Cornell Univ. Extension Bulletin 464, 1941.

[2] For the control of gullies of all kinds, see Ayres, Q. C., *Recommendations for the Control and Reclamation of Gullies*, Bulletin 121, Ia. Eng. Exp. Sta., Iowa State College, 1935. Also, Jepson, Hans G., *Prevention and Control of Gullies*, Farmers' Bulletin 1813, U. S Dept. of Agriculture, 1939.

dam and the gully is slowly filled. The use of semipermanent check dams, flumes, paved channels, and diversion ditches are also recommended on occasion. The only difficulty with engineering features at all extensive is that the cost may exceed the benefits derived or even the value of the land to be served. They thus may prove uneconomical.

108. *Wind erosion*

The movement of soil by wind is so closely related to water erosion that it will be discussed briefly at this point. This type of soil destruction, while most common in arid and semiarid regions, occurs to some extent in humid climates as well. It is essentially a dry-weather phenomenon and hence, in a sense, is a moisture problem. All kinds of soils and soil materials are affected and at times their more finely divided portions are carried to great heights and for hundreds of miles. In the great dust storm of May, 1934, which originated in western Kansas, Texas, Oklahoma, and contiguous portions of Colorado and New Mexico, clouds of powdery debris were carried eastward to the Atlantic seaboard and even hundreds of miles out over the ocean. Such aeolian activity is not a new phenomenon but has been common in all geologic ages. The wind energy that gave rise, due to a combination of favorable circumstances, to the loessial deposits now so important agriculturally in the United States and other countries, belongs in this category.

The destructive effects of wind erosion are obvious. Not only is the land robbed of its richest soil but crops are either blown away or left to die with roots exposed or they are covered up by the drifting debris. Even though the blowing may not be great, the cutting and abrasive effects, especially of sand, upon tender crops often is serious. The area in the United States subject to greatest wind action is that broad expanse called the *Great Plains*. Here the mismanagement of plowed lands and the lowered holding power of the ranges due to overgrazing have greatly encouraged wind work. In dry years, as experience has shown, the results have been disastrous. Two great *dust bowls* (see Fig. 33) exist in this region. One, the larger, occupies much of western Kansas, Oklahoma, and Texas, extending into southeastern Colorado and eastern New Mexico. The other, irregular and somewhat scattered, lies across the centers of three states — Nebraska, and the two Dakotas. Eastern Montana is also affected. Curiously enough, areas of severe water erosion lie contiguous to these so-called dust bowls, while gully and sheet erosion, due to torrential rainfall, are not at all uncommon within their borders.

Possibly 15 per cent of continental United States is somewhat affected by wind erosion, 12 per cent moderately so and perhaps 3 or 4 per cent badly. While most of the damage is confined to regions of low rainfall, some serious wind erosion occurs in humid sections. Sand-dune movement is a good example. More important agriculturally, sandy soils used for vegetables are often affected by the wind, while this type of erosion is especially destructive on cultivated peats, particularly those long and intensively cropped. The drying out of the cultivated and finely divided surfaces of sandy loams and peats leave them both extremely susceptible to wind drift.

The most effective control of wind erosion is, of course, vegetative cover and on the Great Plains the seeding of plowed lands and the strengthening of the grass stands, especially by controlled grazing, are urgent. Great windbreaks have been planted and these are already exerting some influence. Unfortunately they have not been established in the areas where wind action is most serious. On cultivated lands tillage at right angles to prevalent wind direction, deep and rough furrows on land to be left bare, dam-listing, strip cropping, and similar practices are strongly recommended.

In the case of the blowing of sands, sandy loams, and cultivated peat soils in humid regions, various devices are used. Windbreaks and tenacious grasses and shrubs are especially effective. Picket fences and burlap screens, while less efficient as windbreaks than such trees as willows, are often preferred because they can be moved from place to place as crops and cropping practices are varied. Rye, planted in narrow strips across the field, is sometimes used on peat soils. All of these devices for wind erosion control, whether applied in arid or humid regions and whether vegetative or purely mechanical, are, after all, but phases of the broader problem of soil moisture control.

109. *Percolation and leaching — methods of study*

Two general methods of procedure are available for the study of percolation and leaching [1] — the use of an effective system of *tile*

[1] The mechanics of percolation have already been discussed. See page 169.

drains, and the construction of *lysimeters*. For the first method an area should be chosen where the tile drain receives only the water from the land under study and where the drainage is efficient. A record of the amounts of flow throughout a term of years and analyses of the drainage water will throw light on the ordinary losses of water and plant nutrients from a normal soil under a known cropping system. The advantage of such a method of attack is that a large area of undisturbed soil may be studied.

The lysimeter [1] method, however, has been the usual mode of approaching such problems. In one type of lysimeter a small column of soil is entirely isolated by appropriate means from the land surrounding it. Effective and thorough drainage is provided. The advantages of this method are that the variations in a large field are avoided, the work of conducting the study is not so great, and the experiment is more easily controlled.

One of the best known sets of lysimeters of the above type is that at the Rothamsted Experiment Station in England.[2] Here blocks of soil 0.001 acre in surface area were isolated by means of trenches and tunnels, and, supported in the meantime by perforated iron plates, were permanently separated from the surrounding soil by masonry. The blocks of soil are 20, 40, and 60 inches in depth, respectively. Facilities for catching the drainage are provided under each lysimeter.[3] The advantage of such a method of construction lies in the fact that the structural condition of the soil is undisturbed. The possibility of the water passing down between the soil column and the walls of the drain gauge may be urged as a disadvantage. Also, the blocks of soil, although close together, may have been initially somewhat different, especially physically. This, of course, would vitiate comparisons.

With other types of lysimeters, tanks, cans, or jars are used, the soil being placed in the containers and supplied with adequate drainage. The columns of soil may be fertilized and cropped, and field conditions more or less simulated. This is the type of lysimeter commonly in use, especially in the United States. Experiments by such a

[1] From *lysi* meaning loosening and *meter*, to measure.

[2] Lawes, J. B., J. H. Gilbert, and R. Warington, "On the Amount and Composition of the Rain and Drainage Waters Collected at Rothamsted," *Jour. Roy. Agr. Soc.*, Ser. II, XVII:269–271, 1881.

[3] Lysimeters of this type have also been installed at Craibstone, the experimental farm of the North of Scotland College near Aberdeen, Scotland. Hendrick, J., "The Measurement of Soil Drainage with an Account of the Craibstone Drain-Gauges," *Trans. of the Highland and Agr. Soc. of Scotland*, 1921.

method should be conducted for a considerable period in order that the soil may assume a more or less natural structural condition. Even then the data are no doubt in considerable error.

At Cornell University [1] a series of cement tanks sunk in the ground have been constructed. Each tank is 4 feet and 2 inches square and about 4 feet deep. A sloping bottom is provided, with a drainage

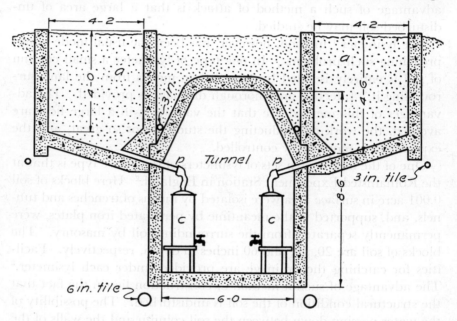

FIG. 34. Cross-section of the lysimeter tanks at Cornell University, Ithaca, New York. Each tank is one of a series, one tunnel serving two rows. Soils under investigation (*a*), outlet (*b*), and can for catching drainage water (*c*).

channel opening into a tunnel beneath and at one side. As the tanks are arranged in two parallel rows, one tunnel suffices for both. (See Fig. 34.) The sides of the tanks are treated with asphaltum in order to prevent solution. Lysimeters of a somewhat similar nature have been constructed in other places in the United States.[2]

[1] Lyon, T. L., "Tanks for Soil Investigation at Cornell University," *Science, New Ser.*, XXIX, No. 746:621–623, 1909. Also, see Lyon, T. L. and Bizzell, J. A., *Lysimeter Experiments*, Memoir 12, Cornell Univ. Agr. Exp. Sta., 1918.

[2] Mooers, C. A. and W. H. MacIntire, *Two Equipments for Investigation of Soil Leaching: I. A Pit Equipment. II. A Hillside Equipment*, Bulletin 111, Tenn. Agr. Exp. Sta., 1915.

MacIntire, W. H. and C. A. Mooers, "A Pitless Lysimeter Equipment," *Soil Sci.*, XI, No. 3:207–209, 1921.

Collison, R. C. and J. E. Mensching, *Lysimeter Investigations: I. Nitrogen and Water Re-*

The soil to be studied is packed into the tanks, layer by layer. Because of the size of the lysimeters, the soils may be cropped, cultivated, and fertilized very much as under field conditions. And a fairly accurate record may be kept of the additions and losses of nutrients that occur. Such data are of great value in fertility-maintenance studies. The main objection to this type of lysimeter is that the soil has been very much disturbed and it probably never assumes its original physical condition. Thus the percolation and leaching data may be somewhat abnormal, probably too high due to the loosened condition of the soil and to the lack of runoff, a greater proportion of the precipitation received passing into the soil than otherwise would be the case. Although the results must be accepted with caution as absolute figures, they are of great value in a comparative way.[1]

A lysimeter of an entirely different type has been perfected in Europe, called in this country the *Russian lysimeter*.[2] A trench is dug beside the soil to be studied, and after the installation, described below, is completed, it is properly walled and covered. Small tunnels at various levels are excavated horizontally under the profile. In each is placed a shallow funnel-shaped pan perforated at the center. This is wedged tightly against the soil horizon above. Drainage tubes are then installed and the tunnels filled with soil. Each funnel drains separately into the trench, where the water of percolation is caught in receptacles and later measured and analyzed.

Such a lysimeter deals with undisturbed soil and thus avoids the objectionable feature of the tank type. Data[3] obtained by this method, however, show a considerable amount of variation and are at times contradictory. Apparently these discrepancies are due to variations in the profile and to possible lateral movements of the water of

---

lations of Crops in Legume and Non-Legume Rotations, Technical Bulletin 166, N. Y. State Agr. Exp. Sta., 1930.

Morgan, M. F., *Soil Changes Resulting from Nitrogenous Fertilizers*, Bulletin 384, Conn. Agr. Exp. Sta., 1936.

[1] For a drastic criticism of the Cornell, Tennessee, and Geneva type of lysimeters, see Joffe, J. S., "Lysimeter Studies: I. Moisture Percolation through the Soil Profile," *Soil Sci.*, XXXIV:123–142, 1932.

[2] Joffe, J. S., "A New Type of Lysimeter at the New Jersey Agricultural Experiment Station," *Science*, LXX:147–148, 1929.

[3] Joffe, J. S., "Lysimeter Studies; I. Moisture Percolation through the Soil Profile," *Soil Sci.*, XXXIV:123–142, 1932.

Collison, R. C., *Lysimeter Investigations: IV. Water Movement, Soil Temperatures, and Root Activity under Apple Trees*, Technical Bulletin 237, N. Y. State Agr. Exp. Sta., 1935.

Lunt, Herbert A., *Forest Lysimeter Studies under Hardwoods*, Bulletin 449, Conn. Agr. Exp. Sta., 1941.

percolation due to wormholes, root passages, and cracks. This type of lysimeter can be expected to operate satisfactorily only in soils with fairly vertical drainage channels.

110. *Percolation losses of water*

When at any time the amount of rainfall entering a soil becomes greater than its water-holding capacity, losses by percolation tend to occur. These losses will be influenced not only by the amount of rainfall and its distribution, but also by evaporation, the character of the soil, and the presence of a crop.

As the rainfall increases, percolation also tends to increase, being much greater in New York, for example, than in Utah. Evaporation

Table XXII. Percolation Through a 60-inch Column of Bare Clay Loam. Rothamsted Experiment Station, Annual Average of Forty-two Years [1]

Periods	Rainfall, Inches	Drainage, Inches	Percentage of Rainfall as Drainage
Dec. — Feb.	6.77	5.58	82.4
Mar. — May	5.96	2.11	35.4
June — Aug.	7.83	1.82	23.2
Sept. — Nov.	8.29	4.50	54.2
Mean total	28.85	14.01	48.5

has a marked influence, reducing drainage losses to a considerable degree. The drainage through sandy soils is generally larger than through clayey soils under strictly humid conditions, especially where some runoff takes place. Yet when evaporation is especially high, sandy soils have been known to percolate less than those of a heavier nature. Field crops, in that they not only intercept but also utilize a large amount of moisture, have always been found to reduce percolation losses.

The results from the Rothamsted lysimeters from 1871–1912 on a bare clay loam 5 feet deep are interesting in a comparative way (Table XXII). The actual percolation is probably a little higher than under field conditions because of reduced runoff incident to experimental control.

It appears under the above conditions that about 50 per cent of the rainfall was lost by percolation through this bare soil. It is also to be

[1] Hall, A. D., *The Book of the Rothamsted Experiments*, E. P. Dutton & Company, Inc., New York, 1917, p. 22.

noted that the drainage loss was much lower in summer than in winter, the ratio being about 1 to 3. This was no doubt due to the high evaporation during the warmer season, as the rainfall was as great for the June-August period as for the December-February interval. Such a discrepancy serves again to emphasize the great loss of water from bare soil by vaporization.

These figures compare fairly well with Wollny's [1] summary on eighteen soils in Europe, studied under similar conditions. These soils, most of which were bare, showed a percolation loss of over 41 per cent of the precipitation. It must be remembered, however, that such data also are probably somewhat high, compared to bare field soils, because little runoff occurred.

Table XXIII. Average Annual Loss of Water by Percolation from Bare and Cropped Soils. Cornell Lysimeter Tanks [2]

Conditions	Rainfall, Inches	Percolation, Inches	Drainage as Percentage of Rainfall
Dunkirk silty clay loam:			
Bare	32.41	24.92	76.8
Cropped	32.41	18.70	57.7
Volusia silt loam:			
Bare	33.22	20.90	62.9
Cropped	33.22	19.10	57.5

It is interesting to consider now a situation where plants were growing on the soil. At Cornell University, Ithaca, New York, a study was made of two soils, bare and cropped, held in lysimeters. The crops were corn, oats, wheat, and hay grown in rotation. The data (Table XXIII) for the Dunkirk and Volusia soils are for ten and fifteen years respectively.

Under the climatic conditions of Ithaca the percolation from the bare soils much exceeded that of the Rothamsted experiments, being about 70 per cent of the total rainfall compared to approximately 50 per cent for the latter. As might be expected, the presence of ordinary field crops much reduced the amount of drainage. In this case

[1] Wollny, E., "Untersuchungen über die Sickerwassermengen in verschiedenerarten," Forsch, a. d. Gebiete d. Agri.-Physik., II:1–68, 1888.

[2] Lyon, T. L., J. A. Bizzell, B. D. Wilson, and E. W. Leland, Lysimeter Experiments, III, Memoir 134, Cornell Univ. Agr. Exp. Sta., 1930.

Lyon, T. L. and J. A. Bizzell, Lysimeter Experiments, IV, Memoir 194, Cornell Univ. Agr. Exp. Sta., 1936.

the reduction was about one-fifth. In the above experiment it was necessary to prevent surface runoff. Assuming that the water, which otherwise would have been lost as runoff, appeared as drainage, it may not be unfair to conclude that runoff and percolation combined account for at least one-half of the normal rainfall. How near such a figure characterizes humid-temperate regions in general, it is difficult to say. That this figure has reliability in a broad way is suggested by Newell's report [1] on the discharge of North American rivers, which, of course, represents roughly runoff and percolation combined. When the flow was of such magnitude as to indicate humid conditions, it constituted 50 per cent or more of the total precipitation received by the watershed.

111. *Leaching losses of nutrients*

Due to variable weather conditions, to inherent differences in soils, and to diversity in management, especially as to fertilization and cropping, it is practically impossible to indicate what the magnitude of the percolation losses of nutrients from any soil is likely to be. Reference to almost any lysimeter data will substantiate this conclusion. Data thus obtained must, therefore, be used with caution and by no means subjected to unwarranted interpretation and application.

From the great mass of lysimeter data [2] available condensed figures

[1] Newell, F. H., *Results of Stream Measurements*, 14th Report, 1892–1893, *U. S. Geol. Survey*, pp. 89–155.

[2] Data regarding the loss of nutrients in drainage, other than quoted will be found as follows:

Hall, A. D., *The Book of the Rothamsted Experiments*, E. P. Dutton & Company, Inc., New York, 1917, pp. 237–239.

Russell, E. J. and E. H. Richards, "The Washing Out of Nitrates by Drainage Water from Uncropped and Unmanured Land," *Jour. Agr. Sci.*, X:22–43, 1920.

Mooers, C. A., W. H. MacIntire, and J. B. Young, *The Recovery of Soil Nitrogen under Various Conditions as Measured by Lysimeters of Different Depth*, Bulletin 138, Tenn. Agr. Exp. Sta., 1927.

Collison, R. C. and J. E. Mensching, *Lysimeter Investigations: I. Nitrogen and Water Relations of Crops in Legume and Non-Legume Rotations*, Technical Bulletin 166, N. Y. State Agr. Exp. Sta., 1930.

Collison, R. C., H. C. Beattie, and J. D. Harlan, *Lysimeter Investigations: III. Mineral and Water Relations and Final Nitrogen Balance in Legume and Non-Legume Crop Rotations for a Period of 16 Years*, Technical Bulletin 212, N. Y. State Agr. Exp. Sta., 1933.

Morgan, M. F. and O. E. Street, *Seasonal Water and Nitrate Leachings in Relation to Soil and Source of Fertilizer Nitrogen*, Bulletin 429, Conn. Agr. Exp. Sta., 1939.

Joffe, J. S., "Lysimeter Studies: The Translocation of Cations in the Profile of a Gray-Brown Podzolic Soil," *Proc. Soil Sci. Soc. Amer.*, V:187–190, 1940.

Lunt, Herbert A., *Forest Lysimeter Studies Under Hardwoods*, Bulletin 449, Conn. Agr. Exp. Sta., 1941.

(Tables XXIV and XXV) will be quoted from only two experiment stations, those at Cornell University in the United States and at Aberdeen in Scotland. The diversity of the results lend weight to the caution voiced above.

The two soils studied at the Cornell University Agricultural Experiment Station — the Dunkirk silty clay loam and Volusia silt loam — are fairly high and rather low in lime respectively. The one has developed from a calcareous lake clay; the other from noncalcareous glacial till derived from sedimentary rocks. The soil columns were 4 feet deep. While the soil was packed in the lysimeters at Cornell, the work at Aberdeen was done with blocks of field soil, isolated for the purpose. The percolation studies at the latter station were made with a cropped and fertilized granitic glacial soil. The gauges were 40 inches deep. The experimental error of all of the figures presented is probably rather high and the two sets of data are not exactly comparable due to differences in climate and soil.

Table XXIV. Average Annual Loss of Nutrients by Percolation through Bare and Cropped Soils. Cornell Lysimeters [1] Average of Ten and Fifteen Years Respectively

Soil Condition	Pounds to the Acre a Year					
	N	P_2O_5	K_2O	CaO	MgO	SO_3
Dunkirk silty clay loam:						
Bare	69.0	Trace	86.8	557.2	104.4	132.5
Rotation	7.8	Trace	69.1	322.0	73.2	108.5
Grass	2.5	Trace	74.5	364.0	83.1	111.1
Volusia silt loam:						
Bare	43.0	Trace	77.3	452.6	68.3	88.5
Rotation	6.6	Trace	68.9	350.5	45.7	82.0

Aside from the great variability of the data from the different sources, which is, of course, to be expected, certain features are particularly outstanding. In the first place, the amount of lime carried away by drainage is always large for humid-region soils no matter what the soil condition or treatment may be. This accounts for the tendency of such soils to become acid. Second, there is a negligible loss of phosphorus by leaching due to the small amount present in the

[1] Bizzell, J. A. and T. L. Lyon, "Composition of Drainage Waters from Lysimeters at Cornell University," *Proc. and Papers, First Internat. Cong. Soil Sci.*, II:342–357, 1927.

Lyon, T. L. and J. A. Bizzell, *Lysimeter Experiments IV*, Memoir 194, Cornell Univ. Agr. Exp. Sta., 1936.

soil and the tenacity with which it is held. Third, crops markedly reduced the removal of nutrients in drainage. This is especially true in respect to the nitrogen, the loss of which is very low from cropped soil. It is obviously poor management to allow a soil to remain bare during the summer season in a humid region. Plants differ markedly, however, in their influence, grass especially reducing the drainage loss of nitrogen. This may be due in part to the restraint that is exerted upon nitrate accumulation. (See page 379.)

Table XXV. Average Annual Loss of Nutrients by Percolation through Soils Cropped to a Rotation. Craibstone Lysimeters [1]
Average of Six Years

| Soil Treatment | Pounds to the Acre a Year | | | | |
	N	P_2O_5	K_2O	CaO	MgO
Untreated	6.7	Trace	10.6	69.6	25.5
Manure and fertilizers	6.3	Trace	9.9	78.5	26.5
Manure, fertilizers, and lime	7.9	Trace	9.2	111.4	31.2

In addition to the generalizations above another phase is particularly interesting — the magnitude relatively of leaching losses as compared to the nutrient removal by crops. This may be effected (Table XXVI) by using the drainage loss figures for the Dunkirk silty clay loam cropped to a standard rotation (see Table XXIV) and the calculated average annual removal of nutrients by a common field-crop rotation.

Table XXVI. A Comparison of the Average Annual Loss of Nutrients by Drainage from the Dunkirk Silty Clay Loam, Cropped to a Standard Rotation, with the Nutrients Removed by an Average Rotation Crop

| | Pounds to the Acre, Annually | | | | | |
	N	P_2O_5	K_2O	CaO	MgO	SO_3
Leached from Dunkirk silty clay loam	8	Trace	69	322	73	108
Removed by average rotation crop	60	25	50	30	20	20

While such comparisons must be made with caution, the differences in data magnitude are such as to admit of certain practical conclu-

[1] Hendrick, J. and H. D. Welch, "The Substances Removed by the Drainage from a Scottish Soil," *Proc. and Papers, First Internat. Cong. Soil Sci.*, II:358–366, 1927.

sions. As the boldface type indicates, nitrogen and phosphorus, particularly with soils of medium to heavy texture, are removed to a greater extent by crops, but the reverse is true in respect to calcium, magnesium, and sulfur. Potash is lost to drainage and crops in about the same degree in this particular case. The seriousness of leaching thus centers in a practical way on the high losses of lime and magnesia, the increase of acidity in humid-region soils, and the biochemical changes that result. Were it not for leaching, we would have no lime, sulfur, and potash problems or they would sink into insignificance. The idea that crops in themselves and alone are responsible for fertility decline is absurd. Leaching and erosion play their part, and it is a large one, in reducing the productivity of soils.

Chapter X. Soil Moisture Control (*Continued*).
Drainage, Weeds, Evaporation, and Temperature

While percolation, especially in humid regions, causes the loss of an appreciable proportion of the rainfall received and carries away in addition many tons of soluble material, it is generally wise to facilitate it, at the same time checking as much as possible by means of crops the loss of available nutrients. The encouragement of percolation is spoken of as *land drainage*, which is the process of removing the excess or superfluous water from the soil as rapidly as possible. While the drainage of swamps and the reclamation of overflow areas are urgent, the drainage of lands already under tillage is often more important. Practical farm drainage is paramount in almost every community, even in arid regions especially where irrigation is practiced.

112. *Types of drainage*

Two types of drainage are feasible, *open* and *closed*. Ditch drainage is the usual type of the first group. Ditches have the advantage of large capacity and are able to carry water at a low grade. On the other hand, they waste land, are ineffective and inconvenient, encourage erosion and weed distribution, and demand a yearly upkeep expenditure. While ditches have a place in land drainage, closed or underdrains should be used wherever possible.

Tile drains are the only reliable means of underdrainage under most conditions. While stone drains [1] are of value in certain cases, they must always be short and are likely to clog. Besides, their drain-

---

[1] Stone drains are built by arranging stone in a properly located and graded trench in such a manner as to provide a continuous channel or throat from the upper end of the drain to the lower. One of the safest modes of construction from the standpoint of clogging is to place flat stones on edge in the trench with their faces parallel to the walls of the ditch. They are capped with a layer of flat stone before the ditch is filled in. The spaces between the stones provide for the movement of the drainage water.

age is slow and rather inefficient. On silty soil, they do not long remain in service. Mole drains,[1] brush drains, box drains, and the like
are recommended only under special conditions.

The operation of the tile drain is simple. The tile (see Fig. 35),
generally 12 or more inches long with a diameter varying with the
water to be carried, are laid end to end in strings on the bottom of a

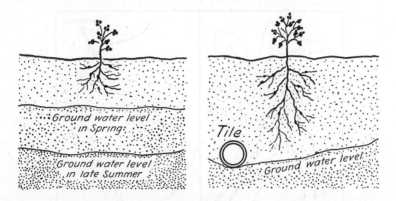

FIG. 35. *Left*, root zone restriction that occurs when natural drainage is too slow.
Right, enlarged root zone and lower water-table that is developed by a properly installed tile drain.

trench of sufficient slope. A carefully protected outlet should be provided. The tile are then covered with earth, straw or surface soil
often being placed directly around the tile to facilitate the entrance of
the water. The superfluous water enters the tile through the joints,
mostly from the sides and bottom. [2] As a consequence, the tops of the
joints may be covered with paper, cloth, or even cemented in order to
prevent the entrance of silt or quicksand. The function of a tile-drain
system is twofold: (1) to facilitate the collection of the superfluous
water, and (2) to discharge it quickly from the land.

[1] A mole drain is simply an unwalled cylindrical channel, 3 or 4 in. in diameter, located
below the soil surface and with a grade sufficient to provide for the satisfactory flow of
water, yet not such as to encourage erosion. This channel is established by means of a
special plow equipped with a sharp blade to which is attached the *mole*, a pointed cylindrical metal plug that looks much like the shell of a field gun. As this plug is pulled through
the soil, it leaves a compressed-wall channel with the proper depth and fall. Although this
type of drain is best used on heavy mineral soils, it is employed at times in peat. Needless
to say, the life of such a drain usually is short.

[2] For flow patterns into tile drains, see Kirkham, Don, "Pressure and Streamline Distribution in Waterlogged Land Overlying an Impervious Layer," *Proc. Soil Sci. Soc. Amer.*,
V:65–68, 1940.

Where the land possesses considerable natural drainage, the tile are laid only along the depressions. This is spoken of as the *natural* system of drainage in that the tile facilitate the quick removal of the water from the places of natural accumulation. But where the land is level or gently rolling, it often needs uniform drainage. A *regular* system must then be installed. This may be either of the *fishbone* or *gridiron*

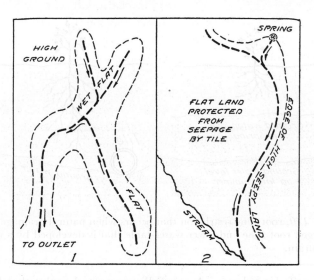

Fig. 36. Natural (*1*) and interception (*2*) systems for laying tile drains. The object in both cases is to give efficient drainage at a low cost.

style, or a modification or combination of the two, natural drainage being taken advantage of when possible. Where spring or seepage occur, cutoff systems must be devised. (See Figs. 36 and 37.)

Every regular system consists of two parts, the laterals and the main drain. The laterals are usually constructed of 3- or 4-inch tile. These laterals should always enter the main at an angle of about 45 degrees. This causes a joining of the water currents with no loss of impetus and allows the more rapidly moving lateral streams to speed up the flow in the main drain. The size of the main depends on the amount and intensity of the rainfall, the acres drained, and the slope. The main, of course, must be larger near the outlet than at any other point. Any good text on land drainage will present tables from which the size of the main drain may be determined.

The grade necessary for the satisfactory operation of a tile-drain system varies with the system itself and the portion under consideration. The grade of the main drain may be very low, especially if the laterals deliver their water with a high velocity. In general, the grade will vary from 2 to 20 inches to the hundred feet, 3 to 6 inches being more or less ideal. When the grade is reduced abruptly the installation of a siltwell may be advisable. The depth of the tile beneath the surface and the distance between laterals will vary with the soil. With sandy soils, the tile may be placed as deep as 3 or 4 feet. With clayey soils, the depth must be shallower, ranging from 15 to 30 inches, while the interval is reduced as the soil becomes more compact or finer in texture. On a clayey soil, the distance between the strings is sometimes as low as 35 feet, although 50 to 75 feet is commoner.

The maintenance cost of a tile-drain system is low, the only especial attention needed being at the outlet. All outlets should be well protected, so that the end tile may not be loosened and the whole system endangered by clogging with sediment. It is well to imbed the end tile in a masonry or a concrete wall or block. The last 8 or 10 feet of tile may even be replaced by a galvanized iron pipe or with sewer tile, thus ensuring against damage by frost. The water should flow freely from a tile-drain system, as a drowned outlet interferes with efficient drainage. The end tile of the system may be protected by a gate or by wire in such a way as to allow the water to flow out freely but preventing rodents from entering in dry weather.[1]

113. *Benefits of drainage*

Draining the land promotes many conditions favorable to higher plants and soil organisms. By giving a freer rein to the forces of aggregation, granulation (see page 57) is greatly encouraged. At the same time, heaving is reduced, as it is only when the soil approaches saturation with water that alternate freezing and thawing have their most disastrous effects on plant roots. It is the heaving of small grain crops and the disruption of such taprooted plants as alfalfa and sweet

[1] There are many state experiment station bulletins available on the installation of tile drains. The following books also deal with the subject:

Elliott, C. G., *Engineering for Land Drainage*, John Wiley & Sons, Inc., New York, 1912.

Powers, W. L., and T. A. H. Teeter, *Land Drainage*, John Wiley & Sons, Inc., New York, 1922.

Ayres, Q. C., and D. Scoates, *Land Drainage and Reclamation*, McGraw-Hill Book Company, Inc., New York, 1928.

clover that are especially feared. Also, drainage, by quickly lowering the water table at critical times, increases the effective root zone (Fig. 35). By this means, the current availability of nutrients is maintained at a higher level.

The removal of excess water also lowers the specific heat of soil, thus reducing the energy necessary to raise the temperature of the layers thus drained. At the same time, surface evaporation, which

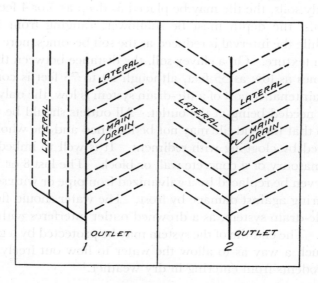

Fig. 37. Gridiron (1) and fishbone (2) systems for laying tile drains. Drainage on heavy level land can be effected only by a uniform layout system.

has a cooling effect, may, to a certain extent be checked. The two together tend to make the warming of the soil easier. The converse of the old saying that in the spring "a wet soil is a cold soil" applies here. Good drainage at all times is necessary that the land may be cultivated and is imperative in the spring if the soil is to warm up properly. At this season of the year, an inadequately drained surface soil may be from 5° to 15° F. cooler than contiguous areas relieved of their excess water (see page 64).

It is perhaps in respect to aeration [1] that the greatest benefits, both directly and indirectly, arise from drainage. A comparison of dia-

[1] For an excellent paper on the condition of orchard soils in respect to aeration, see: Boynton, Damon, *Seasonal and Soil Influences on Oxygen and Carbon Dioxide Levels of New York Orchard Soils*, Bulletin 763, Cornell Univ. Agr. Exp. Sta., 1941.

grams 1 and 2 of Fig. 30 (page 184) clearly indicates the magnitude
of air intake that occurs when the water-clogged interstices are cleared
by gravity pull. In a well-drained soil, perhaps one-half of the pore
space in general may be occupied by air. Under such a condition, the
furrow-slice and the upper subsoil, if the latter is not too compact,
are usually adequately supplied with oxygen, the air of the macropores
almost equalling the atmospheric air in respect to this gas. In the
case of heavy soils, however, especially if poorly granulated, the air
space may remain well below 50 per cent of the total porosity because
most of the interstices are of microsize, and they tenaciously retain
water against gravity. Moreover, the air that is present is likely to be
too low in oxygen to supply the needs of plant roots and desirable
microorganisms. Here granulation as well as drainage is needed.
The situation in the subsoil may even be worse. A compact horizon
with a total pore space of 30 per cent may remain almost totally
saturated with water. Hence, the amount of air is low, its oxygen content restricted, and its interchange very slow. For shallow-rooted
crops, however, this is not so serious, but such a soil should be avoided
in the location of orchards, since tile drains can do little to rectify
the situation until some change in structure has been effected.

A final phase of drainage and aeration that merits separate mention
is the influence upon soil microorganisms. The satisfactory coordination of their various activities requires oxygen and, while some groups
may obtain this element by reduction, acceptable group cooperation
exists only when oxygen is present in a gaseous condition and in
sufficient amounts. The situation is well exemplified by nitrification
which is greatly reduced when the oxygen content drops below a certain minimum. Even the cultivation of surface soils exerts a noticeable stimulation on this process. Thus, the aeration effected by drainage is just a beginning, granulation and other means of introducing
air following up and intensifying the influence initiated by the removal of excess water.

114. *Transpiration — weed control*

One of the main objectives of moisture control is to provide an
adequate and well-regulated supply of water for crop use; that is, to
satisfy this type of transpiration. Transpiration by weeds, however,
is quite a different matter and, in general, should in most cases be

eliminated. This means weed control. In fact, weed control is one of the important crop-management problems in almost all parts of the the world.

Weeds, especially if they are active during the early part of the season, usually retard the growth of crops, often to a serious extent. The detrimental influence is due to the absorption of nutrients that might otherwise be used by the crop and to competition for water. The magnitude of such transpiration is known to be great. The control of weeds is, therefore, to a certain extent a control of moisture, the attempt being to eliminate the transpiration of certain plants to the advantage of others.

While tillage tends to maintain the physical condition of the soil, the killing of weeds thereby is an important consideration also. In fact, often cultivation can be justified only for such a purpose. One of the advantages of a good rotation relates to the discouragement of weeds. Cultivated crops alternating with small grains and meadow so change the conditions of growth and seeding as to aid in weed control. Plowing at particular times, the growing of crops that exert a smothering effect, and the use of clean seed are specialized attempts to accomplish the same result.

It must not be inferred, however, that weeds are always detrimental. When developing late in the season, they may hasten the maturity of the crop by using available water and nutrients. Again, they may act as a green-manuring crop, increasing the organic residues that enter the soil when it is plowed. In orchards, weeds sometimes are used as a cover-crop and aid materially in protecting the soil and in increasing its humus supply.

115. *Evaporation losses*

Evaporation of water takes place almost entirely at the soil surface, exceptions being where large cracks occur which allow a thermal loss directly from the subsoil. This loss of water by direct evaporation from the soil is usually large and may result in a considerable reduction of crop yield, since it affects moisture that would otherwise be used by higher plants. Since the mechanics of the loss have been fully dealt with on page 175, let us turn directly to the magnitude of such removals.

The results with the Rothamsted lysimeters (see page 208) show that about 50 per cent of the annual rainfall appeared in the drainage water. Since the lysimeter soils bore no crop, the remaining 50 per cent must have been lost by evaporation. Thus, in this case, with a bare soil and no runoff, evaporation and drainage were about equal. These figures suggest that, under most conditions, a considerable proportion of the rainfall received by soils is likely to be lost by thermal movement. Let us generalize further.

It has already been estimated (page 210) that in a humid-temperate region runoff plus percolation account roughly for 50 per cent of the annual rainfall received by land. The remainder is divided between the vegetative cover and evaporation. It has been shown (page 181) that a good crop of corn or oats will require the equivalent of from 9 to 10 inches of rain. Assuming a precipitation of from 36 to 40 inches annually, this would indicate that from 9 to 10 inches are lost by evaporation. In short, representative humid-region cropped land probably loses about one-half its annual rainfall as runoff and percolation, while the other half is divided more or less equally between the crop and evaporation, assuming evaporation to include the water intercepted by crops and turned back to the atmosphere as well as that so lavishly vaporized at the soil surface. Such a generalization would not hold, however, for an arid region or for the high-rainfall tropics, yet significant interpolations may be made.

In a rough generalization of this kind, it is well to recognize that the comparative moisture losses bear a different significance practically. Some of the runoff and much of the percolation are considered necessary in that such water is superfluous. Moreover, some of this removal occurs at a time when there is no crop on the land or when plants are inactive. In general, there is no great competition between the removal of drainage water and the plant, except insofar as nutrients are involved. Surface runoff, however, removes some water that might well go into the soil, and erosion always means a loss of valuable nutrients.

With weed transpiration and surface evaporation, the situation is somewhat different. Both of these losses effect water that might otherwise be used readily by the crop, and thus the competition is direct and often keen. Again, these losses frequently are at their maximum at the time that crop demands are greatest. If weeds are critical in soil management, evaporation because of its magnitude must be doubly so.

116. *Evaporation control*

Any material applied to the surface of a soil primarily to prevent loss by evaporation or to keep down weeds may be designated as a *mulch*. Mulches are of two general sorts, *artificial* and *natural*. In the former case, foreign material is merely spread over the soil surface. Manure, straw, leaves, and other litter may be used successfully. Such mulches, while highly effective in checking evaporation and in preventing weed growth, are not generally applicable to field crops. Their use is, therefore, limited to such crops as strawberries, blackberries, and the like.

A specially prepared paper has met with some favor as a mulch.[1] This paper is spread and fastened down either between the rows or over the rows, the plants in the latter case growing through suitable openings. This mulch can be used, however, only with crops planted in rows or in hills. As long as the ground is covered, evaporation and weeds are checked and, in some cases, remarkable crop increases have been reported. Unless the rainfall is torrential, the paper does not seriously interfere with the distribution of the rain water.

The paper mulch has been employed with considerable success in the culture of pineapples in Hawaii where the idea originated and with other crops elsewhere. Whether this type of mulch will be adopted in trucking and vegetable gardening in the United States is doubtful. The cost of the paper and the difficulty of keeping it in place may be such as to offset entirely any increase in crop that may result.

The second type of mulch is spoken of as *natural*, since it is formed from soil itself. With proper tillage and favorable weather, a loose,

[1] Flint, L. H., *Crop-Plant Stimulation with Paper Mulch*, Technical Bulletin 75, U. S. Dept. of Agriculture, 1928.

Magruder, Roy, *Paper Mulch for the Garden*, Bimonthly Bulletin 133, XIII, 4, Ohio Agr. Exp. Sta., 1928.

Edmond, J. B., *Mulch Paper for Vegetable Crops is Tested*, Quarterly Bulletin II, Mich. Agr. Exp. Sta., No. 3:115–117, 1929.

Smith, Alfred, "Effect of Paper Mulches on Soil Temperatures, Soil Moisture, and Yields of Certain Crops," *Hilgardia*, VI:159–201, 1931.

Robbins, P. W., "The Use of Paper Mulch in Forestry Nursery and Field Plantations," *Jour. Forestry*, XXX:315–418, 1932.

Hutchins, A. E., *Mulch Paper in Vegetable Production*, Bulletin 298, Minn. Agr. Exp. Sta., 1933.

Magistad, O. C., C. A. Farden, and W. A. Baldwin, "Bagasse and Paper Mulches," *Jour. Amer. Soc. Agron.*, XXVII:813–825, 1935.

dry layer of soil may be established on the surface by sacrificing much of the water it contains. Such a layer tends to obstruct the upward capillary adjustment of water from the moist soil below to such an extent as to reduce evaporation losses to a considerable degree. This interruption in the capillary transfer of water may be due (1) to a lack of contact with the moist horizons underneath, (2) to an increase in the noncapillary pores and a reduction in those favoring capillarity, and (3) to the resistance to wetting that most dry soils exhibit. In short, when the film tension of the water front is in the neighborhood of pF 2.7, as will be the case with the moist underlayer, conditions as to size and continuity of the capillary channels and especially as to the amount of moisture that they contain must be particularly favorable if effective capillary adjustment is to take place (see page 169). Hence, as long as the mulch is loose, granular, and dry, it will effectively obstruct film movement from below and hold surface evaporation at a minimum. But whether the over-all influence of such mulching will result in a conservation of moisture is another matter which will be considered in the next section.

In theory, a soil mulch should be formed as quickly as possible so that the only moisture sacrificed will be that which was present in the dried layer. Moreover, the mulch should be renewed after every rain and, except in special cases, should not be more than 3 inches deep. Late in the season, especially for corn and similar crops, the cultivation should be shallow to prevent root-pruning and a consequent reduction in crop yield. No matter what may be the object of the cultivation, injury to roots must, by all means, be avoided or at least reduced to a minimum.

117. *Do the establishment and maintenance of a soil mulch conserve moisture?*

For many years, cultivation has been advocated for three reasons: (1) the maintenance of a more satisfactory physical condition of the surface soil, (2) the killing of weeds, and (3) the conservation of moisture. The validity of the first two is unquestioned, but there is some doubt as to the third, especially when a crop is on the land.

Experimental results seem to indicate, particularly in a humid region, that no more moisture is supplied to an intertillable crop cultivated, and thereby mulched, than is available to a comparable crop unmulched, providing weeds are under control and the physical condition of the soil is satisfactory in both cases. Three reasons, all more or less valid, commonly are advanced. In the first place, a large amount of moisture has already escaped by evaporation before the soil is dry enough for cultivation. The moisture left near the surface is much reduced and is held at a high tension, considerably above pF 2.7. Capillarity in this zone is now sluggish. In many cases, this precultivation loss has already established a protective layer of air dry soil, which, although thin, may be successfully coping with evaporation by obstructing capillarity.

Second, the crop itself, if its root spread is wide and comparatively dense, may intercept moisture that might otherwise reach the soil surface, thus making a mulch unnecessary. And third, cultivation and the creation of a mulch deeper than that naturally occurring wastes just that much more water, since surface evaporation is well under control, thanks to the two influences already mentioned. All of this presupposes, remember, that weeds and the physical condition of the soils are not disturbing factors. Nor does it consider the possibility of detrimental root-pruning if the cultivation is deep or prolonged too late in the season. The waste of time in useless labor is also ignored.

A simple calculation will serve to suggest the possible magnitude of the sacrifice of water due to ordinary cultivation. Consider that the soil on which a 3-inch mulch is to be formed weighs 85 pounds to the cubic foot when dry. This would make the 3-inch layer over a square foot weigh about 21 pounds. Also assume that this layer, when first cultivated, contains 16 per cent of water based on dry soil and that, when the mulch is air-dry, this percentage has been reduced to 4 per cent. This means a sacrifice in mulch formation of 12 per cent of water, or, on the basis of the 21 pounds of soil, 2.52 pounds of water to the square foot. Since an inch of water over a square foot weighs approximately 5.2 pounds, the waste due to mulch formation is equivalent to about 0.5 of an inch of rain. This is a very appreciable loss and, under field conditions, no doubt often ranges considerably higher.

In light of the arguments above, it seems doubtful whether cultivation, strictly from the standpoint of mulch formation, ordinarily will conserve enough moisture to benefit the accompanying crop. In fact, the cultivation probably wastes water in spite of the mulch. Such a conclusion is borne out by data from Illinois (Table XXVII) which indicate that, when weeds and physical conditions are controlled, the mulching effect of cultivation is of little benefit to the crop. In fact, the data hint that cultivation may have been somewhat detrimental, possibly through root-pruning or waste of water. The main service of cultivation seemed to be the killing of weeds and the encouragement of a desirable tilth. These results are corroborated by a number of other investigations.[1]

Table XXVII. Effects of Various Methods of Tillage on the Yield of Corn and the Average Percentage of Moisture in the Soil to a Depth of 40 Inches. Average of Eight Years' Test at the University of Illinois. Mean Rainfall, 33.7 inches [3]

Treatment	Yield of Corn, Bushels to the Acre	Average Percentage of Moisture in Soil
Plowed and seedbed well prepared:		
1. Kept bare of weeds only	45.9	22.3
2. Weeds allowed to grow	7.3	21.8
3. Three shallow cultivations	39.2	21.9
Seedbed poorly prepared:		
4. Kept bare of weeds only	31.4	23.1

The failure of cultivation to be of benefit is by no means limited to field crops. Thompson,[2] after six years of experimentation with vegetables in New York, reported that cultivation and mulch formation gave no increase in the yields of carrots, cabbage, and tomatoes over uncultivated plats also kept free of weeds. The influence of

[1] Young, H. J., The Soil Mulch, 25th Annual Report, Neb. Agr. Exp. Sta., 124–128, 1912.

Barker, P. B., The Moisture Content of Field Soils under Different Treatments, 25th Annual Report, Neb. Agr. Exp. Sta., 106–110, 1912.

Cates, J. S., and H. R. Cox, The Weed Factor in the Cultivation of Corn, Bulletin 257, Bureau of Plant Industry, U. S. Dept. of Agriculture, 1912.

Alway, F. J., Studies on the Relation of the Non-Available Water of the Soil to the Hygroscopic Coefficient, Research Bulletin 3, Neb. Agr. Exp. Sta., 1913.

Burr, W. W., The Storage and Use of Soil Moisture, Research Bulletin 5, Neb. Agr. Exp. Sta., 1914.

Call, L. E., and M. C. Sewell, "The Soil Mulch," Jour. Amer. Soc. Agron., IX:49–61, 1917.

Merrill, E. D., Irrigation Investigation and Practice, Report, 1923–1924, Univ. Calif. Agr. Exp. Sta., 46–47, 1924.

Veighmeyer, F. J., "Some Factors Affecting the Irrigation Requirements of Deciduous Orchards," Hilgardia, II:125–284, 1927.

Handbook of Experiments in Agronomy, Special Circular 53, Ohio Agr. Exp. Sta., 36–37, 1938.

[2] Thompson, H. C., Experimental Studies of Cultivation of Certain Vegetable Crops, Memoir 107, Cornell Univ. Agr. Exp. Sta., 1927.

[3] Mosier, J. G., and A. F. Gustafson, Soil Moisture and Tillage for Corn, Bulletin 181, Ill. Agr. Exp. Sta., 1915.

mulching on beets and onions was very slight, probably within the experimental error. The yield of only one vegetable crop, celery, was definitely increased by the maintenance of a mulch. The benefit here may have been due to the influence on the physical condition of the soil and not to the conservation of water, since the aerating effects of cultivation are often very important, especially with heavy soils and deep-rooted crops. In cases in which the rainfall came in light showers, the cultivation, by immediately dissipating it, reduced the water content below that of the unmulched soil. This, of course, occurred at critical times. In contrast with the influence of weed control, the beet yields were increased only 4 per cent by the maintenance of a mulch and 550 per cent by an adequate reduction of weed competition.

The mere fact that a soil mulch usually fails to conserve water in a humid region, unless the drought period is long, does not mean that cultivation is unnecessary or undesirable. The Illinois experiments show it to be vitally necessary in the preparation and maintenance of a good seedbed and in the control of weeds. But once these phases are taken care of, it is questionable, especially in a humid area, whether enough benefit is derived from a soil mulch to make its creation and maintenance worth while. In fact, the waste of water and root-pruning may render overcultivation decidedly objectionable and expensive.

118. *Dry-land farming*

When the annual rainfall is below 20 inches, it would seem that crop production would be impossible without irrigation. Yet between the limits of 12 to 20 inches, certain crop plants may be grown successfully, especially when much of the rainfall comes in the spring and early summer. The system adopted is called *dry-land farming* and consists essentially (1) in using special varieties of such crops as wheat, corn, sorghums, rye, and the like, (2) in reducing the rate of seeding to correspond to the limited amounts of moisture available, and (3) in employing tillage practices that conserve and economize water. It is only the latter phase that concerns us here.

The tillage operations practiced in dry-land agriculture should keep the wind erosion at a minimum. This means rough furrows at right angles to the prevailing high winds, listing, strip-cropping, and the use of a vegetative cover when practicable. At times of rain, the land should be highly permeable and retentive, and protected from water erosion if the rainfall is torrential. Dry-land farming, in many cases, includes a *summer fallow*, the idea being to catch and hold as much of one season's rain as possible and carry it over for use during the next. The soil profile is used as a reservoir, and the success in this respect depends in part upon a soil mulch.

In a semiarid region, if much of the precipitation comes in the spring and early summer, it is practicable to establish the soil mulch near the beginning of the dry season. As cultivation during the summer and fall is necessary only to control weeds, the sacrifice from stirring the soil is largely that occurring when the mulch is first established, since it is seldom wetted during the dry period. Under such a climatic condition, further loss of water is not great, and possibly one-half of the season's precipitation may, in some sections, be carried over to the next year. Then, if that season is not too dry, a satisfactory crop will be grown, the current rainfall being supplemented by the carry-over.

Here then is a situation where an appreciable amount of moisture may be conserved by the proper handling of the land. But it is a special case and should not be confused with the situation in humid regions. In the latter, summer fallowing is detrimental and unnecessary. Moreover, the creation of a soil mulch by cultivation occurs when crops occupy the lands. This is quite a different setup, climatically as well as otherwise, from the simple summer fallowing practiced in dry-land agriculture, where the mulch remains dry over a considerable period.

119. *Moisture control and irrigation*

In areas of low rainfall or when precipitation, although relatively high, is so distributed as to be insufficient for crops at critical times, irrigation, the artificial application of water to land, is common. While irrigation has been practiced for centuries, it is only in recent years that its use, due to engineering facilities, has been extended to great areas the world over. Now, thousands of acres, that otherwise would be barren desert, are producing abundant crops of every kind. In the United States, most of the irrigated land lies west of the 100th meridian and embraces perhaps 20 million acres. Nevertheless, some irrigation, especially for vegetables, will be found in humid regions where the growing season is subject to severe drought and where crop values are such as to admit the added expense.

Much could be said regarding water-supply projects, such as reservoirs, flumes, ditches, and dams; water measurement and control; methods of applying to the land; the amounts adequate for different crops; and the hundred and one details of the art and science of irrigation practice. For this, you are referred to books and bulletins. Here we will consider briefly only those phases of moisture control that are important after the proper application of the irrigation water has been accomplished.

In this respect, it is hardly necessary to emphasize that the principles already discussed relating to the movement and distribution of moisture through the soil, its losses, and its plant relationships, should be applied just as rigidly for irrigation water as for that reaching the soil in natural ways. Hence, erosion, which may become serious when the land is steep or where overirrigation occurs, must be guarded against. Also, drainage is often necessary when water concentrations take place in lower lands or where hardpan interferes with vertical distribution. The movement of water by percolation and capillarity require especially careful attention, as they are taking place, in most cases, in soils that have originated under aridic conditions. Such soils, due to their unique physical and chemical characteristics, respond somewhat differently on receiving water than do those of humid sections. Farmers from regions of heavy rainfall are often deceived by these unsuspected differences. Not only is percolation likely to be unusually rapid due to the pervious nature of the soil, but evaporation is an especially serious problem. Let us consider this latter phase further.

There are two evaporation features under arid region irrigation that usually require especial attention: (1) the magnitude of the evaporation and its control and (2) the possible concentration of soluble salts at or near the soil surface. The first is closely related to climate, the second depends not only on climate but also on the chemical nature of the soil and of the irrigation water.

It is, of course, realized that in dry regions, with their low humidity, high wind velocities, and intense sunshine, vaporization is at a maximum. Consequently, the loss of water from moist soils is rapid and competition with crops often extremely serious. The increase in transpiration is also a factor, reducing to a considerable degree the economy with which plants use water (page 179). Methods of moisture conservation, especially after irrigation water has been added are, therefore, as important as with dry-land farming. Not only must economy be used in the application of water but also in respect to its utilization once it is in the soil. Tillage methods both before and after irrigation thus become extremely important and a soil mulch is probably of some value especially if the intervals between irrigations are long and the weather hot and dry. Here the situation is somewhat analogous to that of dry-land farming where the soil is used as a reservoir for water and the mulch once established will remain effective without further stirring (page 226).

Soluble salt concentrations are related to the chemical nature of aridic soils, which will be discussed in some detail later (page 311). At this point, it suffices to say that soils developed under low rainfall, and hence with practically no percolation loss, usually contain a considerable amount of soluble salts. As long as these salts, largely the carbonates, bicarbonates, sulfates, and chlorides of calcium, magnesium, potassium, and sodium, are more or less uniformly distributed through the profile, no great detrimental effect is exerted upon plants. But, when these soils are irrigated and a plentiful supply of water is present in the upper part of the profile, the situation is radically changed. Evaporation occurs at the soil surface, this in turn sets up capillarity, and moisture moves upward carrying its burden of soluble salts. Even though film adjustment may be effective to a depth of only 15 or 20 inches, it cannot fail but effect, if continued over a period of time, a considerable concentration of salts at or near the surface. Soils that originally were mildly alkaline become loaded with salts, which, if those of calcium and magnesium, give *white alkali*, without much change in pH. But if sodium is the dominant cation, highly alkaline and extremely toxic *black alkali* may appear, often as a surface incrustation (see page 312).

The problem of alkali has no counterpart in humid-land agriculture, and due to ignorance and neglect thousands of acres of fertile land have been practically ruined. Although physical and chemical means of eradication are practiced (page 315), the control lies fundamentally in careful irrigation and a reduction of any surface evaporation that tends to cause an upward movement of salts. Irrigation practice thus not only calls for the usual moisture regulations but some corollary features as well.

120. *Soil moisture and soil temperature*

The temperature of field soils is subject to no radical human regulation, yet soil-management methods, especially those that influence soil moisture, provide for small but biologically vital modifications. Soil moisture exerts an influence on soil temperature (1) by varying specific heat, (2) by encouraging conduction, (3) by surface evaporation, and (4) by percolation.

Since the specific heat of dry soil is low (about 0.2 by weight for a mineral soil), the addition of water will raise its heat capacity to a marked degree. Hence, it is always advisable to remove excess water as quickly as possible. Good drainage is, therefore, especially important early in the spring. Because of differences in water-holding capacity, a sandy soil is recognized as a warm soil and a clay as cold and backward (see page 63).

The principle means by which heat transfers are effected within a soil profile is by conduction (see page 64). Since energy passes from soil to water 150 times easier than from soil to air, the insulating tendencies of the latter and the opposite influence of the former are obvious. A dry soil mulch acts as a blanket while the moisture in the layers below greatly facilitate heat flow. It must be remembered, however, that heat adjustments within the profile are always slow and that a considerable lag may be expected. This is why the subsoil in temperate regions is warmer in winter and cooler in summer than the surface (page 65). It must also be kept in mind that heat distribution in field soils is subject, at best, to but slight control. Such regulation is effected largely by changes in moisture amounts and movements. Hence, the maintenance of water at optimum for crop growth assures practically all of the control that conduction will admit.

The low temperatures of poorly drained soils, especially in the spring, are well known, and experienced men expect a range from 6 to 12 degrees Fahrenheit lower in the surface layer than in comparable well-drained areas. Drainage is, of course, the only practicable expedient, since it not only reduces the specific heat but also makes possible a lowering of evaporation. The tremendous cooling effects of the latter are realized by everyone and need no further emphasis (see page 64).

Besides the three control relations already mentioned, there is the influence of percolation on soil temperature. In general, it has a cooling effect except possibly in the early spring. Precipitation is usually cooler than the soil in temperate regions, especially in the summer. Even if rain water should be 10° F. warmer than the soil, an improbable assumption, an average rain would raise the temperature of the surface 6 inches only slightly, and this would be quickly offset by the cooling effects of evaporation.

Soil moisture control is obviously an important factor in the regulation of soil temperature. From the practical standpoint, the whole question may be summarized by saying that, if a farmer adopts a proper system of moisture control and at the same time employs methods that continually encourage a better physical condition of the soil, he will favorably regulate soil temperature as much as is possible under field conditions.

121. *Summary of soil moisture regulation*

The control of moisture seems to fall logically under four heads: (1) runoff, (2) percolation, (3) weed transpiration, and (4) evaporation. The detrimental influence of runoff over the surface is due to erosion, the loss of the water itself in some cases being of minor importance. Similarly, percolation loss is serious because of the nutrients carried away, rather than because of the waste of the water. In fact, the removal of such water is necessary in order to promote soil sanitation and encourage other desirable conditions.

Weed transpiration and surface evaporation, by drawing on the available soil water, compete directly and seriously with the crop. Cultivation is the remedy commonly recommended. It may eliminate weeds and aid in the creation of a favorable tilth but apparently does not diminish evaporation to any degree. Such conclusions betoken the importance of crop cultivation only as long as the physical condition of the soil is promoted and weeds are a factor. Otherwise, cultivation is usually a waste of time and may even be detrimental if the crop roots are greatly disturbed.

The proper control of soil water has many beneficial influences other than those noted. The regulation of the chemical and biochemical changes in the soil, the circulation of the soil air, and especially the influence on temperature are a few of the correlary relationships that may be specifically mentioned.

Chapter XI. The Origin, Nature, and Classification of Soil Materials

The influence of weathering, a manifestation of climate, is evident on all sides. Nothing escapes it. It breaks up the country rock, it modifies or destroys their physical and chemical characteristics, and carries away the soluble products and even some of the solids as well. The unconsolidated residues left behind, the *regolith*, are extremely variable from place to place in depth, in color, in texture, and in mineral and chemical composition. But weathering goes further. It synthesizes a soil from the upper layer of this heterogeneous mass. Hence, the regolith, or at least the upper portions, may be designated as *soil material*.[1]

Nor are these soil materials always allowed to remain undisturbed on the site of their development. Climatic agencies often shift them from place to place, with further trituration and leaching, until at last they are allowed to rest long enough for profile development to take place. A study of weathering and of the soil materials that result is not only interesting in itself, but it is also a necessary introduction to soil formation and classification. For weathering not only prepares the materials, but, with endless variety and detail, it builds our soils and endows them with character.

122. *Weathering processes classified*

Weathering processes,[2] while diverse both in action and product,

[1] Soil material may be defined as "the unconsolidated and more or less chemically weathered mineral material from which soils may be synthesized." It is the C horizon of the pedologist and is often designated as the *parent material*.

[2] For detailed discussions of weathering, see: —

Merrill, G. P., *Rocks, Rock Weathering and Soils*, The Macmillan Company, New York, 1906.

Emerson, H. L., *Agricultural Geology*, John Wiley & Sons, Inc., New York, 1928.

Joffe, J. S., *Pedology*, Rutgers University Press, New Brunswick, N. J., 1936.

Polynov, B. B., *The Cycle of Weathering*, Trans. by A. Muir, Thomas Murby & Co., London, 1937.

Lobeck, A. K., *Geomorphology*, McGraw-Hill Book Company, Inc., 1939.

may be classified under two heads, mechanical and chemical. The former is often designated as *disintegration*, the latter as *decomposition*.

I. Mechanical (disintegration)

1. Temperature — differential expansion of minerals, frost action, and exfoliation
2. Erosion and deposition — by water, ice, and wind
3. Plants and animals

II. Chemical (decomposition)

1. Hydrolysis (water)
2. Hydration (water)
3. Carbonation (carbon dioxide)
4. Oxidation (oxygen)
5. Solution (water charged with CO_2)

123. *Mechanical forces of weathering*

Variations of temperature, especially if sudden or wide, greatly influence both consolidated and clastic materials. Rocks become heated during the day and at night often cool much below the temperature of the air. This warming and cooling is particularly effective as a disintegrating agent. Rocks are mineral aggregates, the minerals varying in their coefficients of expansion. With every temperature change, differential stresses are set up which eventually must produce cracks and rifts, since the minerals assume their original position with difficulty. Incipient foci for further physical and chemical changes are thus established.

The presence of water, if freezing occurs, greatly increases the mechanical effects just mentioned. The force developed by the freezing of water is equivalent to about 150 tons to the square foot, an almost irresistible pressure. Mountaintop rubble, talus slopes, alluvial fans, and similar formations are evidences of such action. The load of sediment carried by streams is often partially due to the prying action of temperature change, especially where crevice water is present. Nor is this influence of temperature ended when rocks are reduced to fragments, but it carries onward in the soil material and the resultant soil. Freezing and thawing are of great practical importance in altering the physical condition of field soils, especially if they are heavy in texture (see page 58).

The influence of temperature change is manifested on rocks in another way. Due to slow conduction, the outer surface of a rock mass often maintains a markedly different temperature than the inner and more protected portions. This differential heating and cooling tend to set up lateral stresses which, in time, may cause the surface layers to peel away from the parent mass. This phenomenon is spoken of as *exfoliation* and is accelerated at times by the freezing of included water.

Water, as it beats down upon the land as rain and travels ocean-ward, is continually shifting, sorting, and reworking unconsolidated materials of all kinds. Moreover, when thus loaded with sediments, it has a tremendous cutting power as is amply demonstrated by the gorges, ravines, and valleys the country over. Some of the sediments have been carried into lakes, gulfs, and oceans, there to lie submerged for untold ages, before they could serve as soil material (see page 246). But some were deposited as stream terraces, deltas, alluvial fans, and as outwash. As such, they have been available as soil material and have provided some of our most productive lands. The erosive power of water, if uncontrolled, may in turn destroy the very soil for which it has provided the parent material. The erosion of arable lands is now receiving the attention it justly deserves, and the disastrous re-moval of surface soil is being subjected to a certain amount of practical control (see page 198).

Ice is an erosive and transporting agency of tremendous capacity, next to water, perhaps the most important and spectacular physical agent of weathering. One must visit Greenland or Alaska to realize its power. While little in evidence at present in temperate regions, it was active there a mere yesterday as geologic time is reckoned. The glaciation of northern North America and northern Europe is com-mon knowledge, and the erosion, transportation, and deposition that resulted are noticeable at every hand. Deposits directly by the ice and by water running from the glacial front cover thousands of square miles in the United States. From these, soils of many kinds have been evolved. The importance of ice as a mechanical agent is not to be minimized (see page 247).

Wind has always been an important carrying agency and, when armed with fine debris, exerts an abrading action also. Dust storms of almost continental extent may occur, with the result that tons of material are filched from one section and transferred to another. Thus, untold damage is done to arable lands (see page 203). In ages past, much fine material has been thus transported, and millions of acres of soil, especially in the Middle West, central and eastern Europe, in China, and elsewhere have been formed from such wind-borne debris. The extensive loessial deposits of the Missouri and Mississippi valleys are examples of the importance of wind as an agency in the deposition of soil materials (see page 254).

Simple plants, such as mosses and lichens, grow upon exposed rock, there to catch dust until a thin film of highly organic material accumulates. Higher plants sometimes exert a prying effect on rock which results in some disintegration. Such influences, as well as those exerted by animals, are, however, of little import in producing soil material, compared to the drastic physical effects of water, ice, wind, and temperature changes. But the physical influence of biological agencies, while minimized here, assumes considerable importance within the soil itself, as anyone acquainted with the action of plant roots and earthworms will attest.

124. *Chemical processes of weathering*

Scarcely has the disintegration of rock material begun than its decomposition is also apparent. This is especially noticeable in humid regions where chemical and physical processes are particularly active and markedly accelerate each other. Of the chemical changes, *hydrolysis* probably occurs first, especially in the weathering of the feldspars, micas, and similar minerals. Hydrolysis is a double decomposition, water being one of the reacting substances, and a hydroxide of some kind usually results. The change may be illustrated tentatively as below, using microcline as the mineral so affected, although many others react in the same way.

$$KAlSi_3O_8 + HOH = HAlSi_3O_8 + KOH$$

The hydrated aluminum silicate that results under these circumstances undergoes further changes, in part synthetic, and colloidal clay slowly develops. The genesis of this important constituent has already been discussed in some detail (see page 85). The hydroxide that is formed cannot long exist in the presence of carbon dioxide *Carbonation*, therefore, quickly follows, a soluble carbonate resulting in this particular case:

$$2 KOH + H_2CO_3 = K_2CO_3 + 2 HOH$$

If, as hydrolysis proceeds, organic matter should accumulate, the influence of carbon dioxide becomes more intense and carbonation is pronounced. Thus, plant and animal residues may exert a chemical influence in the preparation of soil materials that is much more important than their physical activities.

Water functions as a weathering agent in another way — as water of combination or crystallization. And its assumption is called *hydration*. Many minerals, especially the olivine, feldspar, and mica groups, are so affected. They become soft and lose their luster and elasticity on the assumption of this chemically combined water, and an increase of bulk occurs. As a result, minerals so affected succumb readily to physical and chemical forces. Clay minerals are also highly hydrated, having assumed much water in the course of their synthesis. Two simple examples may be cited. They are the change of hematite to limonite and the development of limonite when ferrous oxide undergoes oxidation.

$$2 \ Fe_2O_3 + 3 \ H_2O = 2 \ Fe_2O_3 \cdot 3 \ H_2O$$
Hematite   Limonite (yellow)

$$4 \ FeO + 3 \ H_2O + O_2 = 2 \ Fe_2O_3 \cdot 3 \ H_2O$$
Ferrous   Limonite
oxide

When the products of hydration dry out due to varying weather conditions, dehydration may occur. Thus, limonite may readily be reduced to a lower hydrate or to hematite, with a noticeable change in color, especially in the latter case.

It cannot be emphasized too strongly that the various forces, both chemical and physical, are closely interlocked. If they were not, weathering would be very slow. In fact, this interrelationship is so close as to make differentiation difficult, the sequence of separate reactions appearing to be one phenomenon. The weathering of microcline, as it is conventionally written, well illustrates this point.

$$2 \ KAlSi_3O_8 + 2 \ H_2O + CO_2 = H_4Al_2Si_2O_9 + K_2CO_3 + 4 \ SiO_2$$
Microcline   Hydrated   Potassium   Silica
                                    silicate   carbonate

Hydrolysis and carbonation have produced the carbonate, a salt in this case very soluble in water and easily removed. The acid silicate that remained has quickly assumed water of combination and may readily be synthesized into colloidal clay. The silica may crystallize to quartz or, perhaps more commonly, pass into a colloidal condition. This type example is illustrative of the many complex chemical changes occurring not only during the production of soil material but also within the soil itself.

Of the various chemical changes due to weathering, *oxidation* is usually one of the first to be noticed. It is particularly manifest in rocks carrying iron in the sulfide, carbonate, or silicate forms. The oxidation of the iron is indicated by a discoloration of the affected rock. The amphibole and pyroxene groups are easily influenced, until, as the process continues, these minerals waste away into hardly recognizable forms, so weakening the rock as to cause it to crumble easily. The way is now open for vigorous chemical changes of all kinds.

Oxidation may be illustrated chemically, using olivine as the iron-carrying mineral. On the assumption of water, serpentine, a hydrated product, and ferrous oxide may result. The latter may now be oxidized to the ferric state.

$$3 \ MgFeSiO_4 + 2 \ H_2O = H_4Mg_3Si_2O_9 + SiO_2 + 3 \ FeO$$

Olivine Serpentine Ferrous oxide

$$4 \ FeO + 3 \ H_2O + O_2 = 2 \ Fe_2O_3 \cdot 3 \ H_2O$$

Ferrous oxide Limonite

While weathering produces many complex compounds, it is evident that there is a considerable amount of simplification as well. And since water is universally present, *solution* occurs. Such cations as calcium, magnesium, sodium, and potassium, as well as many others, are found in the water that circulates through rocks and soil materials. These metallic ions, when in solution, are generally associated with such anions as chlorides, bicarbonates, carbonates, and the like. Carbon dioxide intensifies to a marked degree the solvent action of water and, consequently, increases its power as a weathering agent. The presence of decaying organic matter is of tremendous importance in this respect.

Solution, accelerated by both mechanical and chemical means, is particularly important in that it facilitates a continual loss of constituents as weathering proceeds. A comparison of fresh rock with its weathered equivalent shows this removal to be very large, especially in humid regions. This constant drain accounts for the deficiencies of certain elements not only in the soil material but also in the soil for which it has been the parent.[1]

On the other hand, this solution, however wasteful, is essential, since the intervention of water is necessary in order that the various changes, especially hydrolysis, hydration, and carbonation, may, with sufficient vigor and celerity, reduce rocks to soil material and finally provide for the genesis of soils.

125. *Weathering in action — genesis of soil material*

An understanding, even though it may be limited, of the influences of the separate forces of weathering makes it possible to picture in a simple way the development of soil material from bedrock. A physical weakening, due usually to temperature changes, initiates the process, but it is accompanied and supplemented by certain chemical transformations. Such minerals as the feldspars, mica, hornblende, and the like suffer hydrolysis and hydration, while part of the combined iron is oxidized and hydrated. The minerals soften, lose their luster, and increase in volume. If hematite or limonite is formed, the

---

[1] Following such a general statement of weathering, it is interesting to study the changes in more detail and in specific cases. This may be done by comparing the chemical analysis of a clay with that of the unweathered rock mass beneath. The assumption must be accepted, of course, that the rock analyzed is of the same composition as that from which the soil material was derived. The data are in terms of percentage.

Fresh Granite and Its Residual Clay [a]

Constituents	Rock	Clay	Percentage Lost
SiO_2	60.69	45.31	52.45
Al_2O_3	16.89	26.55	0.00
Fe_2O_3	9.06	12.18	14.35
CaO	4.44	0.00	100.00
MgO	1.06	0.40	74.70
K_2O	4.25	1.10	83.52
Na_2O	2.82	0.22	95.03
P_2O_5	0.25	0.47	0.00
Ignition	0.62	13.75	gain

Virginia Limestone and Its Residual Clay [b]

Constituents	Rock	Clay	Percentage Lost
SiO_2	7.41	57.57	27.30
Al_2O_3	1.91	20.44	0.00
Fe_2O_3	0.98	7.93	24.89
CaO	28.29	0.15	99.83
MgO	18.17	1.21	99.38
K_2O	1.08	4.91	57.49
Na_2O	0.09	0.23	76.04
P_2O_5	0.03	0.10	68.78
CO_2	41.57	0.38	99.15
H_2O	0.57	6.69	gain

[a] Merrill, G. P., *Weathering of Micaceous Gneiss*, Bulletin, Geol. Soc. Amer., VIII: 160, 1879.
[b] Diller, J. S., *Educational Series of Rock Specimens*, Bulletin 150, U. S. Geol. Survey, p. 385, 1898.

decomposing mass becomes definitely red or yellow. Otherwise, the colors are subdued.

Coincident with these changes, such active cations as calcium, magnesium, sodium, and potassium suffer carbonation, and soluble mineral products appear in the water present in the mass. When this water drains away, these soluble constituents are removed, leaving a residue more or less bereft of its easily soluble bases. As the process goes on, all but the most resistant of the original minerals disappear, and their places are occupied by secondary hydrated silicates that often recrystallize into highly colloidal clay. When this clay is small in amount, a sandy soil material is developed, but when dominant, the mass is heavy and plastic.

Such a brief statement of rock weathering demands certain supplementary explanations. In the first place, it must be recognized that the intensity of the various agencies will fluctuate with climate. Under arid conditions, the physical forces will dominate, and the resultant soil material will be coarse. Temperature changes, wind action, and water erosion will be accompanied by a minimum of chemical action.

In a humid region, however, the forces are more varied, and practically the full quota will be at work. Vigorous chemical changes will accompany disintegration, and the result will be shown in the greater fineness of the product. Clayey materials will be more common, and a higher colloidicity can be expected.

Again, it must be remembered that the forces of weathering not only lose their intensity in the lower layers of the mass, but also the transformations are somewhat different. At the surface, the full effects of climatic agencies are apparent, the influence of decaying organic matter usually greatly augmenting the chemical and physical changes. Below, the action is much less vigorous. This is due to the presence of larger amounts of water and a decrease both in porosity and aeration. This differentiation is the forerunner of a definite profile development and the genesis of a soil from the decomposing mass of rock materials.

It is well to remark also that the soil material, developing as described, may be subject to considerable transportation. Thus, new forces are brought to bear, initial processes are intensified, and the whole course of the weathering may be greatly modified. Glacial debris, alluvium, and wind-blown materials are common examples of such mass transfers.

126. *The color of soil materials*

The presence of iron, as already noted, is a very important factor in rock weathering, and the discoloration due to its oxidation is an unfailing indication of chemical decay. The iron in decomposing minerals usually emerges as the ferrous oxide (page 237) and, as such, is soluble, especially if the circulating waters carry carbon dioxide. Under this condition, oxidation goes on rapidly, and the iron passes to the ferric state and probably is first deposited as a relatively insoluble hydrated oxide — limonite or one of the other members of this indefinite group.[1] The yellow coloration so common on weathered minerals is an indication of this. Later, sufficient dehydration may occur to develop hematite and its various shades of red. Thus, it seems that iron, due to its initial instability, imparts a fatal weakness to the rocks and minerals of which it is a part; yet the relative insolubility of its higher oxides causes it to persist as a coloring matter both in soil material and in fully developed soils. Whether the color is yellowish or reddish or a mixture depends on the degree and uniformity of the hydration of the sesquioxide.

The high temperatures in the tropics and semitropics and in the warmer portions of temperate regions encourage the development of such intense red and yellow colors as to excite frequent comment. The soil materials of the Piedmont Plateau and the Appalachian valleys in the United States and the red earths of the Mediterranean regions, of Central America, and of Hawaii are examples. Even recently weathered products in the north temperate regions may show distinct yellowish colorations or tinges of pink or red. Not all soil materials, however, have acquired their color since their parent rocks lost their stability and became a part of the regolith. With soil material from red sandstones and shales, the oxidation of the iron has, of course, occurred before or as the rocks were formed. Here is a color carry-over of millions of years — an inherited characteristic.

---

[1] The compositions of hematite and of the limonite group indicate the possibility of a progressive change from red to yellow by hydration. The formulae for the various limonite compounds are more or less conjectural.

Hematite		Fe_2O_3	Red
	Turgite. . . .	$2\ Fe_2O_3 \cdot H_2O$	
	Goethite . . .	$Fe_2O_3 \cdot H_2O$	
Limonite group. . .	Limonite . . .	$2\ Fe_2O_3 \cdot 3\ H_2O$	
	Xanthosiderite . .	$Fe_2O_3 \cdot 2\ H_2O$	
	Limnite . . .	$Fe_2O_3 \cdot 3\ H_2O$	Yellow

Whatever the case may be, however, reds and yellows in all gradations and shades may be expected in soil materials where vigorous oxidation and hydration of iron compounds have been possible. However, where oxidation has made little progress or where deoxidation is definitely in the ascendancy, modest colors predominate — browns, grays, dull green or blues, or even their brighter equivalents.   In northern climates, do not expect highly colored soil materials except as a carry-over from the original rocks.

The significance of soil-material color in respect to the resultant soil has not, it is hoped, passed unnoted. The possibility of a carry-over is so obvious that it seems logical to conclude that many mineral soils inherit their colors, at least in part and with modifications.   In part, because humus has distinct color effects, especially in the surface soil layers, and with modifications, because weathering, as the profile develops, may alter in some degree the shades and tints of the parent material.

127. *Classification of soil materials*

In discussing weathering, it was tacitly assumed that soil material could originate in a number of different ways.   In addition, it was suggested that this unconsolidated debris might lie in position above bedrock for centuries or it might sooner or later be moved to new positions by the mechanical forces of nature.

On the latter basis, two groups of soil materials, designated as *sedentary* and *transported*, are usually recognized.   The latter may be subdivided according to the agencies of transportation and deposition as follows:

I. Sedentary — still at original site	Residual		
	Gravity. . . .	Colluvial	
II. Transported. . .	Water	Alluvial / Marine / Lacustrine	
	Ice	Glacial	
	Wind	Aeolian	

While these terms relate only to the placement of the soil materials, it has become customary to use them loosely in referring to the soils that have been developed by the weathering of these deposits. Hence, much is heard of *glacial* soils, *alluvial* soils, *residual* soils, and the like. Such a grouping is very general, however, as a wide diversity is sure to occur within each soil group so recognized. This renders the terms of little specific significance.

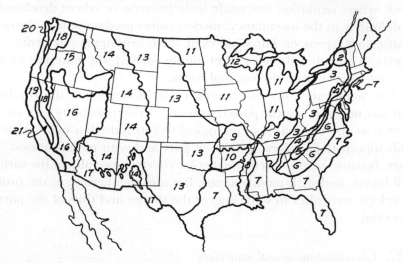

Fig. 38. Generalized physiographic and soil materials map of the United States. The regions located are as follows:

1. New England, mostly glaciated crystalline rocks.

2. Adirondacks, glaciated crystalline and sedimentary rocks.

3. Appalachian Mountains and Plateaus, shales and sandstones.

4. Limestone Valleys and Ridges, mostly limestone.

5. Blue Ridge Mountains, sandstones and shales.

6. Piedmont Plateau, crystalline rocks.

7. Atlantic and Gulf Coastal Plain, sands, clays, and limestones.

8. Mississippi Flood Plain and Delta, alluvium.

9. Limestone Uplands, mostly limestones.

10. Sandstone Uplands, mostly sandstone and shale.

11. Central Lowlands, mostly glaciated sedimentary rocks of many kinds. Great areas are overlaid with loess, a wind deposit of great agricultural importance.

12. Superior Uplands, glaciated crystalline and sedimentary.

13. Great Plains Region, sedimentary rocks of many kinds.

14. Rocky Mountain Region, mountains, uplands and valleys.

15. Northwest Intermountain, mostly igneous crystalline rock, great areas in Columbia and Snake rivers basins, covered by loess.

16. Great Basin, gravels, sands, alluvial fan from various rocks.

17. Southwest Arid Region, gravel, sand and other debris of desert and mountain.

18. Sierra Nevada and Cascade Mountains, mountains, uplands and valleys.

19. Pacific Coast Province, mountains and valleys, mostly sedimentary rocks.

20. Puget Sound Lowlands, glaciated sedimentary.

21. California central valley, alluvium and outwash.

For example, the debris laid down by any particular agency is likely to be exceedingly variable, and this variability will influence the resultant soils for a very long time. Even under the same climatic conditions, many kinds of soil may develop from practically identical parent material because of differences in slope, drainage, depth, and organic accumulation. Again, differences in climate tend to produce, after long periods, soil profiles of great diversity, despite the original similarity of the soil materials.

128. *Residual soil material*

This formation develops in place from the country rock below and has suffered little transportation. Much knowledge of weathering has been obtained by comparing the composition of such debris with that of the bedrock providing the latter is the same as the parent material (see note, page 238).

Residual material, if typically developed, has usually suffered long and often intense weathering. If occurring in a warm humid climate, it is thoroughly oxidized and well leached. And even though it comes from limestone, it may be comparatively low in calcium. Red and yellow colors are characteristic, as may be demonstrated by a trip through the Piedmont Plateau of eastern United States. In cooler, and especially in drier climates, residual weathering is much less drastic, and the oxidation and hydration of the iron may be hardly noticeable. Also, the lime content is higher and the colors of the debris subdued. Tremendous areas of this type of debris are found on the Great Plains and in other regions of western United States.

Residual materials are of wide distribution on all of the continents. In the United States, a glance at the soil-material map (Fig. 38) shows six great eastern and central provinces — the Piedmont Plateau, Appalachian Mountains and plateaus, the limestone valleys and ridges, the limestone and sandstone uplands, and the Great Plains region. The first three groups alone encompass about 10 per cent of the area of the United States. In addition, great expanses of sedentary accumulations are found west of the Rocky Mountains. As might be expected, a great variety of soils occupies these regions of residual debris, since climate, one of the determining factors in soil characterization, varies so radically over this great area.

129. *Colluvial debris*

Colluvial debris is made up of the fragments of rock detached from the heights above and carried down the slopes by gravity. Frost action has much to do with the development of such deposits. Talus slopes, cliff detritus, and similar heterogeneous materials are good examples. Avalanches are made up largely of such accumulations.

Soil material developed from colluvial accumulation is usually coarse and stony, as physical rather than chemical weathering has been dominant. Such deposits are not of great importance agriculturally because of their small area, their inaccessibility, and their unfavorable physical and chemical characteristics.

130. *Alluvial deposits*

There are three general classes of alluvial deposits: (1) flood plains, (2) alluvial fans, and (3) deltas. They will be considered in order.

A stream on a gently inclined bed usually begins to swing from side to side in variable curves, depositing alluvial material on the inside of the curves and cutting on the opposite banks. This results in ox-bows and lagoons, which are ideal for the further deposition of alluvial matter and the development of swamps. This state of meander naturally increases the probability of overflow at high water, a time when the stream is carrying much suspended matter. Part of this sediment is deposited over the flooded areas; the coarser near the channel, building up natural levees; the finer farther away in the lagoons and slack water. Thus, there are two distinct types of first-bottom deposits — *meander* and *flood*. As might be expected, flood-plain deposits are variable, ranging texturally from gravel and sands to clay.

Due to the change in grade, a stream may cut down through its already well-formed alluvial deposits, leaving *terraces* on one or both sides. Often two, or even three, terraces of different heights may be detected along some valleys, marking a time when the stream was at these elevations. Terraces are especially characteristic of streams in or near glaciated regions, the valley fill having taken place during the waning stages of the ice age. Such deposits, however, are usually classified as glacial outwash rather than true alluvium.

Flood-plain deposits are found to a certain extent beside every stream, the greatest development in the United States occurring along the Mississippi. (See Fig. 39.) This area varies from 20 to 75 miles in width and has a length from Cairo to the Gulf of over 500 miles. The soils derived from such sediments usually are very rich, but if they are first bottoms, they require drainage and protection from overflow.

Where streams descend from uplands, a sudden change in gradient sometimes occurs as the stream emerges at the lower level. A deposition of sediment is thereby forced, giving rise to *alluvial fans.* They differ from deltas in their location and in the character of their debris. Fan material is generally gravelly and stony, more or less porous and, in general, well drained.

Alluvial fan debris is found over wide areas in arid and semiarid regions, and the soils therefrom, when irrigated and properly handled, often prove very productive. Even in humid regions, such deposits occur at times in large enough areas to be of considerable agricultural importance.

Much of the sediment carried by streams is not deposited in the flood plain but is discharged into

Fig. 39. The flood plain and delta of the lower Mississippi River. This is the largest continuous area of alluvial soil in the United States.

the body of water to which the stream is tributary. Unless there is sufficient current and wave action, the suspended material, in part, accumulates, forming a *delta.* Such delta deposits are by no means universal, being found at the mouths of only a small proportion of the rivers of the world. A delta often is a continuation of a flood plain, its front so to speak, and is not only clayey in nature but is likely to be swampy as well.

Delta sediments, where they occur in any considerable acreage, are rather important. The combination deltas and flood plains of the Mississippi, Ganges, Po, Tigris, and Euphrates rivers are striking examples. Egypt, for centuries the granary of Rome, bespeaks the fertility of soils originating from such soil material.

131. *Marine sediments*

Much of the sediment carried away by stream action is eventually deposited in the sea, the coarser fragments near the shore, the finer particles at a distance. Also, considerable debris is wrenched from the shore line by the pounding of the waves and the undertow of the tides. Such materials are largely clastic and, if there have been many changes in shore line, the alternation of beds will show no regular sequence and considerable variation in topography and texture. These deposits have been extensively raised above sea level along the Atlantic and Gulf coasts of the United States and have given origin to large areas of marine soils.   (See Fig. 40.)

Marine deposits have been worn and triturated by a number of agencies. First, the weathering and erosion necessary to throw them

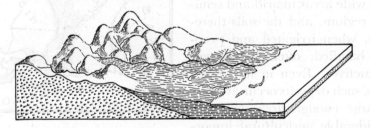

FIG. 40.   Block diagram showing the location of marine sediments and their relation to the uplands.   The emerged coastal plain has already suffered some dissection from stream action.

into stream suspension were sustained. These were followed by the sorting and solvent action of the stream itself. Next, the sediment was swept into the ocean to be deposited and stratified, possibly after being pounded and eroded by the waves for years. At last came the emergence above the sea and the final action of the forces of weathering. The latter effects are of great moment, since they determine the topography and, to a certain extent, the chemical nature of the resultant soil material.

The marine sediments of the United States, although they have been subjected to subaerial weathering a shorter time than some of the residual debris, are usually more worn and generally carry less of the mineral nutrient elements. Their silica content is high, and they are often sandy, especially along the Atlantic seaboard. But in the Atlantic and Gulf coastal flatwoods and the interior pine lands of Alabama and Mississippi, clayey deposits are not uncommon.

In continental United States, the marine deposits of the Atlantic and Gulf coastal provinces (see Fig. 38) occupy approximately 11 per cent of the country and are very diversified due to source of material, age, and climatic conditions under which they now exist. Severe leaching as well as serious erosion occur in times of heavy rainfall. But their soils, although generally quite sandy, support a great variety of crops when adequately supplied with organic matter, properly cultivated and carefully fertilized.

132. *Glacial till and associated deposits*

During the Pleistocene,[1] northern North America as well as northern and central Europe and parts of Asia were invested and invaded by a succession of great ice sheets. The cause was a change in temperature and precipitation accompanied by other fluctuations. But why the climatic changes occurred is highly conjectural. In North America, the major centers of ice accumulation were in central Labrador and the western Hudson Bay region, with a minor concentration in the Canadian Rockies. From the major centers, great continental glaciers pushed outward in all directions but especially southward, covering, at the time, most of what is now Canada and the northern part of the United States. The southernmost extension was down the Mississippi Valley, since here the least resistance was met. (See Fig. 41.)

Central North America and Europe suffered at least four [2] distinct

[1] For supplementary reading as to the Great Ice Age and its influence, see:

Salisbury, R. D., *Glacial Geology of New Jersey*, Vol. V of the Final Report of the State Geologist, Trenton, N. J., 1902.

Coleman, A. P., *Ice Ages Recent and Ancient*, The Macmillan Company, New York, 1926.

Daly, R. A., *The Changing World of the Ice Age*, Yale University Press, New Haven, 1934.

Loebeck, A. K., *Geomorphology*, McGraw-Hill Book Company, Inc., New York, 1939.

Coleman, A. P., *The Last Million Years*, University of Toronto Press, Toronto, 1941.

[2] The ice invasions of central United States are recognized by some authorities as five in number: Nebraskan, Kansan, Illinoian, Iowan, and Wisconsin. Some authors, however, consider the Iowan and the various Wisconsin sheets as belonging to the same stage, thus

ice invasions separated, in each case, by long interglacial periods. So long, in fact, were these ice-free intervals that they are estimated as having covered in total a period considerably longer than the time that ice actually overlay the country.[1] The existence of these interglacial

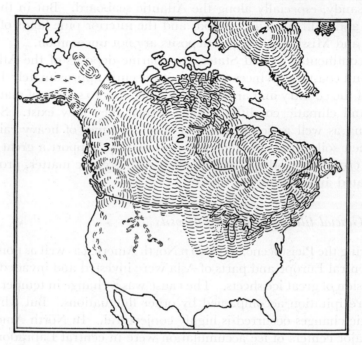

Fig. 41. Sketch map of North America showing the maximum development of the continental glaciation. The three centers of ice accumulation are numbered. Apparently central and eastern United States were invaded from the Hudson Bay and Labradorian centers. Note the marked southerly advance of the ice in the Mississippi valley.

periods is conclusively proved by the presence of forest beds and accumulations of peat between the glacial deposits of different ages and by evidence of the prolonged erosion of the successive layers of glacial

giving a classification that correlates with that established for the glaciation of Europe. The loess covers parts of all of the American till sheets except the Wisconsin, the youngest. The glacial debris of eastern United States and Canada is practically all of Wisconsin age. In New York, it is referred to as the *Ontarian*.

[1] The total length of the Pleistocene ice age as a minimum probably was in excess of 700,000 or even 1,000,000 years. Glacial ice disappeared from northern Iowa and central New York possibly only 25,000 to 50,000 years ago. We may be now enjoying the mildness of another interglacial period.

drift. Some of the interglacial intervals evidently were times of warm or even semitropical climate in regions that are now definitely temperate.

The change in climate that permitted the onset of the Pleistocene ice age evidently not only brought a lowering of temperature and an increase in precipitation but also established such a relation between them that the heat of summer could not melt the winter accumulations of snow. And great snow fields formed at certain centers. As the snow continued to thicken, the increasing pressure and the influence of summer melting gradually changed the snow into ice. Thus, dome-shaped glaciers gradually came into being, incredibly thick at their region of accretion.

Strong lateral thrusts soon inaugurated outward movement, and the ice, coarsely crystalline and with a unique viscosity under this tremendous pressure, was pushed forward, conforming itself to the unevenness of the areas invaded. It rose over hills and often over mountains with surprising ease. Not only was the existing regolith with its mantle of soil swept away, but hills were rounded, valleys filled, and, in some cases, the underlying rocks were severely ground and gouged. Thus, the glacier became filled with wreckage, carrying much on its surface and pushing great masses ahead. And finally, when the ice melted away and the region again was free, a mantle of glacial drift remained — a new regolith and fresh soil material.

Glacial drift is merely ground-up rock, either local or foreign. Some is still fresh and unmodified, while some has been markedly altered by weathering either before or subsequent to its deposition. At times, the original soil was mixed with this detritus, while again the variable accumulations were wholly reworked and considerably stratified by water. The streams of water, which issued from the glaciers, were instrumental in distributing sediments for miles beyond the ice front as outwash plains and river terraces. Glacial lakes, when in existence for sufficiently long periods, furnished basins for the deposition of materials washed from the ice. The glaciation also provided a large amount of detritus so fine as to be susceptible to wind movement, and aeolian influences, as well as fluvial and lacustrine, were concomitant with the deposition of glacial till.

The area covered by glaciers in North America is estimated as 4,000,000 square miles, while perhaps 20 per cent of the United States is either directly or indirectly influenced by the deposits. The greatest glacial extension is often marked by *terminal moraines* wherever the ice margin was stationary long enough to permit an accumulation of debris.[1] (See Fig. 42.) Many other moraines of a *recessional* nature are found to the northward, marking points where the ice front became stationary for a time as it receded by melting. While moraines of this type are generally outstanding topographic features, they are commonly unimportant as soil material due to their small area and unfavorable physiography.

The *ground moraine*, a thinner and more level deposition laid down as the ice front retreated rather rapidly, is of much more importance.

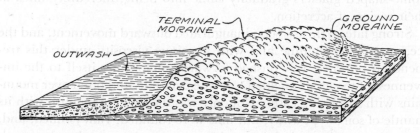

TERMINAL MORAINE

GROUND MORAINE

OUTWASH

Fig. 42. Diagram showing the relationships between a terminal moraine, its outwash and its associated ground moraine. Note the differences in topography and in the nature in general of the three deposits.

It has the widest extent of all glacial deposits and usually possesses a rather favorable agricultural topography. Associated with the moraine in certain places are such special features as *kames*, *eskers*, and *drumlins*.

A third type of deposit is the *outwash* plain, formed by streams heavily laden with glacial sediment. (See Fig. 42.) This sediment is usually assorted and therefore variable in texture. Such deposits are particularly important in valleys and on plains where the glacial waters were able to flow away freely. Such valley fills are common in the United States, both north and south of the terminal moraine, while extensive outwash plains occur on Long Island, New York, and other places. While these depositions usually are not of wide extent, their local importance is often very great. The weathering *in situ* of

[1] The position of the front of a glacier is determined by the relationship between the forward movement of the ice and the rate of melting. When the former is dominant, the ice front advances. When melting is dominant, the ice front recedes. When these two forces are balanced, conditions are favorable for a stand of the ice and the building of a moraine.

the various drift deposits cited has given rise to what are called *glacial soils*. (See Fig. 43.)

The outstanding feature of glacial soil materials is their variability. This is due to the diverse ways by which the debris was laid down, to differences in the chemical composition of the original materials, and

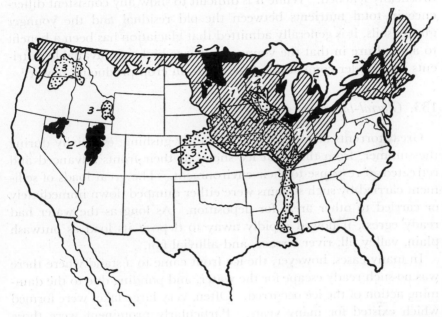

FIG. 43. Areas in the United States covered by the continental ice sheet and the deposits either directly from or associated with the glacial ice. *1*, till deposits of various kinds; *2*, glacial-lacustrine deposits; *3*, the loessial blanket, — note that the loess overlies great areas of till in the Middle West; *4*, an area, mostly in Wisconsin, that escaped glaciation. It is partially loess covered.

to fluctuations in the grinding action of the ice. Of more importance perhaps, these deposits cover a wide area and have been influenced by markedly different climatic conditions. Thus, over the glaciated portion of America, glacial debris of all descriptions may be found, varying as to topography, color, texture, structure, depth, and drainage. As might be expected, the soils derived from such soil material are most heterogeneous. Such variation serves to indicate that the term *glacial soil* is of value only in suggesting the mode in general of deposition of the soil materials. It indicates practically nothing as to the characteristics of a soil so designated.

The Pleistocene glaciation, in most cases, has been a decided benefit, especially agriculturally. The leveling and filling actions, when drift was abundant, have given a smoother topography more suited to farming operations. Also, the soil materials thus supplied are geologically fresh, and the soils derived therefrom usually are not drastically leached. While it is difficult to show any consistent difference in total nutrients between the old residual and the younger glacial soils, it is generally admitted that glaciation has been a benefit to agriculture in that the younger soils are higher in available nutrients and, under comparable conditions, in crop-producing power.[1]

133. *Glacial-lacustrine sediments*

Great torrents of water were constantly gushing, especially during the summer, from the great ice sheets as their fronts advanced and retreated in response to their environment. The great loads of sediment carried by such streams were either dumped down immediately or carried to other areas for deposition. As long as the water had ready egress, it flowed rapidly away to deposit its load as outwash plain, valley fill, river terrace, and alluvial fan.

In many cases, however, the ice front came to a stand where there was no such ready escape for the water, and ponding due to the damming action of the ice occurred. Often, very large lakes were formed which existed for many years. Particularly prominent were those south of the Great Lakes in New York, Ohio, Indiana, Michigan, and in the Red River Valley. (See Fig. 43.) The latter lake, called *Glacial Lake Agassiz*, was perhaps 750 miles long and 250 miles wide at its maximum extension. The others, while individually much smaller, covered in total great stretches of country. Large lakes also occurred in the intermountain regions west of the Rockies as well as in the Connecticut Valley in New England and elsewhere.

With the ice melting rapidly in the hills and higher valleys, these lakes were constantly fed by torrents from above which were laden with sediment derived not only directly from the ice but also from the

[1] Whitbeck, R. H., *The Glaciated and Driftless Portions of Wisconsin*, Bulletin, Geog. Soc. Phil., IX, No. 3:10–20, 1911.

Von Engeln, O. D., *Effects of Continental Glaciation on Agriculture*, Bulletin, Geog. Soc. Amer., XLVI:353–355, 1914.

Ames, J. W., and E. W. Gaither, *Soil Investigations*, Bulletin 261, Ohio Agr. Exp. Sta., 1913.

unconsolidated till sheet over which they flowed. As a consequence, great deposits were made in these glacial lakes, ranging from coarse delta materials near the shore to fine silts and clay in the deeper and stiller waters. Such materials now cover large areas both in the United States and Canada, and their weathering has given rise to what are loosely designated as *glacial lake* soils.

Glacial lake deposits probably present as wide a variation in physical and chemical characteristics as the soil materials of any of the

FIG. 44. When conditions of topography were favorable, the Wisconsin ice sheet acted as a great dam. The diagram shows a stage in the development of glacial lakes Chicago and Warren. (After Daly.)

physiographic provinces. Being deposited by water, they have been subject to much sorting and stratification and range from coarse gravels, on the one hand, to fine clays on the other. There is also considerable variation in respect to lime content, pH, color, and structural characteristics. They are generally found in the lowlands, although they may occur well up on the hillsides if the shores of the old lakes encroached thus far.

The soils developed from these lake sediments are most heterogeneous. Weathering, due to climatic differences, has been variable, and profile contrasts are great. Extending westward from New England along the Great Lakes until the broad expanse of the Red River Valley is reached, these deposits have produced some of the most important soils of the northern states. Such soils are valuable, not only for extensive cropping with grain and hay but also for fruit, trucking, and other intensive types of agriculture.

134. *Glacial-aeolian deposits*

During the glaciation, much fine material was carried miles below the front of the ice sheets by streams that found their source within the glaciers. This sediment was deposited over wide areas by the over-loaded rivers. The accumulations occurred below the ice front at all points, but in the United States seem to have reached their greatest development in what is now the Mississippi and Missouri valleys. Some of the debris found on the Great Plains probably had a similar origin, coming from glaciers debouching from the Rockies. All this, added to the great stretches of unconsolidated till in the glaciated regions and the residual materials unclothed with vegetation on the Great Plains, presented unusually favorable conditions for wind erosion.

It is generally agreed by glacialists that a period of aridity, at least as far as the Great Plains and contiguous eastward areas were concerned, accompanied or immediately followed the retreat of the Iowan ice sheet or perhaps extended well into the Iowan-Wisconsin interglacial interval. The low rainfall of this period was accompanied by strong westerly winds. These winds, active perhaps through centuries, were instrumental in picking up and distributing fine material, both glacial and nonglacial in origin, over wide areas on the Great Plains and particularly in the Mississippi, Ohio, and Missouri valleys. These deposits cover the original soils and soil material, both residual and glacial in origin. The situation, perhaps, was somewhat analogous to the wind erosion now experienced on the Great Plains but, of course, much more severe and under different conditions.

This wind-blown material, called *loess*,[1] is found over wide areas in the United States, in most cases masking the unconsolidated materials below. It covers eastern Nebraska and Kansas, southern and central Iowa and Illinois, northern Missouri, and parts of Ohio and Indiana, besides a wide band extending southward along the eastern border of the Mississippi River. (See Figs. 43 and 45.) Extensive loessial deposits also occur in the Palouse region in Washington and Idaho. In places, notably along the Missouri and Mississippi rivers, its accumulation has given rise to great bluffs which bestow a characteristic topography to the region. Farther from the rivers, the deposits, an upland type, are shallower and smoother in topography.

[1] Aeolian deposits other than loess occur, such as adobe, volcanic ash, and sand dunes. *Adobe* is a term applied to a fine calcareous clay or silt formed in a manner somewhat like loess. It produces an exceedingly rich soil and is very productive when irrigated.

Soils from volcanic ash occur in Montana, Nebraska, and Kansas. They are light and porous and not of great agricultural value. Sand dunes are a menace to agriculture if they are moving.

Not only is loess found over thousands of square miles in central and northwestern United States, but it occurs elsewhere in large areas. It is greatly developed in northern France and Belgium and along the Rhine in Germany where it gives rise to important soils in the valleys that are tributary to that river. Silesia, Poland, southern Russia, Bohemia, Hungary, and Roumania have deposits of this highly fertile soil material. In China, loess is found over a very large part of the valley of the Hwang Ho, a region probably larger in area than France and Germany combined. In South America, loess covers much of the

FIG. 45. Approximate distribution of loess in central United States. The soil that has developed therefrom is generally a silty loam. Note especially the extension down the eastern side of the Mississippi river.

pampa of northern Argentina, while considerable areas occur in eastern New Zealand.[1]

Loess is usually silty in character and has a yellowish-buff color, unless it is very markedly weathered or carries a large amount of humus. The larger particles are usually unweathered and angular. Quartz seems to predominate, but large quantities of feldspar, mica, horn-

---

[1] All of the loessial deposits mentioned apparently are related directly or indirectly to glaciation except that of China. Here the debris originated as residual material in the arid regions to the northwest and, in some places, is still noticeably in motion.

blende, augite, and the like are found. The vertical walls and escarpments formed when this deposit is deeply eroded are one of its most striking physical characteristics.

In spite of the physical and chemical homogeneity of the loess as originally deposited, it has given rise in central United States to soils of considerable diversity because of the climatic differences now existent in the various parts of the loessial area. A glance at the map of the Great Soil Groups (Fig. 49) will show the presence of loess in six distinct soil regions — brown aridics, chestnut, chernozems, prairie, gray-brown podzols, and even the forest soils of the coastal plains may, in places, claim loess as a parent material. This situation, while indicating the probability of great differences in the fertility and productivity of loess soils, especially emphasizes the influence of climate as the final determinate of soil characteristics.[1]

[1] See Vanderford, H. B., and W. A. Albrecht, *The Development of Loessial Soils in Central United States as it Reflects Differences in Climate*, Research Bulletin 345, Missouri Agr. Exp. Sta., 1942.

Chapter XII. Soil Formation, Classification and Survey

To study any heterogeneous group of materials profitably, some sort of a classification is necessary. This is especially true of soils. The value of experimental or research work of any kind is seriously restricted and may even be misleading unless the relation of one soil to another is known. Practical knowledge of crop relationships in any region is of uncertain application without some understanding of the formative processes of the soils in question and of their present profile similarities and differences.

In arriving at such an understanding three phases must be considered: (1) soil genesis or the evolution of a soil from its parent material, (2) soil classification, in this case especially as it applies to the United States, and (3) soil survey, its interpretation and utilization. It will be observed, as the viewpoint is amplified, that these phases are progressively interlocked, and that this sequence is fundamental to the satisfactory understanding and study of soils as they occur in the field.

135. *Weathering and soil formation*

To every thinking person it is obvious that mineral soils have originated, through the operation of climatic agencies, from the unconsolidated materials that mask, more or less completely, the country rock. And that this mantle, the regolith, has in turn been differentiated from solid rock by the same agencies. The general trend of events as bedrock is disintegrated and in part decomposed to give soil material has already been sketched (page 238). Even a superficial examination will show that the process seems in a broad way to be disruptive and to a considerable degree destructive also. The formation of clay and the oxidation of iron are the outstanding examples of synthesis and stabilization as the weathering proceeds and the regolith, or in a narrower sense the soil material, is slowly prepared.

257

At this point a very pertinent question logically arises. How can the soil, a natural body and a derivative, in part at least, of synthesis, result from the activity of forces that are recognized the world over as wasteful and destructive? Why do not the original changes continue until the upper layer of the regolith is reduced to an inert mass, free of soluble constituents, and hence incapable of supporting plant life?

In the first place the disruption of the original silicate minerals paves the way for clay formation. And gradually this highly colloidal material is synthesized. Its genesis has already been discussed (page 85). Its importance in relation to soil fertility is fully recognized. In fact, the natural fertility of mineral soils cannot be high without this synthesized product of weathering.

But this is by no means all. The time finally comes when living organisms decisively intervene, organic matter accumulates, especially at the surface, and the whole trend of the weathering is sharply modified. It now becomes biochemical and biocolloidal, and unique constructive influences are initiated without which a real soil cannot be formed. The accumulation and activity of organic matter, both living and dead, is the real secret of what may be termed *constructive* weathering. Thus weathering, a producer of soil material and weathering, a builder of soil, seem antithetical. Yet fundamentally the same processes are involved in both cases. The difference lies in the types of materials worked on and the internal environments governing the transactions.

Gradually the mineral and organic materials, especially at the surface, become thoroughly blended, the active colloidal portion of the soil representing an intimate mixture of the two. The physical and biochemical changes, more complex than at the beginning and affecting a mass of substance differing profoundly from the original soil materials, cease to be soil-forming except in the lower subsoil. They are now peculiar and inherent to the soil itself and are recognized as true soil processes. A profile, characteristic and unique, gradually develops. A new natural body — a soil — has come into being.

136. *Factors influencing soil character* [1]

While weathering forces are the active agents in soil genesis, their influences are drastically modified by a number of different factors.

[1] For a thought-provoking treatise on this subject see, Jenny, Hans, *Factors of Soil Formation*, McGraw-Hill Book Company, Inc., New York, 1941.

These determine in large degree the kind of soil that finally develops. For purposes of discussion they may be grouped under two heads — *climatic* and *soil material*.

Climatic . . . . . . $\left\{\begin{array}{l}\text{Nature of the climate, especially as to tempera-} \\ \text{ture and precipitation} \\ \text{Vegetative cover and organic accumulations} \\ \text{Time that climatic forces are in action}\end{array}\right.$

Nature of the soil
material as to . . . . . . $\left\{\begin{array}{l}\text{Topography and drainage} \\ \text{Texture and structure} \\ \text{Mineralogical and chemical compositions}\end{array}\right.$

Climate determines in part the nature of the weathering that occurs, or better, the coordinated influence of the forces effective. Vegetation and the drastic changes induced thereby may, except in special cases, be considered as phases of climate. The magnitude of the combined influences is, of course, a function of time. Soil material, as everyone admits, is tremendously variable from place to place, in respect to the phases listed above. Hence it provides an endless variety of environments for weathering activities. The interlocking of all of these variables, climatic and geologic, accounts for the soil heterogeneity that we expect to encounter in the field.

137. *Development of soil characteristics — soil age*

When soil formation begins the characteristics of the parent mass are almost entirely those of the soil material. They are lithological or *inherited*. There is no profile in a soil sense, although layering may be evident. If so, it is geological, that is, related to the deposition of the regolith. Such materials for purposes of classification are spoken of as *azonal* — that is, they belong to no well-defined soil group. Nevertheless, they usually support plant growth, often luxuriantly, and in this sense at least, are soils. Sands and alluvium are good examples.

As the influence of weathering becomes constructive in a soil sense and the presence of organic matter begins to exert its influence, a *young soil* gradually develops. *Acquired* characteristics, that is, those induced largely by climate, are noticeable but those inherited from the parent material are still in the ascendancy. The profile, however, since the constructive agencies have not had time to impress their pattern, is by no means fully developed.

However, as soil-forming agencies gradually attain the ascendancy, the new or acquired characteristics become dominant and the profile, even when not strongly marked, always shows diagnostic traits. The soil is now *mature* since it has reached the peak of profile development under this particular environment. Inherited characteristics, however, are still in evidence, often markedly as in the case of color or other traits, originally features of the parent material.

As time advances a mature soil may pass into *old age*. At this stage most of the inherited characteristics cease to be noticeable, while some of those of an acquired nature become especially prominent. Sometimes well-established profile characteristics are succeeded by others induced by a change in climate or vegetation. A soil then becomes *degraded*. The encroachment of a forest on a prairie is a good example, the characteristics induced by grass yielding to those of a wooded environment.

But what are these characteristics comprehended by the terms *inherited* and *acquired?* The presence of quartz is perhaps the most common example of the former, although the presence of any mineral, such as feldspar or mica, carried over unchanged into a soil, is a good illustration. Color also is often inherited, as in the case of a red parent sandstone or shale. Even clay, if originally a part of the soil material, may be rated as lithological.

Examples of acquired characteristics are as easily cited. Those due to organic matter, to clay formed as the soil developed and to red and yellow iron oxides, are common. And certainly profile layering and the development of granular and prismatic structural forms within the various horizons, are due largely to climatic and vegetative influences. Acquired characteristics of a more local nature, such as imperfect drainage and the accumulation of alkali salts, should also be mentioned. It is the combination and coordination of all of these influences, inherited as well as acquired, that give character to soils and furnish a basis for profile study and soil classification.

In the sequence of events described above, soil age is accorded especial significance. While time is, of course involved, the development and stabilization of the profiles are the real criteria of soil maturity. A young soil is one that is still in the process of adjustment to its environment and soil-building forces are active. A mature soil, on the other hand, is in dynamic equilibrium more or less, with climatic and vegetative influences, and therefore profile modifications are slow.

Such a soil is on a maintenance basis, normal erosion being met by inclusions from the C horizon. This does not mean, however, that physical and biochemical forces are not active — they may be extremely intense especially if sufficient organic matter is present. Yet the profile horizons of a mature soil are not appreciably changing either physically or chemically. Let us now consider the nature of the profile that a well-drained mature soil, whose characteristics reflect the dominating influence of climate and vegetation, is likely to present.

138. *The soil profile*

As soil material is molded into a soil by the biochemical means described above, a more or less definite layering cannot but develop, especially if drainage is adequate. This zoning is particularly noticeable at the surface where climatic agencies are more intense and particularly where there has been an opportunity for the accumulation of organic matter. A section down through the various layers to, or into, the less weathered soil material is the *profile* already frequently mentioned. The texture, depth, color, chemical nature, and sequence of the various horizons characterize a soil and determine its agricultural value. Profile study is, therefore, of prime importance.

For convenience in study and description the soil layers of a well-drained, uneroded mature soil, whose characteristics are dominately those induced by climate and vegetation, are grouped under three heads: A, B, and C (see Fig. 46). The subdivisions of these are called *horizons*. The A group (eluvial) [1] lies at the surface and includes all of the horizons from which material is being removed by leaching. Beginning at the surface of the mineral matter the horizons are designated as A_1, A_2, etc. If a layer of organic matter covers the surface, as is often the case in forests, it is referred to in mass as A_0. But if it is thick enough to exhibit distinct layers, the terminology is extended. The undecomposed litter on the surface is designated as A_{00} and the layer below as A_0. In the case of forest soils it is convenient to subdivide the A_0 into two parts. The layer of active fermentation just under the litter is labeled F, while the humus in direct contact with the mineral soil is referred to as H (see Fig. 46).

[1] Eluvial from *ex* or *e*, meaning out and *luv*, washed.

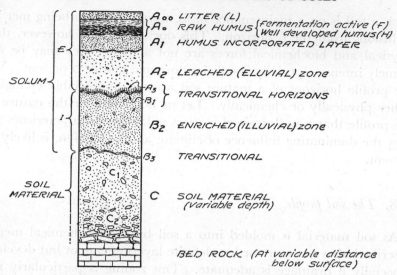

FIG. 46. An ideal soil profile showing all of the horizons usually distinguished. Any particular individual profile, however, generally exhibits clearly only part of these. The horizons most commonly present are labeled in heavy script. The transitional layers usually are faint or absent. E, eluvial and I, illuvial. Further details are as follows:

A_{00}. This horizon consists of loose organic debris. It is usually absent on grass lands but present on forest soils, especially those of temperate regions, and very abundant at certain times of the year. Ordinarily it is but little decomposed.

A_0. A partially or fully humified organic horizon. It may be matted, fibrous or granular. On grass land it is usually absent. On forest soils two distinct layers often may be distinguished — F, the zone of fermentation and H, a markedly humified zone lying just above A_1 or A_2.

A_1. A dark colored mineral horizon containing a relatively large amount of humified organic matter thoroughly mixed with the inorganic layer. In chernozems this layer is very thick; in podzols very thin or absent; and in other soils variable.

A_2. A light colored mineral horizon resulting from a leaching and bleaching action (*eluviation*). It is well developed and very noticeable in true podzols — the gray layer or *bleicherde* of these soils. It is absent from chernozems and certain other soils especially those of arid and semi-arid regions.

A_3. A transition layer, often absent. When it is present it is more like A than B.

B_1. Also a transitional horizon and absent from most soils. But in true podzols it is often present as a characteristic zone of precipitated humus carrying considerable iron and aluminum.

B_2. A zone of accumulation (*illuviation*) especially of iron and aluminum compounds. It is particularly prominent in true podzols as a *reddish-brown* horizon. The hardpan (*ortstein*) of the podzol occurs here when present as does the *clay-pan* of certain other soils. In aridic soil the B_2 is often characterized by special structural forms, frequently columnar or prismatic, and by accumulations of calcium carbonate and gypsum.

B_3. A transitional layer. It may or may not be present.

C.   This unconsolidated *soil material* attains its position in one of two ways — by the weathering in place of the bed-rock or by transportation and deposition by water, ice or wind.   In the former case, when the soil-forming processes are practically coincident with ordinary weathering, the *C* horizon is absent, the solum resting directly on the country rock.   The same may be true for a thin layer of transported material.

The *B* group (illuvial) [1] comes next and includes the layers in which deposition from above is taking place.   In common parlance this is the *subsoil*.   It is the region of accumulation, especially of iron and aluminum.   Here also is concentrated the clay when this washes downward from the surface layers.   In arid regions calcium carbonate and other salts accumulate in the *B*.   Its horizons are labeled in order downward as B_1, B_2, etc.   The *A* and *B* horizons together are called the *solum*, that is, the portion of the profile developed by soil building as distinguished from the soil material below.

The *C* horizon, or soil material, is noticeably less weathered and is usually similar to or identical with that from which the *A* and *B* horizons were derived.   As yet it has not been subjected to soil building but its upper layers will in time become a part of the solum. Since the *C* horizon, especially the upper part, may show considerable chemical weathering, several zones may be distinguished.   Generally, however, little attempt is made to differentiate within this horizon. For further details of the profile see the notes accompanying Fig. 46.

It is at once evident that the profile of any one soil probably will not show, even indistinctly, all of the possible horizons.   The reasons are obvious.   The profile may be immature or may be overly influenced by some local condition such as poor drainage, texture, or topography.   Again some of the horizons are manifestly merely transitional and may at best be very indistinct.   With so many factors involved in soil genesis a slight lack of coordination may prevent the development of such layers.   As a result we can be sure of finding in any well-drained and uneroded mature soil, whose characteristics are dominately those induced by climate and vegetation, only certain horizons.   They are: A_0, if the land is forested; A_1 or A_2 depending on circumstances; B_2; and *C* (see Fig. 46).   Conditions of soil genesis will determine which others are present and their clarity of definition.

When such land is put under cultivation, the A horizons, in part or in whole, become the furrow-slice.   The cultivation, of course, destroys the original layered condition of this portion of the profile, the

[1] Illuvial from *il* or *in*, meaning in and *luv*, washed.

furrow-slice becoming more or less homogeneous. In some soils the A horizons are of sufficient depth to allow a subsurface, but in many cases the plowline is just at the top of or even in the B (Fig. 47).

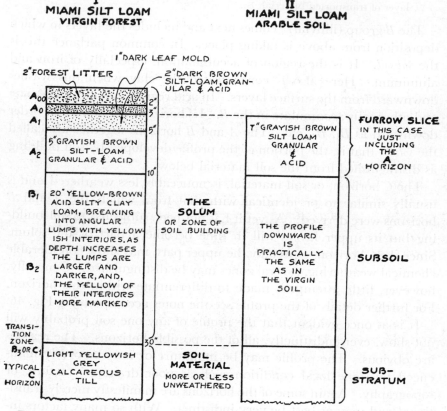

FIG. 47. Generalized profile of the Miami silt loam, one of the gray-brown podzolic soils of Eastern United States. A comparison of the profile of the virgin soil with its arable equivalent shows the changes that may be expected from cultivation. If erosion occurs, the original A horizon may disappear, at least in part, and some of the B horizon will be included in the furrow-slice. (After Baldwin, M., "The gray-brown podzol soils of Eastern United States," *Proc. and Papers of the First Internat. Cong. of Soil Sci.*, IV: 276–282, 1927.)

A profile feature always to be kept in mind is this. Many times, especially on cultivated land, serious erosion has occurred and as a result a *truncated* profile is encountered. As the surface soil was swept away, it was necessary to gradually lower the plowline in order to maintain a sufficiently thick furrow-slice. Hence the furrow, in many cases, is almost entirely within the *B* zone and the *C* material is correspondingly nearer the surface. Many farmers are today cultivating the subsoil without realizing the ravages of erosion. In profile study and description such a situation requires careful analysis.

139. *Climate and soil classification*

Three major ideas are involved in the modern concept of soil genesis and classification. All have been developed in the preceding pages but for purposes of emphasis and clarity they will be restated.

First, soil genesis is a constructive process; unique, distinct, and colorful. No matter where it occurs the same physical and chemical forces are operative. That is, *qualitatively* the forces involved are the same.

Second, due to differences in climate, in vegetation, and in the original soil materials there are great differences from place to place in the intensity and sequence of soil-forming forces, especially in the later stages of soil development. That is, there is a significant *quantitative* variation in the process, correlated very closely with and definitely controlled by climate and vegetation.

Third, when soils are young the original geological nature of the soil materials and the conditions of position apparently determine to a large extent the character of the soil. However, as time passes, climatic agencies become dominant, especially where the topography is level, erosion slight, and drainage good. Hence, inherited characteristics tend in some degree to disappear. Thus most soils apparently are acquiring, some rapidly, some slowly, the characteristics induced by climate and its accompanying vegetation and are losing at a corresponding rate their original geological features.

Under such conditions soils over wide areas, varying greatly as to rock formations and geological origin in general, tend after a considerable lapse of time to become alike in general characteristics if the climatic influences are reasonably uniform and continuous and if erosion is not a serious factor. Such soil groups, therefore, are spoken of as *zonal* — that is, they are of such wide expanse as to be thought of as continental. They constitute the *great soil groups* of the world. Thus climate, with its associated vegetation, becomes the first and the major factor to be considered in the initiation of soil classification.

Associated with zonal soils are two other groups — *intrazonal* and *azonal*. The former includes those soils that, in spite of climate and vegetation, reflect the influence of some local condition such as poor drainage, alkali salts, or some unique inherited or otherwise acquired characteristic. Since they cross zonal boundaries they are termed *intrazonal*. Azonal soils are merely those that are without profile characteristics. Most alluvial and colluvial soils belong in this group.

140. *Humid versus aridic soils*

As the classification of soils is followed still further it seems logical to first consider the zonal soils because of their wide expanse and world importance. And since climate must still be accorded first place, the two great subdivisions become *humid* and *aridic* zonal soils. A further division gives the *great soil groups* of the world (see Table XXVIII).

Humid regions, as far as temperature is concerned, may be broadly grouped under three heads: (1) cold or frigid, (2) temperate, and (3) tropical and semitropical. And since climate is so omnipotent three corresponding zonal groups of soil occur: *tundra*, *podzolic*, and *lateritic*. The vegetation of the tundra consists of mosses, lichens, and shrubs. The ground cover of the podzolic group may be forest or grass, according to conditions, while lateritic soils originate under tropical and semitropical forests. Vegetation and its decomposing accumulation play a major role in the development of soil characteristics, especially in the humid temperate regions. In addition, the podzolic and lateritic groups are characterized by the concentration of iron and aluminum in certain horizons and by the absence in mature soils of calcium carbonate in the solum. And since much leaching has occurred the concentration of soluble salts is low and the surface soils usually are acid.

The aridic group, as the term implies, includes all soils whose profile characteristics are adjusted to a low rainfall, usually not over 25 inches annually. The temperature may be low, medium, or high. A fully and normally developed zonal profile usually reveals a calcium carbonate accumulation at some point in the *A* or *B* horizons higher in percentage than the lime content of the parent material. As the rainfall decreases this layer of calcium carbonate, accompanied by more soluble salts, is found nearer the surface. Unlike humid-region soils, there is little translocation of iron and aluminum. Aridic soils are variable in color, ranging from black through brown or chestnut

Table XXVIII. A Classification of the Great Soil Groups [1] of the World

I. Zonal Humid Soils

Climate	. . . .	Humid and subhumid — cold, temperate, tropical
Vegetation	. . .	Forests, grasses and with tundra, mosses, lichens, shrubs
Iron and aluminum	. . .	Definite translocation and concentrations in certain horizons
Calcium carbonate	. .	Ordinarily no accumulation in mature profiles

Tundra . . . .
- Dark gray peaty accumulations over gray mottled mineral horizons
- Subtratum ever frozen and often the subsoil as well

Podzolic . . . .
- Typical podzol (gray forest soils)
- Brown podzolic
- Gray-brown podzolic
- Red and yellow podzolic (lateritic)
- Prairie — dark brown and reddish brown

Lateritic . . . .
- Typical and well-developed laterites
- Yellowish-brown lateritic soils
- Reddish-brown lateritic soils
- Terra-rossa

II. Zonal Aridic Soils

Climate	. . . .	Arid and semiarid — temperate, semitropical and tropical
Vegetation	. . .	Grass and desert plants
Iron and aluminum	. . .	Little or no movement and concentration
Calcium carbonate	. .	Characteristic accumulations in B and sometimes in A horizons

Direction of arrows indicates a progressive reduction in effective rainfall
- Chernozems (black earth)
- Chestnut and reddish chestnut
- Brown and reddish-brown aridics
- Gray desert (Sierozems)
- Reddish desert soils
- Noncalcic brown soils

[1] *Intrazonal Groups in Association*

Planosols — strongly leached surface soils over clay pan.
Rendzinas — dark-colored grassland soils from soft limy materials.
Brown forest soils — similar to gray-brown podzolics but neutral.
Meadow lands — Wiesenböden.
Bog — peat and muck soils of swamp and marsh.
Half-bog — peaty soils over gray mineral horizons.
Ground-water podzol — poorly drained sandy podzols with cemented subsoils.
Saline soils (solonchak) — high content of soluble salts of Ca, Mg, and Na. Mildly alkaline.
Alkali soils (solonetz) — moderate content of soluble salts but with those of Na dominant. Strongly alkaline.
Solodized-solonetz — partially leached solonetz with acid surface and often with dense clayey columnar B horizon.

Azonal Groups in Association

Alluvial — soils from recently deposited alluvium and with little or no profile development.
Lithosols — shallow soils. An imperfectly weathered mass of mineral debris.
Dry sands — very sandy soils with no profile characteristics.

to gray, as the annual precipitation becomes more scanty. Where the temperature is high, shades and tints of yellow and red occur (see Table XXVIII).

While the A horizon of aridic soils is usually alkaline or neutral, a pH below 7 is sometimes encountered. In a well-drained profile the exchangeable ions of the colloidal complex are mostly calcium and magnesium, sodium ions being in the minority. Soluble salts are often high, yet they ordinarily are so uniformly distributed as to interfere but little with plant growth, unless drainage is impeded or over-irrigation occurs (see page 311).

In some cases the profile layers of zonal aridic soils are distinct and well developed. This is especially true of the chernozem, a soil receiving the highest rainfall of the group and occurring in the United States and Canada just west of the central prairies (see Fig. 49). The surface horizon is deep and black, due to the great accumulation of organic matter and its peculiar type of decay, with a sharp and very distinct transition into the brownish layers underneath. With the other groups of aridic soils, however, the organic matter is low and the profiles less distinct. Yet there is enough difference in temperature and rainfall to account for at least four zonal aridic soils besides the chernozem or black-earth group.

It is apparent that the chemical composition of aridic and humid-region zonal soils must be somewhat different both in the A and B horizons. In contrast with the mildly podzolic gray-brown forest soils of eastern United States, arid soils in general show, when their surface and subsoil horizons are compared, much less difference in respect to the amounts of silica and sesquioxides present. This would seem to indicate a less weathered condition, especially of the feldspars.[1] They also are higher in phosphorus and sulfur but, except for the chernozems, lower in organic matter and nitrogen (see Fig. 4). Due to a greater amount of leaching, humid-region surface soils contain much less lime, potash, and magnesia. The subsoils exhibit the same differences in general except that the gray-brown podzolic soils often show a concentration of iron and aluminum in the B horizon, while zonal aridic soils have an accumulation of lime in this zone or even in the surface.

[1] See Hilgard, E. W., "Die Boden arider und humider Lander," *Inter. Mitt, für Bodenkunde*, I:415–529, 1912; and Marbut, C. F., "Soils of the United States," *Atlas of Amer. Agr.*, Bureau Chemistry and Soils, U. S. Dept. of Agriculture, 1935, Part III, pp. 14–15. The data from Marbut, quoted in part below, are especially significant. A brown

Biologically, organisms may be active at greater depths in zonal aridic than in zonal humid soils because of the loose structure and good aeration of the former. But the intensity of biological activity in arid soils is very largely governed by moisture. When moisture conditions are satisfactory, microbial changes may be expected to take place rapidly. In humid regions such activity is limited very largely to the surface horizons of soil, since only there are the aeration and the food conditions adequate. This microbial activity, however, while more restricted, is very intense.

141. *Tundra soils* [1]

The great soil groups will now be considered in order beginning with the tundra (see Table XXVIII). Since the soils of this category are yet of little agricultural importance except as pasturage for reindeer and caribou, they will be given hardly more than passing mention in spite of their tremendous range in northern Europe, Asia, and North America. Forty per cent of the Soviet Union is thus covered, an area equal to that of the United States.

These soils lie just north of the podzolic group and, as might be expected, the transition from forest to the mosses, lichens, and shrubs of the northlands is most irregular. The accumulation of organic matter gives a peaty surface covering over a bluish-gray sticky and compact subsoil. Since the subtratum, and sometimes even the subsoil, of the

---

forest soil from Indiana is compared with a chernozem from Krydor, Sask., Canada. The figures are in terms of percentage.

	Gray-brown Forest Soil, Indiana, U. S.		Chernozem Sask., Can.	
	3 in. to 5 in.	16 in. to 30 in.	0 in. to 5 in.	15 in. to 24 in.
SiO$_2$	80.64	69.81	64.73	59.26
TiO$_2$	0.72	0.56	0.39	0.40
Fe$_2$O$_3$	3.00	6.18	3.22	3.28
Al$_2$O$_3$	7.79	13.72	9.76	9.95
MnO	0.04	0.03	0.15	0.06
CaO	0.83	0.72	1.70	8.40
MgO	0.49	1.11	1.00	3.13
K$_2$O	1.64	2.48	2.03	1.85
Na$_2$O	1.04	1.11	1.45	1.34
P$_2$O$_5$	0.08	0.07	0.17	0.14
SO$_3$	0.12	0.03	0.20	0.07
Ignition	3.62	4.21	15.55	12.11
N	0.10	0.04	0.56	0.13

[1] See, Nikiforoff, C. C., "The Perpetually Frozen Subsoil of Siberia," *Soil Sci.*, XXVI: 61–81, 1928 and Feustel, I. C., A. Dutilly, and M. S. Anderson, "Properties of Soils from North American Arctic Regions," *Soil Sci.* XLVIII:183–198, 1939.

tundra remains frozen most of the year, a poorly drained boggy condition is sure to be the rule at certain seasons. Much heaving takes place with the alternate freezing and thawing, and explosive blisters sometimes occur. With the tundra soils are associated the muskeg peats, often with perpetually frozen subhorizons.

142. *Podzolization* [1]

Podzolization, to be typical, demands certain conditions. There must be such an adjustment of temperature, rainfall, vegetation, and other factors as to favor, first of all, an abundant surface accumulation of organic matter (duff or mor) (see Fig. 48). Forests are therefore the most common vegetation, although mild podzolization occurs with grasses. Coupled with this there must be a type of decomposition that will develop organic matter yielding acids and other substances of great solvent capacity. When podzolization is intense fungi seem to be the microorganisms engaged in the production of such humus, bacterial activity being at a minimum. In such an acid, low-calcium medium, earthworms are practically absent. pH values as low as 3.5 are often found in this humus, especially the H layer.

Not only should climatic conditions be cool and damp, but also sufficient excess moisture must be present, at least at certain times, to promote leaching. As a result, the acids of the organic horizons are carried downward through the mineral layers below, dissolving and entirely removing carbonates of all kinds, especially those of calcium and magnesium. The colloidal complex of the A horizon thus becomes more or less saturated with hydrogen and it is rendered extremely acid. pH values of 4.0 to 4.5 are common.

Under the conditions described above, the colloidal complexes of the A horizon become unstable and break up. The iron and alumina not already removed are carried away, probably in the sol condition. No doubt humic substances, other than organic acids, have something to do with this chemical eluviation. The A_2 horizon, thus drastically leached, assumes a bleached, gray appearance and is left in a highly acid, siliceous condition. Because of its gray color and ashy appearance the term *podzol* [2] has been applied, and *podzolization* is used to

[1] Joffe, J. S., *Pedology*, Rutgers University Press, New Brunswick, N. J., 1936, Chap. IX. Kellogg, Charles E., *The Soils That Support Us*, The Macmillan Company, New York, 1941, pp. 138–149.

[2] From the Russian *pod*, meaning under and *zola*, ash.

designate collectively the processes that tend to develop such a layer.

While the carbonates, sulfates, and other soluble salts are in large degree carried out of the profile, the colloidal humus with part of the sesquioxides are deposited in the B horizon. Just why the hydroxides, especially those of iron, should precipitate it is difficult to explain

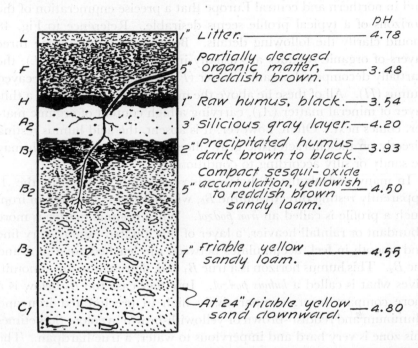

FIG. 48. A well-developed podzol profile at White Lake Lodge, New York, on the Southwestern edge of the Adirondack Mountains. The soil is a stony loam, forested with birch, hemlock and spruce. Note the thickness of the organic cover (mor or duff), the depth of the gray siliceous layer (A_2) and the marked acidity of the whole profile, even the C_1. The layer of precipitated humus (B_1) is unusually well developed.

satisfactorily. The increased base content may finally force them into a gel condition. The humus may also be a factor as it has been found that a humus-sesquioxide mixture becomes more stable as the humus content is reduced. Again the clay carried downward by mechanical eluviation may act as a catch filter and hasten coagulation. Also the upward movements of capillary water in summer may carry sesquioxides into the zone of concentration. The presence of the accumulation near the ground-water level suggests some such relationship. But whatever the cause, a typical podzol profile may exhibit in the B

zone three distinct horizons in order: precipitated humus (B_1), a reddish-brown layer due to a concentration of the sesquioxides with some humus (B_2), and a yellowish horizon (B_3) below, which gradually merges with the soil material (see Fig. 48).

Podzolic weathering is so important in the United States, Canada, and in northern and central Europe that a precise enumeration of the horizons of a typical profile seems desirable. Reference to Fig. 48 should clarify the following details. Beginning at the surface three layers of organic residues are usually in evidence: the litter (L), the partially decomposed organic matter (F), and the black well-decayed humus (H). All of these lie above the mineral soil. Sometimes a thin layer of mineral matter (A_1), carrying a high content of organic matter, comes next. Often, however, it is absent, the acid humus resting directly on the characteristic gray siliceous horizon (A_2), which may be sandy or silty according to conditions.

In many podzols the B_1 horizon is very faintly developed, the A_2 apparently resting directly on the B_2, which is especially high in iron. Such a profile is called an *iron podzol*. When organic matter is more abundant or rainfall heavier, a layer of precipitated humus, very fine and smooth in feel, accumulates between the leached zone (A_2) and the B_2. This humus horizon is a true B_1 and, if present in any amount, gives what is called a *humus podzol*. In either case the B_2 below is a more compact layer, comparatively high in precipitated iron and aluminum and reddish-brown or yellowish-brown in color. Sometimes this zone is very hard and impervious to water, a true hardpan. The B_3 layer is usually friable and yellowish in color. It may merge directly with the C horizon, the more or less weathered substratum, or it may be separated from it by a distinct zone. The whole profile of a well-developed podzol soil is acid, at least until the C horizon is approached. This is a very important point practically, since acidity and the conditions accompanying it have a marked influence on plant growth.

As might be expected, all degrees and gradations of podzolization occur. This is of utmost importance in soil classification. For instance, under conditions of impeded drainage, or a greater accumulation of organic matter, or especially heavy rainfall, the *iron podzol* changes to a *humus podzol* and then into a bog soil whose solum is entirely organic. Again, the process is generally more intense in sandy soils than in clayey ones even under the same climate. This is due to the ready downward movement of water in the lighter soils, the leaching action of the organic acids being more effective.

Gradations also occur as warmer humid regions are approached. The gray podzol soils gradually merge to the southward with those having a brown or gray-brown surface layer and an admixture of the organic matter with the A horizon. These in turn grade into soils whose surface horizons are red or yellow in color. That is, a transition from a podzolic to a lateritic weathering is experienced.

Under such conditions the gray siliceous layer becomes thinner and thinner until it disappears, the precipitated humus zone is no longer evident, and the accumulation of iron and aluminum in the B horizon is less prominent. Moreover, the organic matter becomes more and more mixed with the mineral soil below until the A_0 is very thin, most of the organic matter being a part of the A_1. This layer, now called a *mull*, thus becomes very prominent at the expense of the A_0 and A_2, the latter changing from a gray to a brown color. We now have a mildly podzolized soil, very much higher in fertility than the drastically leached profile with its acid-gray A_2 horizon. Further transition would merge the podzolic soils into the lateritic.

In the same way a marked change in profile is found as progress is made towards a more arid climate. Forest gives way to grass and the podzolic characteristics gradually fade, much as pictured above. Carbonates become evident in the subsoil and, as the rainfall lessens still more, they are found nearer and nearer the surface. Such soils are, therefore, classed as aridic since leaching is not sufficient to deplete the original lime content. In the United States the typical podzols grade westward into prairie soils, then into chernozems, and finally into more pronounced aridic types (see Fig. 49).

143. *Podzolic soil regions of the United States* [1]

The soils of northeastern United States, as already emphasized, show conclusive gradations from podzolic to lateritic conditions southward, and from podzolic to aridic in a westerly and southwesterly direction. This merging is inevitable. As a result five podzolic soil regions may definitely be distinguished.

[1] For an excellent discussion of the soils of the various regions of the United States as t $\prime$ origin, profile characteristics, and agricultural importance, see Kellogg, Charles E., *The Soils That Support Us*, The Macmillan Company, New York, 1941.

The first, drastically podzolic, is designated as the region of *gray* or *typical podzol* soils because of the characteristic color of the A_2 horizon. These soils occur mostly in northern and northeastern United States (Fig. 49). The profile characteristics already have been fully explained (page 272 and Fig. 48). It need only be said further that the soil material is so drastically leached during soil formation and the upper layers are left so acid, that the soils are rather low in agricultural value except in certain cases. Once the organic matter is gone the slump in productivity is rapid. Most of these soils are best left in woodland. Only with certain crops is their cultivation advisable.

Just south of the typical podzols in New England and New York is found a less drastically podzolized soil group of considerable importance in spite of its comparatively small area — the *brown podzolic*. In the soils of this zonal group the gray, infertile siliceous layer is absent or very faint, its place being taken by a friable brown or light-brown A_1 horizon several inches thick, containing a considerable amount of organic matter. It often presents a characteristic salt-and-pepper aspect due to an admixture of sand grains. The B horizons show little evidence of cementation. As a result the brown podzolic soils are loose and well drained and, in spite of their acidity, are much better suited for agriculture than the typical podzols. They are a transitional group peculiar to New England and play an important role in the agriculture of this section.

The *gray-brown podzolic* soils, which lie still further southward (Fig. 49), are also mildly podzolized but due to differences in climate, vegetation, and parent materials present a profile somewhat different from the brown podzolic. The organic matter, mostly from deciduous trees, instead of accumulating on the forest floor as a mat (mor or duff) has, to a considerable extent, become incorporated with the mineral soil (A_1) giving a *mull* layer several inches thick, within which a mild decomposition is occurring. The gray siliceous layer is replaced by a gray or yellowish-brown horizon (A_2) from 5 to 12 inches thick. Considerable exchangeable calcium still occupies the colloidal complex. Consequently these layers are not excessively acid. In fact, at times, only mildly so. Bacteria and actinomyces are active as well as fungi, and earthworms are numerous. The B horizons show some accumulation of clay and often possess a blocky structure that does not always facilitate drainage. Sometimes a clay pan develops. All in all, however, the gray-brown podzolic soils constitute a zonal group of great agricultural value. For further profile details see Fig. 47.

Although the fertility of the gray-brown podzolic soils is only medium, the climate favors crops that assure stable agricultural conditions especially in the United States. The farms are comparatively small, diversification easy, markets close at hand, and social provisions

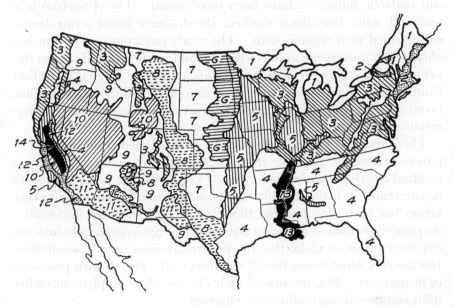

FIG. 49. The great soil groups of the United States (After Marbut and Kellogg). The regions located are as follows:

1. Typical podzol — gray forest soil.
2. Brown podzolic.
3. Gray-brown podzolic.
4. Red and yellow podzolic (lateritic).
5. Prairie — dark brown and reddish brown.
6. Chernozems.
7. Chestnut and reddish chestnut.
8. Brown and reddish brown aridics.

9. Shallow soils (lithosols), mountains, upland and valley.
10. Gray desert (Sierozems).
11. Reddish desert soils.
12. Non-calcic brown soils.
13. Mississippi alluvium.
14. Alluvium and outwash of the central valley, California.

excellent. Opportunities for making a livelihood are such as to render the gray-brown podzolics, covering a great strip from the Middle Atlantic states westward to Iowa and Missouri (see Fig. 49), the bulwark of American agriculture. Great areas of this soil group also occur in western Montana and northern Idaho. Besides, a wide belt extends down the coastal and valley regions of western Washington and Oregon and into California as far south as San Francisco.

The *red* and *yellow podzolic soils* of the southern states (see Fig. 49) indicate clearly that the modifying influence of laterization has been at work. These soils have originated under a mild climate, an abundant rainfall, and a mixed forest, often markedly deciduous. As a result podzolic influences have been most genial. The *A* horizon is a *mull* and, while leaching is marked, the drainage water is not drastically armed with organic acids. The ready oxidation of the iron has checked its movement to lower depths and at the same time has developed colors both striking and significant. The sudden transition from red to yellow surface soils in certain areas is difficult to explain, possibly being due in many cases to a carry-over from the parent materials.

These red and yellow soils have been developed from all sorts of parent materials, ranging from granites to limestones and from residual debris to marine sediments. Yet they have many attributes in common. It is remarkable that climate and its concomitant vegetation has been able to mold them into such noticeable uniformity. As progress is made southward these soils merge so gradually into the semilaterites as to make the line of demarcation merely suggestive. In eastern United States they stand next to the gray-brown podzolics in importance. But, because of their climate, they supplement rather than compete in agricultural production.

The fifth podzolic or perhaps semipodzolic soil region in the United States in that of the *prairie*. Its climate is much the same as that operative in the gray-brown soil region to the eastward. But because the vegetation is grass instead of forest the soils are strikingly different. Under such a cover the organic matter, thoroughly mixed with the *A* horizon, is especially high and the leaching, while sufficient to remove much of the calcium carbonate, has not seriously impaired the natural fertility. This is the only large area of such soils in the world. Just why they are free of woods and whether they would become partially forested in time if undisturbed by man are mooted questions.

The abundant grass cover has resulted in a deep, rich, dark-brown *A* horizon with a varied and active microorganic flora. Southward, the color changes to reddish brown. The structure of the surface is decidedly granular, due to the influence of the grass cover. The exchangeable calcium is high, in spite of the definite acidity, and little

downward movement of iron and alumina has occurred. In places
the presence of clay pans indicate considerable translocation of clay.
The *B* horizon is brownish and grades into a parent material that often
is rich in lime. Podzolic influences, modified by climate and vegetation, have been decidedly beneficial. The marked accumulation of
humus and its dark color, both extremely noticeable to eastern eyes,
are probably due, in part at least, to the hot dry summers which have
impeded and modified microbial activities, so marked in spring and
autumn.

This belt of prairie soils, extending latitudinally through the heart
of the country, varies somewhat in character from north to south and
from west to east with climate, merging with the chernozems on the
one hand and with the gray-brown podzolics on the other. Yet they
are uniformly fertile and, with the red and yellow soils of the South
and the gray-brown forest soils of the East, control the agriculture of
central and eastern United States if not of the nation.[1]

144. *Laterization* [2]

Under the abundant rainfall and high temperatures of the tropics
and semitropics, weathering forces not only work faster and carry
their influence to greater extremes but they also are so coordinated as
to develop a unique product — the *laterite*. Hence the term *laterization* for this type of soil-material development. Here there has been
no glaciation to interrupt the process and the country rock and the
regolith have been subjected to drastic decomposition. Hydrolysis,

[1] Associated with the zonal groups described above are areas of intrazonal soils, very important locally and in some cases of wide extent. Of these in humid United States the
planosols, rendzinas, meadowlands, and *bog soils* deserve especial mention (see Table XXVIII).

The planosols, comparatively level, poorly drained, and with a clay-pan subsoil, occupy
great stretches of prairie in southern Illinois and Iowa and northern Missouri. Their
productivity is considerably lower than that of the zonal prairie. The rendzinas also are
mostly grassland soils, developed from soft limy rocks, and are rather thin. They usually
are neutral or only slightly acid. The famous *Black Belt* extending northwestward across
Alabama into Mississippi is the best known area in the United States (Fig. 49).

Meadowland soils occur in wide areas all along the Atlantic and Gulf coastal plains and
fringe the Great Lakes in Michigan, Ohio, and New York. Bog soils include the peats and
mucks so important in vegetable production. Because of their agricultural significance a
special chapter will be devoted to these organic soils (see page 317).

Of the azonal soils it is necessary to mention only the *alluvial*, the origin of which has already been discussed (page 244). They are important locally along almost every stream.
But the largest and best known development occurs along the Mississippi River (Fig. 39)
and it is justly famed for its high fertility. It figures greatly in the agriculture of the southern states.

[2] A few of the more important articles dealing with laterites are (*See following page*):

as well as oxidation, has been extremely intense and silicate minerals have quickly succumbed. In many parts of the tropics wet and dry seasons alternate, which no doubt greatly intensifies chemical activities, especially those of the organic matter.

In lateritic genesis the soluble bases, such as calcium, magnesium, potassium, and sodium, are quickly released and, according to the season, are subject to removal by leaching. Due to the mobility of these cations the pH is, at least at first, near 7. This condition of low acidity is furthered by the rapid decay of organic residues and the immediate release of the bases of organic combination. As a result, the solubility of the silica is encouraged and that of the iron, aluminum, and manganese retarded. And if drainage is at all satisfactory intense oxidation occurs. Thus as weathering proceeds a red or yellow soil material, high in the sesquioxides and low in silica, results. The intensity of silicon loss and sesquioxide accumulation is remarkable. In Cuba, for example, a soil containing 1.8 per cent of SiO_2 and 71.1 per cent of Fe_2O_3 has developed from parent material showing 41.9 per cent of SiO_2 and only 7.8 per cent Fe_2O_3.[1]

Because of the intensity of lateritic weathering the regolith often becomes very deep and when a soil develops the B horizon extends many feet below the surface. Original differences due to the character of the country rock are often practically eliminated by the vigor of the chemical processes. The oxidation and hydration of iron and aluminum during laterite formation is, of course, intense above the water table and red and yellow hydroxide clays are the final product. Naturally

Campbell, J. M., "Laterite, Its Origin, Structure and Minerals," *Mining Mag.*, XVII: 67–77, 120–128, 171–179, and 220–229, 1917.

Harrassowitz, H., "Laterit," *Fortschr. Geol. Palaeont.*, IV:253–566, 1926.

Bennett, H. H., and R. V. Allison, *The Soils of Cuba*, Tropical Plant Research Foundation, Washington, D. C., 1928.

Harrison, J. B., "The Katamorphism of Igneous Rocks under Humid Tropical Conditions," *Imp. Bur. Soil Sci.*, Harpenden, England, 1934.

Joffe, J. S., *Pedology*, Rutgers University Press, New Brunswick, N. J., 1936, Chap. XII.

Pendleton, R. L., *The Use of the Term Laterite*, Bulletin 17, Amer. Soil Survey Assoc. Rept., 102–108, 1936.

Bonnett, Juan A., "The Nature of Laterization as Revealed by Chemical, Physical and Mineralogical Studies of a Lateritic Soil Profile from Puerto Rico," *Soil Sci.*, XLVIII:25–40, 1939.

Hardy, F., and G. Rodriques, "Soil Genesis from Andesite in Grenada, British West Indies," *Soil Sci.*, XLVIII:361–384, 1939.

Pendleton, Robert I., and Sangar Sharasvana, "Analyses and Profile Notes on Some Laterite Soils and Soils with Iron Concretions of Thailand," *Soil Sci.*, LIV:1–26, 1942.

[1] Bennett, H. H., and R. V. Allison, *The Soils of Cuba*, Tropical Plant Research Foundation, Washington, D. C., 1928, p. 2

no calcium carbonate is present. Iron concretions are found which are indicative of some translocation of the sesquioxides. In fact, where drainage is restricted soft deposits often occur at or near the water table. In some countries these are cut out in conveniently sized blocks, which harden when dry and thus make excellent building material.[1] A true laterite soil always exhibits this layer.

The process of laterization is so intense and leaching is so thorough that the hydroxide clay resulting is very low in exchangeable bases. Under such circumstances one would naturally expect to find the clay very intensively acid. Yet such is not the case, the pH of a typical laterite usually being less acid than silicate clays would be when at the same low-percentage base saturation. A tentative explanation may be offered. Since laterites are made up mostly of the sesquioxides of iron and aluminum, the colloidal acidoids are no doubt largely hydroxides of these metals. Such hydroxide clays are not only extremely insoluble but their dissociation is so weak, compared with silicate clays, that, even when very definitely dominated by adsorbed hydrogen, the surrounding solution is not so greatly affected. In fact, comparatively small amounts of adsorbed bases may serve to maintain the material at a pH near 7. In contrast the percentage base saturation of silicate clay usually must be in the neighborhood of 80 or 90 in order that the pH closely approach 7.

Another feature of laterite clays when well drained is their structural condition. Curiously enough they do not possess the plasticity and cohesion that characterize the silicate clays of temperate regions. Consequently the upper part of the lateritic regolith is loose and porous, with a peculiar granulation that facilitates the entrance of water. Even on steep slopes and under heavy rainfall laterite clay is not susceptible to the erosion that would be expected in temperate zones. These physical characteristics are of course transmitted to the resulting soil, a feature to be remembered in dealing with tropical agriculture.

145. *Laterite soils*

It is not difficult to forecast some of the characteristics of a zonal and well-developed laterite soil. A red or yellow color, especially in the

[1] The term *laterite* is derived from the Latin *later*, brick. It now is used to refer to natural materials characterized by an excess of sesquioxides and, if well drained, red in color.

B horizons, is a foregone conclusion. However, the surface soil, if uneroded, often is brown or gray. In other cases the red or yellow color dominates the surface soil. This is likely to be the case when the parent material was basaltic. And on cultivated soils especially, enough erosion may have occurred to bring some of the bright red or yellowish subsoil into the furrow-slice.

Another characteristic of outstanding importance is the peculiar granular condition, which enables typical lateritic soils to be culti-vated immediately after a heavy rain without the danger of generating an unsatisfactory physical state. In fact, laterites are utilized for agriculture under a weight of rainfall that would render siliceous soils utterly unworkable.

Typical laterite soils are low in total exchange capacity compared to representative temperate-region soils. This is due in part to their lack of organic matter and in part to the nature of their hydroxide clays. Moreover, they are extremely deficient in exchangeable bases and in available nutrients in general. This means that their fertility level is at a minimum. Hence virgin soils, unless precautions are taken, are soon depleted in fertility when put under cultivation. Such soils usually require liberal fertilization if the culture is at all intensive. One disadvantage of the high content of sesquioxides is in respect to the efficiency of superphosphate, the iron and aluminum tending to render the phosphates of the fertilizer not only insoluble but very un-available to crops. For this reason rock phosphate, which is not so readily affected, can be used to advantage. Typical laterite soils usually are moderately or even strongly acid but not so intensely so as a silicate clay would be at the same percentage base saturation. These soils usually respond to lime as well as to commercial fertilizers.

It has already been suggested that the true laterite soil shows at some horizon in the *B* zone the concentration of iron in reference to which the term *laterite* was first used. Soils of a similar nature, but which possess no water table and hence no such impervious accumulation, are simply *lateritic soils* or red and yellow earths. These in general are much more common than the true laterites.

Since humid-tropical and humid-semitropical climates merge more or less gradually into arid as well as into humid-temperate conditions, laterization varies accordingly. All sorts of profile types may thus be found corresponding to climatic gradations. Indeed it is often difficult to decide whether a given soil is essentially lateritic or podzolic. Thus the red earths and red loams of the Mediterranean regions are considered by some to be progressively transitional and without a doubt this is true for the red and yellow soils of our southern states. It is not to be inferred, however, that all soils in the tropics are essentially lateritic. Alluvial soils of all kinds occur as well as colluvial and fan debris that show very little laterization. Moreover, at the higher elevations, podzolization is often the dominant type of soil genesis.

In Europe, laterites and lateritic soils are found in southern France, Spain, Italy, and Greece. In North America they are typically developed in Central America, Mexico, Puerto Rico, Cuba, and other islands in the Caribbean Sea. In northern South America, India, Burma, Thailand, Java, Borneo, Sumatra, and contiguous regions, laterites are common, while on the islands of the central Pacific red earths are abundant. The lateritic soils of Hawaii have received considerable study. Originally forested, lateritic soils will grow many kinds of tropical and semitropical crops — sugar cane, rubber, coffee, bananas, and pineapples being common products.

146. *Aridic soil regions of the United States*

The first and most important soil region west of the central prairies is that of the *chernozems* (see Fig. 49). The rainfall ranges from 15 to 25 inches annually and the vegetation is short grass. While the precipitation is sufficient to support a vigorous growth of herbaceous plants, it is not heavy enough to leach through the profile. As a result calcium carbonate occurs in the B horizons which, therefore, are mildly alkaline and usually grayish or yellowish-brown with white spots or blotches of calcium carbonate. The combined processes of carbonate concentration, in which the influence of the grass is no mean factor, is spoken of as *calcification*. Under the lime accumulation gypsum is often found.

The A horizon of a typical northern chernozem is black [1] due to the accumulation and decay of organic matter under scanty rainfall and hot dry summers.[2] This horizon is surprisingly deep, often 12 to 15

[1] *Chernozem* means black earth.

[2] The chernozem soils, especially those under a cool climate, receive sufficient rainfall during the spring and fall to encourage abundant grass. The summer drought checks rapid decay and thus the organic matter tends to accumulate in large amounts. Such a climatic control, in the presence of abundant lime, seems to promote a type of decay that results in the production of a very black humus. The same explanation may be made for the northern prarie soils of the United States.

inches. In reaction it usually is neutral or even somewhat acid. Its
granular structure is one of its outstanding physical characteristics.
The depth to which the organic matter has penetrated possibly is related to the high-percentage base saturation, since humus dominated
by calcium is considered to be more mobile than that carrying large
amounts of adsorbed hydrogen. The amount of extremely black pigment present may also be related to the percentage base saturation.[1]

A typical chernozem surface soil is surprisingly high in mineral

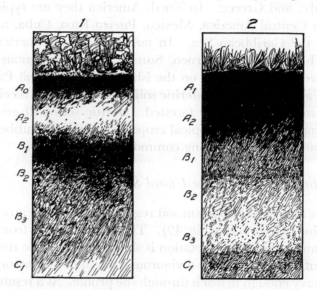

Fig. 50. Sketch contrasting the general characteristics of a well-developed humus
podzol (the precipitated humus, B_1, is especially thick) with those of a typical chernozem. Note the difference in respect to the localization of the organic matter.
A_1 is absent in the podzol and A_0 in the chernozem.

nutrients as well as in nitrogen and sulfur. A chemical analysis has already been cited (see page 269) which fully supports these statements.
On the basis of nutrient the chernozems are the most fertile soils of
large area in the United States but because of low uncertain rainfall
they do not consistently produce so much as the corresponding prairie
types. The southern chernozems are usually lower in organic matter,
lighter in color, and have reddish or yellowish subsoils (see Fig. 50 for
contrast with typical podzol).

The *chestnut* and *brown* aridic soil groups lie, in the order named,

[1] See page 130 for a brief discussion of organic pigmentation.

between the chernozem belt and the Rocky Mountains. They are the principal soils of the Great Plains (see Fig. 49). With a rainfall of only 10 to 15 inches annually, the vegetation is mostly of a steppe type. Due to the scanty precipitation, such soils are much lower in organic matter than are the chernozems and the layer of carbonates is nearer the surface, sometimes even in the *A* horizon. Thus the surface layers are often alkaline. Gypsum also is likely to be present in the subsoil. These soils, as well as the chernozems, are used for cereal production but the agriculture is hazardous because of the low and variable rainfall. The plowing of such soils has increased wind erosion and has magnified the dust storms that in recent years have menaced the agriculture of the Middle West. The dust bowls of Texas, Oklahoma, Colorado, and Kansas, and of the Dakotas and Nebraska lie in these soil regions (see Fig. 33). Much of this extensive area should be in range and again under the protection of native vegetation.

In the intermountain region west of the Rockies are found two zonal groups of some importance — the *gray desert* (Sierozems) in the central part and the *reddish desert* in the south (see Fig. 49). Associated with them and of equal or even greater area are shallow azonal soils hardly more than thin layers of rock fragments mostly on steep slopes. It is hardly necessary to say that all of these soils are largely non-agricultural. Only where irrigation is possible can they be cropped. They are mostly used, when used at all, for grazing. Near them, in the highlands of southern California and central Arizona lie the *noncalcic brown soils*, originally covered with forest and brush. Since they are subhumid, podzolization, though weak, is such as to prevent the accumulation of lime in the profile and to render the surface soil somewhat acid. They are classified with the aridics because of their contiguity. When irrigated these soils in favored localities are fairly productive.

Associated with all of these zonal aridics are surprisingly large areas of *azonal* soils such as the shallow coverings of mountain slopes, already mentioned, and the dry sands of central Nebraska. They are agriculturally nonimportant. Of the *intrazonal* soils little will be said at this time, other than indicate their nature in a general way. When the drainage of aridic soils is impeded and upward capillary movement of water, whether from natural sources or overirrigation, is encouraged by rapid evaporation, soluble salt concentrations may occur at or near the surface. The problem of alkali thus becomes acute. This has already been mentioned under water control in relation to irrigation (page 229) and will be considered in more detail later (page 311). The two intrazonal groups that fall under this head are referred to broadly as *saline* (solonchak) and *alkali* (solonetz).

147. *The subdivision of a soil group — soil series*

The first concept in soil classification is a comprehensive one — the decision as to whether a soil is *zonal*, *intrazonal*, or *azonal* and to what *soil group* it belongs. This already has been discussed, but in passing it is well to emphasize again that a *soil group* is a very broad subdivision based on the recognized tendency of soils within a large area to assume a general similarity as to profile because of the dominating influence of climate and vegetation. And, as may be expected, there are many varieties of soils within each great group. The reasons are not difficult to discover.

In the United States, as elsewhere, many of the soils are young and the original geological characteristics of the soil materials are much in evidence. Again topography is variable and with the accompanying dissimilarities in depth, drainage, aeration, organic accumulation, and the like, a heterogeneity of profile is induced. Thus even if climate were uniform, which of course is not to be expected due to local influences, a great miscellany of soils would still occur within any particular region. Indeed the layman is likely to be impressed by the unlikenesses within a soil group rather than by the similarities that make it possible to establish such a broad division.

Obviously the next step is a subdivision within each *soil group*. This is necessary if any detailed study is contemplated or any agricultural evaluation is to be made. This separation is accomplished by subdividing the great soil groups into lesser groups called *series*. These units are quite distinct. And the soils of any one series are alike, although not absolutely identical, in profile, except for the texture of the surface layer. In more precise terms "a series is a group of soils developed from the same kind of parent material, by the same genetic combination of processes and whose horizons are quite similar in their arrangement and general characteristics. Except for the texture of the *A* horizon, and this is a very important reservation, these characteristics are more or less identical, some range being permissible both internally and externally." Slope and stoniness are examples of external variations.

In field work a more or less standard profile is set up for each series and all soils that approach it closely enough are made a part of this particular subdivision. Ideally, the only differences of agricultural importance that should exist between the various soils of any given series are in the textures of the surface layer and even here the range should not be great.

Series are of course established on the basis of profile characteristics. This requires a careful study of the various horizons as to number, order, thickness, texture, structure, color, organic content, and reaction (acid, neutral, or alkaline). Such features as hardpan at a certain distance below the surface, a distinct zone of calcium carbonate accumulation at a uniform depth, or striking color characteristics greatly aid in series identification.

In the United States each series is given a name, usually from some city, village, river, or county, such as Fargo, Muscatine, Cecil, Mohave, Ontario, and the like. Series names should be common, simple and easy to spell.

It is well to state at this point that similar series are grouped together to give soil *families*.[1] Thus the classification so far runs as follows: (1) the *order*, that is, whether zonal, intrazonal, or azonal; (2) the *suborder*, as podzolic, lateritic, etc.; (3) the *group*, such as gray-brown podzolic or chernozem; (4) the *family*, and finally (5) the *series* just considered.

148. *The soil type*

"The subdivision of the series on the basis of the texture of the *A* horizon gives the soil unit." According to the soil-survey classification used in the United States such a unit is called a *type*. It is well to emphasize, however, that differences in texture between the various types of any given series cannot be great. For instance, a soil with a sandy surface layer could hardly have the same profile otherwise that a soil with clayey *A* horizon would possess. A series should consist, therefore, of a key or dominate type or types with several minor soils varying somewhat as to the texture of the surface horizons.

[1] The *family* grouping is not as yet well worked out and is of interest only to the specialist.

A type, however, is not quite the ultimate subdivision of a series since *phases* are often mapped within types. A *phase* is a subdivision on the basis of some important deviation such as erosion, slope, stoniness, or soluble salt content. It really marks a departure from the normal, or key type, already well established.

All areas of the same soil type, whether normal or phase, in the same general locality are alike (within limits) as to profile characteristics, including the texture of the surface horizon, and were originally similar in fertility. Methods of farming have, of course, developed differences in immediate productivity. This sometimes leads to confusion in comparing soils of different farms.

Areas of the same soil type at some distance from each other usually show certain minor variations. For example, Ontario loam soils 50 or 60 miles apart exhibit certain well-recognized deviations that must be considered in making fertility recommendations. Again variations are to be expected as one soil type grades into another. Thus the heterogeneity of the soil type as to minor characteristics must constantly be kept in mind. A soil type, while conveniently considered as the unit, is still susceptible to subdivision, even beyond a phase, if the necessity should rise. This will depend upon the detail desired in the survey.

Any particular soil of a series is designated for simplicity by the textural name of its surface layer, such as sandy loam, gravelly loam, clay loam, and so on. To this is prefixed the series name. Mohave sandy loam and Carrington silt loam are examples. The type name, therefore, consists of two parts, the first designating the series, and the second indicating the particular individual within the series. This designation is especially valuable as it implies very specifically a great number of characteristics which otherwise would require detailed explanation. It also lends itself to mapping and description.

149. *Soil survey and its utilization*

The classification just outlined is susceptible to enough detail and precision to make it valuable in soil survey. In fact, it was developed for just such a purpose. The function of a soil survey is to classify, locate on a base map, and describe the nature of soils as they occur in the field. The soils, if the system utilized in the United States is fol-

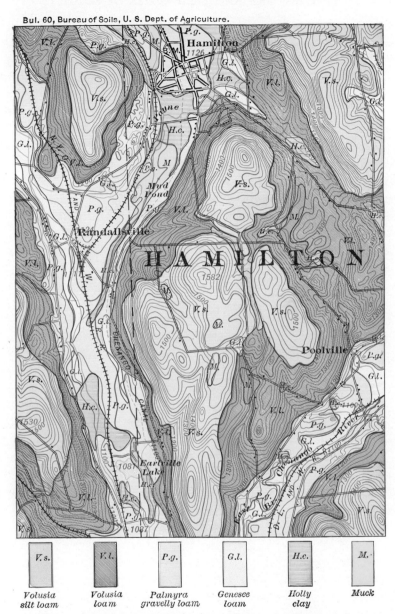

V. s.	V. l.	P. g.	G. l.	H. c.	M.
Volusia silt loam	Volusia loam	Palmyra gravelly loam	Genesee loam	Holly clay	Muck

Fig. 51. Part of the Madison County, New York, soil map showing the topography and drainage and the relation of the various soil types to one another. The Volusia series has been formed from ground moraine, the Palmyra from glacial outwash, while the Genesee and Holly are alluvial. Note the varying elevations of the peat deposits.

lowed, are classified into *series* and *types* on the basis of their profile characteristics. The field man, since his work is localized, concerns himself mostly with series and type separations, giving the broader regional distinctions only general consideration.

As the series and type identification progresses in the survey of any area, the location of each individual soil is shown on a suitable base map using colored pencils. The map often used in the United States is the government topographic map, carrying contours and other information. Aerial base maps are also quite common. In some respects they have considerable advantage over the ordinary contour maps in that land cover and field boundaries show very clearly. The details of topography, however, are not so apparent. If no map of any kind is available, plane-table surveys are made as the field work progresses. This procedure is often necessary when single farms are to be surveyed in some detail.

The field map, after the separations have been carefully checked and correlated, is now ready for reproduction in color. When published it accompanies a bulletin containing a discussion of the topography, climate, agriculture, and soils of the area under consideration. Each soil type is minutely described as to profile and suggestions as to practical management are usually made.

Erosion surveys, which are simply an extension of the usual soil survey, are now common. In addition to soil type, the land use, the slope, and degree of erosion are shown. Colors and suitable symbols are employed to indicate on one map the various factors. Since such a survey is often carried out with the farm as the unit area, the scale of the base map in such cases is likely to be greater than the usual 1-inch-to-the-mile basis. On the other hand when the agricultural value of the land is low a more general survey, called a *reconnaissance* is made. Here much of the usual detail is omitted.

Soil-survey bulletins and maps perhaps attain their greatest usefulness as a basis for other scientific work. Profile studies, whether physical, chemical, or biological, must be preceded by some sort of a survey or classification. Crop research of all kinds is facilitated if a soil survey has previously been made, and correlations and comparisons become possible that otherwise could not be ventured. Land evaluation and appraisal, statistical studies, and sociological investigations are other interests served. Perhaps the soil survey in a technical way is of greatest value in land classification and erosion control. These two phases probably justify the time and money spent in the United States on this work.

In a more practical way the extension specialist and the county agricultural agent find the survey maps and bulletins a guide in making suggestions and recommendations. They afford information that it would be impossible to obtain elsewhere and for a broad, over-all concept of an area nothing better can be consulted. In some cases simpler and more practical bulletins follow the rather technical ones. Opportunity is thus given for the effective presentation of information and up-to-date recommendations that cannot be included in the soil-survey bulletin itself.

While soil classification and survey are too complicated and in some respects too controversial to be expanded further, enough has been said to establish their importance. Without them much work of value would be impossible and thus many activities, now recognized as essential, would be greatly hampered. Soil survey is now so common that its terms and technicalities are recognized as part of the usual fund of agricultural knowledge.

Chapter XIII. The Soil Reaction.
Soil Acidity and Alkalinity

One of the outstanding physiological characteristics of the soil solution is its reaction.[1] And since microorganisms and higher plants respond so markedly to their chemical environment, the importance of soil reaction has long been recognized. Three conditions are, of course, possible: *alkalinity, neutrality,* and *acidity.*

Alkalinity occurs when there is such an accumulation of salts, especially those of calcium, magnesium, and sodium, as to give a preponderance of OH ions over H ions in the soil solution.[2] When the concentration of soluble salts becomes marked, especially at or near the surface, it is spoken of as *alkali.* Under such conditions the soil is usually alkaline and sometimes, especially if sodium carbonate is present, very strongly so. Alkaline soils and alkali are, of course, characteristic of arid and semiarid regions.

Soil acidity, on the other hand, is common in all regions where precipitation is of such magnitude as to leach appreciable amounts of calcium and magnesium from the surface layers of soils. So widespread is its occurrence and so marked is its influence on plants that it has become one of the most discussed phases of the soil. Its importance in a practical way greatly surpasses that of soil alkalinity.

---

[1] The literature dealing with soil reaction, especially that respecting soil acidity, is varied and copious and no specific citations of a general nature can be given. Recent files of such periodicals as the *Journal of the American Society of Agronomy, Journal of Agricultural Research, Journal of Agricultural Science,* and *Soil Science* contain many of the important articles published in English. Certain experiment station bulletins may be consulted with profit.

[2] When salts with strong cations and weak acid radicals, such as Na_2CO_3, K_2CO_3, $Ca(HCO_3)_2$, go into solution they undergo hydrolysis and develop alkalinity. For Na_2CO_3 the reaction is as follows:

$$Na_2CO_3 + 2\ HOH \rightleftharpoons 2\ NaOH + H_2CO_3$$

Since the dissociation of the NaOH is greater than that of the weak H_2CO_3, a domination of OH ions results.

150. *The colloidal control of soil reaction*

A feature of fundamental importance must be examined before any satisfactory consideration may be initiated respecting soil acidity or, for that matter, soil reaction in general. The control mechanism of soil pH is referred to. As is well known, this control lies in the soil colloidal complex, which, according to its nature and condition, exerts a dominating equilibrium restraint and regulation upon the reaction of the soil solution. How is this accomplished?

It has already been explained (page 77) that the colloidal complex of the soil, in spite of its heterogeneous organomineral nature, is in reality a mixture of insoluble acids and salts of these acids. And in spite of the comparative insolubility of the acidoid radicals, some dissociation takes place. For convenience the situation is presented as below, the acids and salts being written separately and calcium, because of its prominence, representing all of the important metallic cations:

$$H(acidoid) \rightleftharpoons acidoid^- + H^+ \quad acidity(\mathbf{H^+}OH^-)$$

$$Ca(acidoid) + 2\,HOH \rightleftharpoons H_2(acidoid) + Ca(OH)_2$$
$$alkalinity(H^+\mathbf{OH^-})$$

The slight dissociation of the hydrogen colloid if present alone tends to maintain an H-ion domination in the dispersive solution and a pH below 7 results. The salts on the other hand, because their weak acid radicals are dominated by such strong metallic cations, tend to give a definite alkaline reaction.

Under natural conditions, where the colloidal acids and their salts exist as a heterogeneous complex, the reaction of the soil solution obviously will depend to a considerable extent upon their relative proportions. That is, a dominance of the acid-producing fractions will give a pH below 7. Reversing this relation will result in alkalinity, while at just the right balance the soil solution will show a pH test of 7. Thus a situation, very complicated as to detail, is susceptible in a broad way to a rather simple explanation.

Since the relative proportions of the adsorbed hydrogen and the exchangeable bases of a colloidal complex ordinarily are expressed in terms of *percentage base saturation*, this terminology is conveniently used in respect to the control exerted by colloidal matter on soil pH.   Obviously a low-percentage base saturation means acidity while a percentage base saturation approaching 100 will result in neutrality or alkalinity.   In general, humid-region soils dominated by silicate clays and whose percentage base saturation is much below 80 or 90, are acid, the acidity increasing progressively as the percentage base saturation goes down.   Soils with percentage base saturations of 80 or 90 or above usually are neutral or alkaline.   Appreciable amounts of calcium carbonate usually will give a soil pH of 8 or perhaps a fraction more.   The presence of sodium carbonate, as is often the case with certain alkali soils, may raise the pH to 10 or above.

The situation respecting laterites is much the same as for soils whose clays are of the silicate type except that the percentage base saturation must fall much lower before acidity results.   As already explained (page 277) these soils where typically developed are drastically leached and as a consequence are low in exchangeable bases.   Yet ordinarily they do not show the high acidity that often characterizes temperate-region soils.   The explanation lies in the nature of the acidoid radicals which are in large degree made up of hydrous oxides of iron and alumina.   The dissociation of these clays when dominated by H ions is much less than that of silicate clays at a correspondingly low-percentage base saturation.   As a result they do not maintain as high an H-ion concentration in the dispersing solution.   Thus a silicate clay with a percentage base saturation of 60 might show a pH of 4.5 or 5, while that of a hydroxide clay similarily devoid of bases might be near 7.   This is a characteristic of lateritic clays that has already been emphasized.

Important as percentage base saturation is in respect to soil pH, there are at least two other factors that exert an important influence. One, the nature of the acidoid, has already been stressed and well illustrated in the reference to hydroxide clays above.   In addition it is well to note that the different acid silicate clays — the kaolin, montmorillonite, and hydrous mica groups — apparently dissociate in somewhat different degrees.   Besides, there are the organic acidoids, which exhibit considerable variety and which apparently are able to maintain lower pH values than the silicate clays at corresponding percentage base saturations.

The second additional factor has to do with the particular bases present in the colloidal complex and especially their ratio relations.

For instance, at a percentage base saturation say of 70, the presence of Ca, Mg, K, and Na ions in the ratio of 10–3–1–1 would certainly result in a lower pH than though the ratio was 5–2–1–7. In the one case calcium is dominant, in the other we are dealing with a sodium-calcium complex.

With the reaction of the soil solution influenced by three distinct and uncoordinated factors — percentage base saturation, nature of the acidoid, and the ratio of the exchangeable bases — one would hardly expect to find a close correlation between percentage base saturation and pH when comparing different soils at random. Yet with soils of similar origin, texture, and organic content a rough correlation does exist. Nevertheless, it should not be counted on with any degree of certainty. Two soils with the same pH seldom possess the same percentage base saturation and vice versa.

151. *Major changes in soil pH*

The most important and most persistent cause of change in the reaction of the solutions of soils in general is carbon dioxide. This gas, developed in most cases so copiously, tends to form carbonic acid and the greater the pressure of CO_2, the higher will be the H-ion concentration resulting. The role of carbonic acid in respect to base exchange has already been duly stressed (page 79) yet the generalized reaction will be repeated in order to lend emphasis and clarity to this vital phenomenon.

$$x\ CarH(acidoid) + y\ H_2CO_3 \rightleftharpoons x\ CarH(acidoid) + y \begin{cases} Ca(HCO_3)_2 \\ r\ carbonates \\ and\ bi- \\ carbonates \end{cases}$$

If the soluble bicarbonates and carbonates are removed, as will be the case in regions receiving sufficient rainfall to cause leaching, the reaction will move towards the right. The colloidal complexes of humid-region soils are, therefore, steadily losing their adsorbed metallic cations, their percentage base saturation is becoming lower, and as a result the H-ion concentration of their solutions is increasing. In other words, a persistent and unremitting inclination towards acidity and its intensification exists in humid-region soils. This in itself is sufficient grounds for considering ionic exchange one of the most important of all soil phenomena. In spite of such a tendency, however, soil solutions may be neutral or even intensely alkaline, since the chemical nature of the colloidal complexes and the soluble salts with which the soil water is in contact determine, at any specific instance, what shall be the reaction of the solution.

Any artificial treatment or manipulation of the soil that increases the loss of calcium and magnesium will, in the course of time, encourage a major change in soil pH. Merely leaving the soil bare allows these cations to be lost more rapidly. In fact, most of the ordinary physical methods of soil management intensify rather than counteract soil acidity. The cultivation of the soil is a case in point.

Certain fertilizers should also be mentioned in this respect. Sulfate of ammonia, for example, by leaving a residue of sulfuric acid and by replacing and encouraging the loss of lime in drainage, hastens the development of acidity. Flowers of sulfur rapidly develop sulfuric acid by oxidation. Nitrate of soda, calcium nitrate, calcium cyanamid, and basic slag, on the other hand, tend to check the swing towards a more acid condition. The addition of lime, if in adequate amount, increases the pH of a soil for reasons that are easy to explain.

152. *Minor fluctuations in soil pH*

Not only do soil solutions suffer major and often drastic changes in H-ion concentration but they exhibit minor fluctuations as well.[1] For instance, the drying of soils, especially above field temperatures, will often cause a noticeable increase in acidity. This is probably due to some change in the organization of the colloidal matter and should be kept in mind in preparing soil samples for pH determination.

Again as summer advances, the pH of a soil may decrease, especially if under cultivation. This may be due to microorganisms possibly through a reduction, directly or indirectly, of the active lime or by the production of acids. The decomposition of humus by changing the nature of the colloidal complex might also be a factor. In winter and

[1] Swanback, T. R., and M. F. Morgan, *Seasonal Fluctuations in Soil Reaction*, Conn. Agr. Exp. Sta. Bul. 311:264–268, 1930.

Smith, A. M., and I. M. Robertson, "The Influence of the Plant upon the Seasonal Changes in Soil Acidity," *Jour. Agr. Sci.* XXI:822–831, 1931.

Hester, J. B., and F. A. Shelton, "Seasonal Variation in pH of Field Soils a Factor in Making Lime Recommendations," *Jour. Amer. Soc. Agron.*, XXV:299–300, 1933.

Stephenson, R. E., "The Nitrification Process and Plant Nutrition," *Soil Sci.*, XLI:188, 1936.

Huberty, M. R., and A. R. C. Haas, "The pH of Soil as Affected by Soil Moisture and Other Factors," *Soil Sci.*, XLIX:455–478, 1940.

spring an opposite tendency sometimes is noted, possibly because there has been some opportunity for the colloidal matter to recoup its reduction in percentage base saturation.

153. *H-ion heterogeneity of the soil solution*

In defining soil acidity as the H-ion concentration of the soil solution it is not to be inferred that one is dealing with an ordinary homogeneous solution. It has been definitely emphasized previously that the solute concentration of a normal soil solution, due to adsorption, is heterogeneous (see page 32). Therefore one is prepared to visualize the H ions as being concentrated near the colloidal interfaces and as becoming less numerous as the outer portions of the films are approached. This means a corresponding increase in OH ions. The attractive forces of the colloidal surfaces are such as to make the differences in H-ion concentration between the inner and outer layers of the capillary water very great indeed. As a result, the drainage water even from a markedly acid soil may be near neutrality due in part to this heterogeneity and the paucity of H ions so far away from the colloidal interfaces.

That this situation is important in many respects cannot be denied. Without a doubt it sets the stage for many different chemical reactions and transfers of variable intensity. Moreover, it affords microorganisms and plant roots a great variety of solution environments. This is especially true in respect to bacteria, actinomyces, and fungi. Organisms that are unfavorably influenced by the physiological conditions of a given H-ion concentration may find, at an infinitesimal distance away, another that is more satisfactory. This may account in part for the many different floral species present in normal soils. The heterogeneity of the soil solution will come to the fore again when the interpretation of a pH determination is under discussion (page 308). As can readily be forecast an analytical figure determined on a heterogeneous solution is likely to be much less significant than one from a solution of uniform concentration.

154. *Exchangeable acidity versus actual acidity*

In an acid soil two more or less distinct sets of hydrogen ions are involved — those of the soil solution itself and those held as adsorbed cations by the colloidal complex. These groups tend towards an equilibrium, are mutually supporting, and must both be considered in any attempt to alter the H-OH ion ratio of the soil solution.

For convenience of distinction the H-ion concentration of the soil solution is designated as *active* or *actual acidity*, while the H ions held in abeyance, or in reserve, so to speak, are referred to as the *exchangeable* or *potential acidity* of the soil. Since the adsorbed hydrogen through equilibrium adjustments becomes active when the acidity of the soil solution is reduced, the term *potential* is particularly significant. Distinct as the two groups apparently are, they no doubt grade into each other since the intensity of attraction at the colloidal interface varies more or less progressively with distance.

The presence of exchangeable or reserve acidity is easily demonstrated. If a sample of acid soil is shaken thoroughly with distilled water, say in a 1 to 3 ratio, and filtered, the percolate if free of colloidal matter will usually show comparatively slight acidity, hardly more than that due to the carbonic acid of the solution in equilibrium with the carbon dioxide of the atmosphere. On the other hand, if a concentrated solution of a neutral salt, such as potassium nitrate, is used instead of distilled water, the filtrate will be intensely acid. The lowering of the pH is due to the liberation of the reserve acidity by ionic exchange. Apparently the K ions are able to replace part of the exchangeable H ions of the colloidal complex and a strong acid, in this case nitric, results, thus demonstrating the existence of reserve acidity.

The relative magnitude of the two types of acidity is not only interesting but, as will appear later, of considerable practical importance as well. In referring to the acidity of a soil as high or very high, the impression may be given that the actual acidity under certain conditions may be exceedingly great, even dangerously so. Actually, however, the reverse is true. For example, $\frac{1}{50}$ pound of calcium carbonate, could it be brought adequately in contact with the soil solution and if the soil colloidal matter did not interfere, would be sufficient to neutralize the active acidity in an acre-furrow-slice of a mineral soil having a pH of 6 and containing 20 per cent of water functioning as a solution. If the same soil should possess a pH of 5, $\frac{1}{5}$ pound of calcium carbonate would be adequate, while if the pH should be lowered to 4, 2 pounds would be ample. Thus the active acidity is evidently ridiculously small even at its maximum.

Since limestone at the rate of 1, 2, or even 3 tons to the acre is often recommended, this neutralizing agent is obviously applied in amounts many times in excess of the active acidity. The reason for such heavy applications is due in large part to the magnitude of the exchangeable acidity. Conservative calculations indicate that the reserve acidity may range from perhaps 1000 times greater than the actual in the case of a sandy soil to possibly 50,000 or even 100,000 times more for a clayey soil high in organic matter. The practical significance of this tremendous difference in magnitude of the active and reserve acidities of soils will be apparent in the next section.

155. *The buffering of soils*

In effecting a definite change of pH in a soil it is usually necessary to have much more acid or alkali than the amounts of H and OH ions in the soil solution would lead one to expect. In other words, there is a distinct resistance to a change in pH other than that offered by the soil solution itself. This is called *buffering* and is due to the influence of weak acids and their salts. While such weak acid radicals as the carbonate, bicarbonate, and phosphates are present and active in soils, the important ones from the standpoint of this phenomenon are those of the colloidal complex. In short, the average soil is colloidally buffered.

Before dealing with the mechanics of soil buffering it might be well to consider a simple case. A solution buffered with acetic acid and sodium acetate will be examined. Once certain basic principles are clearly in mind, soil buffering is easily explained.

When a weak acid, such as acetic for instance, is added in any great amount to water, complete dissociation does not occur. Much of the hydrogen is held back in molecular combination. The equilibrium relation is as follows:

$$CH_3COOH \rightleftharpoons CH_3COO^- + H^+$$

If an attempt is now made to neutralize such a solution by adding just enough alkali theoretically to take care of the dissociated or active acidity, a corresponding amount of the reserve hydrogen of the undissociated acid will immediately appear in the solution and little change in the pH will take place. The solution is thus buffered against an alkali to such an extent that considerable amounts must be added to effectively raise the pH.

When some sodium acetate is added to the acetic acid solution above, it will be buffered against an acid also. Since the salt of this weak acid is quite soluble and dissociates markedly, the equalization now set up will be:

$$CH_3COOH \rightleftharpoons CH_3COO^- + H^+$$
$$CH_3COONa \rightleftharpoons CH_3COO^- + Na^+$$

If a strong acid, such as HCl, in amounts sufficient to change an unbuffered solution, say 1 pH, is added to the comparable buffered solution above, little change in pH will occur. The acid added, in this case HCl, will produce NaCl, a neutral salt, and CH_3COOH. Since the solution is already maintaining its maximum dissociation of acetic acid, these newly associated H ions will be forced back into an inactive molecular condition.

With the fundamental ideas of buffering definitely in mind let us now consider the soil, that is buffered, not so much by simple acids and their salts, but in large degree by a heterogeneous mixture of mineral and organic colloids. If we represent this colloidal complex as being made up of two parts, the acid and salt respectively (page 77), and indicate the probable dissociation, we have a setup identical in general with the acetic acid-sodium acetate buffer already discussed: —

$$H(acidoid) \rightleftharpoons (acidoid)^- + H^+$$
$$Ca(acidoid) \rightleftharpoons (acidoid)^- + Ca^{++}$$

Since the colloidal complex is a mixture of weak acids and their salts and since it apparently functions as a buffer in exactly the same way as does the acetic acid-sodium acetate solution, there is no reason for carrying the explanation further. The mechanism of soil buffering should be clear at least in principle. It might be well to reemphasize, however, that the basis of buffer capacity lies in the reserve hydrogen of the complex and the capacity of this exchangeable hydrogen and its associated metallic cations to react to the impact of additions such as lime and to the unremitting attacks of acids such as carbonic.

156. *Buffer capacity*

Before reviewing the practical importance of soil buffering it might be well to consider the magnitude of this phenomenon, a phase of utmost significance. The first suggestion thereto is as obvious as it is simple. The higher the exchange capacity of a soil the greater, other factors being equal, will be its buffer capacity. This is fully recognized in practice in that the heavier the texture of a soil and the higher its organic content, the larger must be the application of lime to effect a given change in pH.

However, there is a less understood but equally important phase of buffering. Is the buffer capacity of soils the same throughout the

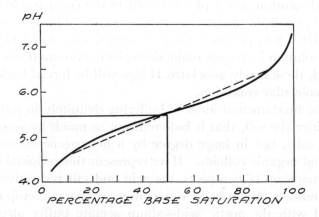

FIG. 52. Theoretical titration curve for a large number of Florida soils. (After Peech.) The dotted line indicates the zone of greatest buffering. The maximum buffering should occur at approximately 50 per cent base saturation.

ordinary pH range? In other words, does it vary with a change in the percentage base saturation? This is best answered by reference to an average theoretical titration curve presented by Peech [1] for a large number of Florida soils (Fig. 52).

Three things are clearly obvious from the curve. First, there is a definite correlation between the percentage base saturation of these soils and their pH. This has already been fully emphasized (page 290) and therefore is not unexpected.

Second, the generalized curve indicates that the degree of buffering varies, being lowest at the extreme pH values. Between, where the curve is flatter, the buffering reaches a maximum. Theoretically, the greatest buffering occurs at about 50 per cent base saturation. This situation is extremely important both technically and practically.

[1] Peech, Michael, "Availability of Ions in Light Sandy Soils As Affected by Soil Reaction," *Soil Sci.*, LI: 473–486, 1941.

Third, the buffering, as indicated by the curve, is more or less uniform over a pH range of say 4.5 to 6.5. This is vitally significant as it indicates, for example, that under field conditions about the same amount of lime will be required to change the soil pH from 5.0 to 5.5 as from 5.5 to 6.0.

Before leaving this phase it is well to remark that the curve of Fig. 52 is generalized and represents the situation in respect to any particular soil only by inference. That the curves for individual soils will deviate more or less widely is to be expected since the colloidal complex of different soils may vary not only with the kinds of clay and humus present but also with their proportionate amounts. As an instance of the difference between the clay groups, Mehlich's [1] results are most significant. He found the pH values of montmorillonite and the hydrous micas to lie between 4.5 and 5.0 when the clays were at 50 per cent base saturation. The pH values of kaolinite and halloysite under comparable conditions were in the neighborhood of 6.

157. *Importance of buffering*

Although the significance of buffering is far-reaching, its importance may be dealt with adequately under two general heads: (1) the stabilization of soil pH and (2) the amounts of amendments necessary to effect a given alteration in soil reaction.

A marked change in pH undoubtedly causes a radical modification in soil environment. And if this environment should fluctuate too widely, as might be the case with an unbuffered medium, higher plants and microorganisms might suffer seriously before they could make adequate adjustments. Not only would they be affected directly by the change in H-ion concentration but also the indirect influences might be most unsatisfactory. Sudden changes in the availability of nutrients, thereby creating deficiencies or oversupplies, could seriously upset the nutritional balance of the soil solution. Such changes, when made, should be gradual or accomplished at a time of year when the biological upset is likely to be least serious. In properly managed cultivated soils and most certainly in virgin lands, buffering, by stabilizing soil pH, seems to be an effective guard against the difficulties described above.

[1] Mehlich, Adolf, "Base Unsaturation and pH in Relation to Soil Type," *Proc. Soil Sci. Soc. Amer.*, VI:150–156, 1941.

The second important feature of buffering is really a corollary of the first since it also relates to the effectiveness of pH stabilization. Obviously the greater the buffering the larger must be the amounts of lime or sulfur, the two most common soil amendments used to effect a given change in pH. Although pH gives some idea as to the degree of base saturation it reveals nothing as to buffer capacity. Hence in deciding as to the amount of lime to apply, for example, soil texture and organic content are the only practicable guides and should not be overlooked (see page 366). Good judgment and experience count for much.

158. *Soil-reaction correlations*

Although the reaction of the soil solution is only one of a number of physiological factors and is more a resultant rather than a cause, certain correlations have been established that are of considerable practical as well as scientific interest. The interrelations between pH values and (1) exchangeability of calcium and magnesium, (2) the solubility of iron, manganese, aluminum, and other elements, (3) the availability of phosphorus, and (4) the activity of soil microorganisms are the phases that receive the most attention.[1]

Exchangeable calcium and magnesium. It has already been shown that as the exchangeable calcium and magnesium are lost by leaching, the acidity of the soil gradually increases. Evidently in any one soil there is a definite correlation between the pH and the activity of these constituents. This is to be expected since the major control of soil pH is percentage base saturation and the latter in turn is determined by the amounts of exchangeable calcium and magnesium present. This correlation is of definite practical significance since it enables a person by means of a pH determination to estimate roughly the percentage base saturation of a soil and hence the activity of the calcium and magnesium. From this it can be decided whether or not a soil for a given crop, or sequence of crops, is deficient in lime (page 362). pH, however, does not, in itself, give much indication as to how much lime to apply. Buffering, as well as a number of other factors, are of major consideration in such a decision (page 366).

---

[1] A graphic representation of these relationships accompanied by a brief discussion has been published by Pettinger. Pettinger, N. A., *A Useful Chart for Teaching the Relation of Soil Reaction to the Availability of Plant Nutrients to Crops*, Bulletin 136, Va. Polytec. Inst., 1935.

Iron, aluminum, and *manganese.* The relationships between soil reaction and the activity of iron, manganese, and aluminum seems to be somewhat more definite than the correlation with calcium and magnesium. When the pH of a mineral soil is low, appreciable amounts of these three constituents are active, so much so in fact that the aluminum may become extremely toxic to certain plants.[1] However, as the pH is increased, precipitation takes place and the amounts of these elements in solution become less and less until at neutrality or somewhat above certain plants may suffer from a lack of available manganese and iron. This is especially likely to be the case if a markedly acid soil is suddenly brought to a neutral or alkaline condition by an overapplication of lime.

While deficiencies of manganese, and especially iron, are not widespread, they do occur on certain soils, particularly if they are sandy and have been heavily limed. But if the reaction of such a soil is judiciously held within a soil pH range say of 5.6 to 7.0, the toxicity of the aluminum may be suppressed, and plant chlorosis due to the unavailability of manganese or iron avoided unless these elements are decidedly lacking in the soil. It should also be noted that overliming and the reduction in H-ion concentration will sometimes develop copper, zinc, and boron (page 361) deficiency symptoms in certain crops. Here is another pH correlation that should not be overlooked.

Available phosphorus. The nature of the phosphate ions seems to vary with the pH of the solution. When the soil is distinctly alkaline, the PO_4 ion apparently is the commonest form. This ion is acquired rather slowly by plants from most soils. But as the pH is lowered and the soil becomes slightly to moderately acid, the HPO_4 ion and the H_2PO_4 ion prevail. At higher acidities H_2PO_4 ions tend to dominate.[2] These two forms are thought by some workers to be absorbed more easily by higher plants and probably by microorganisms also. Thus by the regulation of the pH of a soil, the facility with which phosphorus is absorbed by plants possibly thus is subject to some control, providing of course a sufficient amount of this constituent is soluble.

[1] Hartwell, B. L., and F. R. Pember, "The Presence of Aluminum as a Reason for the Difference in the Effect of So-Called Acid Soil on Barley and Rye," *Soil Sci.* VI:259–277, 1918.

McLean, F. T., and B. E. Gilbert, "Aluminum Toxicity," *Plant Physiol.,* III:293–303, 1928.

[2] McGeorge, W. T., "The Relation of Potential Alkalinity to the Availability of Phosphate in Calcareous Soils," *Soil Sci.,* XXXIX:443–452, 1935.

The activity of the soil phosphorus is related to pH in another way, in this case indirectly. It has already been explained that as the acidity increases there is an enhancement in the activity of the iron and aluminum. Under such conditions soluble phosphates are markedly fixed, perhaps as very complex and insoluble iron and aluminum compounds of some kind. Thus, while an increase in soil acidity promotes the presence of phosphate ions that are readily absorbed by plants, too great a lowering of the pH prevents their availability. It is uneconomical, therefore, to add superphosphate to an overly acid mineral soil.

On the other hand, if the pH of a mineral soil is raised much above 7, say 7.5 or 8.0, not only is the presence in the solution of the PO_4 ion encouraged but also the phosphate nutrition of higher plants, and perhaps of microorganisms as well, is disturbed in another manner. This may be accounted for in several ways.

In the first place at a pH above 7, if abundant lime is present, complex calcium phosphates are formed. These range, in increasing insolubility, from the oxyapatite $[3 \ Ca_3(PO_4)_2 \cdot CaO]$ through the hydroxyapatite $[3 \ Ca_3(PO_4)_2 \cdot Ca(OH)_2]$ to the carbonate-apatite $[3 \ Ca_3(PO_4)_2 \cdot CaCO_3(xH_2O)]$. Moreover, if sufficient fluorine is present, and this may be the case if superphosphate has been applied, the most insoluble phosphate of all, the fluorapatite $[3 \ Ca_3(PO_4)_2 \cdot CaF_2]$ may occur. Thus by a rise in pH the solubility, both of the native and the added phosphorus, may be very seriously impaired.

The situation is further complicated by interrelations of a more speculative nature. As the pH is raised by the addition of lime, the excess calcium may hinder in some way the passage of the phosphate ions through the cell walls of the root hairs or even interfere with the proper metabolism of such ions once they are absorbed.[1] But whatever the explanation may be there undoubtedly is a definite relationship between high soil pH and the satisfactory utilization of phosphorus by higher plants.

The correlation of phosphorus and soil reaction cannot be considered as complete without some mention of the situation in the intermediate pH ranges of mineral soils, say from 5 to 7. At the lower pH figure there undoubtedly is some repression of phosphate avail-

[1] Pierre, W. H., and G. M. Browning, "The Temporary Injurious Effects of Excessive Liming of Acid Soils and Its Relation to the Phosphate Nutrition of Plants," *Jour. Amer. Soc. Agron.*, XXVII:742–759, 1935.

ability due to soluble iron and aluminum but this probably is not serious. Also near pH 7 the active lime tends to reduce somewhat the ease of phosphorus absorption by plants, but here again this is not a major factor. Apparently within the intermediate range itself, anion adsorption [1] plays the major role, the phosphate ions possibly replacing the silicate or hydroxyl radicals of the colloidal complex. Hence the phosphorus would be susceptible to ionic exchange and yet be held closely enough to ensure only negligible losses in drainage. This may account, at least in part, for the more ready availability of the phosphates at intermediate pH values than at, say, pH 4.5 on the one hand, and 7.5 on the other. In the regulation of phosphorus nutrition it is suggested, therefore, that the soil pH be kept within the conservative limits perhaps of 5.6 to 6.5.

Soil organisms and pH. It is well known that soil organisms are influenced, often markedly, by fluctuations in the reaction of the soil solution. This may be due in extreme cases to the H ion itself [2] but in most soils it must be ascribed to the factors correlated with soil pH and already discussed in the preceding paragraphs. In general, it is recognized that bacteria and actinomyces function better in mineral soils at intermediate and higher pH values, the activity being curtailed when the pH drops much below 5.5. Fungi, however, are particularly facultative, flourishing more or less satisfactorily at all reactions. In normal soils, therefore, fungi predominate at the lower pH values but at intermediate and higher ranges they meet strong competition from the bacteria and actinomyces and hence must yield the field to some degree.

We, therefore, find that nitrification and nitrogen fixation take place vigorously in mineral soils only at pH values above 5.5. However, decay, aminization, and ammonification, although curtailed, will still proceed with considerable intensity at lower pH values because most fungi are able to effect these enzymic transfers. This is

---

[1] See Bradfield, Richard, George Scarseth, and J. G. Steele, "Factors Affecting the Retention of Phosphates by Clays," *Trans. 3rd Internat. Cong. Soil Sci.*, I:74–75, 1935. Also, Midgley, A. R., "Phosphate Fixation in Soils — A Critical Review," *Proc. Soil Sci. Soc. Amer.*, V:24–30, 1940, and Metzger, W. H., "Phosphorus Fixation in Relation to the Iron and Aluminum of the Soil," *Jour. Amer. Soc. Agron.*, XXXIII:1093–1099, 1941.

[2] It is suggested by McCalla that H ions are harmful to microorganisms not lethally but because they are so strongly adsorbed at the cell interfaces. Since H ions are with difficulty displaced by other cations, they may hold their position so tenaciously as to prevent the organisms from obtaining, through ionic exchange, satisfactory amounts of the cationic nutrients. See, McCalla, T. M., "Why Does H+ Become Toxic to Soil Bacteria," *Proc. Soil Sci. Soc. Amer.*, VI:165–167, 1941.

indeed fortunate since higher plants growing on very acid soils are at least provided with ammoniacal nitrogen. All in all, a soil in the intermediate pH range, say in the neighborhood of 6.0, perhaps, is under the most satisfactory biological regime. Here nutrient conditions are favorable without being extreme and the phosphorus relations are at an optimum. Hence all favorable soil organisms flourish vigorously, including the nitrifiers and the nitrogen fixers, and a well-balanced microbial population results.

One very significant exception to the generalized correlation of bacteria to soil reaction should be mentioned. The organisms that oxidize sulfur to sulfates (page 127) seem to be markedly facultative. Apparently they not only function vigorously in soils at medium to higher pH values but under markedly acid conditions as well. This is extremely important as it is therefore possible to apply large amounts of sulfur to soils and develop, through the intervention of these bacteria, highly acid conditions. If these organisms were at all sensitive to changes in pH, as sensitive as the nitrifiers for instance, their activity would soon be retarded and finally brought to a halt by their own acidic products.

159. *The relation of higher plants to soil reaction*

On the basis of the preceding considerations, it is possible to distinguish in a general way three physiological conditions in mineral soils. A very acid soil will present a low pH, low exchangeable calcium and magnesium, soluble aluminum, iron, and manganese, possible organic toxins, and a low availability, if not an actual lack, of nitrogen and phosphorus. At the other extreme will be a slightly acid to alkaline soil. Here will be found a moderately high pH, plenty of exchangeable lime, no toxic aluminum, a mild yet active type of humus, a ready availability of the nitrogen and, if the pH is not too high, adequate iron, manganese, copper, zinc, and perhaps phosphorus.

The third and intermediate physiological setup is presented by a moderately to slightly acid soil, which seems for the average plant to be quite satisfactory since the chemical and biological agencies are well in balance. In fact, the ideal as well as the representative soil in a humid-temperate region is one that is somewhat acid, a conception more or less at variance with the popular notion.

Because of the many physiological factors involved it is very difficult to correlate the optimum growth of plants on mineral soils with pH figures except over a considerable range. On the other hand, the relationship of higher plants to the physiological setups described above is easy to establish and in a practical way just as significant. In fact, these three physiological conditions are really just another way of indicating pH range but they explicitly include, and this is most significant, other factors as important or even more important than the H-ion concentration.

On this basis a few of the common plants will be listed. But because so little is known definitely, the grouping (Table XXIX) is not only somewhat tentative but abbreviated as well.

With such crops as alfalfa and sweet clover abundant calcium, and not the H-ion concentration, seems to be the essential factor.[1] The pH is high because the percentage base saturation must be near 100 in order that adequate lime may be supplied. These plants are calcium-loving and are adjusted to the physiological conditions of a high-lime soil. Except under especially favorable conditions, humid-region soils must be limed in order to grow crops of this group satisfactorily.

Rhododendrons and azaleas apparently require a considerable amount of iron and this constituent is only copiously available at low pH values and consequently at low percentage base saturations. Undoubtedly highly acid soils also present other conditions physiologically favorable for this type of plants. Incidentally, soluble aluminum apparently is not detrimental as it is to certain plants higher up the scale. If the pH, and this of course applies to the percentage base saturation also, is not low enough, plants of the low-lime type will show chlorosis and other symptoms indicative of an unsatisfactory nutritive condition.

A glance at Table XXIX will reveal that field crops in general seem to prefer, or at least exhibit a tendency toward, an intermediate physiological condition, neither high nor low in respect to active lime,

---

[1] See, Truog, E., "Soil Acidity: Its Relation to the Growth of Plants," *Soil Sci.*, V: 169–195, 1918; also "Soil Acidity; Its Relation to the Acidity of the Plant Juices," *Soil Sci.*, VII: 469–474, 1919.

True, R. H., "The Function of Calcium in the Nutrition of Seedlings," *Jour. Amer. Soc. Agron.*, XIII: 91–107, 1921.

Kelley, W. P., "The Agronomic Importance of Calcium," *Soil Sci.*, XL: 103–109, 1935.

Pierre, W. H., and W. H. Allaway, "Calcium of the Soil: II. Biological Relations," *Proc. Soil Sci. Soc. Amer.*, VI: 16–26, 1941.

Table **XXIX**. Relation of Higher Plants to the Physiological Conditions Presented by Mineral Soils

PLANTS	PHYSIOLOGICAL CONDITIONS PRESENTED BY		
	Alkaline, neutral & very slightly acid soils	slightly and moderately acid soils	Strongly and very strongly acid soils
Alfalfa	▬▬▬▬		
Sweet clover	▬▬▬▬		
Asparagus	▬▬▬▬		
Spinach	▬▬▬▬		
Sugar beets	▬▬▬▬		
Lettuce	▬▬▬▬		
Garden beets	▬▬▬▬▬	▬	
Cauliflower	▬▬▬▬▬	▬	
Red clover	▬▬▬▬▬	▬▬	
Field peas	▬▬▬▬▬	▬▬	
Cabbage	▬▬▬▬	▬▬▬	
Kentucky bluegrass	▬▬▬	▬▬▬▬	
White clover	▬▬▬	▬▬▬▬	
Timothy		▬▬▬▬	
Barley		▬▬▬▬	
Wheat		▬▬▬▬	
Corn		▬▬▬▬	
Tomatoes		▬▬▬▬	
Soy beans		▬▬▬▬	
Oats		▬▬▬▬	
Alsike clover		▬▬▬▬	
Crimson clover		▬▬▬▬	
Field beans		▬▬▬▬	
Winter vetch		▬▬▬▬	▬
Millet		▬▬▬▬	
Cow peas		▬▬▬	▬▬
Lespedeza		▬▬▬	▬▬
Rye		▬▬▬	▬▬▬
Buckwheat		▬▬	▬▬▬
Red top		▬▬	▬▬▬
Tobacco		▬▬	▬▬▬
Potatoes		▬▬	▬▬▬
Bent grass {other than creeping}		▬	▬▬▬
Fescue			▬▬▬
Poverty grass			▬▬▬
Blue berries			▬▬▬
Cran berries			▬▬▬
Azaleas			▬▬▬
Rhododendron			▬▬▬

percentage base saturation, or pH. The latter enters into the picture, not because it is such a causal factor, but because it is controlled in large degree by percentage base saturation. Hence it is indicative of the physiological setup presented.

As most arable soils in a humid region are tending toward a greater hydrogen-ion concentration, it is indeed fortunate that cultivated plants, except for certain types, not only grow well on moderately acid soils but seem to prefer the physiological conditions therein. Since pasture grasses, many legumes, small grains, cultivated field crops, and a large number of vegetables are included in this broadly tolerant group, soil acidity is not such a calamity as it was once considered. In fact, as already remarked, the ideal and representative humid-region soil obviously is somewhat acid, often moderately so, and should be left in this condition unless the crops grown require a higher or lower lime adjustment.

160. *The determination of soil pH and the limitations of the values obtained*

It has already been emphasized that soil pH is an indication in a broad way of the physiological condition of a soil. Because of this, it is extremely valuable in deciding whether lime is needed for certain crops and how much should be applied. With low-lime plants pH again is most useful. In fact it is a diagnostic figure of unique value and as a result its determination has become one of the commonest routine tests made on soils. Moreover, its determination in competent hands is easy and rapid.

The most accurate method of determining soil pH is by means of a *potentiometer*, an *electrometric* method in which the H-ion concentration of the soil solution is balanced against a standard hydrogen electrode or an electrode that functions in a similar way. In the hands of a skilled operator the instrument gives very consistent results, but the mechanism is rather complicated. Hence figures obtained by a person unable properly to check and standardize the apparatus may be subject to doubt.

A second method, very simple and easy but much less accurate than the electrometric, consists in the use of certain *indicators*. Many dyes change color with an increase or decrease of pH, making it possible, within the range of the indicator, to estimate the approximate H-ion concentration of a solution. By using a number of dyes, either separately or mixed, a range of pH from 3 to 8 is easily obtained. In making such a pH determination on soil, the sample is saturated with the dye and after standing in contact a few minutes a drop of the liquid is run out and its color observed in thin layer. By the use of a color chart and several dyes the approximate pH may be ascertained.

The dye method works most satisfactorily when the soil is air-dry, as a better contact is then obtained between the soil and the indicator. Also the drop of dye isolated is less likely to be muddy. Care should be taken to prevent contamination as the dyes used are extremely sensitive. When properly manipulated the indicator method is accurate within a half of a pH and sometimes much more closely.[1]

Because of the precision with which potentiometer results can be duplicated, it is often assumed that the pH so determined is a very accurate figure. As a matter of fact, data so obtained are most uncertain and speculative. The reason is this: the H-ion concentration of an acid soil solution, as already emphasized, is markedly heterogeneous, ranging, if considerable moisture is present, from a low acidity at the surface of the capillary films to a very high acidity near the colloidal interfaces. Such being the case, the pH figure as obtained by the potentiometer is, at best, only a questionable average. Moreover, it is uncertain how much of the active H ions is compassed by the potentiometer electrodes. Since there apparently is no sharp demarcation between the active and potential acidities, a new doubt is raised as to exactly what is being measured. Thus the colloidicity of a soil prevents an accurate determination of its H-ion concentration.[2]

In the light of such a situation it might seem peculiar that so much reliance is placed on soil pH. In the first place, it is easily and quickly determined. More important, however, is its susceptibility, in spite of its apparent inadequacies, to certain correlations that are of great practical significance. These have already been discussed (page 300).

---

[1] For a comparison of the different dye tests see: Mason, D. D., and S. S. Obenshain, "A Comparison of Methods for the Determination of Soil Reaction," *Proc. Soil Sci. Soc Amer.*, III:129–137, 1938.

[2] Chapman, H. D., J. H. Axley, and D. S. Curtis, "The Determination of pH at Soil Moisture Contents Approximating Field Conditions," *Proc. Soil Sci. Soc. Amer.*, V:191–200, 1940.

Mattson, Sante and Lambert Wiklander, "The Laws of Soil Colloidal Behavior: XXI B. The Amphoteric Points, the pH and the Donnan Equilibrium," *Soil Sci.*, XLIX: 150, 1940.

They may be summarized, however, by saying that a great deal may be inferred regarding the physiological condition of a soil from its pH value; much more, in fact, than from any other single bit of analytical datum.

161. *Soil acidity problems*

Other than the maintenance of fertility in general, two distinct procedures are often necessary on acid soils, especially those at intermediate pH values. One is the intensification of the acidity in order to encourage such plants as azaleas and rhododendrons. The other is the application of active calcium, usually in such amounts as to raise the pH to 6.5 or even to 7.0, thus so modifying physiological conditions as to favor alfalfa, sweet clover, red clover, and other lime-loving crops. For plants other than those of the extreme groups, the maintenance of soil organic matter and the nutrient elements are the principal fertility problems.

Since liming is such an important agricultural feature, its consideration will be reserved for later and fuller discussion (Chap. XV). However, the methods of intensifying the acidity of the soil are briefly discussed in the following section.

162. *Methods of intensifying soil acidity*

A reduction of the pH of soils is often desirable, not only to favor such plants as rhododendrons and azaleas, as suggested above, but also to discourage certain diseases, especially the actinomyces that produce potato scab.

In dealing with the so-called low-lime plants, the change in pH is made under the assumption that as the acidity increases, the physiological condition of the soil will so adjust as to favor the plant in question. Since the availability of iron seems to be one of the critical factors, particularly with azaleas and rhododendrons, a change in pH plus perhaps an increase in organic matter should bring about satisfactory conditions.

With the plants mentioned above the safest and surest procedure is to bring in a soil of such acidity and other characteristics as to present the desirable physiological setup. When this cannot be conveniently done, acid organic matter may be mixed with the soil already at hand. Leafmold, pine needles, tanbark, sawdust, and moss peat, if highly acid, are quite satisfactory. Farm manure may be alkaline, while a peat soil, even though acid, may contain considerable amounts of calcium. Consequently they should be used with caution for such a purpose.

When neither of the above methods are feasible, chemicals may be used. For rhododendron, azaleas, and other plants that require considerable iron, ferrous sulfate is sometimes recommended. This salt by hydrolysis develops sulfuric acid which drastically lowers the pH and liberates some of the iron already present in the soil. At the same time soluble and available iron is being added. Such a chemical thus serves a double purpose in effecting a change in the physiological condition of a soil.

Another material that is even better in many respects is flowers of sulfur. This usually undergoes vigorous microbial oxidation in the soil (see page 127) and under favorable conditions is four or five times more effective in developing acidity than ferrous sulfate. Moreover, it is comparatively inexpensive, easy to obtain, and is a material used for other purposes on the farm.

Sulfur is effective in the control of potato scab since the actinomyces that cause it are discouraged by acidity. Ordinarily when the pH is lowered to 5.5 or perhaps better to 5.3, their virulence is much reduced. Soils, which at pH 5.8 might favor the disease, at a half a pH unit lower are likely to give clean, marketable potatoes. In using sulfur to thus increase soil acidity the management of the land, and especially the rotation, should be such that succeeding crops are not unfavorably affected.

No definite recommendation can be made as to the amounts of ferrous sulfate or of sulfur that should be applied, since the buffering of soils and their original pH are so variable. With composted soils to be used in greenhouses, in nurseries, and around ornamental plants, the best way is to make several preliminary treatments using different amounts of the amendments with definite increments of the soil. After incubating at optimum temperature and moisture for several weeks, pH determinations may be made and a decision arrived at as to the amounts of ferrous sulfate or sulfur that probably would give the desired result.

For rhododendrons and azaleas 1 to 2 pounds of sulfur per 100 square feet for each half a pH that the soil is to be lowered, is perhaps not too much. The dosage should, of course, be varied according to the texture of the soil and its organic content. For the control of potato scab the amount of sulfur applied varies from 100 to 300 pounds to the acre, depending on circumstances. Experience and good judgment are the major factors in such a decision. The results both on the pH and the crop should be checked and additional applications made in succeeding years if they are deemed necessary.

163. *The alkali problem*

When for any reason the drainage of an arid-region soil is impeded, conditions become such as to favor the accumulation of soluble salts at or near the surface. This phenomenon is due to evaporation accompanied and abetted by an upward capillary adjustment of the soil water, which gradually carries the excess salts into the surface horizon. Such a concentration or accumulation is called *alkali*. A condition therefore results that often renders the soil practically useless for agricultural purposes.

Alkali salts usually originate through the ordinary processes of weathering and in profiles where little percolation occurs. Impeded drainage is especially favorable. Almost any rock will give rise to soils rich in alkali if vigorous leaching is not a feature of the weathering processes.

During periods of dry weather alkali salts are carried upward by the capillary rise of the soil water, while during periods of rainfall they may move downward again in proportion to the leaching action. At one time the lower soil may contain considerably more soluble salt than the upper; at another period the condition may be reversed, in which case the solution in contact with roots of plants may contain so much soluble matter that vegetation is injured or destroyed. Very often alkali is localized in small areas called *alkali spots*. These vary in size from a few square yards to several acres. In years of good rainfall these areas may be productive, but in dry years they are often quite sterile. Their appearance in otherwise fertile fields is of serious concern, since their presence indicates that something is radically wrong with the soil management, perhaps the irrigation methods, and that appreciable areas of good land may ultimately be rendered unfit, either temporarily or permanently, for agricultural purposes.

164. *Alkali soils* [1]

The typical aridic soil is *zonal*, that is, climate with its associated vegetation has been the major factor in the determination of its profile characteristics (see page 265). Moreover, it is adequately drained. Alkali soils, in contrast, are *intrazonal;* that is, their outstanding characteristics, in this case soluble salts, are a reflection of some local condition. As already stated, impeded drainage is the immediate cause of the excess of soluble matter. Fortunately, alkali soils are not widespread. Moreover, the presence of salts in concentrations sufficient to be harmful to crops often occurs in soils that, even if not so infested, would be of little or no agricultural value.

Sulfates and chlorides of sodium, calcium, magnesium, and potassium, when concentrated in the *A* horizon of an aridic soil or on the surface as a white incrustation, are common in alkali regions especially during dry periods. A salt mixture of this character is called *white alkali* and the soil containing it a *solonchak* (see Table XXVIII). Sodium chloride is usually one of the prominent salts in such an accumulation. Such a soil is only mildly alkaline and its profile presents no outstanding structural characteristics.

Carbonates of the common metals, particularly sodium carbonate, dissolve organic matter from the soil, thus giving a dark color to the solution and to the incrustation. For this reason, alkali containing large quantities, especially of carbonate of soda, is called *black alkali* and the soil bearing it a *solonetz*. Black or brown alkali may also be produced by calcium chloride or by an excess of sodium nitrate. A well-developed solonetz is very strongly alkaline in reaction and its *B* horizon is characterized by a columnar or prismatic structure. When the impeded drainage of such a soil is rectified it slowly changes, due to leaching, into a *solodized-solonetz*, a soil with a slightly acid surface layer and a dense clayey *B* horizon (see Table XXVIII).

Black alkali is much more destructive to vegetation than is the white. A quantity of the latter which would not seriously interfere with the growth of most crops might completely prevent the development of useful plants if the alkali were of the solonetz type.

The preponderance of sodium chloride is almost always a feature

[1] For a treatise on alkali see, Harris, F. S., *Soil Alkali*, John Wiley & Sons, Inc., New York, 1920.

of all alkali. Sodium and chlorine ions seem to be as little adsorbed as any of the soluble soil constituents. They are thus free to be carried away to the ocean when rainfall is high or to accumulate when little leaching occurs. Their union of necessity produces large quantities of sodium chloride or common salt.

The presence of so much sodium as the chloride, carbonate, and sulfate tends more or less to saturate the colloidal matter of typical alkali soils with this element, resulting in what is called a *sodium complex*. Colloidal matter so dominated tends to assume a dispersed condition, which results in a puddled, undesirable physical state of the soil. This is recognized as particularly characteristic of alkali land of the solonetz type. Solonchak soils, which contain less sodium and more calcium, have a more open structural condition.

165. *Effects of alkali on plants — alkali tolerance*

The presence of relatively large amounts of salts dissolved in water and brought into contact with a plant cell will cause a shrinkage of the protoplasmic lining. This action, called *plasmolysis*, increases with the concentration of the solution until the plant finally dies. The phenomenon is due to the osmotic movement of the water, which passes from the cell towards the more concentrated soil solution. The nature of the salt, the species and even the individuality of the plant, as well as other factors, determine the exact concentration at which the individual succumbs.

The carbonates of the alkali bases have, in addition to a plasmolyzing influence, a corroding effect on the tissues, dissolving the parts of the plant with which they come into contact. When this occurs it is most noticeable at the root crown.

The tolerance of crops to alkali depends on: (1) the physiological constitution of the plant, and (2) the rooting habit. The former is little understood, so much depending on the character of the alkali solution, the nature of the cell wall, and the constitution and activity of the cell contents. It has long been known that the toxicity of two salts, when together, is considerably less than the sum of their detrimental action when used alone. This ameliorating or antagonistic action varies for different salts. This is an example of the complexities which arise when an attempt is made to study the physiological relationships of alkali injury.

The rooting habits of plants in their relation to alkali tolerance are more easily understood. The advantage is always with deep-rooted crops, such as alfalfa and sugar beets, probably because some portion of the root system may always be in contact with soil carrying a minimum of soluble salts. It is interesting to note in this regard that young alfalfa is rather sensitive to soil alkali, while old alfalfa is one of the most resistant of field crops.

Of the cereals, barley and oats are the most tolerant, these being able, in some cases, to produce good crops on soil containing more than 0.2 per cent of black alkali. Of the forage crops, a number of valuable grasses are able to grow on soil containing even more. Timothy, smooth brome, and alfalfa are the cultivated forage plants most tolerant, although they do not equal the native grasses in this respect. Sorghum and sugar beets are quite resistant, as also is cotton. Of the fruits, pears, oranges, and especially grapes are noticeably resistant.

Although observations as to the resistance to alkali of the various crops are conflicting, Dorsey presents data (see Table XXX) that give a general conception of the situation.

Table XXX. Alkali Tolerance[1]

Percentage of Total Salts in Soil	Percentage of Black Alkali in Soil	Crops
0.00–0.20	0.00–0.05	All crops grow
0.20–0.40	0.05–0.10	All but most sensitive
0.40–0.60	0.10–0.20	Old alfalfa, sugarbeet, sorghum, barley
0.60–1.00	0.20–0.30	Only most resistant plants
1.00–3.00	above 0.30	No plants

166. Alkali management[2]

Ordinarily there are three general ways in which alkali lands may be handled in order to avoid at least partially the injurious effects of soluble salts. The first of these is eradication; the second is a conversion of some of the salts to less injurious forms; while the third may be designated as control. In the first two methods an attempt is made actually to eliminate by various means some of the alkali or to render it less toxic. In the third, soil-management procedures are employed

[1] Dorsey, C. W., *Alkali Soils of the United States*, Bulletin 35, Bureau of Soils, U. S. Dept. of Agriculture, 23–25, 1906.

[2] All of the experiment stations of those states having alkali problems have published bulletins relating to its practical management.

which keep the salts well distributed throughout the soil. In many cases land will grow excellent crops if the alkali can be kept so well dispersed through the horizon layers that no toxic concentration occurs within the root zone.

Eradication. Of the methods used at least partially to free the soil of alkali, the commonest are: (1) leaching with underdrainage, (2) scraping and (3) flushing. Of these, flooding after tile drains have been installed is the most thorough and satisfactory. When this method is used in an irrigated region, heavy and repeated applications of water can be made and the alkali leached from the soil and drained off through the tile.

Removal of the alkali incrustations that have accumulated at the surface through excessive evaporation is sometimes resorted to, but it is never very effective as large quantities of salts still remain in the soil. Such a removal may be effected by scraping or by flushing the soil surface. Lands carrying enough alkali to permit either of these procedures is usually so heavily charged that any type of reclamation is unsatisfactory.

Conversion.[1] The use of gypsum on black alkali land is sometimes recommended for the purpose of converting part of the alkali carbonates into sulfates, thus reducing the injurious effects of the soluble salts. The soil must be kept moist, in order to bring about the reaction, and the gypsum should be cultivated into the surface, not plowed under. The reaction is as follows:

$$Na_2CO_3 + CaSO_4 \rightleftharpoons CaCO_3 + Na_2SO_4$$

It is also recognized that sulfur can be used to advantage on both white and black alkali lands, especially where carbonates abound. The sulfur usually oxidizes readily, forming sulfuric acid which not only changes the carbonates to the less harmful sulfates but also tends to reduce the intense alkalinity. Wursten and Powers report sulfur to be the most effective and economical single chemical treatment in the elimination of black alkali.[2]

$$Na_2CO_3 + H_2SO_4 \rightleftharpoons Na_2SO_4 + CO_2 + H_2O$$

[1] Hibbard, P. L., "Sulfur for Neutralizing Alkali Soil," *Soil Sci.*, XI:385–387, 1921.

Kelley, W. P., and A. Aarny, "The Chemical Effect of Gypsum, Sulfur, Iron Sulfate, and Alum on Alkali Soils," *Hilgardia*, III, No. 14, 1928.

[2] Wursten, J. L., and W. L. Powers, "Reclamation of Virgin Black Alkali Soils," *Jour. Amer. Soc. Agron.*, XXVI:752–762, 1934.

Control. The retardation of evaporation is, of course, an important feature of alkali control. The intensive use of the soil mulch is, therefore, very desirable, especially on irrigated lands when alkali concentrations are likely to occur. Such a method of soil management not only may save moisture, but also may retard the translocation of soluble salts into the root zone. This method of control is the most economical, the cheapest, and the one to be advocated wherever possible. It is needless to say that, where irrigation is practiced, an excess of water should be avoided.

The use of alkali-resistant crops is another important feature of alkali control. Sugar beets, sorghum, barley, and alfalfa are especially to be recommended. Moreover, temporary eradication of alkali will allow less-resistant crops to be established. Farm manure is especially useful in this respect. A crop, such as alfalfa, once it is growing vigorously, will probably maintain itself in spite of the alkali concentrations that may occur later.

Chapter XIV. The Nature and Utilization
of Organic Soils

On the basis of organic content two general groups of soils are commonly recognized — mineral and organic. The so-called mineral soils vary in organic matter from a mere trace to as high as 12 or 15 per cent. Organic soils, as the term implies, possess much more organic material, the content ranging from 20 to as high in some cases as 90 or 95 per cent.

Organic soils are by no means so important as mineral soils, yet their acreage, while broken in extent, is in the aggregate very great. Their use in certain localities for the intensive production of crops, especially vegetables, has become so important as to attract considerable public notice. As the development of such lands goes on, more and more attention will be given to their investigation. In the past organic soils have not received the study that they deserve and, as a result, less exact knowledge regarding their physical, chemical, and biological characteristics is available than for mineral soils.

167. *Genesis of organic deposits*

Marshes, bogs, and swamps provide the conditions suitable for the accumulation of organic deposits. The highly favorable environment in and adjacent to such areas has encouraged the growth of many plants, such as pondweed, cattails, sedges, mosses, shrubs, and also trees. These plants in numberless generations thrive, die, and sink down to be covered by the water in which they grew. The water shuts out the air, prohibits rapid oxidation, and thus acts as a partial preservative. The decay that does go on is largely through the agency of fungi, anaerobic bacteria, algae, and certain types of microscopic aquatic animals, that break down the tissue, liberate gaseous constituents, and aid in the synthesis of humus. As the process continues, the organic mass becomes brown or even black in color. And if decomposition proceeds far enough, this mass of organic soil material acquires such profile characteristics as to justify its designation as a true organic soil.

As one generation of plants follows another, layer after layer of organic residue is deposited in the swamp or marsh. The constitution of these successive layers changes as time goes on since a sequence of different plant life is likely to occur. Thus deep-water plants may be supplanted by reeds and sedges, these by various mosses, and these in turn by shrubs, until finally forest trees, either hardwoods or conifers, with their characteristic undergrowth, may gain a foothold. The succession is by no means regular, or definite, as a slight change in climate or water level may alter the sequence entirely. The profile of an organic deposit is, therefore, characterized by layers, differing not only as to their degree of decomposition but also as to the nature of the original plant tissue. In fact these layers later may become soil horizons, their final character being determined in part by the nature of the original materials and in part by the type and degree of decomposition. Thus the profile characteristics of organic soils, as with those dominately mineral in nature, are in part inherited and in part acquired.

168. *Extent and distribution of peat accumulations*

As might be expected, peat deposits are found all over the world wherever the conditions, as outlined above, are favorable. But only in certain countries are these accumulations utilized in any intensive way. In Germany, Holland, Norway, Sweden, Russia, Poland, Ireland, and Scotland, economic use has long been made of peat and peat products. Organic deposits in Germany occupy perhaps 5,000,-000 acres, in Sweden 12,000,000 and in Ireland 3,000,000 acres. Canada possesses approximately 12,000,000 acres of peat, mostly undeveloped.

Organic deposits of the nature described occur in many parts of the United States.[1] In Florida the Everglades, spread out over a vast plain, contain considerably over 2,000,000 acres of saw-grass (sedge) accumulations. Along the Atlantic coastal plain great marsh deposits are found, especially in North Carolina. In California there are

[1] For tabular information as to acreages see, Gustafson, A. F., *Soils and Soil Management*, McGraw-Hill Book Company, Inc., New York, 1941, p. 395.

the tule-reed beds of the great central valley, approximately 300,000 acres in extent. Louisiana alone possesses about 3,000,000 of organic accumulations of various kinds. All of these are southward and outside of the glaciated areas of the United States and related, if at all, only indirectly to the glaciation.

Northward in the regions covered by glacial debris of various kinds, organic deposits are even more extended. In fact about 75 per cent of the peat deposits of the United States occur in the glaciated areas. Minnesota, Wisconsin, and Michigan are especially favored in this respect, their combined acreage running well above 12,000,000 acres. Washington, with about 2,000,000 acres, ranks highest of all the western states. Indiana, Massachusetts, New York, and New Jersey fall into the 300,000- to 500,000-acre class. Other states contain smaller but often very important areas. The total acreage of peat deposits in the United States proper is in the neighborhood of 25,000,-000 acres. In Alaska and northern Canada, and doubtless in northern Asia and Europe as well, there occur great areas of peat derived from sedges and mosses called *muskeg*. In many cases the subhorizons of such accumulations are perpetually frozen. They are closely related to the tundra soils that characterize these regions.

The glaciation by impeding drainage caused the formation of swamps and bogs and, as the climate after the disappearance of the ice gradually attained its present status, conditions became ideal for swamp vegetation to flourish. As a result certain parts of the glaciated region are liberally dotted with organic accumulations ranging from a few inches to 50 or even in places 100 feet in depth. Some areas a number of square miles in extent are solidly occupied as in Minnesota, while in others the peat lies in isolated patches or in long ribbons as in southeastern Wisconsin and in central New York. The latter accumulations are in many cases associated with drumlins. These long cigar-shaped hills often alternate with narrow swamps several miles in length that are filled with organic matter in various stages of decay. Thus peat accumulation in these northern areas is distinctly a glacial concomitant even though of postglacial origin. It is easy to explain, therefore, why peat so often accumulated during the long interglacial periods that separated the various glacial invasions. Conditions immediately after the disappearance of the ice apparently were most favorable for the development and persistence of organic matter.

169. Classification of peat

Peat, regardless of its stage of decomposition, may conveniently be classified according to its parent materials and under three general heads as follows: [1]

Classification of Peat Materials

1. Sedimentary peat . . . . $\left\{\begin{array}{l}\text{mixtures of water lilies, pondweed, horn-} \\ \text{wort, pollen, plankton, etc.}\end{array}\right.$

2. Fibrous peat . . . . . $\left\{\begin{array}{l}\text{sedges of various kinds} \\ \text{mosses — sphagnum, hyp-} \\ \text{num, and others} \\ \text{reeds and other grasses} \\ \text{cattails — latifolia and an-} \\ \text{gustifolia}\end{array}\right\}$ and their mixtures

3. Woody peat . . . . . $\left\{\begin{array}{l}\text{deciduous trees} \\ \text{coniferous trees}\end{array}\right\}$ and their undergrowth

Sedimentary peat, the first listed, usually accumulates in comparatively deep water and therefore generally is found well down in the profile. It is derived from plant materials that decompose freely and rather completely. Due to the nature of the original tissue and perhaps also to the type of decay, a highly colloidal and characteristically compact and rubbery substance develops. This material is unique and so different from the other types of peat commonly found in the profile that it always attracts considerable attention when encountered.

Not only is sedimentary peat rubbery in character but it is usually olive-green in color when in its natural position. On exposure to the atmospheric air it darkens, sometimes becoming almost black. Due to its highly colloidal nature, its moisture capacity is high, perhaps five times its dry weight. Water thus imbibed is held tenaciously and therefore this peat dries out very slowly. The colloidal materials of

---

[1] In Germany peats are classified in a general way into *high-moor* and *low-moor* in reference to the shape of the deposits. The high-moors are convex, that is, raised in the center, while the low-moors are concave. The former is usually quite acid and low in calcium, the latter less acid and quite high in exchangeable calcium.

In England the corresponding terms are *moor* and *fen*. The term *heathland* refers to a shallow acid peat.

For a discussion of American peats and their classification see Dachnowski-Stokes, A. P., and V. Auer, "American Peat Deposits," *Handbuck der Moorkunde*, Gebrüder Borntraeger, Berlin, 1933, Band VII.

sedimentary peat are largely irreversible. Consequently when once dry, this peat absorbs water very slowly and persistently remains in a hard and lumpy condition. Sedimentary peat is thus very undesirable as a soil, not only because of its unfavorable physical condition but also because of other characteristics that render it unsatisfactory for use in the growing of plants. Fortunately, in most cases, it occurs well down in the profile and ordinarily does not appear above the plowline. Therefore its presence usually is unnoticed or ignored unless it obstructs drainage or otherwise interferes with the agricultural utilization of the peat deposit.

As indicated by the classification, a number of fibrous peats occur, often in the same swamp deposit. They are all heterogeneous in character, high in water-holding capacity, and may exhibit varying degrees of decomposition. They differ among themselves especially as to their filamentous or fibrous physical nature. Undecomposed moss and sedge are fine enough to be used in greenhouses and nurseries and as a source of organic matter for gardens and flower beds. Reed and cattails, however, are somewhat coarse, especially the latter. In fact, the cattail accumulations are of little value unless well decomposed. All of these materials as they decay make satisfactory field soils, the cattail soil perhaps being the least desirable, the sedge or moss usually receiving a preferred rating. Fibrous peats may occur at the surface of the organic accumulation of which they are a part or well down in the profile. They usually lie above the sedimentary deposit when this type of peat is present. Nevertheless, if just the right fluctuation of conditions has occurred a stratum of the latter may lie imbedded within the fibrous-peat horizons.

Since trees are the climax vegetation in swamp deposits, woody peat, when it occurs, is usually at the surface of the organic accumulation. This is not an invariable rule, however, since a rise in water level might kill the tree growth and so favor reed, sedge, or cattail as to give a layer of fibrous material over the woody accumulation. It is not particularly surprising, therefore, to find subhorizon layers of woody peat. Woody peat is brown or black in color when wet, according to the degree of humification. It is loose and open when dry or merely moist, and decidedly nonfibrous in character. It is thus easily distinguished from the other two types of peat unless the samples are unusually well decomposed.

Woody peat results from the residues not only of deciduous and coniferous trees but also from the shrubs and other plants that occupy the forest floor. Maple, elm, tamarack, hemlock, spruce, cedar, pine, and other trees occur as the climax vegetation in swamps of temperate regions. In spite of the great number of plants that contribute to its accumulation, woody peat is rather homogeneous unless it contains admixtures of fibrous materials. Its water capacity is lower than that of the fibrous peats, especially those formed from mosses and sedges. For that reason woody peat is less desirable than these peats for use in greenhouses and nurseries where such materials, undecayed or only slightly decomposed, are used as a means of moisture control. Woody residues produce a soil, however, that is quite superior and much prized for the growing of vegetables and other crops.

170. *Various uses of peat*

Peat is utilized in a number of ways, depending on the nature of the material. In the United States, Canada, and Europe the more or less undecomposed products are very commonly employed as a source of organic matter. This is true of moss and sedge peat. When incorporated with mineral soil in sufficient quantities, peat not only ensures a good physical condition but greatly increases the water capacity of the mixture. Artificial soils for potting and other purposes are greatly benefited physically by its use. It is thus valuable in greenhouses, gardens, flower beds, and nurseries both as a soil amendment and as a mulch around growing plants of all kinds.[1]

Peat is likewise useful in the preparation of lawn soils, of golf greens, and in numerous other ways where tilth and organic matter are important factors. While the undecayed materials are generally utilized for such purposes, the humified products are also employed. They are often just as satisfactory and in some instances even superior to the less decayed material. In no case, however, can peat be used as a commercial fertilizer in spite of its relatively high content of nitrogen, which is generally between 2 and 3 per cent. Such nitrogen is so slowly available that it cannot be classed with that normally supplied by nitrate of soda and sulfate of ammonia. Besides, the percentage, while high for a soil, is too low to rate peat as a fertilizer.

[1] Feustel, Irvin C., "The Present Status of Research Relating to the Use of Peat and Muck as Soil Amendments," *Proc. Soil Sci. Soc. Amer.*, IV:271–274, 1939. This article carries an excellent bibliography.

Peat is also used in stables as bedding and litter. It readily absorbs and conserves the liquid manure and when the mixture is applied to the soil the peat contributes considerable valuable although slowly decomposable organic matter. However, the presence of the liquid and solid manure activates the organic matter of the peat and renders its decomposition more rapid than otherwise would be the case. Peat is likewise utilized in chicken houses as a litter under the roosts and in the runways. Sphagnum and other suitable forms of fibrous peats even serve as packing materials in place of excelsior and the other usual substances. They also are good insulating materials.

In Holland, Germany, Belgium, Ireland, and other countries of Europe, peat is dug out in brickette form, dried thoroughly, and used as fuel. Thus vast amounts of Dutch and German peat have not only been used locally, but also shipped considerable distances for in- dustrial purposes. In lands where wood is scarce and coal expensive, peat deposits are a most valuable natural resource. In Holland the excavation of peat has been so regulated as to leave the site well drained and in such a condition that field crops can be grown, aided by the part of the organic matter that, by law, must be left behind. Some of the most productive agricultural areas in Holland lie on the site of these reclaimed and properly exploited bogs.

In the United States the most extensive use of peat is as a field soil, especially for vegetable production, although other crops are grown to some extent. Thousands of acres are now under cultivation, often producing two crops a year. In some respects the vegetable industry has been revolutionized by the exceedingly favorable nature of these organic soils. Peats for such use should be well decomposed, the decay often having gone so far as to make it impossible to identify with certainty the various plants that have contributed to the accumula- tion. As the following pages indicate, the edaphological interest in peat relates mainly to its use as a natural soil and not as an artificial and commercial product for greenhouse, nursery, or factory consump- tion.

However, more and more of the processed peat, locally produced and mostly moss and sedge, undecomposed or only slightly so, is ap- pearing on the market both in Canada and the United States. With great quantities of suitable material available, there is no reason why the domestic demand in the United States should not be met with a domestic product. rather than, as heretofore, with imports. As

people become more familiar with peat and peat products, an in=
creased use by florists, gardeners, and nurserymen is inevitable.

171. *Muck versus peat — muck soils*

Organic deposits are conveniently classified on the basis of the
amount of organic matter that they contain. When the quantity of
this constituent ranges from 20 to 50 per cent, the accumulation is
technically designated as *muck*. When the percentage is above 50,
the material is referred to as *peat*. This distinction is somewhat confused in certain parts of the United States by the use of the term *muck*
in reference to all peat that is well enough decomposed to serve as soil.[1]
Also mineral soils relatively high in organic matter but whose percentage thereof is less than 20 are sometimes designated as muck. In
the pages that follow the chemical distinction between peat and muck
above will be adhered to.

When the organic matter of muck is well decomposed, this material
makes a very satisfactory soil. The large content of mineral matter,
50 per cent or more, is usually due to an inwash of sand and silt.
Fringes and tongues of muck are therefore common at the edges of
peat deposits, especially if conditions of rainfall and topography are
favorable for erosion. One of the best known areas of true muck
occurs on the southern and eastern shores of Lake Okeechobee in
Florida. It is locally known as *custard-apple* land. While muck may
be used successfully for the production of vegetables and other crops,
peat soils are far greater in extent and agriculturally are much more
important. Peat soils for this reason will receive the major attention.

172. *Peat soils — their classification and profile sequence*

Peats may be divided for convenience into two general groups:
(1) undecomposed or only slightly so, and (2) those that are moderately or very definitely decayed. The former are usually brownish or
reddish-brown in color, while the latter, especially when wet, are
dark brown or black and finely divided. Well-decomposed, or even

---

[1] Soil survey men as well as farmers often use the terms *peat* and *muck* in reference to the
state of decomposition of the organic matter, peat referring to the slightly or nondecayed
deposits and muck to those materials markedly decomposed. This further adds to the
confusion of terminology.

partially decayed peat, when suitably located, may be utilized as a field soil, its value agriculturally depending on climate, drainage, lime content, markets, and particularly upon the nature of the original materials that have contributed to the surface layers.

Since the parent materials influence so definitely the physical and chemical properties of peat soils, any classification must take them into account. The following grouping is simple and, to anyone familiar with peat soils, very convenient as well. Since sedimentary peat is seldom near the surface on good peat land, and when so located is physically so undesirable, it is not considered important enough to include in the soil classification.

Classification of Peat Soils

Fibrous peat soils . . . . ⎰ sedges of various kinds ⎱ and their
mosses — sphagnum, hypnum and others mixtures
reeds and other grasses
cattails — latifolia and angustifolia

Woody peat soils. . . . . ⎰ deciduous and coniferous trees and undergrowth ⎱

It is to be especially noted that the classification of peat soils is identical with the grouping of the original soil materials. This is because the parent substances so definitely determine the nature of the profile that no other scheme of classification is nearly so satisfactory. With mineral soils the situation is quite different. While parent materials are very important, the profile characteristics of a well-developed zonal mineral soil are a reflection in large degree of climate. In other words acquired characteristics rather than those inherited from the original materials dominate the profile (page 260). The contrast to this presented by peat soils is noteworthy.

It was found in the consideration of mineral soils that their genesis, their outstanding characteristics, and their plant relationship could not be clearly understood without some knowledge of their profiles. The same is true of peat soils. The next logical step, therefore, is to inquire into the profile sequence of organic soils.

Ideally, one might expect that the profile succession of a peat soil would be rather definite for any region. Actually, no regular sequence is found, due in large part to the irregular and uncoordinated fluctuations in the water levels of the swamps and bogs. In central New York, for instance, sedimentary peat theoretically should be near the bottom of the profile, fibrous material of some kind should come next with woody peat, if the climax vegetation is attained, at the surface; but if there should be several radical changes in the water

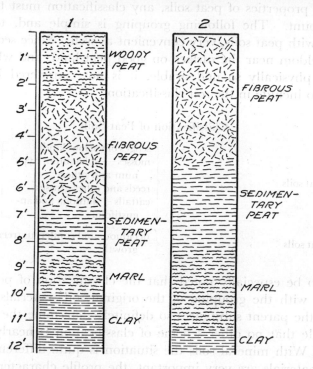

Fig. 53. Representative profiles of a New York woody peat soil (1) and a New York fibrous peat soil (2). The woody peat is, of course, the more desirable as a field soil. Note the presence in both profiles of rubbery sedimentary peat and of marl. (After Wilson and Staker.)

table, the succession ultimately attained might in no way resemble the ideal. Thus woody peat is sometimes found below the surface of the accumulation, covered by deposits that ideally should be encountered beneath, while layers usually encountered at mid-profile are either at the top or the bottom of the organic accumulation. Hence it is difficult to forecast, except in a broad way, the profile order of the peat soils of any particular area.

Again the profile may be immature, the possible succession of plants and their resultant accumulation having only well begun. Thus in New York and other northern and northeastern states, the climax vegetation is forest. Yet the surface peat in many beds may be derived from the decomposition of mosses or sedges or cattail or their intermixture, with a limited sequence or even no other organic horizons below. In fact so variable is the arrangement of the profile layers that every peat bed requires separate investigation. Even the same accumulation, although covered by a uniform surface layer of peat soil, may vary markedly within short distances in respect to the thickness and nature of the underlying horizons. As a result Figs. 53 and 54 are only expected to suggest in a tentative way what actually may be encountered under field conditions.

173. *Physical characteristics of peat soils*

In spite of the many kinds of peat soils — woody, sedge, reed, moss, cattail, and their intermixtures — that are encountered in various parts of the United States, a generalized description will be ventured in respect to their outstanding physical characteristics. Such statements will apply merely to that portion of the organic accumulation that normally occurs in the furrow-slice of cultivated peats and that determines in large part the suitability of the deposits for successful crop production.

The color of a typical cultivated peat soil, dark brown or intensely black when it is wet, is perhaps the first physical characteristic that attracts the attention. Although the original materials may be gray or brown, dark-colored humic compounds appear as decomposition advances and finally dominate the colloidal complex. In general, the changes that the organic matter undergoes seem to be somewhat similar to those occurring in mineral soils in spite of the restricted aeration. Such definiteness in surface coloration is far from characteristic of mineral soils.

The second outstanding characteristic that is likely to be noted is the light weight of the representative peat soil when dry. The volume weight compared with mineral surface soils is surprisingly low, 0.20 to 0.30 perhaps being a fair estimate. A cultivated surface mineral soil will usually fall within the limits of 1.25 to 1.45. A cubic foot of peat soil will contain from 8 to 20 pounds of dry matter, depending on the condition of the soil and the admixture of mineral materials. An acre-furrow-slice of the depth common in mineral soils, while variable, may be considered to weight 400,000 or perhaps 500,000 pounds when

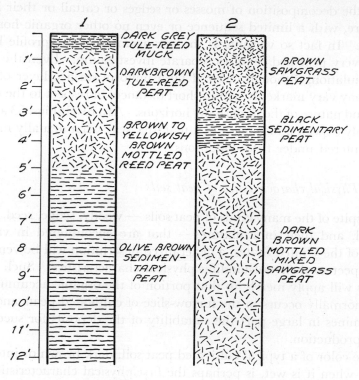

FIG. 54. Generalized profiles of (1) San Joaquin tule-reed peat soil of the Mandeville type and (2) Florida saw-grass peat soil of the Okeelanta type. (After Dacknowski-Stokes' description.)

dry. Compared with the 2,000,000 or 2,500,000 pounds ordinarily considered as the dry weight of an acre-furrow-slice of a representative mineral soil, such figures seem small indeed.

A third important property of peat soil is its high water-holding capacity, one of the characteristics of highly colloidal materials and especially developed by organic matter in such a state. While a dry mineral soil will absorb and hold from one-fifth to two-fifths its weight of water, a peat soil will retain two or perhaps three times its dry weight of moisture, depending on conditions.[1]   This water-holding capacity, possibly ten times greater in general than that of mineral soils, is very important in the growing of vegetables.   With such crops the presence of an abundant water supply is essential.

It must not be hastily assumed, however, that peats greatly surpass mineral soils in their capacity to supply plants with water.   Two conditions militate against the organic soils.   In the first place their amounts of unavailable water are much higher proportionately than that of mineral soils.   Again, since the comparative figures are on the basis of weight, the peat soils with their low volume weights are at a considerable disadvantage.   Yet when considered on the volume basis, the only fair comparison, a cubic foot of peat soil at optimum moisture will supply somewhat more water to plants than a representative mineral soil also at optimum, but not in such excess as the figures quoted in the preceding paragraph might lead one to expect.

A fourth outstanding characteristic of a typical woody or fibrous peat soil is its invariably good physical condition.   While decayed organic matter is, in large degree, colloidal and possesses high adsorptive and catalytic powers, its cohesion and plasticity are rather low. A peat soil of good quality is therefore porous, open, and easy to cultivate.   These characteristics make it especially desirable for vegetable production.   During dry periods, however, the lightness and looseness of peat, especially if its granular condition has been reduced by cultivation, may lead to serious trouble, since it may drift badly in a high wind and extensive crop damage thus result.   It may also become ignited when dry and burn to such an extent as greatly to decrease or even destroy its usefulness.

In referring to the surface layer of an arable peat soil as likely to be granular, unless subject to overcultivation, it is not to be inferred that the whole profile is in this structural condition also.   Far from it. All sorts of physical arrangements are encountered in the subhorizons, such as laminated, vertical, fragmental, fibrous, and rubbery.   The variability from horizon to horizon is determined not only by the character of the original materials, but also by the nature and degree of decomposition.

[1] Undecayed or only slightly decomposed moss or sedge peat in contrast with their soils have a much greater water-holding capacity.   Not uncommonly such materials can absorb and hold water to the extent of eight, twelve or even fifteen times their dry weight.   This explains in part their value in greenhouse and nursery operations.

174. *The colloidal nature of peat soils* [1]

Because of the very high content of organic matter and the particular type of humification, the colloidicity of peat soil is striking, far beyond that exhibited by any mineral-soil colloid. The interface exceeds even that of montmorillonite clay perhaps three and four times, and adsorption, catalysis, and base-exchange capacities are correspondingly great. However, in spite of differences as to original tissue and conditions of genesis, the humus of peat soils greatly resembles that of mineral soils except for the intensity of the colloidal properties. For instance, it has been suggested that the total exchange capacity of a mineral soil is enhanced approximately 2 milliequivalents for every 1 per cent increase in humus (page 88). The figure for peat is somewhat higher in general, perhaps in the neighborhood of 3 milliequivalents for every 1 per cent of organic matter.

Not only can the same graphic formula — x CarH(acidoid) — be used to represent the colloidal complex of peat, but it is noteworthy that the same cations are adsorbed and in the same order of magnitude, namely, Ca > Mg > K > Na. This important difference is to be noted, however. The amount of adsorbed calcium in respect to the other exchangeable metallic cations is very much greater, not only actually, but proportionately, than is the case with mineral soils. As a consequence, calcium is an omnipresent and exceedingly mobile constituent in most peat soils. That this is likely to be true, whether the peat is comparatively low lime or high lime is apparent from the data of Table XXXI. The two soils in question are New York woody

[1] McGeorge, W. T., *The Base Exchange Property of Organic Matter in Soils*, Technical Bulletin 30, Univ. Ariz. Agr. Exp. Sta., 1930.

Baver, L. D., "The Nature of Soil Buffering Action," *Jour. Amer. Soc. Agron.*, XXIII: 587–605, 1931.

Powers, W. L., "Characteristics of Dispersable Organic Colloids in Peats," *Jour. Agr. Res.*, XLIV:97–111, 1932.

Muller, J. F., "Some Observations on Base-Exchange in Organic Materials," *Soil Sci.*, XXXV:229–237, 1933.

Anderson, M. S., and H. J. Byers, *Character and Behavior of Organic Soil Colloids*, Technical Bulletin 377, U. S. Dept. of Agriculture, 1933.

Wilson, B. D., and M. J. Plice, *The Buffer Capacity of Peat Soils*, Memoir 146, Cornell Univ. Agr. Exp. Sta., 1933.

Wilson, B. D., and E. V. Staker, *Ionic Exchange in Peat Soils*, Memoir 172, Cornell Univ. Agr. Exp. Sta., 1935.

Millar, H. C., F. B. Smith, and P. E. Brown, "The Base Exchange Capacity of Decomposing Organic Matter," *Jour. Amer. Soc. Agr.*, XXVIII:753–766, 1936.

Feustel, I. C., *The Acidic Properties of Peat and Muck*, Technical Bulletin 690, U. S. Dept. of Agriculture, 1939.

peats. The total calcium content of the low-lime peat is 1.40 per cent of CaO and its total exchange capacity is 184 milliequivalents. The corresponding figures for the high-lime soil are 6.00 per cent of CaO and 265 milliequivalents total exchange capacity.

Table XXXI. Cationic Condition of Two New York Woody-peat Soils — One Low and the Other High in Lime [1]

Exchange Characteristics	Ca	Mg	K	Na
Exch. cations, m.e.:				
Low-lime peat	55.2	13.4	1.2	1.1
High-lime peat	220.2	16.6	1.6	1.2
Relative numbers of cations — 100 taken as total:				
Low-lime peat	77.9	18.9	1.7	1.5
High-lime peat	91.9	6.9	0.7	0.5
Percentage of each cation in exchangeable condition:				
Low-lime peat	100	100	46	—
High-lime peat	100	72	37	—

Besides supplying milliequivalent figures that indicate the dominance of calcium, the data of Table XXXI show that all of the calcium present in peat soils and a very large proportion of the magnesium are in an exchangeable and hence in an active condition. Moreover, approximately two-fifths of the total potassium is exchangeable. All this is strikingly in contrast with a mineral soil where usually less than 25 per cent of the calcium, 10 per cent of the magnesium, and 2 per cent of the total potassium are exchangeable. Evidently much of the mineral matter of peat is exceedingly mobile.

The pH of peat soils, as with mineral soils, is controlled by the colloidal complex, the percentage base saturation being the major factor (page 290). The ratio of the metallic cations and the nature of the acidoid radical also exert an influence, the latter being especially important. In general the colloidal complex of peat when saturated with hydrogen will develop a lower pH than will an acid clay. In other words the peat complex is the stronger acid. This means that at the same percentage base saturation peats will tend to be somewhat more acid than mineral soils. Also a peat soil must

[1] Wilson, B. D., and E. V. Staker, *The Chemical Composition of the Muck Soils of New York*, Memoir 172, Cornell Univ. Agr. Exp. Sta., 1935.

be practically 100 per cent saturated with calcium and magnesium in order to attain neutrality or alkalinity. As already noted (page 291) humid-region mineral soils at 90 per cent base saturation, or sometimes even at 80 per cent, will show a pH of 7 or above.

Since the buffering of a soil is determined in large degree by the magnitude of its total exchange capacity, peat soils in general show an unusually marked resistance to a change in pH, much greater, of course, than do mineral soils. As a consequence considerably more sulfur or lime is necessary to change the pH of a peat soil than to effect a similar modification in a mineral soil at a corresponding buffer level. However, the buffer curve obtained by plotting pH against percentage base saturation is of the same general order as that for mineral soils (page 298), except that the pH at 50 per cent base saturation is a little less. This means that the buffer zone for peat soils lies at a somewhat lower pH range than for mineral soils. As already suggested, this may be ascribed to the more acid nature of the organic complex.

Because of the large amount of exchangeable calcium and magnesium in representative peat soils and the marked evolution of carbon dioxide if such soils are drained and under cultivation, base exchange is as active as in mineral soils. As a consequence the drainage waters from peat swamps and bogs not only carry copious amounts of lime, but they are likely to be alkaline also. However, the loss of lime from most peat soils is not serious, because of the high initial content of this constituent. Moreover, a rise of the water table in the spring may tend to restore somewhat the bases carried downward during the

Table XXXII. Exchange Data for Two Woody-peat Surface Soils [1] and for a Representative Humid-region Mineral Surface Soil

Exchange Characteristics	Woody Peats		Humid-region Mineral Soil
	Low Lime	High Lime	
Exchangeable Ca	39.8 m.e.	159.7 m.e.	6 to 9 m.e.
Other exch. bases	21.7 "	43.4 "	2 to 3 "
Exchangeable H	122.3 "	62.0 "	4 to 6 "
Total exch. capacity	183.8 "	265.1 "	12 to 18 "
Percentage base saturation	33.5	76.6	66.6
pH	4.0	5.1	5.3–5.6

[1] From Wilson, B. D., and E. V. Staker, *Ionic Exchange of Peat Soils*, Memoir 172, Cornell Univ. Agr. Exp. Sta., 1935.

previous season.   In general the lime content of cultivated peat soils is reduced to the point where this constituent is critical only in special cases.

In order that the exchange properties may be visualized a little more concretely, further data are offered respecting the two woody-peat surface soils already mentioned, one comparatively low in lime, the other rather high.   In contrast the exchange data, already quoted on page 91, for a representative humid-region mineral soil, are given. See Table **XXXII** opposite.

175. *Chemical composition of peat soils*

While peat soils are even more variable chemically than mineral soils, as the data below [1] indicate, certain outstanding and fairly

Chemical Analyses of Certain Representative Peat Soils
in Percentage Based on Dry Matter

Source		Organic Matter	N	P_2O_5	K_2O	CaO
Minnesota [a]	(low lime)	93.0	2.22	0.18	0.07	0.40
Minnesota [a]	(high lime)	79.8	2.78	0.24	0.10	3.35
Michigan [b]	(low lime)	77.5	2.10	0.26	...	0.16
Michigan [b]	(high lime)	85.1	2.08	0.25	...	6.80
German [c]	(low lime)	97.0	1.20	0.10	0.05	0.35
German [c]	(high lime)	90.0	2.50	0.25	0.10	4.00
Austrian [d]	(low lime)	93.3	1.40	0.10	0.06	0.45
Austrian [d]	(high lime)	83.8	2.10	0.18	0.13	2.38
New York [e]	(low lime)	94.2	1.26	0.15	0.10	0.60
New York [e]	(high lime)	81.5	2.56	0.19	0.28	6.51
Minnesota [a]	(low organic)	59.7	2.35	0.36	0.17	2.52
Minnesota [a]	(high organic)	94.0	1.70	0.16	0.04	0.31
Florida [f]	(sawgrass peat)	87.1	2.79	0.41	0.04	5.20
Canadian [g]	(peat soil)	74.3	2.19	0.20	0.16	...
Washington [h]	(woody sedge peat)	89.2	3.52	0.43	0.09	1.29

[a] Alway, F. J., *Agricultural Value and Reclamation of Minnesota Peat Soils*, Bulletin 188, Minn. Agr. Exp. Sta., 1920.

[b] McCool, M. M., and P. M. Harmer, *The Muck Soils of Michigan*, Special Bulletin 136, Mich. Agr. Exp. Sta., p. 23, 1925.

[c] Fleischer, M., *Die Anlage und die Bewirtschaftung von Moorwiesen und Moorweiden*, Berlin, 1913.

[d] Zailer, V., "Die Entstehungsgeschichte der Moore in Flussgebiet des Ems, *Zeitsch. f. Moorkultur und Torfverwertung*, VIII:105–154, 1910.

[e] Wilson, B. D., and E. V. Staker, *The Chemical Composition of the Muck Soils of New York*, Bulletin 537, Cornell Univ. Agr. Exp. Sta., 1932.

[f] Hammer, H. E., "The Chemical Composition of Everglades Peat Soils," *Soil Sci.*, XXVIII:5, 1929.

[g] Rept. Can. Exp. Farms, Rept. of Chemist:160, 1910.

[h] Feustel, I. C., and H. G. Byers, *The Physical and Chemical Characteristics of Certain American Peat Profiles*, Technical Bulletin 214, U. S. Dept. of Agriculture, 1930.

constant characteristics are in evidence. In order to present these more clearly, a representative analysis of the surface layer of an arable peat soil is given, but with the understanding that it is merely suggestive and tentative in nature. The chemical analysis of the upper layer of a representative humid-region mineral soil (see page 23) will be used for comparison and contrast.

Table XXXIII. Suggested Analysis for a Representative Peat and Mineral-surface Soil Respectively, Expressed in Per Cent

Constituent	Peat Surface Soil	Mineral Surface Soil
Organic matter	80.00	4.00
Nitrogen (N₂)	2.50	0.15
Phosphoric acid (P₂O₅)	0.20	0.10
Potash (K₂O)	0.10	2.00
Lime (CaO)	4.00	0.60
Magnesia (MgO)	0.50	0.50
Sulfur trioxide (SO₃)	1.50	0.10

The high nitrogen and organic content of peat soils is so well recognized that these characteristics need no further emphasis. There are certain features in respect to these two constituents, however, that justify further explanation. In the first place, there is no type of peat that can be used as a fertilizer because the nitrogen is not sufficiently available and because the amount, while large for a soil, is too low for a fertilizer. Second, peat soils have a wide nitrogen-carbon ratio, the minimum being in the neighborhood of 1 to 20. In contrast, this equilibrium ratio for a mineral soil is usually between 9 and 16. Third, peat soils, in spite of their wide nitrogen-carbon ratio, show exceedingly vigorous nitrification. In fact the nitrate accumulation, even in a low-lime peat, is usually far greater than that of a representative mineral soil. This can only be explained on the basis of the ready nitrifiability of the peaty constituents, the presence of adequate calcium, and the inactivity of part of the carbon. Thus the effective nitrogen-carbon ratio of peats may be as narrow as that of mineral soils. As a result, the multiplication of the competitive general-purpose heterotrophic organisms is not excessively encouraged and the nitrifiers are given ample opportunity to oxidize the ammoniacal nitrogen.

The phosphorus and potash of peat are both low, the latter exceedingly so in comparison with a mineral soil. Even the phosphoric acid is actually less in pounds, although the percentage figure may be double as in the case cited. On the basis of the acre-furrow-slice (2,000,000 pounds) the representative mineral soil contains 2000 pounds of P_2O_5. An equivalent layer of peat soil (say 500,000 pounds) would furnish only 1000 pounds of P_2O_5 or one-half as much. This explains why, in the growing of crops on a peat soil, phosphorus as well as potash must be applied periodically and in large amounts. This situation is axiomatic in peat fertilization.

The high lime content of peat soils is easily explained. Much of the water entering swamps is from seepage and has had ample opportunity of dissolving lime in its passage through the subsoil and substratum of the contiguous uplands. Moreover, many swamps contain a deposit of bog lime or other calcareous matter in their lower profile. This cannot but exert an influence. Consequently the waters in which swamp and bog plants live and decay are often heavily charged with calcium acid carbonate. As a result the living plants undoubtedly absorb considerable amounts of calcium, and since decaying organic matter is highly adsorptive and the calcium ion exceedingly mobile, the resultant peat horizons cannot avoid the presence of large amounts of exchangeable calcium ions. Nor is leaching, as with mineral soils, such an important factor in robbing the surface layers of lime. High lime, practically all of which is exchangeable, is an outstanding characteristic of many peat soils.

In spite of this high lime content, the majority of peat soils are distinctly acid, often very markedly so. For instance, the average pH of twelve woody-peat soils from Oswego County, New York, was 5.3 in spite of an average CaO content of 3.74 per cent.[1] Cases even more striking are available. At first glance such a condition seems rather anomalous, especially when it is remembered that high acidity in a mineral soil is correlated with low calcium, both actually and relatively. The explanation is obvious. The adsorptive capacity of peat for exchangeable cations is exceedingly high, so great, in fact, that such a soil may be at a low percentage base saturation and yet be carrying actually and comparatively exceptionally large amounts of lime. At the same time the percentage base saturation is such as to assure a markedly acid condition. It must not be forgotten that we are dealing here with the soil solution and not with the alkaline drainage water lower down in the profile.

[1] Wilson, B. D., and E. V. Staker, *The Chemical Composition of the Muck Soils of New York,* Bulletin 537, Cornell Univ. Agr. Exp. Sta., 13, 1932.

The percentage of magnesia in peat soil is usually no greater than that of a mineral soil. The actual amount, however, is much less due to the low weight of peat to the acre-furrow-slice. The situation is thus much the same as that of phosphoric acid, although it is alle-viated somewhat by the high proportion of the magnesium that is held in an exchangeable condition. Peat soils, long intensively cropped, may possibly develop a magnesia deficiency unless fertilizers carrying this constituent have been used. Since most peats are seldom limed, there is little chance of adding magnesium in this particular way.

The abundance of sulfur in peat soils is not at all surprising. Plant tissue always contains considerable sulfur, and as a consequence, or-ganic deposits such as peat should be comparatively high in this constituent. When sulfur oxidation is vigorous, as is usually the case with arable peat soils, sulfates tend to accumulate. At times a white incrustation, probably calcium sulfate (gypsum), can be observed along ditches and at other places on the surface of peat deposits where the upward movement and the evaporation of moisture is taking place. Sulfur is thus so abundant in most peat soils as to preclude any possibility of this element being a limiting factor in plant growth.

Besides the more apparent chemical characteristics, peat soils pre-sent three somewhat anomalous features. These will be restated. First, the representative peat soil possesses a wide nitrogen-carbon ratio and yet in spite of it supports a very vigorous nitrification. Second, peat soils are usually comparatively high in lime and yet may be definitely acid, often highly so. And third, in spite of this acidity, nitrate accumulation takes place far beyond that common in mineral soils. This last feature indicates that calcium is a controlling factor in nitrification, and that the H-ion concentration, unless excessive, does not impede, in itself, this very important biochemical transformation. In fact microorganisms as well as higher plants undoubtedly utilize nutrients most effectively in the presence of a significant concentration of H ions.

176. *Bog lime*

In many cases peat soils are underlaid at varying depths by a soft impure calcium carbonate called *bog lime* or *marl*.[1] Its probable posi-

---

[1] Bog lime is usually spoken of agriculturally as *marl*. Marl, as correctly used by the geologist, refers to a calcareous clay of variable composition. Bog lime, when it contains numerous shells, is often termed *shell marl*.

tion in the profile is indicated by Fig. 53.   Such a deposit may come from the shells of certain of the Mollusca, which have inhabited the basin, or from aquatic plants, such as mosses, algae, and species of Chara.   These organisms have the power of precipitating the calcium of the bicarbonate as insoluble calcium carbonate.   It seems that these plants and animals occupied the basin before or during the formation of the peat, the marl resulting from the accumulation of their residues on the bottom of the basin or farther up in the profile.

Marl, when typically developed, is a white or gray, soft, crumbly material, often full of shells and effervescing freely with dilute hydrochloric acid.   When the deposit is extensive enough and the presence of water or the thickness of the overburden does not interfere, marl may be dug out and used as agricultural lime.   In general, however, it cannot compete in price with ground limestone, although on the basis of calcium content it is often just as satisfactory a form of lime.

In cases in which marl is present, it may not only supply calcium to the circulating waters, but if high in the profile, may actually become mixed with the surface peat.   Thus the exceedingly high lime content of some organic soils may be accounted for, at least in part, on this basis.   As a result, such peats are likely to be low in acidity or alkaline, often intensely so.   In general an alkaline peat is not considered so highly desirable for intensive culture, especially the growing of vegetables.

177. *Factors that determine the value of peat soils*

The value of peat agriculturally will depend on a number of factors. Of first consideration is the possibility of drainage, that is, a more or less permanent lowering and control of the water table sufficient to allow an adequate aeration of the root zone.   This is oftentimes expensive and may require the cooperation of a number of landowners, some of whom may have no interest in the utilization of the peat.

Moreover, it may be advantageous to raise or lower the water table at various times during the season.   For instance, celery at setting is benefited by plenty of moisture.   As the crop develops, the water table should be gradually lowered to accommodate the root development.   The probable cost of drainage and of the seasonal control of the moisture may be such as to make the reclamation of a peat bed economically unwise. Since peat is very often covered with a forest growth, the cost of clearing must be reckoned with. In some cases this cost may be rather high and should be considered before drainage operations begin.

Again the depth and quality of the organic deposit is a factor. Peat settles and shrinks considerably the first few years after drainage and cultivation have become operative. If a depth adequate for cropping does not remain, the expense of reclamation is thrown away. Three or 4 feet of organic material are desirable, especially if calcareous clay or marl underlies the deposit. The quality of the peat is of special importance, not only as to the degree of decay, but also as to the nature of the original plant materials. Woody peat, for example, is generally considered as more desirable than that coming from cattails and reeds, and it usually is highly prized wherever it occurs. Much of the acreage of this type of peat soil lies in Wisconsin, Michigan, and New York.

Besides these factors, market facilities and climatic conditions must be considered. Since peat soils are most profitably used for the growing of vegetables, the possibility of placing the produce on the market with little delay is of prime importance. Hard roads, suitable for trucking, or nearness to railroads influence greatly the acre value of peat lands and the outlay that can be justified in their improvement. The nearness to great centers of population greatly enhances the desirability of such soils. Climate, of course, governs the various kinds of crops that may be produced. These factors determine whether the cropping shall be general farming, trucking, market gardening, or certain specialized crops such as peppermint for instance.

178. *Preparation of peat for cropping*

Since peat soils are often forested or covered with shrubs, the first step is to clear the land. Drainage may then be facilitated further, and the water table lowered and brought under control. The utilization of the area as pasture for a few years is sometimes practiced. The roots and stumps are thus given time to decay, their removal being relatively easy when the land is finally fitted for cultivation. If the area is burned over to remove the brush and other debris, it should be done early in the season while the peat is wet and not likely to catch fire. Such a fire is often difficult to extinguish and may ruin the deposit by destroying the more fertile surface layer. If, however, the surface soil is fibrous with a more desirable layer below, it may be of advantage to burn this part, the resultant ash serving to mineralize the exposed portion.

After breaking the peat soil, preferably with heavy plows drawn by a tractor, it is often advisable to grow such crops as corn, oats, rye, or potatoes for a year or two, as they do well on raw and uneven peat lands. Once the peat is adequately weathered, freed of roots and stumps, and all hummocks eliminated, it is ready for vegetable production. More thorough drainage is now required and is usually obtained by a system of ditches. Sometimes tile drains or even mole drains are used. It is of advantage with certain crops, such as celery, to be able to raise or lower the water table by the use of dams or other adjustments of the drainage system.

179. *Management of peat soils* [1]

All sorts of vegetable crops may be grown on peat soils — celery, lettuce, spinach, onions, potatoes, carrots, asparagus, and cabbage perhaps being the most important. However, beets, parsnips, turnips, and other vegetables may be produced as well as such specialized crops as peppermint. In some cases, peat is used for field crops and a more or less definite rotation is followed. Sugar beets, corn, oats, rye, buckwheat, flax, clover, timothy, and other field crops give good yields when suitable fertilization is provided. In many cases, espe-

[1] A few of the many important publications dealing with the management of peat soil are:

Whitson, A. R., A. R. Albert, and O. R. Zeasman, *Fertilizers and Crops for Marsh Soils,* Bulletin 392, Wis. Agr. Exp. Sta., 1927.

Brown, H. D., *The Culture of Onions in Indiana,* Circular 158, Purdue Agr. Exp. Sta., 1928.

Knott, J. E., *Fertilizing Onions on Muck Soils,* Bulletin 650, Cornell Univ. Agr. Exp. Sta., 1930.

Knott, J. E., *Celery Production on the Muck Soils of New York,* Bulletin 517, Cornell Univ. Agr. Exp. Sta., 1931.

Ogg, W. G., and A. MacLeod, "Reclamation and Cultivation of Peat Lands in Lewis," *Scottish Jour. Agr.,* XV, No. 2, 1932.

Fifield, W. M., *Potato Growing in Florida,* Bulletin 295, Fla. Agr. Exp. Sta., 1936.

Breckenbach, S. R., *A Fertility Program for Celery Production of Everglades Organic Soils,* Bulletin 333, Fla. Agr. Exp. Sta., 1939.

Harmer, Paul M., *The Muck Soils of Michigan, Their Management and Uses,* Special Bulletin 314, Mich. Agr. Exp. Sta., 1941.

cially in Europe, peat soils are used extensively for pasture and meadows. In fact almost any crop will grow on peat soil if properly managed.

Plowing is ordinarily unnecessary every year, as the peat is porous and open, unless it contains considerable silt and clay. In fact, a peat soil generally needs packing rather than loosening. The longer a peat has been cropped the more important compaction is likely to be, since the cultivation tends to destroy the original granular structure, leaving the soil, when dry, in a powdery condition. It is then susceptible to wind erosion, a very serious problem in some sections. For this reason, a roller or packer is an important implement in the management of such land. The compacting of peat allows the roots to come into closer contact with the soil and facilitates the rise of water from below. It also tends to reduce the blowing of the soil during dry weather, although a windbreak [1] of some kind is much more effective. The cultivation of peat, while easier than for mineral soils, is carried on in exactly the same way and should be shallow, especially after the root development of the crop begins. The hilling of potatoes and the banking of celery are special cases and can hardly be classed as cultivation.

Since peat soils are so radically different from mineral soils both physically and chemically, it is not surprising that a somewhat divergent system of fertility management is recommended. In general, peat soils respond to applications of well-rotted farm manure. The manure furnishes plant nutrients, especially nitrogen, and probably increases the rate of decay of the organic matter. This speeding up of the carbon and nitrogen turnover cannot fail to increase the availability of the soil nutrients. As a consequence, farm manure, if available, is sometimes applied every few years even to well-decayed peat. Lime, that so often must be applied to mineral soils in order to raise farm manure to its full effectiveness, ordinarily is less necessary on peat, as this soil usually is adequately supplied with calcium.

Of much greater importance than farm manure are commercial fertilizers. In fact, complete reliance is placed on these materials in the production of most crops, especially vegetables. As organic soils are very low in phosphorus and potassium, these elements must by all means be added. Since vegetables are rapid-growing plants, succulence often being an essential quality, large amounts of readily

[1] For a brief discussion of the control of wind erosion on peat soils, see page 204.

available nitrogen are necessary. The nitrogen of newly broken peat is often rapidly enough available to supply this need. Such peat land, therefore, frequently requires at the beginning only phosphoric acid and potash. This is especially true of woody peats and is taken advantage of in the fertilization of such soil. After peat soils have been cropped for a few years, decay and nitrification are frequently too slow to meet the crop demand for nitrogen. Under such conditions this element is needed and a fertilizer containing nitrogen as well as phosphoric acid and potash is usually recommended.[1]

Peat soils are often not only in need of potassium, phosphorus, and nitrogen, but some of the trace elements as well.[2] On New York woody peats, copper sulfate has given good results in the control of certain diseases of lettuce and has aided in the coloration of onions. In fact, the application of this salt at the rate of 100 to 200 pounds to the acre is becoming a recognized treatment for these soils when they are first put under cultivation. In Florida and elsewhere not only copper sulfate, but salts of manganese and zinc, are used to better the physiological condition of both peat and muck soils. Boron deficiencies are also becoming evident. Just what function the trace elements perform is not definitely known, but their fertilizer value is now well established on such soils, and they must be considered in any well-balanced fertilizer program.

[1] Such analyses as a 0–8–12, a 0–12–12, a 0–12–18, or others of similar ratios are recommended when commercial nitrogen is unnecessary. When nitrogen is required, a 3–12–18, a 4–8–24, a 5–10–5, a 15–30–15, a 5–10–15 or other mixtures of similar ratio may be utilized depending on soil conditions and the crop to be grown. In many cases nitrate of soda or other fertilizers are applied as a side-dressing.

[2] The use of trace elements as fertilizers is discussed more fully on page 419.

Chapter XV. Lime and Its Soil-plant Relationships

It is generally agreed that soil acidity and the physiological conditions that accompany it are induced by a lack or an inactivity of certain metallic cations, especially calcium and magnesium, that tend, when active, to reduce the H-ion concentration of the soil solution. Consequently an artificial rectification of the physiological setup of an acid soil is logically attained by adding compounds carrying the necessary metals in such forms and amounts as to modify the colloidal complex to the extent desired.

The cation most commonly used to alleviate the physiological conditions that characterize acid soils and to correct, at least in part, their acidity is calcium, although magnesium is also applied, sometimes in considerable amounts, since it is associated with calcium in most of the commercial limes. These cations are employed because they are effective with all types of acidity and because they are comparatively cheap and plentiful. Moreover, their carbonates, hydroxides, and oxides are mild and beneficial in their action. In humid-region soils calcium and to a lesser extent magnesium are the metallic cations that usually predominate in the colloidal complexes (see page 72). It is only natural, therefore, that an attempt should be made to restore them by artificial means.

As a means of controlling soil acidity potassium salts in active form are too expensive, while sodium compounds are likely to generate an undesirable physical condition or be otherwise harmful. Besides, even their carbonates are too drastic in action and too caustic to be handled with comfort. Moreover, sodium and potassium are not the metallic cations that normally dominate the colloidal interfaces. Most higher plants and microorganisms are immutably adjusted to a calcium regime.[1]

[1] The following articles bear on this phase:
Kelley, W. P., "Agronomic Importance of Calcium," *Soil Sci.*, XL:103–109, 1935.
Albrecht, W. A., "Calcium-Potassium-Phosphorus relation as a possible factor in Ecological array of Plants," *Jour. Amer. Soc. Agron.*, XXXII:411–418, 1940.
Pierre, W. H. and W. H. Allaway, "Calcium in the Soil, II. Biological Relations," *Proc. Soil Sci. Soc. Amer.*, VI:16–26, 1941.

180. *Forms of lime*

Lime from the strictly chemical standpoint refers to one and only one compound — calcium oxide. Agriculturally, however, the term has a broader meaning. Thus used it "includes all compounds of calcium and magnesium employed in a practical way, not only to raise the pH of an overly acid soil but especially to rectify its physiological condition." It is to be noted that the definition includes magnesium as well as calcium and that the prime objective is not merely to decrease the H-ion concentration but rather to alleviate the factors associative and concomitant with it. A rise in pH takes place because the increase in percentage base saturation, induced by the addition of the compounds usually considered as lime, results in a lowering of the H-ion concentration of the soil solution (page 291).

Three compounds of lime are in common use: *oxides, hydroxides*, and *carbonates*. All these have the advantage of leaving no residues of an objectionable nature in the soil. The oxides and hydroxides change to the carbonate and bicarbonate forms and the latter, when the calcium and magnesium are selectively adsorbed by the colloidal complexes, produce carbonic acid. Since the soil usually is already carrying an excess of carbonic acid and since this weak acid breaks up into water and carbon dioxide at the slightest provocation, undesirable aftereffects ordinarily are not encountered, unless excessive amounts are applied. The direct effects when such limes are adjusted to the soil system (colloidal solids — CO_2 — water) are (1) a rise in percentage base saturation, (2) an increase in active calcium and magnesium, and (3) a lowering of the H-ion concentration of the solution.

The application to the soil of calcium and magnesium salts of strong acids, such as calcium sulfate (gypsum) and calcium chloride, are not usually recommended. The reason is simple. When by base exchange the metallic cations are adsorbed and some of the exchangeable hydrogen of the colloidal matter is liberated, strong acids result. Such acids as sulfuric and hydrochloric, for instance, are not so easily disposed of as weak carbonic acid, and while the amount of active calcium may increase, the soil pH may go down. For this reason gypsum and calcium chloride are not usually considered as an agricultural lime in the sense defined above and seldom are recommended in place of the forms listed.

Certain other compounds of calcium may at some future time be classed as agricultural lime if their use becomes common. For instance, by-product calcium silicate ($CaSiO_3$ and Ca_2SiO_4) has been used successfully in an experimental way [1] and seems to fulfill three prime requisites of ordinary lime — a ready source of active calcium, no objectionable residue since the silicate ion produces a very weak acid, and a capacity to reduce soil acidity. Moreover, when an excess of the powdered silicate is applied to soils, detrimental effects to higher plants, often obtained from overdoses of calcium carbonate, are not observed. One thing, however, must be guarded against — impurities that might be detrimental. If, for instance, the by-product silicate should contain fluorine, even in small amounts, the influence on superphosphate when the two come in contact in the soil would be very undesirable. This is because a reversion of the available phosphoric acid to the very insoluble and unavailable fluorapatite very likely would occur (page 302). The effectiveness of the phosphate might thus be markedly reduced if not entirely negated.

As is to be expected, liming materials do not appear on the market as single compounds of magnesium or calcium, nor are they by any means pure. The better grades of the oxides and hydroxides are generally used in the trades, the less pure materials having an outlet as agricultural lime. The carbonated forms of lime have a number of different sources and vary to a marked degree in purity.

181. *Oxide of lime*

Commercial oxide of lime is commonly spoken of as *burned lime*, *quicklime*, or often simply as the *oxide*. It is usually marketed in paper bags and as a finely ground powder. Some, however, is still sold in the lump condition. The two forms are distinguished by the terms *ground burned* and *lump lime* respectively. Oxide of lime is quite caustic and rather disagreeable to handle.

The devices for producing burned lime are various, ranging from the farmer's lime heap to the large cylindrical kilns of commerce. In any case the general result is the same. The limestone with which the kiln is charged is decomposed by the heat, carbon dioxide and

---

[1] See MacIntire, W. H., et al., "Nature and Liming Value of Quenched Calcium Silicate Slag," *Soil Sci.*, L:219–232, 1940. Some of the important articles on the subject are cited.

other gases are driven off, and calcium and magnesium oxides are left behind.[1] The purity of burned lime, as it is sold for agricultural purposes, is variable, ranging from 85 to 98 per cent. The impurities of burned lime consist of the original impurities of the limestone, such as chert, clay, and iron compounds, etc.

A number of compounds are present in commercial oxide of lime. Calcium oxide and magnesium oxide are, of course, most prominent. With them are small amounts of the hydroxides since the oxides readily take up water from the air and slake to some extent. Also the contact with the atmosphere will tend to produce carbonates as well. Besides these there are the inert impurities already mentioned. Sometimes, as in the case of semicalcined lime,[2] a very considerable amount of carbonate may be encountered.

While commercial oxide of lime varies greatly in composition, a representative sample may possess a purity of perhaps 95 per cent. The calcium and magnesium present in all forms, and expressed in the conventional chemical way, may tentatively be set about 77 per cent of CaO and 18 per cent of MgO. The ratio of calcium oxide to magnesium oxide is usually 4 or 5 to 1. In highly magnesium limes the percentage of MgO may rise as high as 45 per cent with a corresponding lowering of the CaO.

182. *Hydroxide of lime*

This form of lime is commonly, and of course improperly, referred to as the *hydrate*. And since it is produced by adding water to burned lime, the hydroxides that result are often spoken of as *slaked lime*.[3] It appears on the market as a white powder, highly caustic and not at all pleasant to handle.

In order to maintain the concentration of this form of lime at a high point, the slaking often is not carried to completion. As a result, considerable amounts of the oxides are likely to remain. Moreover, the

[1] $CaCO_3 + Heat = CaO + CO_2$.
   $MgCO_3 + Heat = MgO + CO_2$.

[2] Magnesium carbonate burns at a much lower heat than does calcium carbonate. This is taken advantage of in producing semicalcined lime. The temperature of the kiln is raised just high enough to decompose the magnesium carbonate, leaving the calcium carbonate little affected. The product, which is later ground, consists of a mixture of oxides and carbonates.

[3] Impure CaO and $MgO + 2 H_2O = Ca(OH)_2 + Mg(OH)_2 +$ impurities.

hydroxide of lime carbonates very readily.[1] A few weeks after its manufacture the lime will usually effervesce freely when treated with dilute hydrochloric acid.[2] Besides the impurities, six important lime compounds are thus present: the oxides, the hydroxides, and the carbonates of calcium and magnesium. The hydroxides, of course, greatly predominate.

Representative slaked lime may possess a purity perhaps of 96 per cent and show on analysis 60 per cent of CaO and perhaps 12 per cent of MgO. The ratio of the oxides is about the same as that for the representative commercial burned lime. And the maximum percentage of MgO may range as high as 35.

183. *Carbonate of lime*

A number of lime compounds are sold under the head of carbonated lime. Of these, pulverized or ground limestone is the most common. There are also bog lime or marl, oyster shells, and precipitated carbonates. Great deposits of marl occur under peat beds (page 336) and when dredged out, dried, and crushed, make excellent lime. However, the cost usually is too high to allow successful competition with limestone. Also lime carbonates are by-products from certain industries. All of these forms of lime are variable in their content of calcium and magnesium.

Ground limestone, which is used to a greater extent than all other forms of lime combined, varies in purity from approximately 75 to 99 per cent. The average purity of this natural product may be put at perhaps 94 per cent. The only important compounds of lime present are the two carbonates. Representative pulverized limestone contains possibly 80 per cent of $CaCO_3$ and 14 per cent of $MgCO_3$. These, when expressed in the conventional way, are equivalent to 44.80 per cent of CaO and 6.70 per cent of MgO. The ratio of the two oxides is about 7 to 1, somewhat wider than in the case of the burned and hydroxide forms of lime. In highly dolomitic limestone the magnesium carbonate may rise as high as 45 per cent.

184. *Chemical guarantees of limes*

Since the various forms of lime are sold on the basis of their chemical composition, the commercial guarantees in this respect become a mat-

[1] $Ca(OH)_2 + CO_2 = CaCO_3 + H_2O.$

[2] $CaCO_3 + 2 HCl = CaCl_2 + H_2O + CO_2.$

ter of great importance. The caustic forms, that is the oxide and hydroxide, may bear composition guarantees stated in one or more ways — the *conventional oxide content*, the *calcium oxide equivalent*, the *neutralizing power*, and *percentages of calcium and magnesium*. In order to facilitate the explanation and comparison of the various methods, the oxide figures already suggested for commercial burned and hydroxide of lime are drawn together in Table XXXIV and stated in terms of the other methods of expression.

Table XXXIV. Composition of a Representative Commercial Oxide and Hydroxide of Lime Expressed in Different Ways

Forms of Lime	Conventional oxide content, percentage	Calcium oxide equivalent	Neutralizing power	Elemental, percentage
Commercial oxide	CaO, 77 MgO, 18	102.0	182.1	Ca, 55.0 Mg, 10.8
Commercial hydroxide	CaO, 60 MgO, 12	76.7	136.9	Ca, 42.8 Mg, 7.2

Since the oxide form of expression is so commonly used, this type of guarantee is designated here as the conventional method. The *calcium oxide equivalent*, as the term implies, is a statement of the strength of the lime in one figure, namely, CaO. The magnesium oxide is calculated to calcium oxide equivalent and this figure is added to the calcium oxide already present. This may be conveniently done by means of conversion factors.[1] Thus for the commercial oxide of Table XXXIV, 18 per cent of MgO is equal to 25 per cent of CaO and 77 + 25 = 102, the calcium oxide equivalent. This means that every 100 pounds of the impure burned lime is equivalent in neutralizing capacity to 102 pounds of *pure* calcium oxide.

The *neutralizing power*, as the term is arbitrarily used in respect to lime, is nothing more than a statement of the strength in terms of calcium carbonate — that is, its $CaCO_3$ equivalent. Thus by dividing by the factor 0.56 in the case above, the calcium oxide equivalent of 102 becomes 182.1, the $CaCO_3$ equivalent. This means that every

[1] Conversion factors for lime calculations:

$MgO \times 1.389 = CaO$ $MgCO_3 \times .288 = Mg$
$CaCO_3 \times 0.560 = CaO$ $MgO \times .602 = Mg$
$MgCO_3 \times 0.664 = CaO$ $CaCO_3 \times .400 = Ca$
$MgCO_3 \times 1.186 = CaCO_3$ $CaO \times .714 = Ca$

100 pounds of the impure burned lime is equivalent in neutralizing capacity to 182.1 pounds of *pure* calcium carbonate.

The elemental method of expression, while not so common as the other modes of statement, is required in some cases. It may readily be calculated from the conventional oxide guarantee. Or, if given alone, the other forms of statement may be derived from it. Sixty-five per cent of total calcium plus magnesium is a conservative figure for a representative oxide of lime and 50 per cent for a commercial hydroxide.

Commercial caustic limes practically always carry the conventional oxide guarantee and sometimes the elemental. Thus the amount of magnesium, as well as calcium, present is indicated. This is an important consideration. In addition, one or even both of the other forms of guarantee may be given. The latter are especially desirable as they show the strength of the lime in one figure, thus making comparisons between different brands easy.

The guarantees on ground limestone differ in two respects from those of the caustic forms of lime. Usually the separate percentages of calcium and magnesium carbonates are given. These are almost always accompanied by the percentage of total carbonates. In addition one or more of the other four modes of guarantee may be used. By way of illustration the six methods of expression are presented in Table XXXV for a representative ground limestone. Its carbonate composition has already been tentatively suggested.

Table **XXXV**. Composition of a Representative Commercial Ground Limestone Expressed in Different Ways

Lime	Separate Carbonates, Percentage	Total Carbonates, Percentage	Neutra-lizing Power	Conventional Oxide, Percentage	Calcium Oxide Equivalent	Elemental, Percentage
A representative limestone	$CaCO_3$, 80 $MgCO_3$, 14	94	96.6	CaO, 44.80 MgO, 6.70	54.10	Ca, 32.00 Mg, 4.03

Considerable controversy has arisen over the total carbonate method of guarantee, in that it is not so true an expression of the chemical strength of the lime as is the neutralizing-power figure. It has many advocates, however, because it is so simple and requires no chemical explanation. Moreover, in the field a pound of calcic limestone seems as effective in rectifying physiological conditions as a pound of dolomitic limestone. Then why give the lime credit for the higher neutralizing power of the magnesium carbonate and magnify the importance of the magnesium, the lime element of lesser importance? Moreover, the differences between the two guarantee figures are usually so small that the variations of application will effectively cover them up. The argument, therefore, is that, if it makes little difference which type of guarantee is used, why not choose the simpler one?

Those that favor the neutralizing-power method of expression demand accuracy and uniformity. This type of guarantee is accepted for the caustic limes, so why make an exception in the case of limestone? Again, the neutralizing power can be very easily and quickly determined. This is an important consideration in a control laboratory when many samples must be analyzed. Moreover, there is the advertising phase of the controversy. For instance, a dolomitic limestone containing 46 per cent of $CaCO_3$ and 43 per cent of $MgCO_3$ has a neutralizing power of 97 but its total carbonate figure is only 89. When competition is keen, such a difference may lead to much misunderstanding and controversy.

185. *Fineness guarantee of limestone*

The application of the different forms of lime in chemically equivalent quantities to soils does not necessarily mean that equivalent results will be attained. This is especially true in regard to pulverized limestone, the particles of which are quite variable in size as well as hardness. Since it is well known that the finer the division of any material the more rapid is the solution, the importance of knowing the fineness of this form of lime is apparent. The caustic limes usually appear on the market as almost impalpable powders, consequently their fineness is always satisfactory.

The rate of solubility in the soil water is not in itself the only consideration. Lime seems by direct contact to react with the acid colloidal complexes of the soil, effecting thereby an ionic exchange. Since one of the influences sought is an increase in the percentage base saturation of the soil, the more rapidly the adsorbed hydrogen is replaced by calcium and magnesium, the better.

Consequently in producing commercial limestone that may be advertised as *fine* the aim is to turn out a product that has a large percentage of floury material, giving rapid action in the soil, and yet one that carries enough of the coarser grades to ensure lasting qualities.

This type of lime is not so expensive to produce as a limestone that is all very fine and, over the period of the rotation, it apparently is just as satisfactory.

Therefore, in order to rate a limestone as to its probable effects in comparison with other limes, a fineness guarantee is desirable. This is usually one of the requirements of laws controlling the sale of agricultural limestone. A mechanical analysis is made by the use of screens of different mesh, a 10-mesh sieve, for example, having ten openings to the linear inch.[1] The proportion of the limestone that will pass through the various screens used constitutes the guarantee. The following rating gives an idea as to the degree of pulverization exhibited by a representative *fine* limestone: 100 per cent through a 10-mesh screen, 75 per cent through a 50-mesh, and 60 per cent through a 100-mesh. Limestones finer and also considerably coarser than this are on the market.

186. *Interpretation of a fineness guarantee*

Before a statement can be made as to the degrees of fineness a limestone should attain to be satisfactory, some of the experimental work available on the subject should be considered. White presents the following significant data (Table XXXVI) as a result of certain laboratory and greenhouse studies at State College, Pennsylvania.

Table XXXVI. A Comparison of Various Grades of Limestone When Applied at the Same Rates. Pennsylvania Agricultural Experiment Station.[2]
100-mesh Taken as 100

Conditions	100-mesh and smaller	60–80-mesh	20–40-mesh	8–12-mesh
Solubility in carbonated water	100	57	45	28
Value in correcting acidity	100	57	27	18
Formation of nitrates	100	94	56	12
Plant growth	100	69	22	5

[1] The diameter of the individual openings will, of course, be much less than 0.1 in., the exact size depending on the wire used in making the sieve. Usually the diameter of the openings in inches is a little more than one-half of the quotient obtained by dividing 1 by the mesh rating. For instance the openings of a 10-mesh screen are approximately .07 in. diameter; those of a 50-mesh, .0122 in.; and those of a 100-mesh screen, approximately .0058 in. Unfortunately there is no standardization of sieves used for grading agricultural limestone.

[2] White, J. W., *The Value of Limestone of Different Degrees of Fineness*, Bulletin 149 Penn. Agr. Exp. Sta., 1917.

These figures show that the finer grades of limestone are much more rapidly effective. Further data by the same author indicate that, while the coarser lime is less rapid in its action, it remains in the soil longer and its influence should be effective for a greater period of years. Other investigators [1] have published results that substantiate the conclusions above. The proportionate responses are somewhat different, however. This is to be expected, as limestones of different hardness applied to various soil types are sure to respond rather diversely.

Everything considered, a pulverized limestone, "all of which will pass a 10-mesh screen, and at least 50 per cent of which will pass a 100-mesh sieve," should give excellent results and yet be cheap enough to make its use worth while. Such a lime is sufficiently pulverized to rate as a *fine* lime. Nevertheless, many limes are finer than this, 50 per cent sometimes passing a 200-mesh screen. However, because of the cost of grinding the stone to a very fine condition and the rapidity with which such material disappears from the soil, a medium ground lime, such as specified above, seems to be a more desirable commercial product. Such material has enough of the finer particles to give quick results and yet a sufficient amount of the coarser fragments to make it last over the period of the rotation.

A limestone which does not approximate the fineness designated above should be discounted to the extent to which it falls short. It may be necessary, for example, to consider 3000 pounds of one limestone as equal to 1 ton of another, even though their chemical analyses are the same. Considerable judgment in the interpretation of fineness guarantees is necessary in order that such an adjustment be correctly made. Much limestone that falls below the standard set above is now being used because, as a by-product, it is very cheap. When the amounts put on the land are properly adjusted, as good results may be expected from the coarser limes as from the finer limestones and the effects should last considerably longer.

187. *Changes of lime in the soil*

In considering the changes that lime undergoes when added to the soil two things must always be kept in mind: (1) that the calcium and

---

[1] Lyon, T. L., *Relative Effectiveness of Limestone Particles of Different Sizes*, Bulletin 531, Cornell Univ. Agr. Exp. Sta., 1931. Some of the more important literature is cited by this author.

magnesium compounds applied undergo solution under the influence of a variable pressure of carbon dioxide [1] and (2) that the colloidal complex, unless already fully satisfied in respect to bases, which will not be the case with acid soils, will adsorb considerable amounts of calcium and magnesium ions. In short, there is a competition for bases as lime is added to this complex and heterogeneous solid-liquid-carbon dioxide system we call the *soil*.

When lime, whether the oxide, hydroxide, or the carbonate, is applied to an acid soil, the movement, as solution occurs, is toward the bicarbonate form. This is because the partial carbon dioxide pressure, usually several hundred times greater than that of the atmospheric air, is intense enough to prevent the existence of the hydroxide or even the carbonate. The reactions, written only for the calcium limes, are as follows:

$$CaO + H_2O = Ca(OH)_2$$
$$Ca(OH)_2 + H_2CO_3 = CaCO_3 + 2H_2O$$
$$CaCO_3 + H_2CO_3 = Ca(HCO_3)_2$$

This, however, represents only the solution of the lime in carbonated water. The soil situation is not so simple as one might be led to assume. This is because the soil colloidal matter continually upsets the equilibrium tendencies by adsorbing, very vigorously if the soil is quite acid, the ions of calcium and magnesium. These ions may be taken from the soil solution proper or directly from the solid phase if the contact is sufficiently close. The adsorption in respect to calcium may be indicated as follows:

$$x \; CarH(acidoid) + y \begin{cases} Ca(HCO_3)_2 \\ \quad or \quad \rightleftharpoons \\ CaCO_3 \end{cases}$$

$$x \; CarH(acidoid) + y \begin{cases} H_2CO_3 \\ r \; carbonate \\ or \; bicarbonate \end{cases}$$

As the above reaction proceeds the carbonic acid that is formed evolves carbon dioxide. This explains why the application of ground limestone causes for a time an increase in the carbon dioxide pressure of the soil. This increase is especially important since it occurs at the

[1] For a discussion of this phase see Bradfield, Richard, "Calcium of the Soil: I Physico-Chemical Relations," *Proc. Soil Sci. Soc. Amer.*, VI:8–15, 1941.

interface where the solvent action of carbon dioxide is particularly effective. In addition, the adsorption of the calcium and magnesium raises the percentage base saturation of the colloidal complex and the pH of the soil solution is pushed up correspondingly (see page 291). The calcium and magnesium, especially if a limestone containing some fairly coarse as well as fine particles is applied, will exist in the soil, at least for a time, in three forms: (1) as solid calcium and magnesium carbonate, (2) as exchangeable bases adsorbed by the colloidal matter, and (3) as dissociated cations in the soil solution mostly in association with bicarbonate anions. When the calcium and magnesium carbonate has all dissolved the lime system, now a two-phase one, becomes somewhat simpler.

In respect to the situation described above two things should be particularly noted. In the first place the equilibrium tendencies referred to do not result in a homogeneous distribution of calcium and magnesium through the soil solution. Far from it. This is due to variations in carbon dioxide pressure and to the disturbing effects of colloidal adsorption. In the immediate neighborhood of the coarse particles of lime a noticeable concentration of calcium and magnesium ions will be found and, if the carbon dioxide pressure is about that of the atmospheric air, the pH will be near 8, perhaps a little above. At the interface of the colloidal complex, especially if the latter has been raised to a rather high percentage base saturation, the concentration of calcium and magnesium ions, in contrast, will be very much greater. At the same time, however, due to carbon dioxide pressure, the H-ion concentration in this zone may become great enough to give a pH considerably below 7. Between these two extremes variable concentrations of Ca, Mg, and H ions will be found in the soil solution depending upon carbon dioxide pressure of the soil air and other factors. Heterogeneity in respect to the above cations is the rule rather than the exception.

Second, it must be remembered that even a heterogeneous equilibrium of the calcium and magnesium added in lime is not likely to be attained under field conditions. This is due to a number of influences of which changes in moisture content, absorption by higher plants and microorganisms, and leaching, due to excess water, are especially important.

While it is not possible to follow the calcium and magnesium added in lime through all of the intricate chemical and biological changes to which they are subjected in the soil, it is feasible to deal with the broader aspects of the subject. As these metallic cations are withdrawn from the soil solution by higher plants, soil organisms, or by leaching, readjustments occur and calcium and magnesium, previously held in the solid phase or as exchangeable ions, become active largely as the bicarbonate. Not only does the calcium carbonate, which might be present, gradually disappear, but also the colloidal complex is depleted of its bases. This is effected by H ions generated largely by the carbon dioxide that is evolved so copiously from decaying organic matter. In this way the so-called reserve lime is gradually fed into the soil solution, there to be used in many different ways. The transfers described above and written only for calcium proceed as follows:

$$CaCO_3 + H_2CO_3 \rightleftharpoons Ca(HCO_3)_2$$
$$x \; CarH(acidoid) + y \; H_2CO_3 \rightleftharpoons x \; CarH(acidoid) + y \; Ca(HCO_3)_2$$

If the soluble calcium and magnesium are continually removed, as is the case particularly in humid regions, the reactions are persistently forced to the right, since the carbon dioxide pressure usually is fully maintained by the decomposition of the organic matter. And as the percentage base saturation of the colloidal complex is gradually reduced, the pH of the soil sinks (see page 291) until the latter at last presents such an unsatisfactory physiological condition that another application of lime is necessary. This is the cycle through which much of the calcium and magnesium of the soil swings in arable lands.

188. *Loss of lime from arable soils*

In following calcium and magnesium through the lime cycle one cannot escape the possibilities of loss, nor the fact that these removals not only must be large in humid regions but also must exert a drastic physiological effect on the land. Three ways of loss exist: (1) by erosion, (2) by crop removal, and (3) by leaching.

Since erosion has already been rather fully discussed (page 193), little more need be said here regarding it, except to emphasize one fact. Erosion exerts a sorting effect, the finer portions of the soil, both mineral and organic, being carried away to a much greater extent than the coarser fractions. The soil is thus especially depleted of clay and humus. Since a very large proportion of the calcium and magnesium of surface soil occurs in the colloidal fraction, erosion causes a loss of lime much greater than though the soil was affected uniformly. Data suggestive of the magnitude of erosion removal of calcium and magnesium will be presented later (Table XXXVII).

It might be inferred from what has been said regarding the solubility of lime in the soil that higher plants absorb their calcium and magnesium from the freer portion of the soil solution, and largely in a bicarbonate association. This no doubt is true to a considerable extent, yet higher plants may have a share in the transfer of the lime elements from an insoluble and unavailable state to a soluble and available condition. This has already been discussed (page 101), the important point being the production of carbon dioxide by root hairs themselves and by microorganic life at their adsorptive surfaces while they are in very intimate contact with calcium carbonate and particularly with colloidal matter carrying exchangeable lime. As a result an exchange, such as indicated by the reactions on page 354, might readily be forced within the interfacial zones by the high pressure of the carbon dioxide, the plant thereby obtaining calcium and magnesium directly and more readily than otherwise might be the case.

Since calcium and magnesium are so readily thrown into the soil solution by the influence of carbonic acid, these elements are especially susceptible to loss by leaching. The presence of nitrates in the soil, either from biological activity or fertilizer addition, also greatly facilitates the loss of lime in drainage since calcium and magnesium nitrates are very soluble. Sulfates function in a similar way since the solubility of calcium and magnesium sulfates is appreciable. The lime elements are thus susceptible to leaching in three major forms: bicarbonate, sulfate, and nitrate. The relative magnitude ordinarily is in the order given, the losses in association with the bicarbonate anion usually being much in excess of the other two forms.

In order to give some idea of lime losses from soils, data are quoted in Table XXXVII. It must be remembered, however, that these figures are tentative and suggestive only. The data for erosion removal are for a silt loam in Missouri, cropped to a rotation of corn, wheat, and clover (see page 199). The slope was approximately 4 per cent, under a rainfall of about 40 inches. The experiment was carried on for fourteen years. The acre annual removal by crops was calculated for a standard and representative rotation assuming reasonable yields (see page 200). The leaching losses are from the Cornell lysimeters (see page 211). The soil used was the Dunkirk silty clay loam, cropped to a regular rotation. The annual acre losses are averages for a ten-year period. All data are in pounds an acre a year expressed in the conventional *oxide* form and also in the more practical terms of *calcium* and *magnesium carbonates*.

Table XXXVII.   Loss of Lime from Soil Pounds, an Acre, a Year

Manner of Removal	Calcium		Magnesium	
	CaO	CaCO₃	MgO	MgCO₃
By erosion, Missouri experiments, 4% slope	120	214	48	100
By the average crop of a standard rotation	30	53	20	42
By leaching, Cornell lysimeters	322	575	73	153
Total		842		295

The greater loss of calcium than magnesium, especially in drainage, no doubt is due to the fact that the soil colloidal matter usually carries a much larger amount of the former in an exchangeable condition. And, since the average lime supplies six or seven times more calcium than magnesium, this loss ratio will in general be maintained in arable lands as liming proceeds. This does not mean, however, that the magnesium in lime is of minor importance. Far from it. In fact, judging from the figures of Table XXXVII, there should always be at least one-fourth as much magnesium as calcium in the lime applied in order to proportionately meet the outgo of the two constituents. Other things being equal, it is always wise to select a magnesium lime.

Particularly noticeable are the large amounts of lime lost from arable lands. Even if the figures quoted in Table XXXVII are cut in half, they would indicate that 500 pounds of limestone an acre a year were none too great to meet the loss from cropped soils in humid regions. This amounts to about 2 tons of carbonate of lime during the period of the average rotation. Such a conclusion, even though tentative, justifies the attention that is paid to lime in any scheme of fertility management in areas of medium to heavy rainfall.

189. *The effects of lime on the soil*

It has already been emphasized that the changes of lime in the soil are many and complicated. It logically follows, therefore, that the influences of liming cannot be less intricate or less difficult to explain in detail satisfactorily. The discussion that follows must of necessity, rather than choice, be more or less general in nature. The better known effects of liming will be considered under three heads: (1) physical, (2) chemical, and (3) biological.

Physical effects. In heavy soils there is always a tendency for the fine particles to become too closely associated. Such a condition interferes with air and water movement and granulation is necessary. A desirable crumb structure is somewhat encouraged in an acid soil by the addition of any form of lime. This is due, not so much to flocculation as to the influence upon biotic forces, especially those that have to do with the decomposition of the soil organic matter and the synthesis of humus. The presence of the latter greatly encourages granulation (see page 59). In practice the amounts of lime applied are generally too small to influence the structural condition of the soil except in indirect ways.

Chemical effects. Chemically, lime brings about many complex changes in an acid soil. If added in sufficient amounts, it reduces the hydrogen-ion concentration and tends to force such metallic cations as aluminum, iron, and manganese into an insoluble condition (see page 301). This is not undesirable in respect to aluminum, which is toxic to many plants, but too much lime may create an iron and manganese deficiency. The chlorotic influence on plants of overliming may be due in some cases to such a chemical repression. Caution is thus necessary in the use of lime.

Lime undoubtedly is very important in respect to phosphorus. By repressing iron and aluminum, the reversion of the soluble phosphates to very unavailable iron and aluminum combinations is much reduced. Not only is the native phosphorus so affected but especially that added in superphosphate. On the other hand, too much lime may raise the pH well above 7 and thereby encourage the formation of insoluble and unavailable calcium phosphates ranging from the oxyapatite to the carbonate-apatite or even the fluorapatite (see page 302). An adjustment of the pH within the range of 5.6 perhaps to 6.5 probably is most desirable. Here the native as well as added phosphates seem to be particularly soluble. Besides, the phosphate ions presented within these pH limits ($HPO_4^=$ and $H_2PO_4^-$) seem to be easily absorbed by plants.

The liberation of mineral nutrients, particularly potassium, by the addition of lime is somewhat uncertain although it evidently must occur, at least to some extent. The process is probably a very complicated and coordinated chemical and biological change. Consequently the stimulation to plants by such an action is difficult to establish, since so many compensating factors are involved.

Theoretically calcium should by base exchange liberate potassium to the extent that it is exchangeable. Actually, however, the potassium in the drainage water from limed soil is likely to be less than that removed from those untreated.[1] Jenny [2] ascribes this to the stimulating influence of the lime on the microorganisms, the liberated potassium being appropriated by the vigorously multiplying soil flora. The difficulty of measuring potash release under such a condition is obvious.

Of the specific chemical effects of lime already mentioned, the reduction in acidity and the rise in pH are the ones commonly uppermost in the popular mind. The mere correction of the soil reaction is, in itself and insofar as higher plants and microorganisms are concerned, important very largely in indirect ways and these are mostly nutritional. Hence in considering the benefits of lime, the stress should be upon the nutritional effects, both direct and indirect, rather than upon the mere change in soil pH. In fact it is possible to obtain definite benefits from an application of lime without appreciably reducing the hydrogen-ion concentration of the soil. It should be recognized also that the changes due to liming are so many, so complex, and so interrelated, that it is impossible to ascribe the influences observed to any one factor.

Biological effects. The influence of lime upon the general-purpose, heterotrophic soil organisms, thereby increasing the activity of the

[1] MacIntire, W. H., W. M. Shaw, and J. B. Young, "The Repressive Effect of Lime and Magnesia upon Soil and Subsoil Potash," *Jour. Agr. Sci.*, XX:499–510, 1930.

[2] Jenny, Hans, and E. R. Shade, "The Potash-Lime Problem in Soils," *Jour. Amer. Soc. Agron.*, XXVI:162–170, 1934. See also, Dean, H. C., "The Effect of Liming on the Liberation of Potassium in Some Iowa Soils," Research Bulletin 197, La. Agr. Exp. Sta., 1936.

And Gilligan, G. M., "The Effect of Fertilizers and Lime Upon the Electro-dialyzable and Exchange Potash of Cropped Soil," *Jour. Agr. Res.*, LIII:61–65, 1936.

organic matter and nitrogen of an acid soil, is especially significant, as the rate of the turnover of these constituents often is more important than the actual amounts present. This stimulation of enzymic processes not only favors the formation of humus but also encourages the elimination of certain organic intermediate products that might be toxic to higher plants.

Most of the favorable soil organisms, as well as some of the unfavorable ones such as those that produce potato scab, are encouraged by liming. Aminization, ammonification, and sulfur oxidation are markedly speeded up by active calcium. The bacteria that fix nitrogen from the air, either alone or in the nodules of legumes, are especially stimulated by the application of lime. Nitrification, a biological phenomenon of great importance, requires active metallic cations of which calcium is most favored. When lime is inadequate, this desirable transformation will not proceed rapidly. In fact the successful growth of most soil microorganisms so definitely depends upon lime that certain biological activities cannot be expected if soils fall below a given calcium and magnesium level.

190. *Crop response to liming* [1]

The biological effects of lime will now be extended to include higher plants, obviously a consideration of great practical concern. Much experimental work has been done in various parts of the world in determining the relative response of different crops to liming and the reason for certain well-known differences. The results, while in close agreement as to some crops, show striking disagreements as to others. This is to be expected, since the varying conditions of the tests, especially in respect to fertility, no doubt have had a marked influence on the response of the plants under consideration.

Of leguminous crops, sweet clover, alfalfa, and red clover react most markedly to lime. The response of white clover, Ladino clover, soy beans, garden peas, and field peas, while less, is still noticeable. Alsike clover requires less lime than red clover and, as the soil of a region declines in active calcium, it is common to find it gradually replacing

---

[1] Table XXIX, page 306 indicates the lime level at which various plants seem to grow most satisfactorily, thereby indicating whether or not a particular crop is likely to be benefited by liming.

the latter. Lespedeza, cowpeas, vetch, and field beans do not seem to be so definitely benefited by lime.

Of the nonlegumes, asparagus, spinach, sugar beets and garden beets, cabbage, and cauliflower are especially influenced by lime even though the soil is not strongly acid. Barley, blue grass, timothy, and wheat are somewhat affected while corn, oats, millet, rye, sorghum, and other crops show little direct response. However, the stimulation of a legume by the use of lime when the soil is acid will often produce an indirect effect of great practical importance on the crops following. In fact, lime on acid soils used for general and dairy farming is especially important in its influence on the legumes of the rotation, since through their stimulation the nonlegumes of the sequence are greatly benefited. The greater the growth of a leguminous crop, the larger usually are the amounts of active nitrogenous residues left in the soil. Under favorable conditions these decompose rapidly, producing a maximum of humus, at the same time liberating large amounts of available nitrogen. Because of this influence lime is often called an *indirect nitrogen fertilizer*.

Certain crops such as redtop, cotton, buckwheat, fescue, bent grass, potatoes, millet, and rye will grow satisfactorily on soils low in active calcium. To what extent they are directly benefited by lime it is difficult to say. Potatoes, while responding somewhat to lime, are best grown on soils somewhat low in active calcium if scab is prevalent. This disease, an actinomyces infection, is favored when pH values rise above 5.4 or 5.6.

When plants are benefited by lime, a number of possible reasons may be suggested. These are listed as follows: (1) direct nutritive or regulatory action of the calcium and magnesium; (2) removal or neutralization of toxins of either an organic or inorganic nature; (3) retardation of plant diseases; (4) increased availability chemically of plant nutrients; and (5) encouragement of biological activities favorable in a nutritive way. The crop response to liming is thus a complicated phenomenon and only the broadest conclusions may be drawn.

A number of plants is definitely injured by liming, prominent among which are cranberries, blueberries, watermelons, laurel, azaleas, and rhododendrons. It is therefore advantageous not only to know the condition of the soil but also to understand the influence of active calcium and magnesium on the crop to be grown. Lime is too often used as a cure-all, little attention being paid to the widely differing responses exhibited by plants.

This brings us to the question of *overliming*, that is, the addition of lime until the pH of the soil is well above 7, approaching or even somewhat exceeding 8. Under such conditions many crops that ordinarily respond to lime are deterimentally affected especially during the first season following the application. With heavy soils and where farmers can afford to apply only moderate amounts of lime, the danger is negligible. But on sandy soils, low in organic matter and therefore lightly buffered, it is easy to injure certain crops even with a relatively moderate application of lime.

Although overliming can be easily guarded against, it has attracted attention and study far greater than its possible danger warrants. This is because in many cases the reason for the injury has not been satisfactorily explained. A number of possibilities have been suggested. For instance the drastic rise in pH might for a time immobilize iron or manganese (page 301), thus creating a temporary deficiency of one or both of these nutrients. This has happened in a number of cases. Copper and zinc might be affected in the same way. With boron,[1] if this should be the constituent influenced, the situation probably is more complicated. Although neither the soil untreated nor the lime alone appreciably precipitate boron, some authors feel that the two, when in combination, fix it markedly. Possibly also the excess of calcium hinders in some way the movement of boron into the plant, in spite of its solubility. Or too much calcium in the plant cells might even interfere with boron metabolism even though plenty of the latter should be present. It has also been suggested that lime creates a serious competition for boron by a stimulation of soil microorganic activity.

With phosphorus there is even greater chance for speculation. It is well known that an excess of lime in the soil and a pH above 7 are

[1] See, Drake, Mack, Dale H. Sieling, and G. D. Scarseth, "Calcium-Boron Ratio as an Important Factor in Controlling the Boron Starvation of Plants," *Jour. Amer. Soc. Agron.*, XXXIII: 454–462, 1941.

Purvis, E. R., "The Present Status of Boron in American Agriculture," *Proc. Soil Sci. Soc. Amer.*, IV: 316–321, 1939.

Midgley, A. R., and D. E. Dunklee, "The Effect of Lime on the Fixation of Borates in Soils," *Proc. Soil Sci. Soc. Amer.*, IV: 302–307, 1939.

Naftel, James A., "Soil Liming Investigations: V. The Relation of Boron Deficiency to Over-Liming Injury," *Jour. Amer. Soc. Agron.*, XXIX: 761–771, 1937.

Parks, R. Q., and B. T. Shaw, "Possible Mechanisms of Boron Fixation in Soil: I. Chemical," *Proc. Soil Sci. Soc. Amer.*, VI: 219–223, 1941.

favorable for the formation of rather insoluble and unavailable calcium phosphates ranging from an oxyapatite to a fluorapatite (see page 302). A phosphorus deficiency might reasonably be induced in this way. Besides, calcium might affect the passage of phosphate ions through the cell walls of the absorbing root hairs or even interfere with the subsequent metabolism of the phosphorus [1] in a manner similar to that already suggested for boron. With so many possibilities and with such complex, bio-colloidal interrelations to deal with, it is easy to see why overliming injury in many cases has not been satisfactorily explained.

191. *Practical problems respecting lime*

The use of lime in a practical way raises three questions. If the first is answered in the affirmative, the other two present themselves in logical sequence. The three questions are: (1) Shall lime be applied? (2) Which form shall be used? (3) What shall be the rate of application? These queries will be considered in order.

192. *Shall lime be applied?*

The old idea respecting lime was that of a *cure-all* — that there would be no harm in trying it; and perhaps it might be beneficial. Such an attitude should now be a thing of the past as it may lead to a waste of money and perhaps to overliming. The chlorotic condition of plants due to a suppression of iron and manganese and the possibilities of unbalancing their phosphate or boron nutrition are too real to be ignored. Besides, only a few plants require other than moderate amounts of active calcium and even these will grow vigorously on slightly acid soils. In many cases the fertility level is the critical thing. Hence caution is necessary.

In coming to a decision as to the desirability of applying lime, the crop or series of crops to be grown must be considered as well as the condition of the soil itself. In respect to the latter a pH determination commonly is made either by means of a glass electrode and potentiometer or by the less accurate indicator method (page 307). Representa-

[1] See, Pierre, W. H., and G. M. Browning, "The Temporary Injurious Effects of Excessive Liming of Acid Soils and Its Relation to the Phosphate Nutrition of Plants," *Jour. Amer. Soc. Agron.*, XXVII:742–759, 1935.

tive subsoil as well as surface samples should be examined.[1] From such tests the physiological condition of the soil in respect to lime may be inferred. Before a recommendation can be made, however, the lime needs in general of the crop should be considered. The decision rests upon the proper coordination of these two types of information.

A test, which may be used instead of or in connection with the determination of soil pH, has been devised by Comber [2] and is commercially available. A sample of air-dry soil held in a test tube is treated with about double its volume of an alcoholic solution of potassium sulfocyanate (KSCN). The contents of the tube are then well shaken and allowed to stand for an adequate time. The intensity of the red color that develops in the supernatant liquid, if the soil is acid, is an indication of the need for lime.

The theory of the test is simple. As a soil becomes depleted in active lime its acidity increases. At the same time the solubility and activity of its iron becomes greater, the three conditions being roughly correlated (page 301). Potassium sulfocyanate in the presence of soluble iron gives a red color [$Fe(SCN)_3$]. Consequently the more definite the test, in any particular case, the greater is considered to be the acidity of the soil. Hence, the more pronounced is its need for lime.

It must be noted that the test cannot be made successfully with a wet soil nor can it be satisfactorily performed in the field. In this latter respect it is not so useful as the dye method for pH. Moreover, it cannot be used with peat soils as they usually contain only small amounts of iron. Besides peats may, because of their very high exchange capacity, contain adequate amounts of active lime and yet be highly acid.

In deciding whether or not to apply lime to a soil it would seem more logical to test directly for the two constituents involved. Therefore, why not determine the amounts of exchangeable calcium and magnesium present rather than depend on pH or the Comber test? The situation seems to be this: The activity of the exchangeable calcium and magnesium, as well as the physiological condition of the soil, depend very largely on the percentage base saturation; the higher the

[1] Care should be used in the taking of soil samples. They must be representative and before testing should be thoroughly mixed. It is well to pass the sample through a medium-fine screen.

[2] Comber, N. M.. "A Qualitative Test for Sour Soils," *Jour. Agr. Sci.*, X, Part 4:420–424, 1920.

latter the less lime need be applied. Hence, unless the total exchange capacity of a soil is known, the milliequivalents of exchangeable calcium and magnesium cannot be interpreted in terms of percentage base saturation and thereby be used in deciding whether or not the soil needs lime. On the other hand the pH, since it is correlated fairly closely with percentage base saturation is, in itself, an excellent indicator of the activity of the lime elements and of the physiological condition of the soil. Besides it is very easily and quickly determined.

193. *Forms of lime to apply*

The experimental data regarding the relative effectiveness of the various forms of lime are somewhat contradictory. In practice it seems best to assume that the effectiveness of the lime depends on the amount of magnesium and calcium carried and is influenced to a much less degree by the particular combinations in which these bases may occur. For example, 1½ tons of medium to finely ground limestone carrying 50 per cent of calcium oxide or its equivalent should be as effective during the period of the rotation as 1 ton of slaked lime analyzing 75 per cent calcium oxide.

It should be noted that the caustic forms of lime give a little more rapid and drastic effect than does ground limestone. This is to be expected and is taken advantage of in practice. But over the period of a rotation there seems to be little difference between the various forms of lime when they are applied in equivalent chemical amounts. The charge that quicklime, even at the usual rates of application, produces an extremely rapid and detrimental rate of organic-matter dissolution is not to be taken seriously. The rapidity with which hydrolysis and carbonation occur precludes any undesirable effects.

On the basis of the ideas already presented, it is evident that four major factors should be considered in deciding on a specific brand of lime to apply. These factors are as follows:

1. Chemical guarantees of the limes.
2. Total cost applied to the land (price a ton, freight, trucking to farm, and application to land).
3. Fineness of the limestone.
4. Miscellaneous considerations (rapidity of action, handling, storage, bag or bulk, etc.).

By a purely arithmetical calculation based on factors 1 and 2 above, the cost of equivalent amounts of lime as applied to the land can be determined. These factors will show which lime will furnish the greatest amount of neutralizing power in total for every dollar expended.

For instance the *neutralizing power* ($CaCO_3$ equivalent) of two limes, a hydroxide and a ground limestone, are guaranteed at 135 and 95 respectively. The cost of applying a ton of each to the land (all charges, including trucking and spreading) for purposes of calculation will be considered to be $10.00 in the case of the hydrate and $6.00 for the carbonate. Obviously it will require only $95/135$ or 0.7 of a ton of the former to equal 1 ton of the latter. The cost of equivalent amounts of neutralizing power, based on 1 ton of limestone, will therefore be $7.00 for the hydroxide of lime and $6.00 for the limestone. The latter looks like the better buy.

One very important factor is the fineness of the limestone. If it is not sufficiently pulverulent to rate as a so-called fine lime (see rule on page 351), allowance must be made for the lack of rapid acting material. For instance, if 1¼ tons of the limestone considered in the above calculation must be used to equal 1 ton of its satisfactorily fine equivalent, $7.50 would of necessity be expended rather than $6.00. This lack of fineness in the limestone would throw the cost advantage to the hydroxide form.

There are several miscellaneous factors that must be considered. The handling of the caustic limes, even when bagged, is somewhat more disagreeable than working with limestone. The necessity for storage also comes in, since it is often desirable to carry lime from one season to another. The limestone has the advantage here, as it does not change in storage, if kept dry, as do the others. The rapidity of action of the various limes should also receive some consideration. Where the soil is quite acid and quick action is necessary, the caustic limes are preferable. Moreover, there is the question of purchasing the lime, especially the limestone, in bags or in bulk. The extra cost of the bags is often more than offset by the ease of handling and storage. And the decision should not be finally approved until the nature of the soil and the probable response of the crops have again been reviewed.

It would seem, therefore, that the decision as to the particular brand of lime to apply to a soil is a question of good judgment based on a knowledge of the various forms of lime, the significance of their guarantees, and their probable influence on the soil and the crops grown.

194. *Amounts of lime to apply*

In respect to the amounts of lime to apply, it is well to emphasize at the outset that all recommendations thereto are estimates. It is impossible to decide with accuracy and certainty. Too many factors are involved, especially that of buffering. It must always be remembered that we are dealing with a colloidal complex, the buffering of which we are never quite sure of. Besides the objective of the lime addition is to rectify properly the physiological condition of the soil, a very indefinite condition. We are never quite certain what amounts of calcium and magnesium will accomplish this or just what pH should be temporarily established. With crops that respond noticeably to lime, the pH should be raised to at least 6 or perhaps above. This probably ensures a percentage base saturation in mineral soils of 80 or 90 and sufficient active calcium and magnesium.

A situation that adds to the difficulty of deciding how much lime to apply is the practice usually of adding lime only once in a rotation. Hence the rate of application must be stepped up sufficiently to ensure enough active lime during this period. This requires good judgment and experience.

In arriving at a practical decision, a number of factors should be considered. The principle ones are as follows:

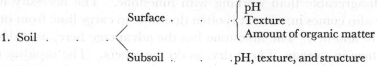

1. Soil
   - Surface . . . . . { pH, Texture, Amount of organic matter
   - Subsoil . . . . . pH, texture, and structure
2. Crops to be grown
3. Length of the rotation
4. Kind of lime used
5. Fineness of the limestone
6. Experience

The pH (or, if preferred, Comber's test) is invaluable as it gives some idea as to the percentage base saturation of the soil and how acute is the need for lime. The texture and organic matter are important since they are indicative of the adsorptive capacity of the soil and the strength of buffering. Naturally the higher the buffer capacity of a soil the greater must be the amount of lime applied in order to attain a satisfactory activity of calcium and magnesium and a given change in pH. The subsoil also should be tested for pH and examined as to texture and structure. Advice as to the cropping of any soil should not be given without a knowledge of subsoil conditions.

The other factors listed have already been discussed. Besides, their importance is self-evident. As to the kinds of lime, the three forms in respect to their effects on the soil are roughly in the ratio of 1 ton of representative finely ground limestone to 0.7 of a ton of commercial hydroxide to a little over 0.5 of a ton of representative oxide. The experience factor has been listed to emphasize the wisdom of taking advantage of lime knowledge wherever it may be found.

Table XXXVIII. Suggested Amount of Finely Ground Limestone that Should Be Applied to the Acre of Mineral Soil for Red Clover

Need for Lime	Limestone, Pounds to the Acre	
	Sandy Loam	Clay Loam
Moderate	1500–2000	2000–2500
High	2000–2500	2500–3500

In ordinary practice it is seldom economical to apply more than 2 tons of finely ground limestone to the acre of mineral soil, unless it is very acid and the promise for increased crop yield exceptionally good. The data cited above (Table XXXVIII) while merely tentative serve in a general way as guides in practical liming operations for a four- or five-year rotation with average mineral soils. It is assumed that red clover is the principal legume of the rotation. The recommendations are in terms of finely ground limestone. If the lime is coarser than the minimum already quoted (see page 351), or if an oxide or hydroxide is used, due allowance should be made. If alfalfa or sweet clover are to be grown the amounts should be increased perhaps 500 to 1000 pounds in each case.

195. *Methods of applying lime and its place in the rotation*

As already suggested, the activity of lime is greatly encouraged by contact. Hence the more thoroughly it is mixed with the soil, the greater will be the number of active centers and the more rapid and effective will be the treatment.

Lime is best applied to plowed land and worked into the soil as the seedbed is prepared. It should be mixed thoroughly with the surface half of the furrow slice. Top-dressing with lime is seldom recommended except on permanent meadows and pastures. Even though it does go in solution at the surface, it is carried downward through the larger channels and fails to have much effect on the soil.

The time of year at which lime is applied is immaterial, the system of farming, the type of rotation, and related considerations being the deciding factors. Winter application may even be practiced. The soil should not be too moist when the application is made, as the lime, especially the slaked and ground-burned forms, tends to ball badly and thus thorough distribution is prevented.

A lime distributor should be used, especially if the amount to be applied is at all large. A manure spreader can be utilized and even an endgate seeder may be pressed into service. Small amounts of lime may be distributed by means of the fertilizer attachment on a grain drill. Special types of distributors are available for spreading the very coarse forms of limestone. The evenness of distribution is as important as the form and amount of lime used and should by no means be neglected.

The addition of small amounts of limestone, say 300 to 500 pounds an acre, often gives remarkable results, when drilled in with the crop that is being seeded. Even though the lime is not mixed thoroughly with the soil and there is little change in the pH and the physiological condition of furrow-slice as a whole, the results may be favorable. Apparently the lime in this case is functioning more as a fertilizer and as a means of rectifying conditions within the crop and at its root-soil interfaces rather than as a soil amendment.

A discussion of the application of lime is never complete without some consideration being given to the place in the rotation at which the liming is best done. In a rotation of maize, oats, fall wheat, and two years of clover and timothy, the lime is often applied when the wheat is seeded in the fall. It can then be spread on the plowed ground and worked in as the seedbed is prepared. Its effect is thus especially favorable on the new seeding. With potatoes in the rotation, the lime usually should follow this crop, especially if scab is prevalent. In practice, the place of lime in the rotation is often determined, in part at least, by expediency, since the vital consideration is, after all, the application of lime regularly and in conjunction with a suitable rotation of some kind. The rule is, however, to apply the lime with or ahead of the crop that gives the most satisfactory response.

196. *Lime and soil-fertility management*

The influence of successively liming a soil over a period of years may tend to raise or lower its fertility, according to the system of management that accompanies the applications of the lime. The use of lime alone will undoubtedly increase crop yields for a time. Chemical reactions will be encouraged, soil organisms will be stimulated, and more nutrients will become available for crop use. Such stimulation, however, will soon wane and, if nothing is returned to the land, productivity must ultimately drop back to even a lower level than before the lime was applied.

This being the case, farm manures, crop residues, legumes, and superphosphate should be utilized to the fullest extent in connection with the lime. And when this combination is insufficient to keep up the fertility, especially the nitrogen and potash, fertilizers other than those of a phosphatic nature should be resorted to. Trace elements may be required in addition. Lime improperly used exhausts the soil, but when rationally supplemented it becomes one of the most important factors in the maintenance of soil fertility and productivity.

Chapter XVI. The Nitrogen Economy of Soils

Of the various plant nutrients, nitrogen probably has been subjected to the greatest amount of study and even yet its higher plant and microbiotic relationships are receiving much attention. And there are very good reasons. The amount in the soil is small, while the quantity withdrawn annually by crops is comparatively large. At times the soil nitrogen is too readily soluble and is lost in drainage; at other times it is definitely unavailable to higher plants. Its effects are very marked and rapid. Thus overapplications may occur which are harmful. All in all, nitrogen is a nutrient element that should not only be conserved, but also regulated.

197. *The nitrogen cycle*

In all soils there is a very considerable intake and outgo of nitrogen in the course of a year, accompanied by many complex transformations. Some of these changes may be controlled more or less by man, while others are entirely beyond his command. This interlocking succession of reactions, reversible, infinitely recurrent, and largely biochemical, constitutes what is known as the *nitrogen cycle* (see Fig. 55). It has attracted scientific study for years and its practical significance is beyond question.

The nitrogen income of arable soils is derived from such materials as crop residues, green manures, farm manure, commercial fertilizers, and ammonium and nitrate salts brought down by rain. In addition, there is the fixation of atmospheric nitrogen accomplished by certain microorganisms. The outgo is due to crop removal, to drainage, to erosion, and to loss in a gaseous condition.

Much of the nitrogen added to the soil undergoes many transformations before it is removed. Crop residues, green manures, farm manure, and other organic carriers undergo complex changes as soon as they are incorporated with soil. Proteins are converted into various decomposition products and finally their nitrogen appears in the nitrate form. Even then it is allowed no rest, as it is either appropriated by microorganisms and higher plants, or lost in drainage, or by volatilization. And so the transfer goes on and on. The mobility of nitrogen is remarkable, rivaling carbon in ease of movement and surpassing calcium in the variety and complexity of its transformations.

198. *Nitrogen transformations in soils* [1] — *aminization*

Organic nitrogenous compounds, when incorporated in the soil, are immediately attacked, if conditions are at all favorable, by a great variety of organisms. In forests especially, millipedes, sowbugs, springtails, and mites have much to do with the initial processes as well as earthworms, if the active lime is not too low. In cultivated lands animal life, except for the earthworms, is not so prominent, the general-purpose heterotrophic bacteria, fungi, and actinomyces accounting for most of the dissolution. In any case, as the decomposition proceeds, these latter groups seem, in most cases, to dominate and the microbial tissue increases at a rapid rate.

The proteins and allied compounds, which largely constitute the nitrogenous matter commonly added to soil, are not absorbable by higher plants, but they can be used by the heterogeneous soil fauna and flora. As a result of their enzymic digestion, such compounds readily break down into proteoses, peptones, and finally to amino acids. These protein building blocks, the amino compounds, are usually considered as one of the initial end products of the decay of complex nitrogenous compounds. Hence the process is spoken of as *aminization.* The hydrolytic transformation may be indicated more or less graphically as follows:

$$\begin{array}{l} \text{Proteins and} \\ \text{near-proteins} \end{array} + \begin{array}{l} \text{Enzymic} \\ \text{digestion} \end{array} = \begin{array}{l} \text{Complex amino} \\ \text{compounds} \end{array} + CO_2 + E + \begin{array}{l} \text{Other} \\ \text{prod-} \\ \text{ucts} \end{array}$$

Soil organisms of many kinds acquire energy by this type of digestion and also utilize some of the nitrogen as the enzymic processes take place. At the same time carbon dioxide is freely evolved as the amino compounds and other products emerge. The fate of the nitrogen (Fig. 55) is thus twofold — synthesis by the general-purpose organ-

---

[1] The amount of nitrogen in mineral soils and its relationship to the soil organic matter is dealt with on pages 138 and 139.

isms into complex cell contents and tissue, and the appearance of by-product nitrogen in the form of amino acids and no doubt in other and simpler combinations as well. The acquisition of energy and of tissue materials by soil organisms accounts for the phenomenon, the nitrogen not in immediate demand playing, temporarily at least, the role of a residue or surplus.

Aminization is greatly influenced by soil conditions, temperature and aeration being especially important. Good drainage greatly encourages it, as also does active calcium. Moisture optimum for higher plants seems to favor the fauna and flora having to do with the dissolution. In fact, the nature of the processes that take place are determined by soil conditions rather more than by the particular general-purpose organisms that are present.

As the digestion above described continues and the soil organisms, both animal and plant, utilize the amino compounds, produced either by themselves or by other individuals, as a source of energy and of tissue-building material, the nitrogen involved may go in one of two directions. It may be synthesized into cell contents and again become a part of complex proteinaceous compounds, or it may appear as a simple waste or by-product — ammonium. The enzymic process that results in the latter form of nitrogen is called *ammonification* (Fig. 55).

Before dealing with ammonification, let us consider for a moment the utilization of amino compounds by soil organisms, especially the microflora.

Microorganisms, particularly those of a heterotrophic nature, when in need of nitrogen seem to use this form readily. Such a source is of great advantage, as the acquisition is attended with a minimum of energy expenditure. And if the fungi of mycorrhiza can use amino nitrogen, which is quite probable, and pass the nitrogen on to the host, certain higher plants may benefit indirectly from such a capacity. While higher plants may possibly directly synthesize amino nitrogen, such an appropriation occurs so sparingly as to merit here no more than passing notice.

199. *Ammonification*

As already indicated, the same organisms, in general, that facilitate aminization also promote ammonification. In so doing, they tap ready sources of energy as well as appropriate some of the nitrogen involved. The enzymic process may be tentatively indicated as follows: —

$$\text{Amino compounds of various kinds} + \text{Enzymic Hydrolysis} = \begin{bmatrix} NH_4 \text{ ions} \\ \text{assoc. esp.} \\ \text{with } CO_3 \\ \text{and } HCO_3 \\ \text{ions} \end{bmatrix} + CO_2 + E + \text{Other Products}$$

In the acquisition of energy by ammonification, the organisms evolve copious amounts of carbon dioxide and leave behind a number of by-products other than the ammonium compounds that now engage our attention. Of the ammonium forms, the carbonate and bi=

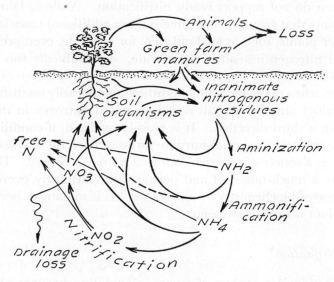

FIG. 55. The main portion of the nitrogen cycle. In tracing the transfers, it is well to begin with the nitrogenous organic residues. Additions due to microbial fixation of nitrogen, rain and fertilizers are not shown.

carbonate no doubt are prominent, as is to be expected when the abundance and activity of carbon dioxide is considered.

While ammonification seems to proceed to the best advantage in well-drained aerated soils with plenty of active basic material present, it will take place to some extent under almost any condition, due to the great number of different organisms capable of accomplishing the change. This is one of the advantages of a general-purpose flora and fauna.

The fate of the ammoniacal nitrogen (as shown in Fig. 55) is three-fold. First, considerable amounts are appropriated by some of the ammonifiers themselves or by other soil organisms capable of using this type of compound. Mycorrhizal fungi, no doubt, are able to absorb ammoniacal nitrogen and pass it on to the host.

Second, higher plants are able to synthesize, often very readily indeed, this form of nitrogen.[1] Young plants of almost all kinds are especially capable in this respect, although they seem to grow better if some nitrate nitrogen is also available. Mature plants such as certain grasses, forest trees, and their undergrowth apparently are forced to use ammoniacal nitrogen because the soils on which they grow often do not support ready nitrification. Azaleas, laurel, and other plants that require a low-lime soil are additional cases in point. Still other plants, such as lowland rice, for example, even prefer ammoniacal nitrogen instead of the nitrate. Undoubtedly this type of synthesis is extremely important.

Finally, when plant and animal synthesis temporarily is satisfied, and if by-product ammonium still remains unused, nitrogen in this form may go in a third direction. It is readily oxidized, if conditions are favorable, by certain special-purpose forms of bacteria that use it, not so much as a source of nitrogen, but as a source of energy. Thus one arrives at a much-talked-of and perhaps comparatively overemphasized phase of biochemistry — *nitrification*. It is so named, because its end product is nitrate nitrogen.

200. *Nitrification*[2]

Nitrification is a process of enzymic oxidation brought about by certain special-purpose bacteria. Fungi, actinomyces, and soil animals apparently have no important capacity in this respect. The ammonium compound most readily influenced is ammonium carbon-

[1] See Allison, F. E., "Forms of Nitrogen Assimilated by Plants," *Quart. Rev. Biol.;* VI: 313–321, 1931; and "The Comparative Effects of Concentrated Nitrogenous Fertilizers on Permanent Soil Acidity," *Jour. Amer. Soc. Agron.*, Vol. XXIII:878–908, 1931.

Also Tiedjins, V. T., "Factors Affecting Accumulation of Ammonia and Nitrate Nitrogen, Particularly in Tomato and Apple," *Plant Physiol.*, IX:31–57, 1934.

[2] The literature on nitrification is voluminous. For a comprehensive discussion, consult Waksman, S. A., *Principles of Soil Microbiology*, The Williams & Wilkins Company, Baltimore, 1932.

ate, possibly because this is the more common ammoniacal salt found in soils, and the special organisms have become adjusted to its oxidation.

Nitrification is considered to take place most commonly in two coordinated steps, two distinct groups of bacteria being involved. As shown below, the first step is the production of a salt of nitrous acid by one group of bacteria, followed immediately by its oxidation to the nitrate form by another. Some carbon dioxide is evolved as the conversion progresses as well as other products. The presence of active calcium, or some other cation that can function in a similar manner, seems to be necessary for satisfactory nitrification.

$$NH_4 \text{ ions} + \begin{bmatrix} \text{Enzymic oxida-} \\ \text{tion in presence} \\ \text{of active Ca.} \\ \text{Nitrite bacteria} \end{bmatrix}^1 = \begin{bmatrix} NO_2 \text{ ions} \\ \text{in assoc.} \\ \text{with bases,} \\ \text{esp. Ca} \end{bmatrix} + CO_2 + E + \text{other products}$$

$$NO_2 \text{ ions} + \begin{bmatrix} \text{Enzymic oxida-} \\ \text{tion in presence} \\ \text{of active Ca.} \\ \text{Nitrate bacteria} \end{bmatrix} = \begin{bmatrix} NO_3 \text{ ions} \\ \text{in assoc.} \\ \text{with bases,} \\ \text{esp. Ca} \end{bmatrix} + CO_2 + E + \text{other products}$$

The organisms in this case are special purpose and autotrophic (see page 109) instead of general purpose and heterotrophic, as are those concerned with aminization and ammonification. They obtain most of their energy by the oxidation of inorganic compounds. Like plants, they acquire carbon from carbon dioxide, at the same time respiring quantities of this gas.

Collectively, the nitrifying organisms are called *nitrobacteria*. *Nitrosomonas* and *Nitrosococcus* are concerned in the conversion of ammonia into nitrites. The organisms having to do with the oxidation of nitrites to nitrates are generally designated as *nitrobacter*. In practice

[1] The enzymic oxidations involved in nitrification are exceedingly complex. Hence this simple method of representation is somewhat misleading.

Mumford has shown that hydroxylamine and hyponitrous acid are intermediate between ammonium nitrogen and the nitrite.

$$NH_3 \rightarrow NH_2OH \rightarrow H_2N_2O_2 \rightarrow HNO_2$$

Mumford, E. M., "The Mechanism of Nitrification," *Chem. Soc. Proc.* (London), XXX:36, 1914. Also Corbet, A. S., "Formation of Hyponitrous Acid as an Intermediate Compound in the Biological or Photochemical Oxidation of Ammonia to Nitrous Acid. I. Chemical Reactions," *Biochem. Jour.*, XXVIII, No. 4:1575–1582, 1934; and "II. Micro-Biological Oxidation," *ibid.*, XXIX, No. 5:1086–1096, 1935.

these two groups of bacteria are usually spoken of as *nitrite* and *nitrate* organisms.

Since the conditions favoring the nitrite and nitrate bacteria are practically the same, the second transformation is thought to follow so closely on the first as to preclude any great accumulation of the nitrite. This is fortunate, as this salt in any concentration is toxic to higher plants. As a consequence, nitrification is generally discussed as though the transformation was only one step and dependent on one group of organisms.

It is necessary to remark in this connection that other soil organisms probably are able to produce nitrate by-products. There is some evidence that nitrates are formed from ammonium compounds without a detectable appearance of the intermediate nitrites.[1] It is reasonable to suppose that simple amino compounds may be subject to the same type of transfer. It is also possible that photochemical oxidation may take place in tropical soils.[2] How extensive such forms of nitrification are cannot be stated. Apparently, however, the bilateral oxidation already emphasized is the most important in a practical way.

201. *Soil conditions affecting nitrification*

The nitrifying bacteria are not only a special-purpose type, but they are extremely sensitive to their environment, much more so than the heterotrophic aminizing and ammonifying organisms. As a result, nitrification is often spoken of as the weak point of the nitrogen cycle. Consequently, soil conditions that influence the vigor of nitrification deserve practical consideration. They are: (1) aeration, (2) temperature, (3) moisture, (4) active lime, (5) fertilizer salts, and (6) the nitrogen-carbon ratio.

Aeration. Since nitrification is a process of oxidation, any procedure that increases the aeration of the soil should, up to a certain point, encourage it. Plowing and cultivation, especially if granulation is not impaired, are recognized means of promoting nitrification. It is perhaps not incorrect to say that the influence of the intertillage of

[1] Kaserer, H., "On Some New Nitrogen Bacteria with Autotrophic Habits of Life," (Trans.), *Ztschr. Angew. Chem.*, XIX:1681, 1906.

[2] Rao, Gopala G., "Newer Aspects of Nitrification: I," *Soil Sci.*, XXXVIII:143–159, 1934. And Corbet, A. S., "The Formation of Hyponitrous Acid as an Intermediate Compound in the Biological and Photochemical Oxidation of Ammonia to Nitrous Acid, II. Microbiological Oxidation," *Biochem. Jour.*, XXIX:1086–1096, 1935.

crops upon the nitrifying bacteria is in many cases as important as the capacity of cultivation to control weeds and maintain a suitable physical condition. The influence of cultivation will, of course, depend on circumstances. Call and Sewell report that intertillage did not promote nitrate accumulation in a friable Kansas soil, while Lyon, working with a compact soil in New York, obtained a considerable increase of nitrates.[1]

Temperature. The temperature most favorable to the process of nitrification is from 80° to 90° F. At a temperature of 125° F. nitrification practically ceases. At freezing or below, nitrification will not take place, but at about 40° F. it begins and slowly increases in intensity until the optimum temperature is reached. The lateness with which nitrification attains its full vigor in the spring is well known, and nitrate of soda is sometimes used to offset it. Greenhouse soils, because of favorable conditions including high temperature, sometimes accumulate undesirably high amounts of nitrates.

Moisture. The rate with which nitrification proceeds in a soil is governed to a marked extent by the water content, the process being retarded by both very low and very high moisture conditions. In practice, it is safe to assume that the optimum moisture as recognized for higher plants is also optimum for nitrification. This means for the average soil that excess or drainage water must have disappeared from the surface horizons and the upper subsoil. The pore space under such a condition would then be occupied by water, perhaps to the extent of 50 per cent, and the pF would stand approximately at 2.7 (see Fig. 23). It must be remembered, however, that nitrification will noticeably progress at moisture contents below the wilting point (pF 4.2) for higher plants.

Active lime. It is a very common observation that lime stimulates nitrification in soils, even in those that may already contain a fair amount of active calcium. Apparently the process of oxidation requires active bases. While potassium, magnesium, and ammonium will enable the action to proceed, calcium gives the best results. This accounts for the feeble nitrification in acid mineral soils and the seeming sensitiveness of the organisms to a low pH. As a matter of fact, however, acidity within reasonable limits seems to have little influence

[1] Call, L. E., and M. C. Sewell, "The Relation of Weed Growth to Nitric Nitrogen Accumulation in Soils," *Jour. Amer. Soc. Agron.*, V:35–44, 1918.

Lyon, T. L., "Intertillage of Crops and Formation of Nitrates in Soil," *Jour. Amer. Soc. Agron.*, XIV:97–109, 1922.

on nitrification when adequate calcium is present. This is especially true of peat soils. At pH values even below 5 these soils may show remarkable accumulations of nitrates. This is because of their high total exchange capacity and the presence in consequence of unusually large amounts of active calcium despite the low percentage base saturation.

Fertilizers. Small amounts of many kinds of salts, even those of the trace elements, stimulate nitrification. Sodium nitrate, unless applied in excessive amounts, promotes the nitrification of dried blood and cottonseed meal. Phosphates are especially effective with all types of soil organisms, as well as the nitrifiers, and so intensely is the phosphorus utilized that competition with higher plants may result. The same is no doubt true in respect to potash salts. In general, the stimulation of soil bacteria by the application of fertilizers is coordinate with the stimulation ordinarily observed in higher plants. Rational fertilization, therefore, promotes nitrification and other microbial activities as well as the growth of crops.

Nitrogen-carbon ratio. The addition to the soil of sugars, celluloses, or other easily decomposed substances with a wide nitrogen-carbon ratio causes, if conditions for decay are favorable, a disappearance, wholly or in part, of the nitrates originally present. This suggests why the application of straw or coarse manure will frequently retard the growth of plants, if sufficient time is not allowed for at least partial decomposition of the added organic matter to take place before the crop is planted. The disappearance of nitrates from this cause does not necessarily mean that nitrates are not being formed at all; but if they are, they are being assimilated as rapidly as produced.

The significance of the nitrogen-carbon ratio has already been considered (page 136) so that the explanation here may be brief. Added carbohydrates supply a ready source of energy to the general-purpose organisms of the soil, and, under favorable conditions, a tremendous multiplication is initiated. Nitrogen is necessary for the synthesis of the new protoplasm. As a result, all that is available in the soil is commandeered, and there is little chance for nitrate accumulation even though it should be formed. In fact, nitrification is probably more or less at a standstill, because of a lack of ammoniacal nitrogen, this also having been swept up by the multiplying organisms. Thus there is competition with higher plants for nitrogen, often of a most serious nature.

After the carbonaceous matter has partially decomposed so that energizing material is no longer abundant, nitrogen assimilation slows down and ammonium compounds appear. Conditions may now become favorable for nitrification, and nitrates may again accumulate in the soil. The nitrogen-carbon ratio, particularly of easily decomposable compounds, is therefore a factor in determining the form of the nitrogen present.

The practical importance of the nitrogen-carbon ratio in respect to nitrification is unquestioned. The tendency of green manures, strawy farm manure, and other crop residues to suppress nitrate accumulation are excellent examples. Insofar as nitrogen is conserved, the influence is to be encouraged; but in many cases, competition with crops is unduly severe. If this is to be avoided, the residues should be applied some time before the crop is planted. Thus an interval will be provided for rapid microbial activity whereby the nitrogen-carbon ratio will be reduced to the point where nitrification is adequate.

One more phase of the nitrogen-carbon ratio should be mentioned. There is evidence to show that plant roots exude or slough off organic matter of a highly carbonaceous nature.[1] Thus there is a widening of the nitrogen-carbon ratio near the roots and an increase in microbial activity in the rhizosphere. Nitrates consequently disappear from certain critical zones. The presence of more organisms near the roots of plants than at some distance,[2] lends support to such a conclusion, as also does the greater evolution of carbon dioxide from cropped soils than from those uncropped.[3] Apparently living roots locally stimulate the heterotrophic flora of the soil, and thereby retard nitrate accumulation. Higher plants may thus directly and notably encourage microbial competition.

There is considerable evidence that competition of soil organisms induced in this way may be, under some conditions, a serious handi-

[1] Lyon, T. L., and J. K. Wilson, "Liberation of Organic Matter by Roots of Growing Plants," Memoir 40, Cornell Univ. Agr. Exp. Sta., 1921.

[2] Wilson, J. K., and T. L. Lyon, The Growth of Certain Microorganisms in Planted and Unplanted Soils, Memoir 103, Cornell Univ. Agr. Exp. Sta., 1926.

Starkey, R. L., "Some Influence of the Development of Higher Plants upon the Microorganisms of the Soil: IV. Microscopic Examination of the Rhizosphere," Soil Sci., XLV:207–227, 1938.

Timonin, M. I., "The Interaction of Higher Plants and Soil Microorganisms: III. Effect of By-products of Plant Growth on Activity of Fungi and Actinomyces," Soil Sci. LII: 395–408, 1941.

[3] Neller, J. R., "The Influence of Growing Plants on Oxidation Processes in the Soil," Soil Sci. XIII:139–158, 1922.

cap to certain crops. The poor growth of apple trees on sod to which no nitrogen is applied and their vastly better growth when top-dressed with a large quantity of nitrate of soda is an indication of this. Apparently the grass, by the continual sloughing off of root tissue and by the death of the finer roots themselves, maintains a rather wide nitrogen-carbon ratio in the soil. Also the grass itself may absorb some nitrates, although it no doubt must absorb much of its nitrogen in other forms. As a result, the apple trees suffer from a lack of available nitrogen traceable directly to the nitrogen-carbon ratio. One of the reasons for cultivating orchards rests upon this biochemical relationship.

202. *The fate of nitrate nitrogen*

The nitrate nitrogen of the soil may go in four directions (see Fig. 55). It may (1) be synthesized by microorganisms, and (2) by higher plants, it may (3) be lost in drainage, and under certain conditions it may (4) leave the nitrogen cycle in a volatile condition.

The assimilation of nitrate nitrogen by soil organisms and higher plants has already been dealt with, and only a few words more are necessary thereto. So voracious is the microorganic flora at times that it competes seriously with higher plants. It is probable that a large proportion of the nitrate formed during the year is appropriated by soil organisms. Higher plants thus not only feed on by-product nitrogen, but they must also be satisfied with what is left by the general-purpose soil flora and fauna. No doubt this is small in comparison with the total nitrogen that, during the growing season, passes through the amino, the ammoniacal, and the nitrate forms.

The amount of nitrate nitrogen found in drainage water, the third avenue of loss, is not usually very great if the soil is properly managed. It is evident from data already quoted (page 212) that perhaps the average annual removal of nitrogen from a representative arable mineral soil by leaching is in the order of 5 or 10 pounds an acre. Compared to the removal by crop plants, this loss is moderate. With bare soils, however, the withdrawal is much greater, amounting in the case of the Cornell lysimeter soils (page 211) to 69 pounds an acre a year. This is equivalent to 431 pounds of commercial nitrate of soda. Such a loss is, of course, serious and indicates that care should be used in respect to leaching control.

Under certain conditions, especially those of poor drainage and aeration, it seems probable that nitrate, nitrite, ammoniacal, and even simple amino compounds in the soil may be reduced and nitrogen in an elemental condition allowed to escape. This is the fourth direction in which nitrate nitrogen may move, and with it go other forms as well. The various phases of reduction will be considered in the next section.

203. *The volatilization of soil nitrogen*

The conditions under which the volatilization of soil nitrogen occurs are not well understood, but most authorities agree that this loss is greatly encouraged by poor drainage and lack of aeration. The maintenance of the soil in a bare condition and the presence of excessive amounts of mobile nitrogenous compounds may also be important factors. The meagre data in respect to nitrogen volatilization indicate that this form of loss not only is common, but also is of considerable magnitude from well-managed cropped soils and probably also from lands still in a virgin condition.

The reduction of nitrate nitrogen to the elemental state has been most studied, and for a considerable time this was thought to be the principal type of volatilization. The organisms involved seem to be the general-purpose heterotrophic forms that under favorable soil conditions promote aminization and ammonification. However, under imperfect drainage and aeration at least some of them are facultative and may readily abstract oxygen from nitrates and their reduced products. The trend of the reaction may be represented as follows:

$$NO_3 \longrightarrow \quad NO_2 \longrightarrow \quad NO \longrightarrow \quad NH_2OH \longrightarrow \quad N$$

| Nitrates | Nitrites | Hyponitrites | Hydroxylamines | Gaseous nitrogen |

Not only can such organisms reduce nitrates and nitrites, but ammonium compounds may also be subjected to dissolution,[1] elemental nitrogen being one of the resultant products. It is possible also that simple amines and amides may be acted on in the same general way (Fig. 55). It is to be noted that all of these changes apparently are

[1] Kaserer, H., "On Some New Nitrogen Bacteria with Autotrophic Habits of Life," (Trans.), *Ztchr. Angew. Chem.*, **XIX**:1681, 1906.

directly biochemical and are thought to be encouraged by poor aeration and drainage and the presence of abundant amounts of easily affected nitrogenous compounds.

There is one other way [1] by which nitrogen may possibly be thrown out of the nitrogen cycle in the elemental form, conceivably in appreciable amounts. It can readily be shown that nitrites in a slightly acid solution will evolve gaseous nitrogen when brought in contact with ammonium salts, with amines, with amides such as urea, and even with nonnitrogenous sulfur compounds and carbohydrates. This type of reduction is only indirectly biological, the last stages being purely chemical.

It is well to note that this type of volatilization does not necessarily require adverse soil conditions such as poor drainage and aeration and may take place as commonly as does aminization, ammonification, and the oxidation of nitrites to nitrates. Elemental nitrogen could even be a by-product coordinate with nitrates as nitrification proceeds under what are considered favorable conditions. Hence volatilization thus induced might be a normal feature of the nitrogen cycle rather than dependent, as are those of a strictly biological nature, upon soil conditions adverse to higher plants.

Since gaseous nitrogen is unavailable to higher plants, reduction, no matter what the mechanism may be, undoubtedly is, if at all extensive, a serious drain on the nitrogen cycle. In a fifteen-year lysimeter experiment at Cornell University [2] with a soil cropped ten years and kept bare five, the nitrogen loss, unaccounted for by crop removal and drainage, amounted to about 25 pounds an acre a year. Volatilization losses obtained in the same way at the New York State Experiment Station [3] with cropped lysimeter soils ranged from 11 to 80 pounds. Unpublished results from the Cornell lysimeters covering a period of fifteen years show a loss of nitrogen of from 40 to 45 pounds an acre, a year unaccounted for. The soil studied was a well-drained sandy loam cropped to vegetables and heavily fertilized either with nitrate of soda or sulfate of ammonia. That such losses are not con-

---

[1] Wilson, J. K., "Soil Algae as Reducers of Nitrate to Nitrite," *Proc. Soil Sci. Soc. Amer.*, VI:196, 1941. The suggestions made in the abstract cited are elaborated in a later article.

[2] Lyon, T. L., and J. A. Bizzell, "Nitrogen Economy in Dunkirk Silty Clay Loam," *Proc. and Papers, First Internat. Cong. Soil Sci.*, III:619–627, 1927.

[3] Collison, R. C., H. G. Beattie, and J. D. Harlan, "Lysimeter Investigations. III. Mineral and Water Relations and Final Nitrogen Balance in Legume and Non-Legume Crop Rotations for a Period of 16 Years," Bulletin 212, N. Y. State Agr. Exp. Sta., 1933.

fined to humid-region soils is indicated by the work of Bracken and Greaves [1] with samples from twenty-one localities in the Cache and Juab valleys of Utah. Conservative calculations indicated that at least one-half of the total loss of nitrogen from cropped soils as compared to virgin land was not accounted for by leaching, erosion, and crop removal.

Although these figures are not conclusive, it would seem that the volatilization of nitrogen from a normal arable soil may be a serious factor. The data suggest an order of loss very much greater than the removal of nitrate nitrogen in the drainage water of cultivated land (see page 212). The only suggestions that can be made at present for the control of volatilization is to keep a crop on the land as much as possible, provide for adequate drainage and tillage, and avoid an excess of active nitrogenous compounds in the soil.

204. *The two main divisions of the nitrogen cycle*

The discussion so far has concerned itself with the main part of the nitrogen cycle and with nitrogen already in the soil or plant. Its transformations are shown graphically in Fig. 55. It is to be noted that two general types of enzymic activities are current: (1) synthetic or building-up processes, and (2) transformations such as aminization, ammonification, nitrification, and reduction, all resulting in progressively simple products. Most of the soil nitrogen is involved in the former activity, a very small proportion appearing at any time in the ammoniacal, nitrite, or nitrate forms. This is fortunate, as the loss of much nitrogen by drainage and volatilization is thus avoided. Most people do not realize the importance of this situation or of the fact that higher plants are by-product feeders, living on the nitrogen left over from the metabolism of the soil fauna and flora.

The other part of the nitrogen cycle, not shown in Fig. 55 and which will now be considered, concerns itself with the acquisition of nitrogen from various sources. Four ways of addition are recognized in arable soils: (1) nitrogen fixation by legume bacteria, (2) free fixation or azofication, (3) additions in rain water, and (4) application of nitrogen in fertilizers, farm manure, and green manures. They will be considered in order.

[1] Bracken, A. F., and J. E. Greaves, "Losses of Nitrogen and Organic Matter from Dryland Soils," *Soil Sci.* LI:1–15, 1941.

205. *Fixation of atmospheric nitrogen by nodule bacteria* [1]

It has long been recognized that certain crops such as the clovers, alfalfa, peas, beans, and others improve the soil in some way, making it possible to grow larger yields of cereals after these plants have occupied the land.   Within the last century the benefit has been traced to the fixation of nitrogen through the agency of bacteria contained

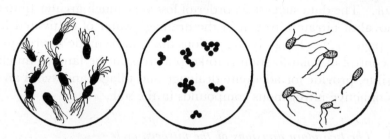

FIG. 56.   Some soil organisms especially important in the nitrogen cycle.   Left to right: *Azotobacter*, nitrate bacteria, and nodule organisms of alfalfa.

in nodules on the roots of the host.   The specific plants so affected belong, with a few exceptions,[2] to the family of legumes.

It has furthermore been demonstrated that the host plant is generally able to appropriate some of the nitrogen so fixed and thus benefit by the relationship.   For this reason the fixation is often spoken of as *symbiotic*.   The organism is a *rhizobium* and there are a number of strains depending on the host plants.   They are therefore classified according to the host as *Rhizobium meliloti* for those of alfalfa and sweet clover, *Rhizobium trifolii* for the clovers, *Rhizobium japonicum* for soybeans, and so on.   As a group, they will be referred to here as the *nodule* or *legume organism* instead of by the more technical terms.

The legume organisms live in the root nodules, take free nitrogen from the air of the soil, and synthesize it into complex forms.   The nodules are not normally a part of leguminous plants, but are evidently the result of an irritation of the root surface, much as a gall is

[1] The literature on the fixation of nitrogen by microorganisms is exceedingly copious One may best begin with Waksman, S. A., *Soil Microbiology*, The Williams & Wilkins Company, Baltimore, 1932.

[2] Alnus, Coriaria, Elaeagnaceae, and a few other nonlegumes carry root nodules similar to those of legumes.   See, Fred, E. B., I. L. Baldwin, and Elizabeth McCoy, *Root Nodule Bacteria and Leguminous Plants*, Madison, Wis., 1932.

caused to develop on a leaf or on a branch of a tree by an insect. In
a culture containing the proper bacteria, the prick of a needle on the
root surface of a legume will cause a nodule to form in the course of a
few days. The entrance of the organisms normally is effected through
the root hairs. The infection tube ultimately extends the entire length
of the root hair and into the cortex cells of the root, where the growth
of the tubercle starts and where the fixation of nitrogen occurs. How
the plant absorbs this nitrogen after it has been secured by the bacteria
is not well understood, nor is it known in exactly what form the
nitrogen is at first fixed, although amino and amide forms very soon
appear.[1] It seems likely that the nitrogen compounds produced
within the bacterial cells are diffused through the cell wall and absorbed by the host plant.

While the nodule bacteria are considered to be common to all
leguminous plants, it is well known that the organisms from one
species of legumes are not necessarily well adapted to the ready production of tubercles on other leguminous species although infection
may be effected by proper culturing.[2] Certain cross-inoculations are,
however, very easy and successful in practice. The organisms seem
to be readily interchangeable within the clovers, the vetches, and the
beans. Those from sweet clover and bur clover will inoculate alfalfa,
while the bacteria may be transferred from vetch to field pea or
from cowpea to velvet bean.[3] The part played by the plant is
doubtless to furnish the carbohydrates that supply energy to the nitro-
gen-assimilating bacteria. The stimulating influence of carbohydrates

---

[1] This is a complex and highly controversial question. See, Virtanen, A. I., "Mechanism of Symbiotic Nitrogen by Leguminous Plants," *Proc. Soil Sci. Soc. Amer.*, IV:221–
222, 1939. And Wilson, P. W., *The Biochemistry of Symbiotic Nitrogen Fixation*, University of
Wisconsin Press, Madison, 1940.

[2] Wilson, J. K., *Leguminous Plants and their Associated Organisms*, Memoir 221, Cornell
Univ. Agr. Exp. Sta., 1939.

[3] A partial listing of the groups within which inoculation may easily be made is given
below:

Group   I. Alfalfa, bur clover, white sweet clover, yellow sweet clover, fenugreek, and yellow
             trefoil.
Group   II. Mammoth and red clover, alsike clover, crimson clover, hop clover, white clover,
             zigzag clover.
Group   III. Lespedeza, peanut, acacia, tick trefoil, kudzu, cowpea, partridge pea, jack bean, vel-
             vet bean, lima bean, etc.
Group   IV. Garden pea, sweet pea, horse bean lentil, Canada field pea, hairy vetch, common
             vetch, purple vetch, etc.
Group   V. Soybean.
Group   VI. Garden bean (numerous varieties) pinto bean, and scarlet runner.
Group   VII. Lupine, serradella, blue lupine, yellow lupine, and white lupine.

Pieters, A. J., *Green Manuring*, John Wiley & Sons, Inc., New York, 1927, pp. 140–141.

sometimes is taken advantage of in the inoculation of legumes. The coating of the legume seeds with sugar prior to sowing seems to encourage inoculation, possibly because of the direct influence of the carbohydrates upon the nodule bacteria.

Even when the nodule bacteria are present in the soil, a legume may secure, through their intervention, but little atmospheric nitrogen. This is especially true if there is an abundant supply of soil nitrogen upon which the organisms as well as the host plant may draw. The nodule bacteria have the ability to utilize combined nitrogen as well as the gaseous form. As a matter of fact, they may prefer it, since its acquisition requires less energy expenditure. On soils rich in nitrogen, nodulation therefore often occurs sparingly and the legume may be forced to draw most of its nitrogen from the soil itself. A decrease in soil nitrogen may readily result. On the other hand, legumes growing on soils somewhat deficient in nitrogen may, if properly inoculated, cause a very considerable gain in this constituent.

If legumes, especially of certain types, are to be grown most successfully, the specific strains of nodule organisms for that crop must be present. Such organisms may never have been in the soil or may have disappeared because of unfavorable influences. Under such conditions the inoculation either of the soil or preferably of the legume seed with the desired organism is a practical necessity. Since inoculation is not expensive, it apparently is worth while as an insurance, so worth while, in fact, that it should be employed with certain legumes every time they are seeded. Commercial cultures may readily be obtained accompanied by full directions for their use.

206. *Amount of nitrogen fixed by nodule bacteria*

The amount of nitrogen fixed by the legume bacteria depends on many factors. The condition of the soil, especially as to aeration, drainage, moisture, and the amount of active calcium, is of prime importance. Many soils are in such a condition as to harbor only a meagre, nonvirulent flora of legume bacteria. Even when the above factors are favorable, a large amount of readily available nitrogen will obstruct nodulation and consequently fixation.

Besides, there is the nature of the host plant. Some legume field crops, such as alfalfa and sweet clover, facilitate a nodule fixation of especially large amounts of nitrogen. The clovers are less effective, while some legumes can be credited with but a scanty acquisition. Lyon and Bizzell [1] in a ten-years' experiment at Ithaca, New York, report the order and relative magnitude of fixation, taking alfalfa as 100, as follows:

Alfalfa	100	Soybeans	42
Sweet Clover	67	Hairy vetch	27
Red Clover	60	Field beans	23
Alsike Clover	56	Field peas	19

Alfalfa grown continuously under the favorable conditions of the above experiment acquired symbiotically 251 pounds of nitrogen an acre yearly. A fixation ranging from 188 to 260 pounds an acre a year was recorded by Collison [2] at Geneva, New York, for the same crop.[3] Perhaps for an average crop of alfalfa, 200 to 250 pounds of nitrogen an acre would be a conservative figure. The corresponding estimate for red clover might well be 100 to 150 pounds an acre.

207. *Fate of the nitrogen fixed*

The nitrogen fixed by the nodule organisms may go in three directions. It may be absorbed by the host plant, the latter benefiting greatly by the association. Second, the nitrogen may pass in some way into the soil itself, either by excretion or more probably by a sloughing off of the roots and their nodules,[4] and thereby benefiting a crop associated with the legume. This influence is a matter of common observation. The more vigorous development of timothy or bluegrass in association with clover than when grown alone is a well-known example. Third, when the legume sod is turned under, some of the nitrogen becomes available to the succeeding crop. Because of its narrow nitrogen-carbon ratio, organic nitrogen of this type swings through the nitrogen cycle with remarkable ease and may quickly appear in the nitrate form.

The influence of inoculation upon the host plant usually is very

[1] Lyon, T. L., and J. A. Bizzell, "A Comparison of Several Legumes with Respect to Nitrogen Accretion," *Jour. Amer. Soc. Agron.*, XXVI: 651–656, 1934.

[2] Collison, R. C., H. C. Beattie, and J. D. Harlan, *Lysimeter Investigations. III. Mineral and Water Relations and Final Nitrogen Balance in Legume and Non-Legume Crop Rotations for a Period of 16 years*, Bulletin 212. N. Y. State Agr. Exp. Sta., 1933.

[3] For further data regarding amounts of nitrogen fixed by the various legume organisms, see, Fred, E. B., I. L. Baldwin, and Elizabeth McCoy, *Root Nodule Bacteria and Leguminous Plants*, Madison, Wis., 1932, p. 218.

[4] Wilson, J. K., "The Loss of Nodules from Legume Roots and Its Significance," *Jour. Amer. Soc. Agron.*, XXXIV: 460–471, 1942.

striking and naturally is of great practical importance, as there is likely to be an increase not only in crop yield, but also in the percentage of nitrogen. Data bearing upon the latter phase were obtained by Arny and Thatcher [1] who analyzed both the tops and roots of sweet clover and alfalfa grown on soil inoculated and not inoculated. The soil originally was not known to carry the legume organism. The results are shown in Table XXXIX.

Table XXXIX. Effect of Inoculation with the Legume Organism on the Nitrogen Content of Sweet Clover and Alfalfa
(Calculated as percentages based on dry matter)

Soil Treatment	Sweet Clover		Alfalfa	
	Tops	Roots	Tops	Roots
Inoculated	2.29	2.01	2.56	2.14
Not inoculated	1.37	0.88	1.51	0.71

208. Do legumes increase the soil nitrogen?

Apropos of the fate of the nitrogen fixed by legumes, it is generally assumed that legumes leave the soil on which they have been growing richer in nitrogen. As a matter of fact, the result is likely to be just the opposite when the soil is already high in nitrogen or the crop is harvested and removed from the land. Beans and peas are especially likely to leave the land depleted since their fixation is low, and their roots often are partially removed in harvesting. Swanson [2] determined total nitrogen in the soil of a considerable number of fields in Kansas that had grown alfalfa continuously for twenty to thirty years, at the same time analyzing soil from contiguous land in native sod. In most cases, the alfalfa soil was lower in nitrogen than the sod. This tendency for legumes actually to lower instead of raise the total nitrogen of soils is substantiated by Collison [3] in his carefully controlled lysimeter experiments with alfalfa and clover.

However, it may be expected that soils will gain some nitrogen if

[1] Arny, A. C., and R. W. Thatcher, "The Effect of Different Methods of Inoculation on the Yield and Protein Content of Alfalfa and Sweet Clover," *Jour. Amer. Soc. Agron.,* IX: 127–137, 1917.

[2] Swanson, C. O., "The Effect of Prolonged Growing Alfalfa on the Nitrogen Content of the Soil," *Jour. Amer. Soc. Agron.,* IX:305–314, 1917.

[3] Collison, R. C., H. C. Beattie, and J. D. Harlan, *Lysimeter Investigations. III. Mineral and Water Relations and Final Nitrogen Balance in Legume and Non-Legume Crop Rotations for a Period of 16 Years,* Bulletin 212, N. Y. State Agr. Exp. Sta., 1933.

leguminous crops, including the aboveground portions, are plowed
under or otherwise become incorporated, or if a leguminous flora remains untouched for a number of years. By growing red clover on
sand very low in nitrogen and allowing the crops to remain on the
ground to be plowed in every second year, Saunders and Shutt [1] were
able to secure a gain of 52 pounds of nitrogen an acre a year during a
nine-year period. Hall [2] reports an annual acre gain of 98 pounds on
the broadbalk field which was allowed to run wild for twenty years
carrying a vegetation of legumes and nonlegumes. These latter gains,
of course, include the nitrogen added in rain and by nonsymbiotic
bacteria, offset by volatilization and leaching losses. The accumulations of nitrogen cited are both large. However, they were obtained
in soil very low in nitrogen at the beginning of the experiments and
not very rich in that constituent at the end.

It is not always true, however, that turning under the entire legume
crop will increase the nitrogen of the soil. Mooers [3] conducted experiments for ten years in which wheat, followed by cowpeas, was
grown annually. On one set of plats the cowpea vines were plowed
under each year, and on the other set they were removed. The surface 8 inches of soil into which the vines were plowed under lost 288
pounds of nitrogen to the acre during the experiment. However,
where the vines were removed before plowing the loss was 388 pounds.
It would seem that, in spite of the fixation of nitrogen that may have
occurred, the influence of the wheat and other sources of loss were
such as to reduce the nitrogen content of the soil.

It is evident, therefore, that the influence of legumes on the amount
of nitrogen in the soil is uncertain. When the total soil nitrogen is
high, legumes may produce a decrease, especially if the crop is removed from the land. Even when the aboveground parts are plowed
under, there may still be a decrease, although some accretion is likely
if the nitrogen level of the soil is low. In general, however, the draft
of legumes on the soil nitrogen is less than that of nonlegumes, and as
a consequence, their use is to be encouraged in a rotation where the
maintenance of soil nitrogen is important. Legumes are so economi-

[1] Saunders, Wm., and F. T. Shutt, *Clover as a Fertilizer*, Bulletin 40, Centr. Exp. Farms,
Ottawa, Canada, 19–21, 1902.

[2] Hall, A. D., *Book of the Rothamsted Experiments*, E. P. Dutton & Company, Inc., New
York, 1905, p. 139.

[3] Mooers, C. A., *Effects of Liming and Green Manuring on Crop Yields and on Soil Supplies of
Nitrogen and Humus*, Bulletin 135, Tenn. Agr. Exp. Sta., 1926.

cal in their use of soil nitrogen that a high protein crop may often be harvested with little or no depletion of the land in respect to this element. They are nitrogen savers.

209. *The effect of legumes on the activity of soil nitrogen*

Although leguminous crops do not always, nor probably usually, bring about an increase in soil nitrogen, they do produce, under comparable conditions, a better growth of the succeeding crops than do nonlegumes unless the soil is already very high in available nitrogen. Under most circumstances, they render the organic matter of the soil more active by adding to it plant residues with a narrow nitrogen-carbon ratio. Such residues are of course very readily decomposed and ammonification and nitrification soon take place. If nonlegumes such as rye are plowed under while young, when their nitrogen-carbon ratio is narrow, they too may activate the soil nitrogen; but it is only the legumes that so markedly exert this effect on the soil when the residues of the more mature crop are incorporated.

An experiment by Lyon and Bizzell [1] demonstrates very effectively this property of legumes. Contiguous plats of alfalfa and timothy respectively were plowed up after they had been in these crops continuously for six years. The soil of the two plats at this time contained approximately the same percentages of nitrogen. However, when planted to maize the next season, the yield from the alfalfa soil was much larger than that from the timothy one. Since the better growth on the alfalfa soil could not have been due to more nitrogen, it must be ascribed to the ready nitrifiability of the legume residues. This was shown by a larger accumulation of nitrates. The property of nitrogen activation possessed by legumes is secondary in importance only to the ability of their nodule bacteria to assimilate this element from the atmosphere.

210. *The fixation of atmospheric nitrogen by azofication*

Soils may acquire a part of their nitrogen supply independently of higher plants, fertilizers, and rainfall. There exist in soils certain

[1] Lyon, T. L., and J. A. Bizzell, "The Influence of Alfalfa and of Timothy on the Production of Nitrates in Soils," *Centrlb. f. Bact.* II, XXXVII:161–167, 1913.

Lyon, T. L., and J. A. Bizzell, *Experiments Concerning the Top Dressing of Timothy and Alfalfa*, Bulletin 339, Cornell Univ. Agr. Exp. Sta., 119–143, 1913.

organisms, using the organic matter as a source of energy, that are able to obtain elemental nitrogen from the soil air. This nitrogen is incorporated in the bodies of the organisms and is left in the form of proteins and related compounds upon their death. The process is called *azofication*, because of the *Azotobacter* group of bacteria to which is ascribed a major part of the fixation. Since these organisms use the soil organic matter as a source of energy and are not directly associated with higher plants, as are the legume bacteria, the transformation is often spoken of as *nonsymbiotic* or *free fixation*.

Although several different groups of bacteria, blue-green algae, and perhaps fungi are able to acquire atmospheric nitrogen nonsymbiotically, the major fixation in the representative soil apparently is brought about by two groups of heterotrophic bacteria. One of these is the aerobic *Azotobacter* of which there are several different species. The other is an anaerobic, or perhaps a facultative, bacterium called *Clostridium pastorianum*. Because of the highly colloidal nature of most soils and the great concentration of carbon dioxide at the interfaces, conditions of low oxygen, favorable for the latter organism, are present in all soils, even when in the best of tilth. Consequently these two groups of bacteria probably work side by side in the synthesis of atmospheric nitrogen.

It is not to be assumed that the *Azotobacter* and *Clostridium pastorianum* acquire all of their nitrogen from atmospheric sources. Since less energy is required for the synthesis of ammoniacal and nitrate nitrogen, these forms are probably readily used. In fact, in a soil high in such available nitrogen, it is doubtful whether a great deal of free fixation takes place. In this respect, the nonsymbiotic bacteria resemble the symbiotic types.

Highly carbonaceous organic matter, since it supplies energy readily, greatly encourages azofication. For this reason, an application of sugar, or some other easily available carbohydrate, to a soil is often highly beneficial, even though it temporarily suppresses nitrification. Sod land, because it generally contains a large supply of organic matter with a wide nitrogen-carbon ratio, and because it is likely to be low in nitrate nitrogen, presents almost ideal conditions for azofication. The presence of potassium, iron, manganese, and phosphate ions also increases the suitability of the soil for vigorous nonsymbiotic fixation of nitrogen. The addition of a phosphatic fertilizer is considered especially beneficial.

Azotobacter are notably sensitive to active calcium and unless a fair amount of this metal is present, the fixation lags. In this respect, azofication resembles nitrification. The H-ion concentration in itself does not seem to be a factor unless the pH becomes rather low. In mineral soils free fixation of nitrogen begins to lag noticeably at pH 5.5 and at pH values below 5.0 becomes more or less negligible. Such is not the case, however, with peat soils, since they ordinarily contain suitable amounts of active lime even at relatively high H-ion concentrations. The maintenance of the pH of mineral soils above 5.5 or even 6.0 by judicious liming is to be recommended.

A condition that appears to be exceptionally favorable to azofication is one in which a grass or similar nonleguminous vegetation is allowed to grow year after year and is left to decompose on the land. Under such conditions Hall [1] reports an accumulation of 44 pounds of nitrogen annually to the acre over a period of twenty years. Some of this gain may have been due to nitrogen added in rain water, but probably this did not exceed 6 or 8 pounds an acre a year, and no doubt was more than offset by volatilization and drainage losses. The field was allowed to run wild and contained practically no leguminous plants.

A somewhat similar case is on record at Cornell University [2] where plats of land were kept in grass for ten years without any application of nitrogen in fertilizers. The crop was cut annually, but not removed. Analyses of the soil were made at the beginning and end of the experiment. There was a gain of nitrogen amounting to 415 pounds to the acre at the end of ten years, or 41.5 pounds as an annual average. A small part of this, probably about 6 pounds yearly, was due to additions in rain. Since the loss by volatilization and drainage combined probably was considerably greater than this addition, the fixation ascribed to azofication appears rather conservative. It was under such conditions as those described above, encouraged by hot, dry summers and abundant lime, that the prairie and chernozem soils acquired their high content of organic matter and nitrogen. When mature grasses with their wide nitrogen-carbon ratio become incorporated with the soil, they provide abundant energy for the nitrogen-fixing organisms.

[1] Hall, A. D., *Book of the Rothamsted Experiments*, E. P. Dutton & Company, Inc., New York, 1905, p. 139.

[2] Lyon, T. L., and B. D. Wilson, *Some Relations of Green-Manures to the Nitrogen of a Soil*, Memoir 115, Cornell Univ. Agr. Exp. Sta., 1928.

But when grass is cut and harvested each year, so that several pounds of nitrogen to the acre are removed from the soil, and the amount of carbonaceous material available to the nitrogen-fixing organisms is reduced, the free fixation of nitrogen is likely to be less. In the same field as that in which the last-mentioned experiment was conducted, plats of timothy without nitrogenous fertilization were cut for hay each season for ten years. Instead of a gain in soil nitrogen, there was a slight reduction amounting to an annual average of nearly 5 pounds to the acre. From 20 to 25 pounds of nitrogen were removed in the hay crop each year. Assuming that the loss of nitrogen by drainage and the accretion by rainfall would nearly balance each other, a minimum of 15 to 20 pounds of nitrogen to the acre were fixed annually in this particular case, if no loss by volatilization is reckoned in. If such a loss occurred, the fixation figures would of necessity be that much greater.

Considering the data quoted, meagre and unreliable as they are, it is perhaps fair to assume that azofication fixes in the representative arable soil at least 25 pounds of nitrogen an acre a year. Probably the average figure is nearer 40 or 50 pounds. This is of the same order of magnitude as the removal of nitrogen by volatilization. For purposes of rough calculation, it is perhaps not far wrong to consider that volatilization and azofication may approximately balance each other.

211. *The addition of nitrogen to soil in rain*

Nitrogen occurring in rain water generally is in the nitrate and ammoniacal forms and consequently is readily available to plants. The amounts thus brought down are variable, usually fluctuating markedly with season and location. It is well known that the additions are greater in the tropics than in humid-temperate regions and larger in the latter than under semiarid climates. In Table XL will be found some of the more important data regarding the amounts of nitrogen thus added to the soil in various parts of the world. It will be noted that the figures are, for the most part, from temperate regions.

Apparently the ammoniacal nitrogen added to the soil in rain water is, at least in temperate regions, always larger in amount than that in the nitrate form. It is also noticeable that, while the nitrate nitrogen is about the same for most locations, the ammonium form shows wide variations. Considering the figures as a whole, it seems fair to assume that under a humid-temperate climate, an average of about 4½ pounds of ammoniacal and 1½ pounds of nitrate nitrogen fall on every acre of land yearly in rain water. Allowing for some loss in runoff, perhaps 5 pounds of nitrogen an acre actually enter the soil.

Table XL.   Amounts of Nitrogen Brought Down in Rain

Location	Years of Record	Rainfall in Inches	Pounds to the Acre a Year	
			Ammoniacal Nitrogen	Nitrate Nitrogen
Harpenden, England [a]	28	28.8	2.64	1.33
Garford, England [b]	3	26.9	6.43	1.93
Flahult, Sweden [c]	1	32.5	3.32	1.30
Groningen, Holland [d]	..	27.6	4.54	1.46
Bloemfontein and Durban S. Africa [e]	2	...	4.02	1.39
Ottawa, Canada [f]	10	23.4	4.42	2.16
Ithaca, New York [g]	11	29.5	7.10	0.80

[a] Russell, E. J., and E. H. Richards, "The Amount and Composition of Rain Falling at Rothamsted," *Jour. Agr. Sci.*, IX:309–337, 1919.

[b] Crowther, C., and A. G. Ruston, "The Nature, Distribution, and Effects upon Vegetation of Atmospheric Impurities in and near an Industrial Town," *Jour. Agr. Sci.*, IV:25–55, 1911.

[c] Von Feilitzen, H., and I. Lugner, "On the Quantity of Ammonia and Nitric Acid in Rainwater Collected near Flahult, in Sweden," *Jour. Agr. Sci.*, III:311–313, 1910.

[d] Hudig, J., "The Amounts of Nitrogen as Ammonia and Nitric Acid in the Rainwater Collected at Uithuizer-Meeden, Groningen," *Jour. Agr. Sci.*, IV:260–269, 1912.

[e] Juritz, C. F., "Chemical Composition of Rain in the Union of South Africa," *S. Africa Jour. Sci.*, X:170–193, 1914.

[f] Shutt, F. T., and R. Dorrance, "The Nitrogen Compounds of Rain and Snow," *Proc. and Trans. Roy. Soc. Canada*, XI:63–71, 1917.

[g] Wilson, B. D., "Nitrogen and Sulfur in Rainwater in New York," *Jour. Amer. Soc. Agron.*, XVIII:1108–1112, 1926.

An annual acquisition of 5 pounds of nitrogen in a readily available form to each acre of land affords some aid in the maintenance of soil fertility, as it is equivalent to about 31 pounds of commercial nitrate of soda. This addition by the rainfall nearly offsets the annual removal of nitrogen in drainage water from a soil under a standard rotation and more than meets such loss when the soil is in continuous sod (see Table XXIV). It is not unreasonable to assume, therefore, that in general it more or less completely offsets leaching losses. The accession of nitrogen in rain is, however, small as compared with the

60 or 70 pounds of nitrogen annually removed from an acre by the average crop. Nevertheless, it is an important factor in the nitrogen economy of the land.

212. *Control of soil nitrogen*

The problem of nitrogen control is twofold: (1) the maintenance of an adequate supply in the soil, and (2) the regulation of the turnover in such a way as to assure a ready availability at such times as to meet crop demands. To begin with, it is well to gauge the magnitude of the losses that ordinarily must be met in dealing with maintenance problems.

It has been suggested for a representative humid-region soil that azofication approximately offsets the possible losses of nitrogen by volatilization (page 393). It has also been tentatively assumed that rain-water acquisition equals in general leaching removals (page 394). Therefore the nitrogen in the harvested crops plus that carried away by erosion approximately represents the yearly deficit. Considering the former as 60 or 70 pounds an acre a year, and the latter as possibly 20 or 25 pounds for lands having a moderate slope (see page 200), it seems that in a general way 75 or 100 pounds of nitrogen an acre will be required annually to effect a balance. Such figures should be used guardedly, as they are purely hypothetical and are designed merely to give a general concept of the problem.

Nitrogen deficits are met, partially or wholly, in practice, in four ways — crop residues, farm manure, legumes, and commercial fertilizers. The discussion of their utilization is reserved for a later and more opportune occasion. Suffice to say at this point that, although the deficit can be met and is being met on the better managed farms, the average arable soil in the United States is at the present time probably suffering a slow decline in total nitrogen.[1] That crops do not show a corresponding decrease in yield may be ascribed to better methods of soil management and to a greater activity of the nitrogen still present in the soil. This introduces the second phase of nitrogen control — *turnover* regulation.

By all odds, the more difficult of the two general problems of nitrogen control is the regulation of this element after it enters the soil.

---

[1] Lipman, J. G., *Preliminary Note on the Inventory and Balance Sheet of Plant Nutrients in the United States*, Bulletin 607, N. J. Agr. Exp. Sta., 1936.

Availability at the proper time and in the correct amounts, with a minimum of loss, is the ideal. The influence of climate, of erosion, drainage, tillage, fertilizers, lime, and the N:C ratio must be balanced against the nature of the soil, the crops grown, and their particular influence on the land. There are many factors involved. A knowledge of the various phases of the nitrogen cycle and their practical significance are invaluable in dealing with the situation.

Since soils under any given climate tend to assume what may be called a *normal content* of nitrogen under ordinary methods of cropping and manuring, any attempt to raise the nitrogen content to a point materially higher than the normal will be attended by an unnecessary waste due to drainage and other losses. It would appear to be good practice, therefore, to maintain only a moderate nitrogen level in a soil and keep the nitrogen active by the use of legumes and other organic materials with a narrow nitrogen-carbon ratio, and by applications of lime and commercial fertilizers. This is essentially the recommendation already made for soil organic matter (page 143), and it is known to be both economical and effective. In short, the practical problem is to supply nitrogen to the soil, to keep it mobile, and at the same time to protect it from excessive loss by drainage, volatilization, and erosion.

Chapter XVII. Fertilizers and Fertilizer Effects

While the use of animal excrement on cultivated soils was common as far back as agricultural records can be traced, mineral salts have been systematically and extensively employed for the encouragement of crop growth hardly more than one hundred years. Any inorganic salt, such as nitrate of soda, or an organic substance, such as tankage or fish scrap, regularly on the market and applied to the soil directly to promote crop development is considered to be a commercial fertilizer.[1]

213. *Fertilizer objectives*

The primary objective in the application of a commercial fertilizer to a soil is to supply plant nutrients, but the addition is usually made to supplement the native constituents rather than to constitute the only source of supply. The crop, even though fertilized, continues to depend on the soil for an appreciable proportion of its mineral substance unless the land is very sandy and low in organic matter.

Besides supplementing the nutrients already present in the soil, another function is expected of the fertilizer added. It should establish a proper *balance* between the necessary elements of nutrition. This seems essential in order that an under- or overstimulation of the crop does not occur and that abnormal physiological developments are not encouraged.

There is another feature of fertilization that is usually entirely over-

[1] For further information as to fertilizers and their use, see: Gustafson, A. F., *Handbook of Fertilizers*, Orange Judd Publishing Co., Inc., New York, 1939.

Worthen, E. L., *Farm Soils, Their Management and Fertilization*, John Wiley & Sons, Inc., New York, 1941.

Collings, Gilbeart H., *Commercial Fertilizers*, The Blakiston Company, Philadelphia, 1941.

Bear, Firman E., *Theory and Practice in the Use of Fertilizers*, John Wiley & Sons, Inc., New York, 1938.

looked.   In fact most people know nothing about it.   Commercial fertilizers when applied to the soil influence the microorganisms just as profoundly as they do higher plants.   In fact, the fertilization of the soil flora is an essential feature of successful soil management in spite of the fact that it receives little attention.   Since the bacteria, fungi, and actinomyces are more successful than are higher plants in their competition for nutrients, their needs are satisfied first.   Then if any nutrients are temporarily left over, crops may benefit.   Thus an amount of fertilizer fully adequate for crop needs may fail to give the desired results when added to a soil, because of chemical and bio-chemical fixation.   It has already been shown that microorganisms especially compete with higher plants for nitrogen (page 112), 1 ton live weight of organisms requiring the equivalent of over 300 pounds of nitrate of soda.   Apparently they compete almost as vigorously for phosphorus and perhaps for potash and calcium also.   Proper fertilization is difficult to attain.

214. *The fertilizer elements and their problems*

Of the eleven nutrient elements that plants obtain from the soil, calcium and magnesium when required in any considerable quantity are applied as lime.   And lime is not usually rated as a fertilizer, although it does exert a profound nutritive effect.   Sulfur is present in several commercial fertilizers and its influence is considered important, yet, because it is not critical nutritionally except in certain localities, it receives only secondary attention as a fertilizer.   This leaves three nutrients other than the trace elements — *nitrogen, phosphorus,* and *potassium*.   And since they are so commonly applied in commercial fertilizers they are often referred to as the *fertilizer elements*.

The mobility of the soil nitrogen and the complexity of its transformations have been considered (Chap. XVI).   That its maintenance and activity are vital is a fertility homily.   Undoubtedly it presents a problem that in many cases cannot be solved without commercial fertilizers.

The phosphorus in soils is not only low in amount (see page 25) but rather unavailable.   As a consequence, even when soil conditions are favorable, especially as to pH and active lime, this element is likely to be critical.   There are few soils that do not show a phosphorus deficiency.   In fact, the practical importance of phosphorus in the maintenance of soil fertility is on a par with nitrogen and its attendant organic matter.

A feature of the phosphorus problem that should not be overlooked is the tendency for this element, when added to the soil, to revert to less soluble and available forms. Thus the water-soluble monocalcium phosphate of superphosphate [$CaH_4(PO_4)_2$] changes readily to insoluble and unavailable calcium phosphates if the lime is so abundant as to hold the soil pH much above 7. Or if calcium is lacking and the soil is overly acid, complex iron and aluminum phosphates even more unavailable are formed. Only when the pH falls within a certain range (see page 303) can the most satisfactory result be expected from superphosphate. As a consequence the addition of small amounts of phosphorus may not give the desired results and, since soil conditions are so difficult to gauge, the optimum amount becomes a matter of judgment or even of guess. Moreover, the situation is complicated by microbial utilization. The microflora must be fed as well as the higher plants, and they require no mean amount.

The situation in respect to potassium is somewhat different and in many cases no less critical. Most mineral soils, except those of a sandy nature, are high in total potassium (see page 23). Yet the amount of potash held in an easily exchangeable condition at the colloidal interfaces is usually small. Hence higher plants must depend on the ordinary processes of solution or effect an availability by direct contact with the undecomposed soil minerals and the colloidal complex. Such influences as tillage, the addition of farm manure, the decomposition of organic matter, and the application of lime aid in solving the potash problem of soils. When these are not adequate, recourse to commercial potassium must be made.

An examination of the drainage water from mineral soil will usually show large amounts of potash, at least enough annually to satisfy the needs of higher plants (see page 211). Yet crops may be suffering a deficiency. They apparently must be in contact with a comparatively concentrated solution in order to obtain a satisfactory amount of this element. The problem is not only solubility, but a solubility that is wasteful to an extreme. Phosphorus nutrition, in contrast, is very economical as this element is but sparingly lost in drainage.

The competition of microorganisms for potassium, which may at times be keen, further complicates the situation. For instance, potassium is possibly liberated by ionic exchange when lime is applied to moderately acid soils. Yet such a treatment often lessens the amount of this element appearing in drainage. It is suggested that the soil microorganisms are so stimulated by the lime that they demand exceptional quantities of potassium.[1]

215. *The influence of nitrogen on plant development* [2]

Of the three elements usually applied in commercial fertilizers, nitrogen seems to have the quickest and most pronounced effect, not only when present in excess but also when moderately used. It tends primarily to encourage aboveground vegetative growth and to impart to the leaves a deep green color. With cereals it increases the plumpness of the grains and their percentage of protein. With all plants nitrogen is a regulator in that it governs to a certain extent the utilization of potash, phosphoric acid, and other constituents. Moreover, its application tends to produce succulence, a quality particularly desirable in certain crops such as lettuce and radishes.

Plants receiving insufficient nitrogen are stunted in growth and possess a restricted root system. The leaves turn yellow or yellowish-green and on some plants tend to drop off. The addition of a small amount of available nitrogen will, other conditions being favorable, cause a remarkable change, indicative of the activity of this element within the plant. Its mobility in the soil has already been observed in the study of the nitrogen cycle.

Because of the immediately visible effect from the application of available nitrogen compounds, the average person is prone to ascribe too much importance comparatively to the influence of this element on proper crop development. This attitude is unfortunate, since nitrogen is expensive and is easily lost from the soil. Moreover, of the three fertilizer constituents, it is the only one which, added somewhat in excess, will ordinarily result in harmful aftereffects on the crop. Very dark green, soft, and sappy leaves are an indication of an oversupply of nitrogen. The possible and important detrimental effects of this element may be listed as follows:

[1] Jenny, Hans, and E. R. Shade, "The Potassium-Lime Problem in Soils," *Jour. Amer. Soc. Agron.*, XXVI:162–170, 1934.

[2] Good discussions of the effects of the various nutrients on plant growth are given by Russell, E. J., *Soil Conditions and Plant Growth*, Longmans, Green and Company, New York, 1937.

1. Nitrogen may *delay maturation* by encouraging excessive vegetative growth, which remains green beyond the normal time of ripening. This often endangers field crops to frost, and in some climates may cause orchards to winter badly.

2. It may *weaken the straw* and cause *lodging* in grain. This is due to an extreme lengthening of the internodes, and as the heads fill the stems are no longer able to support the increased weight. Lodged grain does not fill well and is difficult to harvest.

3. It may *lower quality*. This is especially noticeable in certain grains and fruits, as barley and peaches. The shipping qualities of fruits and some vegetables are also impaired.

4. It may *decrease resistance to disease*. This is probably due to a change in the physiological conditions within the plant, and also to a thinning of the cell walls, allowing a more ready infection. Nitrogen in excess of photosynthetic capacity seems to upset the nutrition of the cells, and once infection occurs little resistance can be offered to the progress of the disease.

It must not be inferred, however, that all plants are detrimentally affected by large amounts of nitrogen. Many crops such as the grasses, lettuce, radishes, and the like depend on plenty of this element for their best and most normal development. In fact, standard quality is not attained unless large amounts of nitrogen are available. With such crops, therefore, the detrimental effects above listed are not to be expected unless exceedingly large quantities of nitrogen are made available. Nitrogenous fertilizers may be used freely in such cases, the cost of the materials in respect to the value of the crop being the main consideration.

216. *Influence of phosphorus on plants*

It is difficult to state in detail the functions of phosphorus in the economy of even the simplest plants. Neither cell division nor the formation of fat and albumen take place adequately without it. Starch may be produced when it is lacking, but does not readily change to sugar. As seeds do not form without its presence, it undoubtedly is concerned in the production of nucleoproteids. Its close relationship to cell division may account for its presence in grains and other seeds in comparatively large amounts. Flowering and fruiting depend absolutely upon it.

Phosphorus especially hastens the maturation of the crop and in this respect it counteracts the effect of excessive nitrogen. This influence is particularly important in wet years and in cold climates where the season is short. Phosphorus also encourages root development, particularly of the lateral and fibrous rootlets. This renders it valuable in soils that do not encourage root extension and to crops that naturally have a restricted root development. It is especially serviceable in the production of nursery stock, which should have a strong, fibrous root system. Phosphorus is notably valuable for fall-sown crops such as wheat and alfalfa. A sturdy root growth is developed which tends to counteract winter injury and prepares the plant for a rapid spring development. This is especially important with certain types of crops as for instance fall wheat.

The ratio of grain to straw, as well as the total yield, is increased in cereals by phosphorus. Phosphorus also strengthens the straw, thus decreasing the tendency to lodge, which is likely to occur especially with oats if too much available nitrogen is present. A lack of phosphorus results in a restricted root system and a bronzing or purpling of the leaves. Plants deficient in phosphoric acid seem to find it difficult to obtain sufficient potash. No doubt there is a similar relationship in respect to other nutrients.

Phosphorus decidedly improves the quality of certain crops. This has been recognized in the handling of pastures in many parts of the world, a better bone development of the grazing animals resulting. The effect on the palatability of vegetables is an influence of practical concern. Phosphorus is also known to increase the resistance of some plants to disease, due possibly to a more normal cell development and to a more vigorous metabolism.

Besides the effects noted, phosphorus is valuable because of its balancing influence on potassium and especially on nitrogen. By hastening maturity, strengthening root development, increasing disease resistance, and encouraging flowering and fruiting, it powerfully counteracts possible detrimental effects of excess nitrogen. This is evident when the effects of phosphorus listed above are checked against the undesirable consequences of too much nitrogen (see page 401). Moreover, phosphorus tends at times to alleviate the detrimental effects of overliming, perhaps by restoring the phosphate nutrition that seems to be upset by the absorption of too much calcium (see page 362).

217. *Effects of potassium on plant growth*

The presence of adequate available potash in the soil has much to do with the general tone and vigor of the plant.   By increasing resistance to certain diseases and encouraging the root system, it tends to counteract the ill effects of too much nitrogen, while in delaying maturity it works against undue ripening influences of phosphoric acid. In a general way, it exerts a balancing effect on both nitrogen and phosphorus, and consequently is especially important in a mixed fertilizer, if the potash of the soil is low or unavailable.

Potassium is essential for starch formation and the translocation of sugars, and is necessary in the development of chlorophyll, although it does not, like magnesium, enter prominently into its molecular structure.   It is important to cereals in grain formation, giving plump heavy kernels.   It also seems especially valuable to leguminous crops of all kinds.   Abundant available potassium is absolutely necessary for tuber development and consequently the percentage of this element usually is comparatively high in mixed fertilizers recommended for potatoes.   In fact, all root crops respond to liberal applications of potash.   As with phosphorus, it may be present in large quantities in the soil and yet exert no harmful effect on the crop.   While potassium and sodium are similar chemically, sodium cannot entirely take the place of potassium in plant nutrition, although it may serve in its stead to a certain extent.   When there is an insufficiency of potash, the sodium of the soil, or that added in such fertilizers as nitrate of soda, may be very useful.

The leaves of crops suffering from a potassium deficiency [1] appear dry and scorched at the edges, while the surfaces are irregularly chlorotic.   With such plants as red and alsike clover, alfalfa, and sweet clover, these symptoms are preceded by the appearance of small dots arranged more or less regularly around the edges of the leaves.   As a result photosynthesis is much impaired and the synthesis of starch practically brought to a standstill.   In contrast, adequate potassium encourages the assimilation of carbon dioxide, the utilization of nitrate

---

[1] For the deficiency symptoms of potassium see: *Potash Deficiency Symptoms* distributed by The American Potash Institute, Washington, D. C., 1937.

Also *Hunger Signs in Crops*, American Society of Agronomy and the National Fertilizer Association, Washington, D. C., 1941.   And *If They Could Speak*, Chilean Nitrate Educational Bureau, New York, 1941.

nitrogen in protein synthesis, the intake of water, and adequate root development. The influence on starch production is especially noticeable with root crops, which markedly respond to potassium fertilization.

218. *The nutrient balance*

Before taking up a discussion of the various fertilizing materials, one point should be emphasized. In considering the respective effects on plant growth exerted by the three fertilizer elements, it is noticed that they tend to check, balance, support, and supplement one another. This relationship is very important in fertilizer practice since it influences the results that may be attained by the application of fertilizers and has much to do with the economy and effectiveness of their utilization.

Ideally, the fertilizer added should so supplement the soil nutrients as to present to the plant just the correct proportion of nitrogen, phosphorus, and potassium. At the same time the amounts and availability of the eight other elements should be ideal. In short the fertility balance as a whole should be such as to produce a large and normal crop growth. In practice, however, such an ideal is difficult to attain. The soil is always more or less an unknown quality as to the probable availability of its constituents. Moreover, it is difficult to forecast the reactions that will occur when the fertilizer is applied and the extent to which its constituents will remain active and available in the soil during the course of the growing season. The influence of calcium, magnesium, manganese, iron, aluminum, and other elements upon the efficacy of a fertilizer is always problematical.

Again, crops differ in their response to fertilizers and the whole set of relationships is greatly affected by the weather. A fertilizer that functions almost ideally one year may, in the following season, give somewhat different results. It is difficult to cope with the vagaries of the weather in fertilizer practice.

The situation in respect to fertilizer balance explains why the kind of fertilizer to apply and the amounts to the acre are always somewhat of a guess. Nevertheless, the ideal should be striven for even though it seldom can be closely approached. Obviously much depends in fertilizer practice on good judgment and the ability to anticipate the conditions that must be met. A knowledge of three things is absolutely essential: (1) the nature and influence of the various fertilizers, (2) soil conditions and their dynamics, and (3) the culture and response of the crops being grown. Only the first of these phases will be considered in this chapter.

219. *Three groups of fertilizers*

The emphasis which has been placed on the three nutrient elements leads directly to a very simple fertilizer grouping. On the basis of the elements supplied, commercial fertilizers automatically fall into three groups: (1) those that supply nitrogen, (2) those serving as a source of available phosphoric acid, and (3) those carrying water-soluble potash.

The classification, however, is not so simple as this grouping would imply, as many fertilizers carry two or sometimes all three of the elements of nutrition. As examples of this overlapping, potassium nitrate, ammo-phos, and ammoniated superphosphate may be cited. Each contains two of the fertilizer elements while a complete fertilizer carries all three. The situation will be fully apparent when the fertilizer tables presented later are examined.

Because of the lack of space it will only be possible to discuss each group in a general way, listing the various fertilizers of each, and mentioning the outstanding characteristics of a few of the most important. Fortunately detailed descriptions of the various fertilizers are available in published form [1] from which their physical and chemical characteristics, mode of manufacture or source, and other important properties may be ascertained if the reader cares to go further than these pages will carry him.

220. *Nitrogen fertilizers*

Often referred to as *ammoniates*, nitrogen fertilizers may be divided for convenience into two groups: (1) organic and (2) inorganic. The organic fertilizers, among which are tankage, fish scrap, castor pomace, and cottonseed meal (see Table XLI), must undergo aminization, ammonification, and nitrification before their nitrogen becomes fully available to higher plants. As a result, they are not so quickly effective as nitrate of soda or sulfate of ammonia, and do not

[1] See reference books cited on bottom of page 397.

produce a suitable crop response unless the soil is warm. Their action, however, is mild and natural.

Organic fertilizers are popular because they tend to liberate their nitrogen gradually throughout the season, and especially because they aid in maintaining a good physical condition in any mixture of which they may be a part. This conditioning influence is important as it assures a ready drillability of the mixture. Mixed fertilizers are often supplied with from 200 to 300 pounds of some organic material for this reason. The main objection to the organic ammoniates is the expense of the nitrogen carried, which costs two or three times as much as that supplied as nitrate of soda, sulfate of ammonia, or other inorganics.

Table XLI.   Organic Ammoniates

Fertilizer	Source	Per Cent Nitrogen
Dried blood	Packing house	8 to 12
Animal tankage	Packing house	5 to 10 (3 to 13% P_2O)
Meat meal	Packing house	10 to 11 (1 to 5% P_2O_5)
Garbage tankage	Steam-treated garbage, grease removed	2 to 4 (some P_2O_5 and K_2O)
Process tankage	Waste treated with acid under steam	6 to 10 (some P_2O_5)
Sewage sludge	Sludge dried and ground	5 to 6 (variable amounts of P_2O_5 and K_2O)
Dried fish scrap	Cannery waste and non-edible fish	6 to 10 (4 to 8% P_2O_5)
Cottonseed meal	Ground cake after removal of oil	6 to 9 (2 to 3% P_2O_5 and 1 to 2% K_2O)
Linseed meal	Ground cake after removal of oil	4 to 5 (1.5% P_2O_5 and 1.5% K_2O)
Tobacco stems	Waste tobacco, midribs and stems	1.5 to 3.5 (4 to 9% K_2O)
Castor meal	Ground cake after removal of oil	5 to 7 (about 2% P_2O_5 and 1% K_2O)
Cocoa-cake meal	Ground cake refuse	3.5 to 4.5 (some P_2O_5 and K_2O)

Nitrate of soda and sulfate of ammonia have been for a number of years the main inorganic sources of nitrogen and still continue popular. Nitrate of soda supplies nitrogen in a form that immediately stimulates the crop even if the soil is cold. Hence it is extremely valuable early in the spring and as a side-dressing later in the season. Nitrate of soda tends to reduce the acidity of soils slowly or even render them alkaline [1] due to the residual sodium. This constituent

[1] Hall, A. D., "The Effect of the Long-Continued Use of Sodium Nitrate on the Constitution of the Soil," *Trans. Chem. Soc.* (London), LXXXV:950–971, 1905. Also Brown, B. E., "Concerning Some Effects of Long-Continued Use of Sodium Nitrate and Ammonium Sulfate on the Soil," *Annual Report,* Penn. State Coll., 1908–1909:85–104.

tends to produce sodium carbonate, which is quite alkaline. There-fore, nitrate of soda may, if used year after year in large amounts, not only produce alkalinity but also develop an unfavorable physical condition, due to the dispersive and puddling effects of the sodium carbonate upon the colloidal complex. In practice, however, the amounts of nitrate of soda added are seldom large enough to bring this about.

Table XLII.   Inorganic Ammoniates

Fertilizer	Chemical Form	Source	Per Cent Nitrogen
Sodium nitrate	NaNO$_3$	Chile saltpetre and synthetic	16
Ammonium sulfate	(NH$_4$)$_2$SO$_4$	By-product from coke and gas, and also synthetic	20
Calcium cyanamid [a]	CaCN$_2$	Synthetic	22
Ammonium nitrate	NH$_4$NO$_3$	"	35
Ammonium chloride	NH$_4$Cl	"	26
Calcium nitrate [b]	Ca(NO$_3$)$_2$	"	15
Urea [c]	CON$_2$H$_4$	"	42
Cal-nitro	CaCO$_3$ + NH$_4$NO$_3$	"	16 to 20
Ammoniated superphosphate [d]	NH$_4$H$_2$PO$_4$, (NH$_4$)$_2$SO$_4$ plus calcium phosphates	"	3 or 4 (16–18% P$_2$O$_5$)
Ammo-phos [e]	NH$_4$H$_2$PO$_4$ and other ammonium salts	"	11(48%P$_2$O$_5$)[f]
Potassium nitrate	KNO$_3$	"	13 (44% K$_2$O)

[a] This fertilizer contains over 25 per cent Ca(OH)$_2$ and about 13 per cent carbon besides other ingredients such as CaCO$_3$, CaS, etc. The total amount of calcium expressed as CaO is approximately 53 per cent.

[b] A small amount of ammonium nitrogen is present as well as 25 to 30 per cent of CaO.

[c] The commercial salt is usually treated in some way in order to reduce its deliquescence.

[d] Made by treating ordinary superphosphate with ammonia liquor or anhydrous ammonia. May also contain urea or nitrate nitrogen.

[e] Manufactured by treating ammonia with phosphoric acid

$$NH_3 + H_3PO_4 = NH_4H_2PO_4$$

[f] There are other analyses of this fertilizer.

Sulfate of ammonia, on the other hand, tends to develop an acid residue when added to the soil.[1] There are a number of reasons for this. Since the NH$_4$ ions are readily adsorbed by the soil colloidal

[1] Hall, A. D., and C. T. Gimingham, "The Interaction of Ammonium Sulfate and the Constitution of the Soil," *Jour. Chem. Soc.* (London), XCI:677, 1907.

White, J. W., "The Results of Long-Continued Use of Ammonium Sulfate upon a Residual Limestone Soil of the Hagerstown Series," *Annual Report*, Penn. State Coll., 1912–1913, pp. 55–104. Ruprecht, R. W., and F. W. Morse, *The Effect of Sulfate of Ammonia on Soil*, Bulletin 165, Mass. Agr. Exp. Sta., 1915.

matter, ionic exchange occurs vigorously.   And if H ions are displaced by the entering cations, sulfuric acid is formed.   A similar result is attained if higher plants or microorganisms use the ammonium radical of the fertilizer to a greater extent than they do the sulfate. Undoubtedly this is often the case.   But this is not all.   Apparently the ammonium ion is readily susceptible to nitrification, even after it has entered the colloidal complex.   And since nitrification by oxidation entirely eliminates the NH_4 ion, the chances are excellent that its place in the exchange complex will be taken by H ions.   Thus the percentage base saturation of the colloidal matter is reduced and this, of course encourages acidity.   While these influences are difficult to separate, their combined effect undoubtedly is toward lowering the soil pH.

The development of acidity by sulfate of ammonia, however, is not particularly serious.   A little increase in the amount of lime added or an alternation of nitrate of soda with the ammonium sulfate will counteract this tendency.   Sulfate of ammonia should be nitrified at least in part in order to be most satisfactory for plants in general and therefore does not give quite so rapid an influence in a cold soil as nitrate of soda.   However, in warm weather it usually undergoes nitrification so rapidly that plants are promptly supplied with nitrate nitrogen.

The relative merits of nitrate of soda and sulfate of ammonia have long been in controversy.   With a strongly acid, low-lime soil, sodium nitrate no doubt will give the better results with most crop plants.   At a low pH the NO_3 ions seem to be absorbed more readily than the NH_4 ions and apparently are used to better advantage within the plant.   The nitrate form of nitrogen may function in ways other than as a nutrient, perhaps as a source of oxygen.   Also sodium nitrate tends to reduce rather than accentuate soil acidity.

On the other hand, when a soil contains adequate active calcium and a fairly high pH, there seems no reason why sulfate of ammonia should not be as effective as nitrate of soda for most plants and for some crops even more useful.   At a high pH the NH_4 ions are absorbed by plants more readily than the NO_3 ions, and the energy of synthesis is less.[1]   In fact, ammoniacal nitrogen, principally because it is cheaper, is applied in greater amounts than is the nitrate form.

The great advance in fertilizer production in recent years has been

[1] For articles bearing upon the intake of NO_3 and NH_4 ions see bottom of page 374.

in the industrial development of the so-called synthetics, that is, fertilizers made from by-product nitrogen or nitrogen fixed from the air.[1] Even part of the nitrate of soda on the market is synthetic, the rest being Chilean saltpetre, a natural product. Fully two-thirds of the fertilizer nitrogen used in the United States is carried by synthetics. These materials may supply only nitrogen, as in the case of urea and calcium nitrate, or also contain available phosphoric acid or potash. Such is the case with ammo-phos and potassium nitrate.

One of the most promising of the synthetics is urea, a fertilizer with almost three times more nitrogen than nitrate of soda. It readily undergoes hydrolysis in the soil, producing ammonium carbonate.[2] Thus the immediate effect of this fertilizer is towards alkalinity although its residual influence tends to lower the pH. The ammonium carbonate produced is ideal for rapid nitrification, especially if calcium is present in adequate amounts. Urea thus ultimately presents both NH_4 ions and NO_3 ions for plant absorption. Its one serious objection, high deliquescence, has been adequately overcome by certain treatments.

While the fixation of nitrogen by the cyanamid process is very important commercially, the product, calcium cyanamid, has some objections as a fertilizer. When used to top-dress crops it may cause injury to the foliage if not carefully applied. In the soil its nitrogen changes rather readily to ammonium carbonate but there are certain temporary intermediate products that may be harmful to crops. However, considerable amounts of calcium cyanamid are used satisfactorily in mixed fertilizers, the physical condition of the cyanamid making it especially desirable. Moreover, when properly handled, it may be applied alone to certain crops with excellent results. Since it contains about 25 per cent of calcium hydroxide, it tends definitely to raise the soil pH.

Ammonium nitrate and calcium nitrate theoretically should be excellent fertilizers but their excessive deliquescence renders them difficult and unpleasant to handle. By treating the former with calcium carbonate a more desirable product has been developed. It is sold under the name of Cal-nitro.

Of the synthetics carrying phosphorus in addition to nitrogen,

[1] There are a number of different ways of utilizing air and by-product nitrogen. For details see Collings, G. H., *Commercial Fertilizers*, The Blakiston Company, Philadelphia, 1941.

[2] $CON_2H_4 + 2 H_2O = (NH_4)_2CO_3$.

ammo-phos and ammoniated superphosphate are perhaps the most used in the United States. Since most soils respond to both nitrogen and phosphorus and since both of these products are comparatively cheap sources of the two elements, their use is growing rapidly. Their nitrogen, however, is almost entirely in the ammoniacal form. They are further discussed on pages 411 and 413.

The importance of the synthetic fertilizers lies not only in the range of compounds made available for agricultural use, but also in the lowered cost of the nitrogen supplied. With cheaper nitrogen more of this element will be used and a corresponding influence can be expected on crop production. Commercial nitrogen, if low in price, could be applied with profit where it is now used but sparingly. Fertility practice would thus be simpler and the maintenance of soil nitrogen and humus at suitable levels less serious problems.

221. *Phosphatic fertilizers*

The principal phosphorus fertilizer at the present time is superphosphate. The ordinary grades (16 to 20 per cent available P_2O_5) are made by treating raw rock phosphate with suitable amounts of sulfuric acid. A large proportion of the phosphorus is thus changed to the monocalcic form [$CaH_4(PO_4)_2$], although some is left in the dicalcic condition [$Ca_2H_2(PO_4)_2$] [1]. Much of the superphosphate now used is this ordinary grade, which consists of about 31 per cent phosphates, 50 per cent gypsum, and 19 per cent impurities of various kinds. The total phosphorus to the hundred weight is rather low, ranging from 7 to 9 pounds, while the sulfur and calcium amount to about 12 and 18 pounds respectively.

There are two grades of high-analysis superphosphates, the *double* (32 per cent available P_2O_5) and the *treble* (40–48 per cent available

---

[1] Representing the complex raw rock by the simple formula — $Ca_3(PO_4)_2$, the following conventional reactions may be used to show the changes that occur during the manufacture of ordinary 16 to 20 per cent superphosphate.

$$Ca_3(PO_4)_2 + 2 H_2SO_4 = CaH_4(PO_4)_2 + 2 CaSO_4 + \text{impurities}$$
(Insoluble)   (Water
                                     soluble)

The acid is never added in amounts capable of completing this reaction. Consequently some di-calcium phosphate — $Ca_2H_2(PO_4)_2$, spoken of as *citrate soluble* or *reverted phosphoric acid*, is produced.

$$Ca_3(PO_4)_2 + H_2SO_4 = Ca_2H_2(PO_4)_2 + CaSO_4 + \text{impurities}$$
(Insoluble)   (Reverted)

Table XLIII.   Phosphoric-acid Fertilizers

Fertilizer	Chemical Form	Source	Percentage of P_2O_5
Raw bone meal	$Ca_3(PO_4)_2$	Packing house	20–25
Steamed bone meal [a]	$Ca_3(PO_4)_2$	Packing house	23–30
Rock phosphate	Fluor- and Chlor-apatites	Ground rock	25–30
Superphosphate	$CaH_4(PO_4)_2$ and $Ca_2H_2(PO_4)_2$	Made from rock phosphate	16–47
Basic slag [b]	$(CaO)_5 \cdot P_2O_5 \cdot SiO_2$	Steel slag	15–25
Bone black	$Ca_3(PO_4)_2$	Refining refuse	32–35
Monocalcium phosphate	$CaH_4(PO_4)_2$	Synthesized [c]	50
Calcium metaphosphate	$Ca(PO_3)_2$	Synthesized [d]	62–63
Ammoniated super-phosphate	$NH_4H_2PO_4$ $Ca_2H_2(PO_4)_2$ $Ca_3(PO_4)_2$ $NH_4)_2SO_4$	Synthesized	16–18 (3–4% N)
Ammo-phos	$NH_4H_2PO_4$ mostly	Synthesized [e]	48 (11% N)
Potassium phosphate	Indefinite	Synthesized [f]	32–53 (30–50% K_2O)

[a] The steamed bone meal is cooked under pressure and the fat and oil removed.   The bone is left open and porous.

[b] The formula of this fertilizer is very uncertain.   Basic slag is intensely alkaline because of the presence of large amounts of the hydroxide and carbonate of lime.

[c] Made by treating a high-analysis rock phosphate with H_3PO_4:
$$Ca_3(PO_4)_2 + 4 H_3PO_4 = 3 CaH_4(PO_4)_2 + \text{impurities.}$$

[d] Synthesized from rock phosphate or limestone and P_2O_5:
$$Ca_3(PO_4)_2 + 2 P_2O_5 = 3 Ca(PO_3)_2 + \text{impurities, or}$$
$$CaCO_3 + P_2O_5 = Ca(PO_3)_2 + CO_2 + \text{impurities.}$$

[e] Made with phosphoric acid and ammonia:
$$H_3PO_4 + NH_4OH = NH_4H_2PO_4 + H_2O + \text{impurities.}$$

[f] Made by heating KOH and calcium phosphate.

P_2O_5).   They differ from the ordinary types principally in that they contain more phosphorus and less gypsum, the two varying more or less inversely with each other.   The amount of calcium sulfate in the treble superphosphate is almost negligible.[1]

When added to a mineral soil containing large amounts of active calcium, especially if the pH is above 7, the mono- and dicalcium phosphates of superphosphate immediately revert to more complex

[1] The *treble* superphosphate is synthesized by treating a highgrade phosphate rock with phosphoric acid:
$$Ca_3(PO_4)_2 + 4 H_3PO_4 = 3 CaH_4(PO_4)_2 + \text{impurities.}$$

The *double* superphosphate may be made by mixing ordinary superphosphate and the treble in the proper amounts.   It contains about one-half as much gypsum as do the ordinary grades.

calcium phosphates, which, unfortunately, are quite insoluble and rather unavailable to plants. These reverted forms range with increasing insolubility from oxyapatite through the hydroxy form to the carbonate-apatite. If any amount of fluorine is present the final and most insoluble reversion form is the fluorapatite (see page 302).

On the other hand, if the superphosphate is added to soils that are quite acid, say pH 5 or below, the available phosphates react with the iron and aluminum, which are active at this pH range (see page 302). These reversion products are even more insoluble and unavailable than the calcium phosphates formed when the pH is above 7.

Fortunately at pH values between perhaps 5.6 and 6.5 the fixation of phosphorus seems to be in large degree due to adsorption of some sort, with a minimum of reversion to insoluble iron, aluminum, and calcium phosphates. Within this range the added phosphates seem to be considerably more soluble, and besides the phosphate ions ($HPO_4^=$ and $H_2PO_4^-$) that appear at this pH seem to be readily absorbed by plants. The regulation of soil pH thus is a phase of phosphate economy that should not be overlooked.

Since superphosphate gives a very acid reaction when tested with indicators, it is generally supposed that it must increase the acidity of soils to which it is added. As a matter of fact, it has practically no effect within the ordinary pH range. But at a low pH superphosphate tends to reduce acidity, while at a pH of 7 or above the modification is in the other direction.[1] The slight influence of this fertilizer on soil reaction probably is due to the vigorous reversion that occurs as soon as it is applied to the soil.

Because of the precipitation of the active aluminum, superphosphate seems to alleviate the physiological influence of soil acidity. The balancing of plant nutrition is also a factor. But since lime is cheaper and more effective, it is better suitably to adjust the soil pH with this material before adding the superphosphate. A much greater proportion of the phosphorus will then be available to the crop.

Ammoniated superphosphate,[2] which contains from 3 to 4 per cent of nitrogen and 16 to 18 per cent of phosphoric acid, is gaining in popularity. It affords a chance of easily changing ammonia to a suit-

---

[1] Pierre, W. H., "The Effect of Mono-, Di-, and Tri-Calcium Phosphates on the Reaction of Soils of Different Degrees of Acidity," *Jour. Amer. Soc. Agron.*, XXVI: 278–289, 1924.

[2] Ammoniated superphosphate is made by treating ordinary superphosphate with either

able fertilizer form, at the same time improving the physical qualities of the superphosphate. When a small amount of nitrogen can be used profitably with the phosphorus, the application of this fertilizer is to be recommended as it is a cheap and effective source for both nutrients. Ammo-phos, which commonly analyzes 11 per cent of nitrogen and 48 per cent of phosphoric acid, is also an economical fertilizer and should be used when a larger proportion of nitrogen to phosphorus is desired.

Bone meal is an expensive form of phosphoric acid. Moreover, it is rather slowly available in the soil. It is used extensively in greenhouse and floricultural work, part of its popularity possibly being due to the nitrogen carried. Bone meal can be applied in large amounts and yet produce no detrimental influence on crop growth. This is not so likely to be the case, of course, with some of the more readily soluble phosphatic fertilizers.

Basic slag, while commonly used in Europe, is on the market only to a limited extent in the United States. Because of its alkalinity and the rather ready availability of its phosphoric acid, it is a very desirable phosphatic fertilizer. It seems to be especially effective on acid soils apparently because of its high content of calcium hydroxide.

Raw rock phosphate, due to its insolubility, must be finely ground in order that it may react at all readily when applied as such to the soil. Its availability is markedly increased by the presence of decaying organic matter. For that reason it is often recommended as a reinforcement for farm manure. Ordinarily it should not be used alone unless the soil is rather well supplied with active organic matter. It is the least available of the phosphatic fertilizers already mentioned, the order being: superphosphate and ammo-phos, basic slag, bone meal, and raw rock. Although its chemical formula is given conventionally as $Ca_3(PO_4)_2$, rock phosphate is much more complicated than this

---

ammonia liquor or anhydrous ammonia. The ammonia is thus changed to forms suitable for fertilizer use and the physical condition of the superphosphate improved. The reactions are as follows:

$$CaH_4(PO_4)_2 + NH_3 = NH_4H_2PO_4 + CaHPO_4$$
$$2\ CaHPO_4 + CaSO_4 + 2\ NH_3 = Ca_3(PO_4)_2 + (NH_4)_2SO_4$$

When enough ammonia has been added to give 2 per cent of nitrogen in the mixture practically all of the monocalcium phosphate has been reverted. At this stage the nitrogen is present in two different forms and the phosphorus in three. All of these are considered as readily available to plants.

The percentage of nitrogen may be readily doubled by using an ammonia liquor enriched by adding urea or ammonium nitrate. A third form of nitrogen may thus be present in the final product.

formula would suggest. It apparently approaches the fluorapatite $(3\ Ca_3(PO_4)_2 \cdot CaF_2)$ in its molecular make-up. This no doubt accounts in part for its slow availability.

Considerable discussion as well as controversy at one time arose regarding the relative merits of superphosphate and rawrock phosphate not only when applied to soils on the basis of equal amounts of phosphoric acid but also when compared on the basis of equal money values. Thorne,[1] after a critical review of the field experiments where superphosphate and raw rock were used, came to the conclusion that, while raw rock phosphate is an excellent fertilizer, superphosphate is generally superior. He finds that, while raw rock may be employed with profit on land materially deficient in phosphorus, superphosphate has generally proved the more effective and the more economical carrier of phosphoric acid for crops.

These conclusions, which are amply corroborated by other investigators, do not imply that raw rock phosphate is never equal or superior to superphosphate, nor that raw rock may not have a place as a fertilizer on the average farm. To a soil rich in organic matter it may be added to advantage. It is especially useful in reinforcing farm manure, seemingly being about as effective under such conditions as is superphosphate. However, the trend in fertilizer manufacture seem to be such that raw rock phosphate will continue to be used largely as a source of phosphorus for other and more soluble forms.

Mention should be made of two very high analysis phosphate fertilizers not as yet in general use — monocalcium phosphate [$CaH_4(PO_4)_2$ — about 50 per cent available P_2O_5] and calcium metaphosphate [$Ca(PO_3)_2$ — 62–63 per cent available P_2O_5] (see Table XLIII). Both are in the experimental stage but hold great promise as they seem to be as effective, when used in equivalent amounts, as superphosphate. Their concentrations make them extremely attractive when transportation is a factor. The latter, commonly called *meta-phos*, may be made by treating either phosphate rock or limestone with P_2O_5. The highly concentrated phosphorus penta-oxide can be produced at the mine, shipped to a point where limestone is cheaply available, and the meta-phos manufactured in the territory where it is to be used. Transportation costs would thus be cut to a minimum.

For purposes of evaluation and sale the various phosphorus com-

[1] Thorne, C. E., *Raw Phosphate Rock as a Fertilizer*, Bulletin 305, Ohio Agr. Exp. Sta., 1916.

pounds that are present in phosphatic fertilizers are classified in an arbitrary and empirical way as follows (Table XLIV):

Table XLIV. Fertilizer Classification of Phosphates

1. *Water-soluble*. $\left.\begin{array}{l} CaH_4(PO_4)_2 \\ NH_4H_2PO_4 \\ K \text{ phosphate} \end{array}\right\}$

2. *Citrate-soluble*

  In 15 per cent neutral ammonium citrate
  —$Ca_2H_2(PO_4)_2$
  In 2 per cent solution of citric acid —
  phosphates of basic slag

} . *Available* phosphoric acid [a]

3. *Insoluble*
  Phosphate of bone and raw phosphate rock

} . *Unavailable* phosphoric acid [a]

[a] The various fertilizers studied are rated as follows:
  Available — superphosphate (all grades), ammoniated superphosphate, ammophos, basic slag, monocalcium phosphate, meta-phos.
  Mostly Unavailable — rock phosphate and bone meal.

It is well to note that the classification of the phosphates is in some degree arbitrary and artificial. For instance *available* phosphates, because of the reversion that occurs, are not strictly available when applied to the soil, nor do they remain water-soluble. The term *available* really refers to those phosphates that readily stimulate plant growth when properly used as fertilizers. Those phosphates that are less effective are rated as *unavailable*, yet in the soil they attain a certain amount of availability to crops. The terms are especially valuable in respect to the guaranteed analysis when fertilizers are offered for sale.

In the case of ordinary superphosphate a guarantee, say of 20 per cent P_2O_5, refers to available phosphoric acid and includes both the water soluble $CaH_4(PO_4)_2$ and the citrate soluble $Ca_2H_2(PO_4)_2$. With ammo-phos (11 per cent total nitrogen and 48 per cent available P_2O_5) the available phosphoric acid is carried by the water-soluble $NH_4H_2PO_4$. Since phosphate fertilizers are guarantees in the terms set forth above, it is absolutely necessary that a person be familiar with the distinctions noted. Otherwise the correct interpretation of a guarantee is impossible.

222. *Fertilizers used for their potassium*

One of the largest known deposits of potassium fertilizers occur in Germany, where there are extensive beds varying from 50 to 150 feet in thickness, lying under an area from the Harz Mountains to the Elbe River and known as the Stassfurt deposits. Crude potash salts occur in other sections of Germany, in France, in the United States, and elsewhere.

While potash deposits are found in other parts of the world, the French, German, and American mines are at present the only ones operating extensively. The first World War stimulated considerable investigation regarding possible sources of potash, especially in the United States. Domestic kelp, saline brines, accumulations in old lake beds, underground deposits, and flue dust now furnish practically all of the potash used in America.

Kainit and manure salts (see Table XLV) are the most common of the crude potash fertilizers. The high-grade chloride and sulfate of potash originally imported from Germany and France are their refined equivalents. The potassium chloride, now produced so extensively in the United States, comes mostly from saline brines, old lake beds, and underground deposits.

Table XLV. Potash Fertilizers

Fertilizer	Chemical Form	Percentage of K_2O
Potassium chloride [a]	KCl	48–60
Potassium sulfate	K_2SO_4	48–50
Sulfate of potash-magnesia [b]	Double salt of K and Mg	25–30
Manure salts	KCl mostly	20–30
Kainit	KCl mostly	12–16
Potassium nitrate	KNO_3	44 (and 13% N)
Potassium phosphate	Indefinite	30–50 (and 32–53% P_2O_5)
Wood ashes [c]	K_2CO_3 largely	3–7 (and 1–2% P_2O_5)
Tobacco stems [d]	Organic	4–9 (and 2–4% N)

[a] All of these fertilizers contain other potash salts than those listed.

[b] Contains 25 per cent of $MgSO_4$ and some chlorine.

[c] Intensely alkaline from presence of $Ca(OH)_2$. The other potash fertilizers are neutral or slightly alkaline.

[d] For other organics carrying potash see Table XLI.

All potash salts used as fertilizers are water-soluble and are therefore rated as readily available. While these salts might develop an acid residue if employed in large amounts, there is no indication that this is the case under practical conditions. Some discrimination is made against the chloride (muriate) in the case of potatoes and especially tobacco since large dosages are considered to lower the quality. Hence when large amounts of potash are to be applied for the latter crop at least a part usually is preferred in the sulfate form.

Potassium magnesium sulfate, although rather low in potash, has attained some usage in parts of the country where magnesium is likely to be deficient. In some respects it is a more desirable source of magnesia than dolomitic limestone.

Tobacco stems, as well as other potassium-carrying organics, are used in making mixed goods. They supply nitrogen as well as potash and, what is more important, act as a filler and drier. In some parts of the country wood ashes are sometimes obtainable. They carry potassium in the carbonate form, a combination especially desirable for certain crops. The amount of lime added with wood ashes is usually large and on an acid soil may have a considerable influence. They may render slightly acid or neutral soils overly alkaline and thereby have a harmful effect. It is not wise to buy such a product unless it is accompanied by a reliable guarantee.

223. *Sulfur as a fertilizer*

The possible deficiency of sulfur in the arable soils of the United States was first called to the attention of soil scientists by Hart and Peterson in 1911.[1] They point out that crops remove more sulfur from the soil than is indicated by the earlier analyses of plant ash, since considerable sulfur was lost by volatilization in the former determinations. On the basis of their own analyses they show that crops remove as much or even more sulfur from the soil than phosphorus. The fact that soils are generally as low in sulfur as in phosphoric acid lends weight to the contention that if phosphorus is a limiting factor in productivity, sulfur should be also. This argument seems especially convincing as practically no phosphorus is lost in drainage while the removal of sulfur in this way is comparatively large, being for the Dunkirk silty clay loam at Ithaca, New York, about 43 pounds an acre a year. (See Cornell lysimeter data on page 211).

However, considerable sulfur in the sulfate form is added to the soil each year in rain water.[2] This amount depends on the location

[1] Hart, E. B., and W. H. Peterson, *Sulfur Requirements of Farm Crops in Relation to the Soil and Air Supply*, Bulletin 14, Wis. Agr. Exp. Sta., 1911.

[2] Wilson, B. D., "Sulfur Supplied to the Soil in Rainwater," *Jour. Amer. Soc. Agron.*, XIII:226–229, 1921.

Alway, F. J., "A Nutrient Element Slighted in Agricultural Research," *Jour. Amer. Soc. Agron.*, XXXII:913–921, 1940.

and may range from 2 or 3 pounds of sulfur an acre a year, to perhaps over 100 pounds near industrial centers. The loss of sulfur from the Dunkirk silty clay loam held in the Cornell lysimeters,[1] due to cropping and drainage combined, amounted over a period of ten years to about 56 pounds to the acre yearly from the cropped tanks. The addition of sulfur in the rain water at Ithaca was approximately 26 pounds each year. It is therefore safe to assume that rain water ordinarily will not replace the sulfur removed by normal cropping, erosion, and leaching. How is the deficit to be met?

In general and dairying farming the problem is taken care of in a more or less automatic way. In practical soil management sulfur is returned to the soil in green manures, crop residues, and farm manures. Commercial fertilizers, such as superphosphate, ammonium sulfate, and potassium sulfate [2] contain considerable amounts of sulfur and are now very commonly used. An application to the acre of 10 tons of farm manure reinforced with 500 pounds of ordinary superphosphate adds well over 100 pounds of sulfur. This alone, once in the rotation, would go far toward meeting any deficit. At the Ohio Experiment Station [3] plats treated with sulfate-bearing fertilizers were found over a period of years to contain considerably more sulfur than soils not so fertilized but cropped in a similar manner.

There is another angle to the sulfur problem that until a few years ago escaped attention — the probability that the soil, and perhaps to a much lesser degree higher plants, absorbs sulfur dioxide from the atmosphere. Alway,[4] who has advanced the idea, substantiates his suggestions rather conclusively. The magnitude of this absorption, which, bear in mind, is exclusive of the sulfur added in precipitation, is not known but it may be in excess of that brought down by rain, snow, and dust. Here, then, is another automatic addition, a further insurance against a sulfur deficiency. And incidentally it furnishes a

---

[1] Bizzell, J. A., and T. L. Lyon, "Composition of Drainage Waters from Lysimeters at Cornell University," *Proc. and Papers, First Internat. Cong. Soil Sci.*, II:342–357, 1927.

[2] The amount of sulfur in a ton of farm manure probably averages about 5 lb. Ordinary superphosphate and commercial ammonium sulfate and potassium sulfate contain to the hundred-weight approximately 12, 24, and 15 lb. respectively.

[3] Ames, J. W., and G. E. Boltz, *Sulfur in Relation to Soils and Crops*, Bulletin 292, Ohio Agr. Exp. Sta., 1916.

[4] Alway, F. J., A. W. Marsh, and W. J. Methley, "Sufficiency of Atmospheric Sulfur for Maximum Crop Yields," *Proc. Soil Sci. Soc. Amer.*, II:229–238, 1937. And, Alway, F. J., "A Nutrient Element Slighted in Agriculture Research," *Jour. Amer. Soc Agron.*, XXXII: 913–921, 1940.

second reason why crops requiring large amounts of sulfur, such as alfalfa, can be grown successfully on land receiving no artificial applications of this element.

In the light of the information presented, it seems that the sulfur situation is not comparable with nor so serious as that of the phosphorus. With certain soils in eastern Washington and Oregon, in Minnesota, and in California, sulfur in some form undoubtedly must be added, especially in the growing of alfalfa. However, under ordinary conditions, if the normal residues produced on the farm are utilized, there seems little reason for sulfur being a limiting factor in soil productivity, especially if fertilizers carrying sulfur are used.

224. *Trace elements as fertilizers* [1]

Of the elements usually found in mere traces in soils and used but sparingly by plants, the application of four, under certain soil conditions and with certain crops, often give surprisingly beneficial results. These elements are copper, manganese, zinc, and boron. With iron, which exists in most soils in large amounts (page 23), the situation usually is not urgent except where lime has been added in unusually large quantities.

The reason for the deficiency of the four trace elements listed, either individually or in mass, is not difficult to postulate. In the first place not only are they ordinarily present in the soil in extremely minute amounts (page 22) but also their availability is uncertain, a slight change in soil conditions being sufficient to render them critical. For instance, overliming is likely to reduce their availability often to the danger point. In the second place, practically no attention in the past has been paid to the trace elements in our systems of soil management. It is only in recent years that the essential nature of these constituents has been known. And even then it apparently was assumed that the amounts used by plants were too small to be important or that the elements were incidentally applied in sufficient quantities to forestall any deficiency. We know now that such ideas were fallacious.

[1] The literature dealing with the trace elements is exceedingly voluminous. See Willis, L. G., *Bibliography of References to the Literature on the Minor Elements and Their Relation to the Science of Plant Nutrition*, 3d ed., Chilean Nitrate Educational Bureau, New York, 1939, with First Supplement, 1940, Second Supplement, 1941, and Third Supplement, 1942.

A deficiency diagnosis usually is made from plant symptoms [1] rather than from soil analysis since a fluctuation in availability that is difficult to measure analytically, may determine whether or not the trace element is critical. Already crop specialists are adept in the detection of various deficiencies, while the growers themselves are rapidly becoming familiar with the symptoms that their crops are likely to exhibit.

The influence of overliming in accentuating or actually in creating a trace-element deficiency has already been mentioned. Its effects in respect to manganese, and perhaps copper and zinc also, probably are the result of precipitation, the rise in pH above 7 tending to produce compounds that are unavailable to higher plants.

As to the lime-boron relationship, there is a considerable difference of opinion.[2] Some authors claim that, although the soil untreated and the lime alone do not individually reduce the boron solubility to any extent, the two in combination fix it markedly. Others feel that the large amounts of active calcium influences the plant in such a way physiologically as to interfere either with the entrance of boron or its utilization once it has been absorbed. Still others suggest that lime stimulates microbial activity and thereby raises a competition for boron that seriously affects the crop. But whatever the explanation, it would seem that overliming should especially be guarded against where trace-element deficiencies are suspected.

When a trace-element deficiency is to be corrected, a salt of the lacking nutrient usually is added separately to the soil. Copper, manganese, and zinc generally are supplied as the sulfate while boron is applied as borax. The rate of application should be carefully regulated as an overdose can cause severe injury. All of the above elements are decidedly toxic when above a certain concentration. In case of doubt as to the amounts to apply, expert advice should be sought.

In some cases trace elements are placed in ordinary commercial fertilizers and their presence therein made a special advertizing feature. A stock mixture is compounded using some organic ammoniate, such as cottonseed meal, as a base to which are added the trace-element salts. A few pounds of this mixture are included in each ton of

[1] See *Hunger Signs in Crops*, American Society of Agronomy and National Fertilizer Association, Washington, D. C., 1941, and *If They Could Speak*, Chilean Nitrate Educational Bureau, New York, 1941.

[2] For citations see bottom of page 361.

the fertilizer. The idea, of course, is to ensure against a possible deficiency of the trace elements. The fallacy of the practice is that not enough of any one trace element ordinarily is added to the soil to adequately meet a real deficiency should it occur. Trace elements require a more careful regulation than can be attained in this way.

That the fertilization with trace elements is of great practical importance, cannot be denied. Plant malnutritions, due to such deficiencies, are becoming more and more apparent. All kinds of plants are affected. The next few years undoubtedly will see a tremendous development of this phase of fertility regulation.

225. *Fertilizer brands*

In an attempt to meet the demands for well-balanced fertilizers suited to various crops and soils, manufacturers have for years placed on the market a large number of brands, containing at least two of the so-called fertilizer elements, and usually all three. The former are designated as *incomplete* fertilizers, while the latter are spoken of as *complete*. These various brands commonly carry a significant name, which frequently implies the usefulness of the material for some special crop growing on a particular soil.

The ordinary type of complete fertilizer is made by mixing a considerable number of carriers together in order to supply the necessary nutrients in the percentage amounts desired. Thus for such a ready-mixed complete fertilizer, castor pomace or some other organic, nitrate of soda, sulfate of ammonia, superphosphate or ammo-phos, and muriate of potash might be used. Three forms of nitrogen are thus supplied, the castor pomace acting as a conditioner as well as a fertilizer. The drillability of the mixture may be further encouraged by the addition of dolomitic limestone. The three forms of nitrogen distribute or spread the effect of this element — the nitrate giving rapid action, the ammoniacal a somewhat delayed effect, while the organic nitrogen prolongs the influence into mid-season.

Such incomplete fertilizers as ammo-phos, ammoniated superphosphate, potassium nitrate, and potassium phosphate, carrying only two of the three fertilizer elements, may be applied separately. Their utilization is thus very simple and they are effective if they meet the fertility demands of the situation. If a complete fertilizer is desired, the addition of one other carrier is all that is necessary.

Besides supplying available nitrogen, phosphoric acid, and potash in certain proportions, a commercial fertilizer not only should be drillable when first purchased but also should remain in this condition if properly stored. Of the fertilizers commonly used in mixed goods, nitrate of soda, sulfate of ammonia, and potassium chloride are most likely, because of their deliquescence, to develop an unsatisfactory physical condition. Improperly cured superphosphate may also give trouble. The *condition* of a mixed fertilizer is maintained by the use of driers. In this respect the organic ammoniates, such as castor pomace, tobacco stems, and the like, are especially valuable. Calcium cyanamid performs a like function as well as serving as a cheap source of nitrogen. Dolomitic limestone when used to counteract the acidity developed in the soil by certain of the fertilizer salts, also acts as a conditioner. The manufacturer is as careful regarding the drillability of his fertilizer as he is of the maintenance of its guaranteed analysis. Most complete fertilizers carry at least 300 pounds a ton of materials that will help maintain a suitable physical condition.

Most mixed fertilizers, unless especially treated, tend to develop an acid residue in soils. This is mainly due to the dominating influence of certain of the nitrogen carriers, especially those of an ammoniacal nature. The phosphorus and potash fertilizers commonly used have little effect upon soil reaction unless they contain nitrogen. For many years no particular attention was paid to this tendency. For instance the average mixed fertilizer sold in the United States in 1933 had an acidity equivalent a ton of about 150 pounds of calcium carbonate.[1] At the present time the average mixed fertilizer is what is called *neutral*, that is, it exerts little residual effect on soil pH. This is attained by adding dolomitic limestone to the fertilizer in amounts sufficient to offset the acid residue. Data are available in respect to nitrogen fertilizers that make rather easy the calculation of the amount of dolomitic limestone necessary in any particular case.[2]

Fertilizer concerns have always found it more profitable to sell ready-mixed fertilizers than to deal in the separate carriers, such as nitrate of soda, superphosphate, and the like. However, present conditions greatly encourage the application directly to the soil of certain separate carriers, especially superphosphate, ammo-phos, ammoni-

[1] Mehring, A. L., and A. J. Peterson, "The Equivalent Physiological Acidity or Basicity of American Fertilizers," *Jour. Assoc. Official Agr. Chemists*, XVII:95–100, 1934.
[2] See Pierre, W. H., "Effect of Nitrogenous Fertilizers on Soil Acidity," *Ind. and Eng.*

ated superphosphate, nitrate of soda, and sulfate of ammonia. This is especially true in respect to general and dairy farming where a simple fertilizer system is satisfactory. In more intensive culture, as in vegetable production, complete fertilizers are used more generally.

226. *The fertilizer guarantee*

Every fertilizing material, whether it is a single carrier or a complete ready-to-apply mixture, must carry a guarantee as to its content of nutrient elements. The exact form is generally determined by the state in which the fertilizer is offered for sale. The *total nitrogen* is expressed in its *elemental form* (N). The phosphorus is quoted in terms of *available phosphoric acid* (P_2O_5). In some cases, the bone phosphate of lime [B.P.L. or $Ca_3(PO_4)_2$] equivalent is included. This is likely to be the case with bone meal or raw rock phosphate. The potassium is stated as *water-soluble potash* (K_2O).

The guarantee of a simple fertilizer, such as sulfate of ammonia, is easy to interpret, since the name and the composition of the material is printed on the bag or tag. When the amount of the nutrient element carried is noted, the availability and general value of the fertilizer is immediately known if a person is at all familiar with the common commercial fertilizers. For instance, if the material is sodium nitrate at 16 per cent total nitrogen, it is apparent that the fertilizer is high-grade and should give immediate and definite results when properly applied to growing crops.

The interpretation of an analysis of a complete fertilizer is almost as easy. The simplest form of guarantee is a mere statement of the percentages of N, P_2O_5, and K_2O. Thus a 5–10–5 refers to the percentage of *total nitrogen*, the percentage of *available phosphoric acid*, and the percentage of *water-soluble potash*.

When the fertilizer is made by mixing a number of separate ingre-

---

Chem. XXIII:1440, 1931, and "Determination of Equivalent Acidity and Basicity of Fertilizers," *ibid.*, Analytical Ed., V:229–234, 1933.

The acidifying capacity in terms of pounds of $CaCO_3$ for every 1 per cent of N in 1 ton of fertilizer (when applied to the soil), is as follows:

Ammonium sulfate	107	High-grade tankage	15
Ammo-phos	107	Fish scrap	31
Monoammonium phosphate	107	Cottonseed meal	29
Urea	36	Castor pomace	18

The basicity in the same terms for certain fertilizers is as below:

Nitrate of soda	36	Tobacco stems	86
Calcium cyanamid	57	Cocoa meal	12

dients together, the guarantee printed on the bag or tag is usually more complicated, depending on the requirement of the fertilizer law and the importance which the manufacturer attaches to a long guarantee. The following analysis for a 5–10–5 illustrates the sort of guarantee that is sometimes seen:

5–10–5

	Per Cent		*Per Cent*
Total N	5.0	Water-soluble P_2O_5	9
Equivalent to NH_3	6.1	Reverted P_2O_5	1
		Available P_2O_5	10
Water-soluble K_2O	5.0	Unavailable P_2O_5	1
K_2O as muriate	5.0	Total P_2O_5	11

In some states figures as to *water-soluble nitrogen, water-insoluble nitrogen* and *available insoluble nitrogen* are required.

An *open formula* guarantee is used by some companies. Such a guarantee not only gives the usual chemical composition but a list of the ingredients, their composition, and the pounds of each in a ton of the mixture. Such a type of guarantee is given below for a 5–10–5 neutral fertilizer:

5–10–5

	Per Cent	*Pounds*
Nitrate of soda	16	125
Castor pomace	4½	278
Sulfate of ammonia	20	255
Ammo-phos	11–48	150
Superphosphate	18	712
Muriate of potash	60	167
Dolomitic limestone		313
		2000

Commercial fertilizers are sometimes grouped according to their *ratio*. For instance a 5–10–5, a 6–12–6, a 10–20–10, and a 15–30–15 all have a 1–2–1 ratio. These fertilizers should give essentially the same results when applied in equivalent amounts. Such a grouping is valuable when several analyses are offered and the comparative costs become the deciding factor as to which shall be purchased. Moreover, fertilizer recommendations are sometimes made on the basis of the ratio, the particular analysis being decided on later.

227. *Fertilizer inspection and control*

So many opportunities are open for fraud, either as to availability or the actual quantities of ingredients present, that laws controlling the sale of fertilizers are necessary. These laws apply not only to the ready-mixed goods but to the separate carriers as well. Such regulations protect not only the public but also the honest fertilizer company, since spurious goods are kept off the market.

Certain provisions are more or less common to the various fertilizer laws in the United States. In general, all fertilizers selling for a certain price or over must pay a license fee or a tonnage tax and print the following data on the bag or on an authorized tag:

1. Number of net pounds of fertilizer to a package.
2. Name, brand, or trade-mark.
3. Name and address of manufacturer.
4. Chemical composition guaranteed.

For the enforcement of such laws the states usually provide adequate machinery. The inspection and analyses may be in the hands of the state department of agriculture, of the director of the state agricultural experiment station, of a state chemist, or under the control of any two of these. In any case, inspectors are provided who take samples of the fertilizers on the market throughout the state. These samples are analyzed in order to ascertain whether the goods are up to guarantee. The expense of the inspection and control of fertilizers is defrayed by a license fee or a tonnage tax.

If the fertilizer falls below the guarantee — allowing, of course, for any variation permitted by law — the manufacturer is subject to prosecution in the state courts. A more effective check on fraudulent guarantees, however, is in publicity. The state law usually provides for the publication each year of a bulletin containing the guaranteed and found analyses of all brands inspected. Not only has this proved effective in preventing fraud, but it is a great advantage not only to the fertilizer user but also to the honest manufacturer, as his guarantees receive an official sanction. The found analysis of most fertilizers is generally up to or above the guarantee.

228. *Fertilizer economy*

Whether buying ready-mixed complete commercial fertilizers or the various separate carriers, such as nitrate of soda, sulfate of ammonia, and the like, it is always important to obtain high-analysis goods. Price data indicate that the higher the grade, especially of a ready-mixed fertilizer, both as to availability and the percentage of the constituents carried, the greater is the amount of the various nutrients obtained for every dollar expended. This is a price rule well worth remembering. It holds because the overhead is about the same for every ton of mixed fertilizer, regardless of the amount of nutrients that it contains. Concentration, therefore, reduces the overhead for a unit of nutrient carried. Thus a 10–20–10 is usually a much better buy than a 3–6–3.

In many instances a saving can be effected by purchasing the separate fertilizers and applying them separately to the soil. Superphosphate is often applied alone for all sorts of crops. Nitrate of soda, sulfate of ammonia, and similar nitrogenous fertilizers are employed to advantage in orchards, as top-dressings on meadows and pastures, and as a side-dressing in vegetable production. When farm manure is available, the use of superphosphate with lime and manure in a legume rotation is generally desirable. When little manure is produced, the application of sodium nitrate or ammonium sulfate, especially if superphosphate has previously been used, is good practice. The separate fertilizers may thus be effectively applied without the necessity of mixing and some saving effected thereby.

229. *When to home-mix fertilizers* [1]

For vegetables and often for the regular field crops, a complete fertilizer is desirable. If a ready-mixed fertilizer is not available or is too expensive, the separate fertilizers may be purchased separately and the compounding done on the farm. This is called *home-mixing*.

In general, it is claimed that the factory fertilizers are more finely ground than those mixed by the farmer, and consequently the ready-mixed goods are not only more uniform but also in better physical condition. Besides, the factory-mixed fertilizers generally carry more organic nitrogen than the farmer can afford to put in.

While these reasons are more or less valid, good results may be expected from a fertilizer even though it may not be quite uniform, as the soil tends to equalize this deficiency. Moreover, by screening and

[1] For formula calculations and directions for the mechanical mixing, see the references cited at bottom of page 397.

by using a proper conditioner, a farmer can obtain a physical state which will in no way interfere with the drilling of the material. The important thing, however, is the saving that often can be affected. This makes home-mixing attractive and really is the only excuse for it. While obviously one farmer alone ordinarily cannot afford to buy small lots direct from the wholesaler because of the freight charges, this objection is being met by cooperative organizations of various kinds whereby the single carriers may be purchased in carload lots and shipped directly to the association.

Such arguments do not mean, however, that it always pays to buy and mix the separate materials. As a matter of fact, in most cases it is not worth while, especially where only a small amount of fertilizer is needed, even though it is possible to cooperate with other farmers. In short, fertilizers should be bought by the method that will give the greatest value for every dollar expended, providing of course that the mixture that goes onto the land is high grade and properly balanced.

230. *Methods of applying fertilizers*

Although much emphasis is placed on the selection of the correct fertilizer ratio and on the adequate and economical amounts of the various analyses used, the method of application must not be overlooked. A fertilizer should also be placed in the soil in such a position that it will serve the plant to the best advantage.

Cultivated crops such as corn, cotton, or potatoes are usually fertilized in the hill or the row, with a fertilizer attachment, part or all of the fertilizer being applied at the time of planting. If placed in the hill the fertilizer may be deposited below or better, at one side of the seed. When distributed in the row the fertilizer usually is laid in as a narrow band, on one or both sides of the row, 2 or 3 inches away and a little below the level of the seed. When the amount of fertilizer is large it is often wise to broadcast part and thoroughly cultivate it into the soil before the planting is done. In some cases the crop is side-dressed with an additional amount of fertilizer later in the season.

With small grains and similar crops the drill is equipped with a distributor, the fertilizer entering the soil more or less in contact with the seed. When the amount of fertilizer applied exceeds 300 or 400 pounds, part should be broadcast before the crop is seeded in order to avoid germination injury.

Vegetables when in rows are fertilized much the same as corn or cotton. However, larger amounts are usually applied and side-dressing, especially with a nitrogen fertilizer such as nitrate of soda, is common. This is done after the crop is well started and is in addition to the regular fertilization. When the fertilizer is applied around the hill, as with such crops as melons, the treatment is called a *spot-application.*

Orchard trees usually are treated individually, the fertilizer being applied around each tree within the spread of the branches but beginning out several feet from the trunk. The fertilizer is worked into the soil as much as possible. When the orchard cover-crop needs fertilization it is treated separately, the fertilizer being drilled in at the time of seeding or broadcast later. Ornamental trees are often fertilized by what is called the *perforation* method. Numerous small holes are sunk around each tree, within the outer half of the branch-spread zone and extending through the surface into the upper subsoil. Into these holes, which are afterward filled up, is placed a suitable amount of an appropriate fertilizer. This method of application places the nutrients within the root zone and avoids an undesirable stimulation of the grass generally growing around ornamental trees.

With meadows, pastures, and lawns, it is well to fertilize the soil well at the time of seeding. The fertilizer may be applied with the seed or better, broadcasted, and worked thoroughly into the soil as the seedbed is prepared. The latter method is preferable, especially if the fertilization is heavy. During succeeding years it may be necessary to top-dress such crops with a suitable fertilizer mixture. This method of application requires care. The amount of fertilizer applied and the time of treatment should be so regulated as to avoid injury to the foliage or the root crowns of the plants.

A practice that promises much is the plowing under of commercial fertilizers with organic residues of various kinds, especially for such a crop as corn.[1] The advantages in general are these: (1) The fertilizer, while still well within the root zone, is placed in soil that remains moist during most of the growing season. This ensures maximum and consistent activity. (2) With nitrogenous fertilizers, such as sulfate of ammonia, urea, and calcium cyanamid, nitrification is retarded

[1] Cook, H. L., and G. D. Scarseth, "The Effect of Cyanamid and Potash When Plowed Under with Organic Refuse on the Yield of Corn and Succeeding Crops," *Jour. Amer. Soc. Agron.,* XXXIII:283–293, 1941.

because of the lower temperature and the reduced oxygen content of the placement zone. This means that the added nitrogen remains largely in the ammoniacal form. Hence it is less likely to be leached from the root zone. At the same time it is still in a readily available condition. (3) The nitrogen, if plowed under with organic matter, is more likely to react with the lignins and other carbohydrates and thus be retained in the soil (page 129). At the same time this union encourages humus production (page 137). The experiments so far carried out suggest that the judicious plowing under of commercial fertilizers, especially those carrying nitrogen, may increase not only their current seasonal effects but also their residual influences.

231. *Amounts of fertilizers to apply*

The agricultural value of a fertilizer is necessarily uncertain, since a material easily subject to change is placed in contact with two wide variables, the soil and the crop. Soil conditions are constantly fluctuating not only from year to year but progressively through the season. The kind and the amount of the fertilizer applied should, as nearly as possible, meet this change. Again the soil and the added fertilizer react with each other very vigorously both chemically and biologically. The reversion of phosphoric acid is an example of the first while the decomposition of the organic ammoniates illustrates the latter. The result may be an increase or, more often, a decrease in the effectiveness of the fertilizer application. Due allowance should be made for such contingencies when deciding on the kind and amount of fertilizer to apply.

Again there is the weather which has a tremendous effect on the soil, upon the crop, and both directly and indirectly, upon the fertilizer applied. The situation obviously is so complex that, at best, the kind and the amount of fertilizer to apply can only be estimates or guesses, based of course, upon the technical and practical information at hand. This phase of fertilizer practice has already been discussed from the standpoint of fertilizer objectives (page 397) and the difficulty of attaining a suitable nutrient balance in the soils (page 404).

One factor of outstanding importance in respect to the amount of fertilizer to apply is soil condition. It is essential that the soil be at its maximum fitness — physically, chemically, and biologically. This means that granulation, drainage, aeration, organic matter, lime, and other factors should be as satisfactory as possible in order to realize the best results when fertilizers are applied. It is only when the soil is fit that the amounts of fertilizer can be estimated with any degree of satisfaction.

It must always be remembered that the very high yields obtained under fertilizer stimulation are not always the ones that give the best interest on the money invested. In other words, the law of diminishing returns is a factor in fertilizer practice. Therefore the application of moderate amounts of fertilizer is to be urged for all soils until the maximum paying quantity that may be used for any given crop is approximately ascertained.

With all of the usual crops except those grown under garden, trucking, and market-gardening conditions, the fertilizer applications are relatively light. The rate for ordinary superphosphate seldom exceeds 500 pounds to the acre for grains and is usually less than 1000 pounds for field-grown vegetables. Such fertilizers as a 4–12–4 or 5–10–5 are applied at the rate of 150 to 400 pounds to the acre for grain crops. Somewhat larger amounts are used for vegetables and other special crops produced under field conditions. If more concentrated analyses are utilized, the rate to the acre is correspondingly decreased.

For vegetables, especially those grown intensively on sandy land or peat soils, complete fertilizers are used in rather large amounts, as high as 2000 pounds of such analyses as 4–8–12 or a 5–10–5 often being recommended. With vegetables the expenditure for fertilizers may be large because of the high acre-value of the crop.

232. *The broader aspects of fertilizer practice*

It is obvious that fertilizer practice involves many intricate details regarding soils, crops, and fertilizers. In fact, the interrelations of these three are so complicated and far reaching that a practical grasp of the situation requires years of experience. The lack of exactness in fertilizer decisions should ever be kept in mind.

Leaving the details and viewing the situation in a broad way, it seems to be well established that any fertilizer scheme should provide phosphoric acid and potash in amounts sufficient to balance the nitrogen, since this element is so active and subject to such ready loss from the soil. A plan that calls for an abundance of minerals is a sound one.

This, coupled with a heavy fertilization of the money crop, does not, however, constitute all that is deemed fundamental in a rational system of soil fertilization.

Not only must the soil, the crop, the fertilizer analysis, and the rate of application receive careful study, but the rotation and its management should be considered in addition. The fertilizer applications must be correlated with the use of farm manure, crop residues, green manure, trace elements, and lime. The residues of previous fertilizer additions also merit attention. In short, fertilizer practice is merely a phase, but a very important one, of the scientific management of the soil.

Chapter XVIII. Farm Manure and Green Manure

Farm manure is one of the most important agricultural by-products, since it affords a means whereby the unused portion of the crop may become a part of the soil, there exerting an influence far greater than its nutrient content would portend. The world has already entered an era in which the prevention of agricultural waste is becoming necessary and a nearer approach to a self-sustaining system of soil management more and more essential. Therefore, up-to-date farm management is demanding a careful handling as well as a wiser utilization of the manure produced on the farm.

233. *The composition of farm manure* [1]

The term *farm manure* is employed in reference to the refuse from all animals of the farm, although as a general rule the bulk of the ordinary manure which ultimately finds its way back to the land is produced by cattle and horses. This is supplemented to a greater or less extent by manure from hogs, sheep, and poultry.

Farm manure consists of two original components, the *solid* and the *liquid*, in about the ratio of 3 to 1. On the average, a little more than *one-half the nitrogen*, almost *all of the phosphoric acid*, and about *two-fifths of the potash* are found in the solid manure. (See Fig. 57.) Nevertheless, this apparent advantage of the solid manure is offset by the ready availability of the constituents carried by the urine, giving the latter

[1] For analyses of farm-manure, see:

Storer, F. H., *Agriculture*, Charles Scribner's Sons, New York, 1910, pp. 237–248.

Thorne, C. E., *Farm Manures*, Orange Judd Publishing Co., Inc., New York, 1941, pp. 89–93.

Aikman, C. M., *Manure and Manuring*, William Blackwood & Sons, Ltd., Edinburgh, 1910, pp. 279–292.

Roberts, I. P., *The Fertility of the Land*, The Macmillan Company, New York, 1904, pp. 159–182.

Van Slyke, L. L., *Fertilizers and Crop Production*, Orange Judd Publishing Co., Inc., New York, 1932, pp. 216–226.

about an equal commercial and agricultural value with the solid excrement. Such figures are suggestive of the care that should be taken of the liquid manure.

While extended data are available as to the chemical composition of the liquid and solid portions of the excreta from the various farm animals,[1] it is extremely difficult to quote reliable average figures on mixed farm manure as it ordinarily is applied to the land. This is because a number of variable factors enter in which may radically change the amounts and proportions of nitrogen, phosphoric acid, and potash present. The more important of these factors are: (1) kind of animal, (2) age, condition, and individuality of animals, (3) food consumed, (4) litter used, and (5) the handling and storage which the manure receives before it is spread on the land.

In spite of the marked variability of farm manure, representative composition figures will be suggested. For purposes of calculation and

[1] The Composition of Fresh Animal Excrement [a]

Excrement, percentage		Percentage of			
		H_2O	N	P_2O_5	K_2O
Horse	Solid, 80	75	0.55	0.30	0.40
	Urine, 20	90	1.35	Trace	1.25
	Whole manure	78	0.70	0.25	0.55
Cow	Solid, 70	85	0.40	0.20	0.10
	Urine, 30	92	1.00	Trace	1.35
	Whole manure	86	0.60	0.15	0.45
Sheep	Solid, 67	60	0.75	0.50	0.45
	Urine, 33	85	1.35	0.05	2.10
	Whole manure	68	0.95	0.35	1.00
Swine	Solid, 60	80	0.55	0.50	0.40
	Urine, 40	97	0.40	0.10	0.45
	Whole manure	87	0.50	0.35	0.40
Hens	Whole manure	55	1.00	0.80	0.40

[a] Van Slyke, L. L., *Fertilizers and Crop Production*, Orange Judd Publishing Co., Inc., New York, 1932, p. 218.

Commercial Pulverized Animal Manures [a]

Fertilizer	Percentage of		
	N	P_2O_5	K_2O
Sheep	2.50	1.50	1.50
Goat	1.35	1.40	3.60
Poultry	4.50	3.20	1.35

[a] Van Slyke, L. L., *Fertilizers and Crop Production*, Orange Judd Publishing Co., Inc., New York, 1932, p. 171.

discussion, average farm manure ready for field application will be considered as containing *0.5 per cent of nitrogen, 0.25 per cent of phosphoric acid, and 0.5 per cent of potash.* The tentative nature of such figures, however, must always be kept in mind. Besides nitrogen, phosphorus, and potassium, farm manure contains calcium, magnesium, sulfur, and all of the trace elements. The latter no doubt are in some cases extremely important.

234. *Outstanding characteristics of farm manure* [1]

As a farm manure is essentially a fertilizer, whether it is produced on the farm or purchased outside, it is logical to contrast it with the ready-mixed commercial fertilizers on the market. In such a comparison, seven characteristics are outstanding: (1) the moist condition of manure, (2) its variability, (3) its low analysis, (4) its low grade, (5) its unbalanced nutrient condition, (6) the residual influence exerted by manure, and (7) its rapid fermentative processes.

Of the above characteristics the first two may be disposed of quickly. The variability of farm manure has already been sufficiently emphasized since it is a condition ordinarily to be expected. As to the moisture, whether in fresh or well-rotted manure, the amount may vary from 50 to 80 per cent depending on conditions.

Since representative farm manure is considered to contain 0.5 per cent of nitrogen, 0.25 per cent of phosphoric acid, and 0.5 per cent of potash, a ton of this fertilizer supplies only 10, 5, and 10 pounds of total nitrogen, phosphoric acid, and potash respectively. It is without doubt a low-analysis material when compared to the commercial fertilizers commonly on the market such as a 5–10–5 or a 15–30–15.

It must not be assumed, however, that the amounts of the three

[1] Data as to the amounts of manure likely to be produced by the different classes of farm animals are often useful in fertility calculations.

Tons of Manure Produced Annually by Farm Animals per 1000 Pounds Live Weight [a]

Animal	Weight of Excrement	Weight of Bedding	Total Weight
Horse	9.00	3.0	12.00
Cow	13.50	1.5	15.00
Pig	15.25	3.0	18.25
Sheep	6.25	3.5	9.75
Steer	7.50	1.5	9.00
Hen	4.75	—	4.75

[a] Van Slyke, L. L., *Fertilizers and Crop Production*, Orange Judd Publishing Co., Inc., New York, 1932, p. 287.

fertilizer elements added to an acre of land in an ordinary application of farm manure are correspondingly small. Because of the large acre applications of this fertilizer, the quantities of the nutrient elements added are comparatively large. For example, 10 tons of representative farm manure will supply in total about 100 pounds of nitrogen,

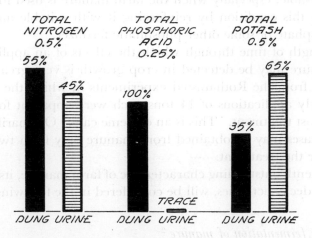

FIG. 57. Diagram showing the distribution of nitrogen, phosphoric acid, and potash between the solid and liquid portions of average farm manure.

50 pounds of phosphoric acid, and 100 pounds of potash. This is equal in terms of total nutrients to 625 pounds of nitrate of soda (16 per cent), 312 pounds of superphosphate (16 per cent), and 166 pounds of potassium chloride (60 per cent).

In considering such figures it is well to remember that only a part of the nutrient constituents of farm manure is readily available. That is, manure is low grade compared to commercial fertilizers. In general, only about *one-half of the nitrogen, one-sixth of the phosphoric acid,* and a little more than *one-half of the potash* are readily available to plants. On the basis of readily available nutrients 1 ton of average farm manure supplies approximately 5 pounds of N, 1 pound of P_2O_5, and 5 pounds of K_2O.

The phosphoric acid of most mineral soils is not only low but rather unavailable. Moreover, the phosphorus added in fertilizers is adsorbed rather strongly by the soil complex and is likely to become inactive. As a consequence, it seems necessary for a complete fertilizer to carry as much or even more phosphoric acid than nitrogen or potash. The ratio of a ready-mixed complete commercial fertilizer in respect to these three constituents ordinarily is seldom less than 1–1–1 or 1–2–1, while in many cases it is as high as 1–3–1 or 1–4–1. Farm manure in comparison is obviously too low in phosphoric acid to be fully effective and is considered as unbalanced for that reason. It is often advisable, especially when the farm manure is used for cereals, to correct this condition by reinforcing it with suitable amounts of superphosphate or some other phosphatic fertilizer.

The length of time through which the effects of an application of farm manure may be detected in crop growth is very great. Hall [1] cites data from the Rothamsted experiments in which the effects of eight yearly applications of 14 tons each were apparent forty years after the last treatment. This is an extreme case. Ordinarily, profitable increases may be obtained from manure only from two to four years after the treatment.

The seventh outstanding characteristic of farm manure, its fermentative and decay activities, will be considered in the following section.

235. *The fermentation of manure* [2]

In the process of digestion, the food of animals becomes more or less decomposed. This condition comes about partly because of the digestive processes themselves and partly from the concurrent bacterial action that takes place. Consequently the fresh excrement, as it comes from the stable, consists of decayed or partially decayed plant materials, with a certain amount of broken-down tissue. This is more or less intimately mixed with litter and the whole mass is moistened with the liquid excrement carrying considerable quantities of soluble compounds of nitrogen, potassium, and other nutrients. Moreover, the whole mass is teeming with bacteria and other microorganisms.

When manure is first produced, it is usually somewhat loose, especially if considerable litter is present. The first microbial action is, therefore, likely to be largely aerobic in nature. Transformations are

[1] Hall, A. D., *Fertilizers and Manures*, E. P. Dutton & Company, Inc., New York, 1928, p. 234.

[2] For discussions concerning the decomposition of manure see: Russell, E. J., and E. H. Richards, "The Changes Taking Place during the Storage of Farm Manure," *Jour. Agr. Sci.*, VIII, Part 4:495–563, 1917.

Waksman, S. A., *Principles of Soil Microbiology*, The Williams & Wilkins Company, Baltimore, 1932, Chap. XXV.

very rapid and are accompanied by considerable heat. This is commonly the case with horse manure particularly. The simple nitrogenous compounds are influenced first, although the more complicated constituents are by no means unaffected. Carbon dioxide is given off in large quantities. Urea is readily influenced by aerobic activities and quickly undergoes hydrolysis. The ammonium carbonate which results is unstable and promptly produces ammonia. The odor of this gas in horse stables gives evidence of such a change.

$$CON_2H_4 + 2\ H_2O = (NH_4)_2CO_3$$
$$(NH_4)_2CO_3 = 2\ NH_3 + CO_2 + H_2O$$

If conditions are favorable for nitrification, and such is likely to be the case, nitrates may appear in abundance. Since such compounds of nitrogen are very soluble and subject to but little adsorption, serious leaching losses may occur.

Moreover, as has already been suggested, the nitrites instead of being quickly oxidized to the nitrate form, may just as readily liberate elemental nitrogen by reacting with other nitrogen compounds such as amides, amines, and ammonium salts (page 382). A twofold loss of nitrogen is likely to result. The nitrites may even react with non-nitrogenous materials such as the carbohydrates. This loss of nitrogen due to the chemical activity of the nitrites may be much more important in the manure pile than most persons suspect. Hence in the earlier and better aerated decomposition stages, farm manure may be depleted of its nitrogen in three forms — ammoniacal, nitrate, and elemental.

As the manure becomes compacted, especially if it is moist and in a pile, the gaseous oxygen is gradually used up and its place is taken by carbon dioxide. The decay now changes from aerobic to anaerobic, it becomes slower, and the temperature is lowered. New organisms may now function, although most of those active under aerobic conditions probably continue to be effective. The products become changed to a considerable degree. Carbon dioxide, of course, is still evolved in large amounts, but instead of ammonia being formed, the nitrogenous matter is converted, at least in part, into the usual putrefactive products. And since conditions are ideal for biochemical reduction, amines, amides, ammonium, nitrites, and nitrates are readily affected in this way. Consequently **considerable amounts** of gaseous nitrogen are no doubt evolved.

The general fermentative changes in any manure pile can readily be recapitulated. First occurs the more aerobic activity, with the escape of copious quantities of carbon dioxide and variable but considerable amounts of ammonia gas and elemental nitrogen. Next, if the manure is wetted and compacted, as is likely to be the case if it is piled up, a slow deep-seated decay sets in with a simplification of some compounds and a synthesis of others. The over-all result is humification. Here again much carbon dioxide is given off and with it gaseous nitrogen since conditions are ideal for the biological reduction of many different nitrogenous compounds. Since the manure is likely to be alternately wetted and dried, the two general processes described become recurrent. This of course hastens the humification but results in larger losses of both carbon dioxide and nitrogen than might otherwise be the case.[1]

Because of the great loss of carbon dioxide and water during the decay processes, there is considerable change in the bulk of the manure. Fresh excrement loses from 20 to 40 per cent in bulk by partial rotting and 50 per cent by becoming more thoroughly decomposed. It is often argued that if the manure is properly stored, this rapid loss of carbon dioxide and water will raise the percentage amounts of the fertilizer elements. This may be true for potash and phosphoric acid. But in practice the losses in handling due to leaching and fermentation are so pronounced as to place well-rotted manure at a disadvantage as far as its supply of plant nutrients is concerned. This is especially likely to be the case in respect to nitrogen which is subject to loss by volatilization as well as to removal by leaching.

Under certain conditions, however, well-rotted manure is more desirable than the fresh material. This is especially true if the fresh manure is strawy. The addition of straw to a soil may widen its nitrogen-carbon ratio and reduce as well as prevent the formation of nitrate nitrogen. Strawy manure apparently will produce the same effect and if a crop immediately follows its application, detrimental influences may be noted. Under such conditions the well-decayed product is more desirable. When manure is used as a top-dressing, as

---

[1] A change of a biological nature which sometimes takes place in loose and rather dry manure is *fire-fanging*. Many people consider this to be due to actual combustion, as the manure is very light in weight and has every appearance of being burned. This condition, however, is produced by fungi and the dry and dusty appearance of the manure is due to the mycelia, which penetrate in all directions and use up the valuable constituents. Manure thus affected is of little value either as a fertilizer or as a soil amendment.

is sometimes the case with fall wheat and other crops, well-rotted material should always be applied if possible. If strawy manure is plowed under, as is usually the practice, sufficient time should be allowed for decay to take place, thus ensuring a narrow nitrogen-carbon ratio when the crop following needs nitrogen.

In trucking and vegetable gardening, well-decomposed manure is generally preferred especially if the soil is sandy. Such is also the case with home gardens, flower beds, lawns, and greenhouses. *Composting*, which is largely a biological process, is often resorted to especially in the latter cases, farm manure being used in building up the compost pile. Because of its high organic content and the influence of its nitrogen and microorganisms, manure is especially valuable for such purposes.[1]

236. *Artificial farm manure*

A product spoken of as *artificial farm manure* was devised in England during the First World War by the decomposition of straw under more or less controlled conditions.[2] The method used in the United States is similar.[3] The straw as it is stacked, or packed into containers, is treated, layer by layer, with a mixture of fertilizer salts of which nitrate of soda or sulfate of ammonia is prominent. Ground limestone and superphosphate are also added. Other salts are sometimes used in addition. The straw is kept thoroughly moist and compacted, and, if the weather is warm, decay begins almost immediately.

The fertilizers, due to the nitrogen, phosphorus, and calcium carried, greatly hasten the decomposition of the wet straw and within six or eight months the artificial manure is ready for use. The product

[1] A compost is commonly made of alternate layers of manure and the vegetable matter that is to be decayed. Layers of sod or of soil high in organic matter may also be introduced. The manure supplies most of the decay organisms which, in the presence of nitrogen, cause a rapid and effective humification. The foundation of such a compost is usually soil, and the pile is preferably capped with earth. The mass should be kept moist in order to prevent loss of ammonia and elemental nitrogen and to encourage vigorous bacterial action. Acid phosphate is often added to balance up the mixture and make it a more effective fertilizer. A nitrogen fertilizer may also be employed with profit.

[2] Hutchinson, H. B., and E. H. Richards, "Artificial Farm Manure," *Jour. Min. Agr.*, Great Britain, XXVIII:398–411, 1921.

[3] Halverson, W. V., and E. F. Torgerson, "Production of Artificial Farmyard Manure by Fermenting Straw," *Jour. Amer. Soc. Agron.*, XIX:577–584, 1927.

Albrecht, W. A., and E. M. Poirot, "Farm Trials with Artificial Manure," *Jour. Amer. Soc. Agron.*, XX:123–132, 1928.

Turk, L. M., *Synthetic Manure Production in Michigan*, Circular Bulletin 157, Mich. Agr. Exp. Sta., 1936.

closely resembles ordinary farm manure in appearance but is somewhat better balanced in chemical composition because of the fertilizers added. Field tests indicate that such material is equal to farm manure as a fertilizer.[1]

A number of different formulae have been suggested for treating the straw. Perhaps the following is as good as any. It calls for 160 pounds of a fertilizer mixture for each ton of dry straw as follows: 70 pounds of sulfate of ammonia, 50 of ordinary superphosphate; 30 of limestone; and 5 pounds each of magnesium sulfate and common salt.

In those parts of the United States in which grain farming is practiced and large amounts of straw are available, the scheme may prove of value in reducing such material to a form whereby it may be applied to the soil without radically widening the nitrogen-carbon ratio. The undesirable effects of plowing under the fresh straw may thus be avoided. In some cases the normal rainfall is depended on to supply sufficient moisture for the decay of the straw, the fertilizers being applied at threshing time. The cost of the fertilizers must, of course, be taken into consideration. How feasible the production of artificial manure is for the growing of vegetables or for use in dairy sections is yet to be demonstrated. In the latter case it is possible, of course, to use much of the surplus straw as bedding.

237. Nutrient losses during manurial production

A certain amount of every crop is lost before it is consumed by animals. Such loss, while important, is usually small on most farms, especially when compared to the nutrients retained by the livestock. Attention is therefore particularly directed towards those losses sustained by the food as it undergoes normal digestion.

As might be expected, the data [2] bearing on this phase are variable,

[1] Brown, P. E., and F. B. Smith, "The Production of Artificial Manure from Oats Straw under Control Conditions," Jour. Amer. Soc. Agron., XXI:310–322, 1929.

[2] Experimental results are reported in the following publications:

Thorne, C. E., Maintenance of Fertility, Bulletin 183, Ohio Agr. Exp. Sta., 200–202, 1907.

Frear, W., Losses of Manure, Bulletin 63, Penn. Agr. Exp. Sta., 1903.

Hall, A. D., Fertilizers and Manures, E. P. Dutton & Company, Inc., New York, 1928, p. 195.

Hopkins, C. G., Soil Fertility and Permanent Agriculture, Ginn and Company, Boston, 1910, p. 201.

Sweetser, W. S., "The Manurial Value of the Excreta of Milch Cows," Annual Report, Penn. State Coll., 321–351, 1899–1900.

Wood, T. B., "Losses in Making and Storing Farmyard Manure," Jour. Agr. Sci., II 207–215, 1907–1908.

depending on the age, conditions, individuality, and class of animal, and the character of the food.   As a generalization and for purposes of calculation, it may be considered that *three-fourths of the nitrogen, four-fifths of the phosphorus, nine-tenths of the potash, and one-half of the organic matter* are recovered in the manure.   This means losses of about 25, 20, 10, and 50 per cent respectively for these constituents (see Fig. 58).   While such losses are necessary and are usually compensated by the animal products, their magnitude must be considered in estimating the value of manure in fertility maintenance.

238. *Losses due to the handling and storage of farm manure*

Since approximately one-half of the nitrogen and three-fifths of the potash of average farm manure are in a soluble condition, the possibility of loss by leaching is usually great, even though the manure is not exposed to especially heavy rainfall.   In addition, decomposition,

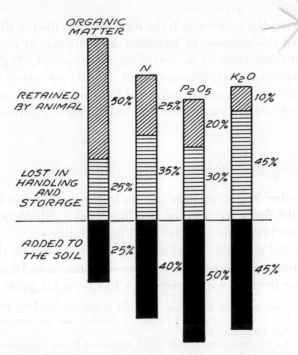

¹Fig. 58.   A tentative representation of the proportion of the organic matter, nitrogen, phosphoric acid and potash originally present in the food (1) retained by the animals, (2) lost in handling and storage of the manure, and (3) applied to the soil.

both of an aerobic and anaerobic nature, will cause a rapid waste of nitrogen in the ammonium, nitrate, and elemental forms, one-half of that present in the manure being rather susceptible to such losses. Packing and moistening the manure will change the decay from aerobic to anaerobic, thus reducing the waste of gaseous nitrogen while encouraging the simplification of the manurial constituents. Tight floors in the stables and impervious bottoms in the manure pit or under the manure pile should considerably diminish leaching losses.

While the figures [1] are variable, it is probable that *one-half of the nitrogen, potash, and organic matter* and at least *one-third of the phosphoric acid* of farm manure are lost even under fairly careful methods of storage. On the average farm where manure very often remains outside for several months, the losses will be much higher. Thus at least one-half of the nutrient constituents of the manure ordinarily is wasted. This represents considerably over one-half of the fertilizing value, since the elements removed are those that would be most readily available to plants.

Considering the losses which the food sustains during digestion and the waste of the manure in handling and storage, it cannot be expected that more than *25 per cent of the organic matter, 40 per cent of the nitrogen, 50 per cent of the phosphoric acid*, and *45 per cent of the potash* of the original crop as removed from the land will, under ordinary conditions, reach the soil again (see Fig. 58). This is a conservative estimate.

239. *Practical handling and storage of farm manure*

Considerable loss to manure occurs in the stable, due to leaching. Therefore the first care is to the bedding, which should be chosen for its absorptive properties, its cost, and its cleanliness.

Coordinated with this are the floors, which should be tight so that the free liquid will be held in contact with the absorbing materials. Preservation in stalls with tight floors has been for years a common

[1] Data respecting manurial losses may be found as follows: Roberts, I. P., and H. H. Wing, *On the Deterioration of Farmyard Manure by Leaching and Fermentation*, Bulletin 13, Cornell Univ. Agr. Exp. Sta., 1889.

Schutt, M. A., *Barnyard Manure*, Bulletin 31, Canadian Dept. Agr., Cent. Exp. Farms, 1898.

Thorne, C. E., *Farm Manures*, Orange Judd Publishing Co., Inc., New York, 1914.

Thorne, C. E., and others, *The Maintenance of Fertility*, Bulletin 183, Ohio Agr. Exp. Sta., 1907.

method of handling farm manure in England. The trampling of the animals, and the continued addition of litter as the manure accumulates, aid in the preservation.

When it is possible to haul directly to the field, this practice is to be advised, since opportunities for excessive losses by leaching and fermentation are thereby reduced. Manure may even be spread on frozen ground or on the top of snow, provided the land is fairly level and the snow is not too deep. This system saves time and labor, and very largely obviates leaching losses since the soluble portions of the manure are carried directly in the soil. Such a practice, however, will not prevent some losses by volatilization.

It is often necessary to store manure outside, fully exposed to the weather. When this is the case, certain precautions should be observed. In the first place, the pile should be located on level ground far enough from any building so that it receives no extra water in times of storm. The sides of the heap should be steep enough to shed water readily, while the depth of the pile should be such as to allow little leaching even after heavy storms. The earth under the manure may be slightly dished in order to prevent loss of excess water. If possible, the soil of the depression should be puddled, or better, covered with cement.

Some farmers, especially if the amount of manure produced is large, find it profitable to construct manure pits of concrete. These pits are usually rectangular in shape with a shed covering. One or even both ends are open to facilitate the removal of the manure. In such a structure, leaching is prevented by the solid bottom while the roof allows a better control of moisture conditions. By keeping the manure carefully piled and well moistened, decomposition may proceed with a minimum waste. Large losses of carbon and nitrogen, however, will still take place.

Another method of storage is in covered barnyards or in sheds where animals are fed and bedded. The floor of such a structure should be more or less impervious. The manure is kept thoroughly packed as well as damp by the animals. This is a common method of handling manure in the fattening of steers in the Middle West and allows a minimum loss, providing hogs are not allowed to follow the steers.

It is evident from this consideration that well-protected and carefully preserved manure will be higher in available plant nutrients than that carelessly handled. Since hauling directly to the field affords less chance of loss by leaching and fermentation, this mode of handling should be adopted wherever feasible. If storage must be resorted to, the precautions already suggested should be observed insofar as possible.

240. *Economic utilization of farm manure*

In the application of manure to the land, the same general principles observed in the use of any fertilizer should be kept in mind. Of these, fineness of division and evenness of distribution are of prime importance. The efficiency of the manure may be raised considerably thereby.

A third important factor is the rate of application. Since the supply of manure is often limited in diversified farming, it is usually better, especially with field crops, to decrease the amounts at each spreading and cover a greater acreage. Thus, instead of adding 20 tons to the acre, 10 tons may be applied and twice the area covered. Applications can then be made oftener and a larger and quicker net return realized for each ton of manure.

Not only is there a greater crop yield a ton from the smaller applications but a greater recovery of the manurial fertility in the crops also results. Ohio experiments [1] show that in the first rotation after the manure is applied, a 25 to 30 per cent higher recovery may be expected from an 8-ton treatment to the acre than from 16 tons.

Evenness of application and fineness of division are greatly facilitated by the use of a manure spreader. This also makes possible the uniform application of small amounts of manure, even as low as 5 or 6 tons to the acre. It is impossible, of course, to spread such small amounts by hand and obtain an even distribution.

Whether manure should be plowed under or not depends largely on the crop on which it is used. On meadows and pastures it is spread as a top-dressing. With other crops, however, it is often plowed under. This is particularly necessary if the manure is long, coarse, and not well rotted. If manure is fine and well decomposed, it may be harrowed into the surface soil as is sometimes done with wheat. Obviously the method employed will depend on the crop, the soil, and the condition of the manure.

[1] Thorne, C. E., and others, *Plans and Summary Tables of the Experiments at the Central Farm*, Circular 120, Ohio Agr. Exp. Sta., 108, 1912.

In the utilization of farm manure it is well to remember that its addition to the soil in large amounts may widen the nitrogen-carbon ratio. This is likely to be the case if the manure is strawy. The injurious effects that are sometimes observed from the use of manure may be due to the reduction of nitrate accumulation induced by the high carbon content of the materials added. When the manure is strawy, a sufficient interval should elapse between the application of the fertilizer and the planting of the crop in order that nitrate accumulation may again take place. The plowing under of manure in the fall is a case in point.

A phase of manurial management that deserves special attention is that of *reinforcement* or the treatment of the manure with a fertilizer, usually phosphatic in nature. This will be considered in the following section.

241. *Reinforcement of farm manure*

As already explained, average manure contains about five times more readily available nitrogen and potash respectively than active phosphoric acid. It is thus badly unbalanced. In comparison with a complete commercial fertilizer, there should be at least five times, and better ten times, more available phosphoric acid in the manure than is usually present to be sure that the nitrogen and potassium are properly balanced. In order to obtain the most economical results with manure, liberal applications of phosphorus are used in the rotation in connection with it. Sometimes, however, part of the phosphatic fertilizer is mixed with the manure before the application is made. It is the latter practice that is spoken of as *reinforcement*.

The amounts of phosphatic fertilizers that should be added to a ton of farm manure depends on the acre-rate of application of the latter. Ordinarily from 500 to 600 pounds of 16 or 20 per cent superphosphate or its equivalent are applied to the acre in this way during the course of a field crop rotation. Thus if 10 tons of manure are spread on an acre, each ton should be reinforced with 50 or 60 pounds of superphosphate. If 15 tons of manure are used, the reinforcement may be at the rate of 35 to 40 pounds of superphosphate a ton. Raw rock phosphate is ordinarily utilized at double the rate of superphosphate on account of its less ready availability.

If the superphosphate is added each day in the stable in the case of dairy cows, 2 pounds per cow will amount to a reinforcement of about 50 pounds to the ton of manure. With this as a gauge any desired rate of superphosphate application to the land may be decided on providing, of course, the tons of manure that are to go on each acre of land are known in advance. Thus if the rate of manuring is to be 10 tons, 3 pounds of superphosphate daily per cow would mean the application of 750 pounds of superphosphate to each acre receiving manure.

If farm manure is to be balanced fully, that is in respect to its total content of nitrogen and potash, at least 100 pounds of ordinary superphosphate to the ton are necessary. If it is to be balanced only to the extent of its readily available nutrients, perhaps half this amount will be adequate. These rule-of-thumb figures are worth remembering when manure is to be used in an intensive way on gardens and flower beds and in nurseries and greenhouses.

In discussing the reinforcement of farm manure, it is well to emphasize that such a practice is unnecessary when only the influence of nitrogen is desired. This is the case when manure is applied as a top-dressing on meadows, pastures, lawns, and orchards. If phosphorus is needed in such cases, superphosphate generally is added alone or in a mixed fertilizer before the manure is spread.

242. *Crops that respond to farm manure* [1]

Since manure is available in limited amounts on the average farm and as mineral fertilizers give good results on grass and legumes, it is often considered judicious to reserve most of the manure for other crops of the rotation. This is especially the case when a feed crop such as maize or such cash crops as cabbage, tobacco, cotton, or potatoes are grown.

The top-dressing of the meadows with farm manure is allowable, especially with a new seeding or when the land is soon to be plowed for a cultivated crop. When the soil is acid and lime cannot be applied, it is practically necessary to top-dress the new seeding in order to ensure a good stand of clover, even though alsike is seeded. Manure thus takes the place of lime, in a way, and strengthens and protects the crop. In many communities a large proportion of the farm

[1] See Thorne, C. E., *Farm Manures*, Orange Judd Publishing Co., Inc., New York, 1914, Chaps. XI and XIII.

manure is applied to the meadows, no doubt for the reasons just suggested.

The value of manure in orchards should not be overlooked, especially on sandy soils, as the maintenance of organic matter as well as nitrogen is a vital factor in orchard practice. In most cases, however, the fertility of an orchard soil can be maintained adequately by means of leguminous cover-crops and a nitrogenous commercial fertilizer, thus releasing the farm manure for use in the regular field rotation or for vegetables.

With trucking, garden, and greenhouse crops, the applications of large amounts of manure when obtainable have always proved advisable. As a matter of fact, manure, when correctly handled, has shown itself one of the best fertilizers for intensive operations. This is due not only to the nutrients carried by the manure, but to the large quantities of easily decomposed organic matter that are at the same time introduced. As large amounts of highly phosphatic fertilizers usually follow the manure in such cases, direct reinforcing is unnecessary.

243. *Farm manure and the maintenance of soil fertility*

It has already been emphasized that the amount of humus in the soil is determined by the quantity of organic nitrogen present and that crop residues ordinarily supply sufficient organic matter, provided that the nitrogen supply is adequate. As a consequence, farm manure is valuable especially because of the nitrogen it supplies. The organic matter that it furnishes probably does not greatly augment the amount of humus in the soil unless the manurial applications are very large. In spite of the fact that farm manure supplies energy and no doubt has a very considerable influence on the physical condition of the soil and on its microorganic flora, it must be considered essentially as a nitrogen, and perhaps to a lesser degree a potash fertilizer.

Viewed in this light the question immediately arises, Can the fertility problems of the representative general or dairy farm be solved by the use of farm manure even if it should be reinforced with superphosphate? The answer, of course, is No, especially if a more or less permanent fertility system is in mind. There are several reasons for such an answer.

In the first place hardly one-half of the nitrogen, potash, and phosphoric acid removed by the crops fed to animals is returned to the soil in farm manure. And, of course, not all crops are used for animal food. Thus the utilization of farm manure alone would obviously result in a gradual reduction of soil fertility unless other sources of nutrients were resorted to.

When adequately reinforced with superphosphate the phosphorus need may be met but the nitrogen and potash and especially the lime losses are hardly challenged. A deficiency in any one of these nutrients will soon unbalance any system of fertility. It is only when farm manure is properly coordinated with lime, commercial fertilizers, and legumes as well as with good tillage, weed elimination, and soil-water control, that the fullest effects from this valuable farm by-product can be realized.

244. *Green manures* [1]

From time immemorial the turning under of a green crop to better the condition of the soil has been a common agricultural practice. Records show that the use of beans, vetches, and lupines for such a purpose was well understood by the Romans, who probably borrowed the idea from other nations. The art was lost in Europe to a great extent during the Middle Ages, but was revived again as the modern era was approached. At the present time, it is given a place, when possible, in every rational plan for the handling of mineral soils. It is also used to a certain extent on peat land.

Green-manuring refers to the practice of turning into the soil undecomposed green plant tissue. The plowing under of some rapid-growing crop, such as oats, rye, or peas is an example. Such material, if the soil is in a proper condition and well managed, brings about a number of favorable effects and may aid materially in maintaining or raising the crop-producing capacity of a soil.

245. *The benefits of green-manuring*

The influence exerted by green-manuring which is generally mentioned first relates to the organic supply of the soil. When there is a shortage of farm manure, the practice becomes of special importance

---

[1] A full discussion of green-manuring in all of its phases may be found in Pieters, A. J., *Green-Manuring*, John Wiley & Sons, Inc., New York, 1927.

since roots and the usual crop residues may not be adequate to maintain the humus content of the land. Even when farm manure is available, a green-manuring crop now and then may do much toward sustaining a suitable amount of organic matter.

The humus compounds resulting from the decay of green manures without doubt increase the adsorptive capacity of the soil, and promote aeration, drainage, and granulation — conditions that are extremely important in successful plant growth. In fact, organic matter is one of the most important factors in determining the tilth of any soil. It serves to bind together a sandy soil and increases its water-holding capacity. In a clay it promotes a crumb structure and practically determines the fitness of such a soil to function as a foothold for plants (see page 59).

The plowing under of a green manure not only adds organic carbon to the soil but nitrogen as well. The amount of nitrogen may be large or small, depending on conditions. If the crop turned under is a legume and the nodule organisms have been active, the store of soil nitrogen is markedly augmented. It has already been emphasized that, as the decay of organic residues takes place, nitrogen is retained and the carbon is reduced, by the evolution of carbon dioxide, to a given level with it. In other words the nitrogen-carbon ratio becomes operative (see page 136). This means that the amount of soil humus is determined by the amount of organic nitrogen present. From this standpoint any increase in soil nitrogen, especially in the form of green residues, is always a welcome addition.

Besides the influence of green-manuring upon the physical condition of the soil and upon its store of humus and nitrogen, the added organic material acts as a food for soil organisms, and tends to stimulate biological changes to a marked degree.[1] Such biochemical action is of special consequence in the production of carbon dioxide, ammonium, nitrites, nitrates, and other simple compounds. The response of the general-purpose flora of the soil and of the Azotobacter to carbonaceous and nitrogenous materials is well known. Even peat soils, made up largely of organic matter, are markedly activated by the turning under of a green-manuring crop.

A green manure also exerts a conserving influence on the nutrients

[1] For the activating influence of green manures, see Lewis, R. D., and J. H. Hunter, "The Nitrogen, Organic Carbon and pH of Southeastern Coastal Plain Soils as Influenced by Green-Manuring Crops," *Jour. Amer. Soc. Agron.*, XXXII:586–601, 1940.

of the soil since it takes up soluble constituents that might otherwise be lost in drainage. In this respect it functions as a *cover-crop*.[1] The nitrates of the soil, which are very soluble and are adsorbed only slightly by the colloidal complexes, are thus conserved by such a crop. The presence of a green manure on the soil at a time when it might otherwise be bare is highly desirable. Besides this, green manures, especially those with long roots, carry nutrients upward from the subsoil, and when the crop is plowed under these constituents are deposited within the root zone.

The increased availability of the inorganic constituents of the soil is a phase that should not be forgotten in this connection. Jensen[2] found that the addition of 3 per cent of green manure raised the solubility of lime and phosphoric acid 30 to 100 per cent. This was over and above the mineral constituents which came directly from the decomposing green crop. Potassium, magnesium, and iron may also be markedly influenced in the same manner. In fact, the potash problem of many soils is solved, at least temporarily, by the activity of the soil organic matter.

246. *Increase in soil nitrogen due to a leguminous green manure*

When a nonlegume is turned under as a green manure, nitrogen originally in the soil is merely returned in an organic form. There is no gain. But if a legume is so utilized there is a possibility of increasing the soil nitrogen to the extent of the symbiotic fixation. Since an increase in the organic nitrogen of the soil means an increase in fertility as well as a possible rise in humus, the probable magnitude of the fixation is worthy of some attention.

Data have already been cited (page 386) which indicate that the nodule organisms of a vigorous crop of alfalfa might fix from 200 to 250 pounds of nitrogen an acre. Comparable figures for red clover are perhaps 100 to 150 pounds an acre. Soybeans compare rather well with red clover but hairy vetch and field beans ordinarily will

[1] A *cover-crop* is one planted for the purpose of covering or protecting the soil at a certain time of year.

A *catch-crop* is one that follows the main crop. It must be rapid in growth as it can occupy the soil a relatively short time. Both a cover-crop and a catch-crop may, on occasion, be used as a green manure.

[2] Jensen, C. A., "Effect of Decomposing Organic Matter on the Solubility of Certain Inorganic Constituents of the Soil," *Jour. Agr. Res.*, IX:253–268, May, 1917.

acquire from the air only a half or a third as much nitrogen. If these crops are turned under, the soil, of course, gains in organic nitrogen to the extent of the fixation.

A rough-and-ready method of calculation is based on the assumption that the nitrogen present in the tops of well-inoculated legumes represents the amount fixed by the symbiotic bacteria.[1] It must be admitted that this provides an extremely uncertain basis for estimation, yet it gives a rough idea of the extra nitrogen acquired by the soil. For instance, a ton of dry red clover contains from 40 to 50 pounds of nitrogen. If a green-manuring crop equivalent to 2 tons of dry substance an acre should be turned under, there would be a gain in soil nitrogen of 80 to 100 pounds. Dry alfalfa hay carries from 50 to 60 pounds of nitrogen a ton. The plowing under of green alfalfa equal to 3 tons of dry matter would mean an addition to the soil of 150 to 180 pounds of nitrogen an acre.

Before leaving this phase something more specific should be said in respect to the significance of such gains. One hundred pounds of nitrogen so added is equivalent in terms of nitrate of soda to 625 pounds of the commercial salt. Moreover, assuming a nitrogen-carbon ratio of 1 to 12, this amount of organic nitrogen should support an increase in humus of perhaps 2000 pounds. Besides, there is the stimulation of soil organisms of all kinds, especially those concerned with the carbon and nitrogen cycles. This activation, common to all green manures when properly used, is especially characteristic of those of a leguminous nature.

247. *The decay of green manure and its influence on nitrate accumulation*

When a green crop is turned under, the trend of its decay is the same as that of any plant tissue as it becomes a part of the soil body.[2] The general-purpose organisms of the soil, both animal and plant, are especially active, together with the decay bacteria carried in by the turned-under crop. The decomposition is probably both aerobic and anaerobic in nature, carbon dioxide being continuously evolved as

---

[1] Hopkins, C. G., *Soil Fertility and Permanent Agriculture*, Ginn and Company, Boston, 1910, p. 217.

[2] Waksman, S. A., "Chemical and Microbiological Principles Underlying the Decomposition of Green-Manures in Soil," *Jour. Amer. Soc. Agron.*, XXI:1–18, 1929.

Martin, T. L., *The Decomposition of Green-Manures at Different Stages of Growth*, Bulletin 406, Cornell Univ. Agr. Exp. Sta.; 1921.

decomposition proceeds. There is, of course, a tremendous increase in microbial tissue and the demand for, and the turnover of, both carbon and nitrogen are exceedingly great. Finally, as the vigorous decay slackens, simple end products other than carbon dioxide begin to appear, intermixed with the humic remains of the green manure. All this in considerable detail has already been explained on page 118.

A phase of the decay process, so briefly sketched above, has a most important bearing on the accumulation of nitrate nitrogen in the soil. As already suggested, the addition of fresh decomposable plant tissue results in a rapid multiplication of organisms of all kinds. As a consequence, nitrates disappear from the soil immediately and no nitrogen in this form may accumulate until the period of rapid decay is past. By this time the population of general-purpose decay organisms is much reduced due to lack of food. Hence the competition for nitrogen is less keen. Nitrifying organisms now become conspicuously active and it is possible for nitrates to accumulate in the soil again. The details of this control are fully set forth on pages 134 and 135.

It is, of course, desirable to so control the period of the rapid decay, with its suppression of nitrates, that the crop following the green manure may not suffer from a lack of nitrogen. In other words, the *time interval* is an important consideration. In some cases it is possible to speed up the process, while at other times it makes little difference whether the rate is slow or rapid. Other things being equal, the higher the nitrogen content of the green-manuring crop, the more rapid will be the decomposition and the shorter will be the period of nitrate suppression.

The time interval during which a depression of the nitrate nitrogen of the soil occurs is also influenced by the succulence of the green manure and its stage of maturity. The younger the crop and the more water it contains, the shorter is the period of rapid decay. The plowing under of a dead dry cover-crop will not give so satisfactory results as though fresh tissue had been used. Whenever a crop immediately succeeds the green manure, the decay should be as rapid as possible. Otherwise, the accumulation of nitrates will be much delayed and the crop will suffer for available nitrogen. From this standpoint the advantage of a young and succulent leguminous green manure is obvious. A crop that has reached maturity not only lacks succulence but also its nitrogen percentage is likely to be lower than that of younger plants.

248. *The desirable characteristics of a green manure and the crops that are suitable*

An ideal green-manuring crop should possess three characteristics: rapid growth, abundant and succulent tops, and the ability to grow well on poor soils. The more rapid the growth, the greater the chance of using such a crop economically as a means of soil improvement. The higher the moisture content of the green manure the more rapid is the decay and the more quickly are benefits obtained. As the need of organic matter is especially urgent on poor land, a hardy crop has great advantages.

When other conditions are equal, or many times even if they are not, it is of course better to choose a leguminous green manure in preference to a nonleguminous one, because of the nitrogen gained by the soil. A little additional nitrogen is sometimes of tremendous importance. However, it is so often difficult to obtain a catch of some legumes and they may be so valuable as animal feed, that it is poor management to turn the stand under until after a crop or two have been harvested. Again, the seeds of many legumes are expensive, almost prohibiting their use in this way. Among the legumes commonly grown as green manures are sweet clover, lespedeza, Ladino clover, crimson clover, cowpeas, soy beans, field peas, vetch, and peanuts. Many of the other legumes do not fit into the common rotations in such a way as to be turned under conveniently as a green manure.

The plants utilized in the various parts of the United States as green manures may be grouped under two heads — legumes, and nonlegumes. Their value, of course, depends on climate, some of those mentioned being unsuited to northern regions and vice versa.

Legumes		*Nonlegumes*	
Southern Section Especially	Wide Range	Wide Range in Most Cases	
Crimson clover	Alfalfa	Rye	Ryegrass
Bur clover	Red clover	Oats	Sudan grass
Lespedeza	Sweet clover	Barley	Mustard
Crotalaria	Soy bean	Millet	Rape
Smooth vetch	Canada field	Buckwheat	Weeds
Austrian winter	pea	Wheat	Winter oats
pea	Cowpea		and barley

The growing of two crops together for a green manure is often recommended. If properly chosen in respect to growth habits, climatic adaptation, and soil requirements, the advantages are numerous. Not only can larger amounts of green material be produced but also, if one of the crops is a legume, nitrogen fixation may be taken advantage of. Also one may offer support to the other, a factor of no mean importance when dealing with plants that tend to lodge.

Oats and peas, and rye and vetch are excellent examples of green-manure combinations. The two nonlegumes in these cases are highly desirable because of their rapid, abundant, and succulent growth and because they may be accommodated to almost any rotation. These crops are hardy and will start under adverse weather conditions and in a poorly prepared seedbed. They are thus extremely valuable on poor soils. Moreover, their influence is especially enhanced by sowing a legume with them. Other combinations just as valuable are possible. In any case the mixtures should be plowed under when at mid-growth or soon after, as at that time their nitrogen-carbon ratio is narrow and a large proportion of the nitrogen which would ultimately have been fixed or otherwise acquired has already been taken up.

249. *The practical utilization of green manures*

The indiscriminate use of green manures is of course never to be advised, as no benefit, or even an injury, may result and the normal rotation much interfered with. The turning under of green crops must be judicious in order that the soil may not be clogged with undecayed matter. Once or twice in a rotation is usually enough for such treatments. Good drainage should always be assured as aeration is of vital importance in the proper decay of plant residues in the soil.

In regions where the rainfall is scanty, great caution must be observed in the handling of green manures. The available moisture that should go to the succeeding crop may be used by the green manure itself or in the processes of decay, and the soil left light and open, due to an excess of undecomposed plant tissue. In the drier portions of the United States, it is still a question whether green manures have any advantage over summer fallowing.

It is generally best to turn under green crops when their succulence is near the maximum and yet at a time when abundant tops have been produced. With a suitable green manure this occurs at about or a little beyond the half-mature stage. A large quantity of water is carried into the soil when the crop is in this condition, and the draft on the original soil-moisture is less. Moreover, the carbon-nitrogen ratio of the green manure is comparatively narrow at this time. Again, the succulence encourages a rapid and more or less satisfactory decay, with the maximum production of humus and other products. The plowing should be done, if possible, at a season when a plentiful supply of rain occurs. The effectiveness of the manuring is thereby much enhanced as the moisture conditions are such as to ensure a rapid and effective decomposition.

Whether to fall- or spring-plow a green-manuring crop is of great practical importance and is decided largely by climate, the nature of the soil, the crop used, and other factors. While fall plowing seems to be of some advantage in the northern states as measured by nitrate accumulations in the following summer, the reverse seems to be true farther south where the winters are milder and shorter and where the spring and summer seasons are longer. Whether the soil is sandy or clayey must also be considered. The question involved is the time interval of decay already emphasized and which so markedly influences nitrate production and accumulation.

Whether or not a green manure, even though suited to the climate and the soil, can be used advantageously is determined by the character of the rotation. In the northern states, due to the shorter season, it is often somewhat of a problem when, in any ordinary rotation, a green manure may be introduced without seriously interfering with the regular crops. Not only is the period for growing the green manure very short, but the time interval between the turning under of the green substance and the planting of the next crop is often inadequate.

For instance, in a rotation of maize or potatoes, oats, wheat, and two years of hay, a green manure might be introduced after the corn or potatoes. This would not be a very good practice, however, as a cultivated crop usually should follow a green manure in order to facilitate decomposition. When a rotation of this kind is used, it is better either to supply organic matter in another way, or to alter or break the crop sequence in such a manner as to admit of a more advantageous use of green crops. In the southern states this disadvantage is not encountered to such an extent, as the season is much longer and the rotation less likely to interfere.

Where trucking crops are raised and no very definite rotation is adhered to, green-manuring is easier. It is especially facilitated when cover-crops are grown, as in orchards or nurseries. The growing of green crops for summer feed also favors the easy and profitable use of green manures. In general, it may be said that the organic matter obtained from such a source should be supplemented by farmyard manure and superphosphate when possible, especially in the growing of vegetables. A better balanced, richer, and more abundant humus is likely to result.

250. *Green-manuring and the maintenance of soil fertility*

It cannot be emphasized too strongly that green manuring is only one of the several practices employed in an attempt to maintain, or partially maintain, the productivity of arable soils. Moreover, it is often the last of the various methods to be resorted to. Crop residues and farm manure under ordinary conditions supply most of the organic residues found in mineral arable soils, and if the nitrogen level is high these should suffice. Whether or not green manures are used should depend on the adequacy of these sources of plant tissue. The plowing under of green plants, therefore, may be considered as a supplementary measure, very important in some cases but ordinarily not so essential in the general fertility scheme as certain other practices.

Chapter XIX. The Fertility Management
of Mineral Soils

While most of the fundamental facts and conceptions regarding the nature and properties of soils and their plant relationships have been presented, they have not been correlated in a practical way. It seems desirable at this point, therefore, not only to interrelate these facts and concepts but also to interlock them in such a manner as to establish a general scheme of fertility management. With this as a background, the data already emphasized should be doubly significant in a practical sense.

The maintenance of a profitable and continuous soil productivity is an intricate problem, since many variable factors are involved. Weather conditions, moisture relations, soil organic matter and tilth, soil reaction, available nutrients, and plant diseases and insect pests are the more important influences. Under such conditions no scheme of soil management and crop production can be perfect, even though it may be fairly profitable.

The sources of knowledge regarding the rational handling of the soil are numerous. Much data have arisen from experience and observation, much are empirical, while some are confessedly conjectural. In spite of the large amount of technical information available regarding the soil and its plant relationships, practical experience has contributed the most.

251. *What a good system of soil management should include*

In outlining a good system of soil management five major features must be cited. Of these good tilth deserves first consideration. This means a suitable condition of the soil physically and implies in addition a satisfactory regulation of moisture. The proper maintenance of soil humus and thereby the encouragement of granulation are the first requisites of tilth.   Plowing and cultivation, so necessary in seedbed preparation and in the incorporation of plant residues of all kinds, should promote crumb structure rather than act as a deterrent.   This assures adequate aeration and the proper drainage, at least of the furrow-slice.   If the subsoil is likely to be wet, especially during the growing season, underdrains such as tiles may be necessary.   Good tilth also implies erosion control and in a broad way is related to crop rotation as well.

The control of weeds, a second major factor in soil management, is associated with good tilth since the cultivation of the land to modify its physical condition may at the same time greatly hinder the development of undesirable vegetation.   At certain times during the growing season tillage is practiced almost wholly for the control of weeds.   Some weeds, however, such as quack grass and bindweed, cannot be discouraged effectively by cultivation, and other means must be employed.   Weeds, by using moisture and nutrients that otherwise might go to the crop, seriously interfere with the production of a successful harvest.   In fact, weeds are one of the most important difficulties with which the farmer must contend.

The control of plant diseases and insect pests is in certain cases a phase of soil management.   Many insects and disease organisms pass a part, or the whole, of their life cycle in the soil.   And the handling of the soil may greatly affect their virulence.   The time of plowing the land, the order of the crops grown, the interval between the successive crops, the burning of residues, and the addition of chemicals are illustrative of the relation of soil management to insect and disease control.   The fall plowing of the land to reduce cutworm activity and the burning or plowing under of cornstalks to suppress the corn-borer organisms are specific examples.   The addition of sulfur to lower the pH in potato-scab control and the use of hydroxide of lime to make the soil alkaline in the suppression of the finger and toe disease of cabbage may also be cited.

A proper sequence of crops is also in part a feature of soil management since the rotation employed greatly influences the soil physically, chemically, and biologically.   For instance, sod crops tend to encourage humus accumulation and to promote granulation.   Cultivated crops on the other hand encourage organic decay and increase the losses of nutrients in drainage.   Whether a crop is a legume or a nonlegume is an important consideration. Again erosion control is in part a question of crop selection. In short, no system of soil management is complete until a suitable rotation has been decided upon. This implies the use of good seed and acceptable varieties.

A good system of soil management should, above all, provide an adequate supply of available plant nutrients. This is the fifth major requisite. If the fertility of the soil is high, the situation is comparatively simple. The good tilth and the adequate aeration and moisture control already emphasized should make the nutrients available in proper amounts. That is, soil processes, both chemical and biological, are so regulated and encouraged as to supply sufficient quantities of nitrogen, phosphoric acid, potash, lime, and other constituents necessary for crop growth.

But, on the other hand, if any of the essential elements are lacking or are in such a condition as to respond too slowly to natural processes, they must be added. The application of farm manure, fertilizers, and lime are cases in point. As most soils soon require such additions, the maintenance of soil fertility has become a most important and widespread problem in the management of soils, particularly in humid regions. Even in arid regions the only feature holding a priority rating is water supply.

252. *The use of chemical analyses and tests in the detection of fertility needs*

In dealing with the fertility problem of any particular soil it is necessary, of course, to know, first of all, what nutrient element or elements are deficient or are not becoming available rapidly enough to meet the current needs of plants. In the popular mind this appears to be a very simple proposition. Chemistry has to its credit so many wonderful accomplishments that it would seem mere routine to analyze the soil for the various nutrient elements and immediately detect the constituents limiting crop growth. Not only this, but the analysis, in the public mind, is conceived to be easily interpreted in terms of the amount of fertilizer that should be applied to rectify the difficulty. As will appear later this is asking rather too much unless the chemical data are supplemented by information from other sources. No phase of soil science has received so much popular recognition as chemical analysis, nor is any other technical soil procedure so little understood in general and at the same time so greatly over-rated.

Two general types of chemical analyses are commonly made in re-spect to the constituents present in soils — *total* and *partial*.   Under the latter is grouped a miscellany of determinations including the so-called *rapid tests* now receiving so much attention.

In a *total analysis* the entire amount of any particular constituent present in the soil is determined, regardless of its form of combination and its mobility.   Such data are of great value in the scientific study of soils and little progress in pedology and edaphology would have been made without this type of analytical results.   The elimination of such data from the pages of this book would seriously impair the technical information and leave the over-all viewpoint of the soil sadly un-balanced both scientifically and practically.

In spite of the great importance of total analyses in soil research and teaching, they fail entirely in one very important respect.   Ordinarily no hint is given as to the availability or nonavailability to plants of the constituents under consideration (see page 465).   And this, of course, is the vital question in fertility decisions.   Unless an element is suffi-ciently mobile, it is sure to be a fertility liability.   For instance, many mineral soils are comparatively high in total potash (page 23), yet they very often respond profitably to potassium fertilization.   A total analysis cannot be expected to detect this sort of a situation.   Thus a soil high in total nutrients may respond to a commercial fertilizer, while one that is much lower may require no such accession.   As a result, total analyses, except in specific cases, are all but valueless in making practical recommendations.

Partial analyses are of many kinds.   At one time it was considered feasible to digest the soil with a weak acid of just such strength as to remove the nutrient, or nutrients, that would, under field conditions, be immediately available or at least easily acquired by plants during the next growing season.   Such a method is so arbitrary and artificial, and leaves out of consideration so many important factors, such as the particular crop grown, seasonal soil processes, and the vagaries of weather, that it has been impossible to correlate data so obtained closely enough with crop response to use them in a practical way.   The fact that numberless extractive agents have been proposed, bespeaks the inadequacy of this type of chemical analysis.

Another type of partial analysis of soils shows much promise, the determination being in this case, not one of solution, but of replacement from an adsorbed condition. The displacement may be affected by electrodialysis or by means of a properly buffered solution, often barium or ammonium acetate, the concentration of the cation being sufficient to saturate the colloidal complex, fully displacing the ions originally present. The methods are now well standardized and the amounts in the soil of such replaceable cations as calcium, magnesium, potassium, manganese, iron, and aluminum are readily determined. Since constituents so held are mobile and therefore more or less easily available to plants, determinations of this nature are of great practical value when properly correlated with crop response. In many cases, however, the percentage extent to which the exchange complex is occupied by a particular nutrient is about as important as the gross amount present. Other factors also enter in, making an interpretation in a practical way difficult. (See page 404.)

Finally there are the *rapid tests* which are now greatly in vogue and are so widely advertised. Some of these are undoubtedly of great value, while others probably will in time be abandoned. The determination of pH and the Comber test have already been discussed (pages 307 and 363). They unquestionably have merit in the control of soil acidity and the factors associated with it. As a basis for lime recommendations they are both of great practical value. Everyone having to do with soil management, whatever its phase, should be fully conversant with the first of these tests and preferably with both.

Of the other rapid tests [1] it is not possible to speak with such assurance. Since a weak solvent is used and the time of extraction re-

[1] Hance, Francis E., *Soil and Plant Material Analyses by Rapid Chemical Methods*, Bulletins 50 and 51, Hawaiian Sugar Planters' Assoc., 1936 and 1937.

Hester, Jackson B., J. M. Blume, and F. A. Shelton, *Rapid Chemical Tests for Coastal Plain Soils*, Bulletin 95, Va. Truck Exp. Sta., 1937.

Spurway, C. A., *Soil Testing — A Practical System of Soil Fertility Diagnosis*, Technical Bulletin 132, 2nd rev., Mich. Agr. Exp. Sta., 1938.

Morgan, M. F., *Chemical Soil Diagnosis by the Universal Soil Testing System*, Bulletin 450, Conn. Agr. Exp. Sta., 1941.

Bray, R. H., *Rapid Tests for Measuring and Differentiating Between the Adsorbed and Acid-Soluble Forms of Phosphate in Soils*, Mimeograph Pamphlet A.G. 1028, Ill. Agr. Exp. Sta., 1942 and *Directions for Modified Tests for Replaceable Potassium in Soils*, Mimeograph Pamphlet A.G. 1033, Ill. Agr. Exp. Sta., 1942.

Truog, E., "The Determination of the Readily Available Phosphorus in Soils," *Journ. Amer. Soc. Agron.*, XXII:874–882, 1930 and Volk, N. J. and E. Truog, "A Rapid Chemical Method for Determining the Readily Available Potash in Soils," *Journ. Amer. Soc. Agron.*, XXVI:537–546, 1934.

duced to a minimum, most of the nutrients removed are those very loosely held by the colloidal complex. The extracting solution, often sodium acetate, is usually buffered at what is considered a suitable pH in order that the supply of active hydrogen may be constant. The idea is, of course, to so standardize the test as to establish a relationship between the amounts of nutrient removed and the fertilizer needs of the crop to be grown. The test may be reported either in general terms, such as *low*, *medium*, or *high* in respect to the amounts in the soil of the nutrient tested for, or more specifically, in pounds to the acre. In either case the final and critical interpretation is yet to be made — the kind and amount of fertilizer to apply.

At best such tests give only a rough idea of the amounts of easily available constituents present in any soil, as they are arbitrary and artificial like many partial determinations. No one pretends that the solvent used takes out the same amount of a nutrient that would be removed by the crop during the growing season. The great number of different solvents recommended attest the artificiality of the procedure. To make matters worse serious technical difficulties are encountered in accurately determining the amounts of the several nutrients even after they are extracted. Hence the results taken alone mean little. They can only be interpreted in light of a practical knowledge of the crop to be grown and of an understanding of the soil type and its environmental conditions. Two soils testing exactly the same might respond quite differently to identical fertilizer treatment in the field. Obviously it is dangerous to place such tests in the hands of amateurs, not only because they might not make the determinations properly but especially because they would lack the knowledge and judgment necessary for a rational interpretation.

It seems, therefore, that soil tests supply, even at their best, only a fractional part of the information that should be considered in making fertilizer recommendations. The kind of crops grown, their culture, their fertility needs, and their rotation come first. Of equal importance are the texture and structure of the soil and its drainage. Moreover, the nature of the particular fertilizer used, its specific influence on the crop, and especially its changes when added to the soil, should be considered. If this is the situation, the practical importance of chemical tests has been overrated and the public confidence to a certain extent misplaced.

Now that the limitations of chemical tests are clear and their value in a practical way defined, it is easy to outline the procedure commonly followed in furnishing the public with fertility advice.   This is best accomplished by experienced and technically trained men, who understand the scientific principles underlying the common field procedures and who also are in practical touch with the experiences of farmers over wide and diverse areas.   These specialists can make the required chemical tests or have them made.   Besides, they possess a background that enables them satisfactorily to correlate the information so obtained with the other phases that bear on the situation.   The following section deals with the principles upon which such advice is grounded.

253. *Fertility management in outline*

The principal contributors to the successful maintenance of soil fertility are six in number.   They are listed below with the means by which they are effectively attained in practice:

1. Addition of soil organic matter by means of	Crop residues Farm manure Green manure . . . ⟨ Legume / Nonlegume
2. Adequate supply of nitrogen from	Crop residues Farm manure Legumes . . ⟨ Regular crop / Green manure Nitrogen fertilizers
3. Application of lime if necessary	Carbonate (usually limestone) or Hydroxide of lime or Oxide of lime
4. Provision for available potassium by means of	Farm manure and crop residues Decay of organic matter Potash fertilizers
5. Addition of phosphorus in . . .	Superphosphate or other phosphatic fertilizers
6. Application of trace elements . . .	As separate salts or in mixtures

The utilization of the above means of maintaining soil fertility vary markedly in different cases and the details become at times rather complicated.   Moreover, they interlock in a most surprising degree, the influence of one being necessary for the successful functioning of another.   For the sake of clarity the various phases will be considered in regular order, with such explanations as are necessary to make their practical significance apparent.

254. *The maintenance and activity of soil organic matter*

An adequate amount of organic residue must, of course, enter the soil at frequent intervals. This alone, however, may not maintain the soil humus at a desirable level or give the rate of energy release and end-product formation most favorable for crop production.

Soil humus accumulation essentially is a nitrogen problem. The nitrogen of the soil organic matter is closely correlated with and exerts a marked control on the amount of humus that results. This is because of the nitrogen-carbon ratio. Under ordinary conditions of decay the organic residues decrease until the humus that results attains a ratio of roughly 20 to 1 with the nitrogen present. The greater the amount of soil nitrogen, the higher will be the organic level maintained in mineral soils. This has already been fully explained (page 137).

As to the rate of turnover, several factors are involved. Of these drainage, insofar as it promotes satisfactory aeration, is absolutely necessary. Decomposition of a desirable type seldom occurs in imperfectly drained mineral soils. Moreover, active calcium as well as sufficient nitrogen is also essential. Unless both of these elements are present in suitable amounts, the turnover of the organic matter will be too slow. In short, the problem is threefold: (1) sufficient residues, (2) enough nitrogen to assure a high level of humus accumulation, and (3) soil conditions that will promote a biological activity capable of keeping the organic-matter cycle in full swing. Then and only then will the energy release be adequate and the production of simple products satisfactory.

Crop residues, both roots and aboveground parts, farm manure, and green crops usually supply organic refuse in abundance if sufficient organic nitrogen is present. This element, rather than the original organic supply, determines the humus accumulation in soils. Therefore the use of legumes is recommended wherever possible instead of nonlegumes, and farm manure is preferable to mere straw.

As to the amount of humus that should be maintained in any particular soil a statement made on page 143 can well be repeated. "Since the rate at which carbon is lost from the soil increases very rapidly as the organic content is raised, the maintenance of the humus at a high level is not only difficult but also expensive. It is, therefore, unwise to hold the organic matter above a level consistent with crop yields that pay best. Just what this level should be will depend on climatic conditions, soil type, and crops grown. In any event maintain the soil organic matter at an economic minimum, consistent with a suitable physical condition, satisfactory biochemical activity, an adequate availability of nutrients, and paying crop yields."

The activity of the soil organic matter, as determined by calcium and drainage, is usually more important than the actual amount of this constituent present. Many productive soils possess much less nitrogen and organic matter than those in the same community whose crop yields are considerably lower. The analysis of the Ontario loam, a soil of high productivity, and that of the Volusia silt loam, naturally a rather poor soil, well illustrate this point (Table XLVI).

Table XLVI. Percentage Composition of Ontario Loam and Volusia Silt Loam as Sampled in New York. The Figures Are Averages of Twelve Analyses in Each Case [1]

Constituents in Total	Ontario Loam	Volusia Silt Loam
Organic matter (N × 20)	3.20	5.00
Nitrogen (N)	0.16	0.25
Phosphoric acid (P_2O_5)	0.11	0.16
Potash (K_2O)	1.98	2.16
Magnesia (MgO)	0.74	0.80
Lime (CaO)	1.04	0.40
Sulfur trioxide (SO_3)	0.14	0.19

The first critical difference between two soils seems to be in the amount of lime, which governs in part the effectiveness both of the nitrogen and the organic matter. The poor drainage of the Volusia is also a vital factor. In spite of the larger amounts of nitrogen and humus in the Volusia silt loam, their turnover, due to the inadequate supply of lime and the slow drainage, is too sluggish to meet the needs of the crop. Other unfavorable physiological conditions no doubt grow out of the lack of lime and the poor aeration.

Incidentally these data are illustrative of the impossibility of using a total chemical analysis as a basis of fertility recommendations. Even if these figures were most carefully weighed, the chances are that the Volusia instead of the Ontario would be chosen as the better soil unless their field performances were known. And as to practical recommendations, a guess even as to the lime requirements would be impossible.

[1] Bizzell, J. A., *Chemical Composition of New York Soil*, Bulletin 513, Cornell Univ. Agr. Exp. Sta., 1930.

255. *The addition and regulation of nitrogen*

Of all the nutrient elements nitrogen is probably the most troublesome to supply and certainly the most difficult to regulate. The control it exerts on the soil humus, its complicated transformations, its ready loss by volatilization and in drainage water, and its notable influence on crops makes it an element of outstanding interest and attention. Once the nitrogen problem is solved, the other factors concerned with fertility maintenance are more readily amenable.

That the upkeep of nitrogen is critical is not difficult to demonstrate. A few figures will suffice. Assuming that drainage and volatilization losses of nitrogen are offset by rainfall and azofication, only the removals by the harvested crop and by erosion are left unmet (see page 395). This deficit in a general way probably amounts to at least 75 and perhaps even 100 pounds of nitrogen an acre a year. Such a loss is equivalent to approximately 470 to 625 pounds of commercial nitrate of soda. A deficit of this magnitude must be met, at least partially, in order that the productivity of the soil should remain at a profitable level.

Of first importance in nitrogen control are crop residues, not only the aboveground parts but the roots as well. By these means a considerable amount of nitrogen is continuously returned in organic form. As aminization, ammonification, and nitrification take place, this nitrogen again becomes available to higher plants. Such returns are more or less automatic and greatly reduce the difficulty of meeting the yearly nitrogen deficit. They are much more important than most farmers realize.

When animals are kept on the farm, a certain amount of manure is produced. This by-product carries approximately 10 pounds of nitrogen to the ton and is too valuable to be neglected. Assuming a 10-ton application an acre once in a five-year rotation, the return to land so treated would amount to 20 pounds of nitrogen an acre yearly. While by no means meeting the nitrogen deficit, farm manure narrows it considerably and maintains production at a higher level than the addition of such a small amount of nitrogen would lead one to expect. This is probably due to its marked promotion of biological activities.

The plowing under of green manures, especially if the crop so utilized is a legume, may notably increase the supply of soil nitrogen. A crop of red clover, sweet clover, or vetch, for example, may conceivably contain from 100 to 125 pounds of nitrogen received from the air through the fixing activity of bacteria found in the root nodules (see page 387). Such a fixation is equivalent to 625 to 780 pounds of commercial nitrate of soda. This amount of nitrogen thrown into the organic-matter cycle cannot but greatly influence the activity of the soil organisms and ultimately increase not only the amount of nitrogen and humus present in the soil but the mobility of other constituents as well.

The use of a legume as a regular harvested crop of the rotation is especially important in the maintenance of soil nitrogen. With legumes such as clover, alfalfa, and vetch, the amount of nitrogen removed in the harvested portions is thought in many cases to be equalled by the nodule fixation (see page 451). It is thus possible to grow and remove a high protein crop with little or no draft on the soil as far as the nitrogen is concerned. Such a possibility is extremely important in any scheme of nitrogen conservation and maintenance. The use of legumes, therefore, compares favorably with the utilization of crop residues and farm manure in the nitrogen economy of the soil.

It is only fair to suggest that commercial nitrogen is used in general and dairy farming primarily to supplement the nitrogen already present in the soil and not permanently to increase its amount. In fact, the crop is usually so stimulated by the fertilizer that it not only uses the nitrogen therein but more of the soil nitrogen than it probably otherwise would. And since fertilizer nitrogen is largely inorganic, its aid in humus build-up may not be great. Fertilizers thus seem to be somewhat less important in the maintenance of soil nitrogen and organic matter than are farm manure, crop residues, and legumes. With vegetable growing on sandy soil, the situation is different. Here the main reliance is placed on commercial fertilizers, the soil functioning more as a medium than as a source of nutrients.

256. *The utilization of lime*

Three practical questions must be answered in respect to lime. *Is lime necessary*, and if so, *what kind* shall be applied and in *what amounts* to the acre? These queries have already been so fully considered (see page 362) that only three points in respect to liming need be reemphasized.

While lime is often spoken of as a soil amendment, its first major benefit is probably nutritional. That is, the calcium and magnesium really function as fertilizer elements, the indirect influence serving to augment and intensify the direct effects. A very good example of this is the case of such legumes as clover and alfalfa. These plants fail to thrive on acid mineral soils not so much because of the low pH but rather on account of a nutritional lack of calcium. This same relationship probably holds for many bacteria and actinomyces as well. Of soil animals, earthworms certainly respond nutritionally to lime.

A second feature, very important but perhaps overemphasized, in comparison with the nutritional phase, is the indirect effects of lime — that is, its influence as an amendment. A very good example of this is its tendency to speed up biochemical activities in the soil, thereby increasing the rate of energy release and the appearance of simple products. Also, the variations in the solubility of iron, aluminum, and manganese, with fluctuations of pH (see page 301) might be cited, these constituents becoming less active as the pH moves from 4.5 to 7.5. When such a change in iron, aluminum, and manganese solubility is brought about by the addition of lime, the latter functions as a soil amendment. A number of other illustrations just as important could be cited.

And third, lime is not to be used carelessly as a cure-all but applied judiciously or not at all. Too much lime or lime for the wrong crop is just as bad as the failure to enlist its benefits when they are possible. Chemical tests are indispensable in making lime decisions.

257. *Adequate available potassium*

Mineral soils, other than those of a markedly sandy nature, contain large stores of potassium. The potash figure for the representative medium to heavy mineral soil is at least 2 per cent. This is equivalent approximately to 40,000 pounds to the acre-furrow-slice, not to mention the vast stores of this constituent in the subsoil layers. The annual acre loss of potash to the average crop and to drainage combined amounts to possibly 130 pounds as a maximum (see page 212). In terms of commercial muriate of potash (60 per cent K_2O) this equals 216 pounds, which seems a large yearly removal. Yet compared with the total potash in the soil it is insignificant. Obviously the potash problem of the average soil is not a question of totals but of availability.

The soil potash situation is somewhat anomalous. Large amounts of this constituent are being carried away by drainage water (perhaps 60 or 70 pounds an acre annually) and yet a crop growing on the soil may benefit from a potassium fertilizer. Apparently adequate absorption by higher plants usually does not occur until there is a wasteful sufficiency of potassium in the soil solution. A mobility of this constituent rivaling that of calcium apparently is demanded.

If the organic matter, nitrogen, and lime are maintained at an adequate level in the soil, the solvent action of the carbon dioxide and other acids will be at a maximum and perhaps potassium solubility lavish enough to meet the needs of higher plants will result. This seems to be the case with many virgin soils. The maintenance of soil organic matter, therefore, may automatically solve the problem, at least for a time, in the heavier soil where the total content of potash is high. However, a time will come when this transfer from complicated combinations to the soil solution, or to an absorbed and exchangeable condition, will be too slow for satisfactory plant nutrition. Then symptoms of potash deficiency will begin to appear.[1]

On arable soils the application of farm manure in addition to the usual organic residues has been found most helpful. Ten tons of average manure supplies about 100 pounds of potash, equivalent to that carried by 166 pounds of commercial potassium chloride (60 per cent K_2O). Up to the present time the potash problem of many of the heavier soils in the United States has been met in the two ways mentioned. Now, as in the case of European soils, even the crops on the heavier and stronger lands are beginning to show an acute need for potassium fertilization. And potash deficiency symptoms now are not difficult to find in eastern United States. Commercial potash must be used in increasing amounts.

With light soils the situation is much more critical. Here the total as well as the available potash is very low and with many crops this element has been added artificially for years. Farm manure and crop residues are entirely inadequate. When potash is a limiting factor, especially on sandy soils, it usually pays to apply nitrogen and phos-

---

[1] While these symptoms are somewhat different for various kinds of plants, a little experience will enable one to detect potash deficiencies readily. See *Potash Deficiency Symptoms* distributed by The American Potash Institute, Washington, D. C., 1937. Also *Hunger Signs in Crops*, American Society of Agronomy and the National Fertilizer Association, Washington, D. C., 1941. And *If They Could Speak*, Chilean Nitrate Educational Bureau, New York, 1941.

phoric acid also, and sometimes trace elements in addition. Thus potatoes and tobacco, crops that require plenty of potassium, usually receive a complete fertilizer when grown on light soils. Most vegetables also respond well to fertilizers carrying potash. The need for potassium on arable soils is rapidly increasing.

258. *The addition of phosphoric acid*

It is well understood that the phosphorus of soils is critical in two respects — low availability and small amounts present (see page 25). Consequently arable lands generally show a phosphorus deficiency long before the nitrogen and organic matter begin to fail or to assume a low level of activity. For many years, therefore, phosphatic fertilizers have been a standard and effective recommendation. There are only a few soils that do not give a crop response to available phosphorus.

Only in special cases are potassium and nitrogen applied singly, but the utilization of a phosphorus fertilizer alone is very common, especially in areas of general and dairy farming. The most common fertilizer carrying this element is superphosphate, although other forms are growing in popularity. In general and dairy farming, crop residues, legumes, farm manure, superphosphate, and lime will maintain the fertility of many soils at a profitable if not at a maximum fertility level for many years. This is the simplest system of soil fertility that has yet been devised for these types of farming.

For crops of a high acre value, such as cotton, tobacco, and vegetables, especially when grown on the lighter soils, commercial nitrogen as well as phosphoric acid is necessary and under such conditions potash usually is critical also. Thus a complete fertilizer may be used as a supplement to crop residues, legumes, and lime. In such cases farm manure is not usually available in important amounts. More and more reliance is thus placed on commercial fertilizers. Hence, whatever trend the system of fertility management takes, the artificial application of phosphorus is necessary.

One phase of phosphate fertilization has already been discussed (page 301) but it is so important as to merit further emphasis. This is the relation of pH to phosphorus availability to plants. When mineral soils are quite acid (say pH 4.5 or 5.0) the activity of iron, aluminum, and manganese is greatly enhanced. Soluble phosphates added to such soils are immediately changed to insoluble and unavailable forms. This is very uneconomic.

On the other hand at a high pH (say 7 to 8) the large amounts of active calcium in mineral soils change the added phosphate to insoluble calcium phosphates ranging from oxyapatite to carbonate apatite or even fluorapatite (see page 302). All of these phosphates are comparatively unavailable to plants, especially the latter two. Because of the relationship described it seems best to adjust the pH of mineral soils some place within the range perhaps of 5.6 to possibly 6.5. Here the added phosphate seems to be considerably more soluble and besides the phosphate ions ($HPO_4^=$ and $H_2PO_4^-$) presented at this pH appear to be quite readily absorbed by plants. The regulation of soil pH thus is a phase of phosphate fertilization that should not be overlooked.

259. *Magnesium and sulfur deficiencies*

Magnesium and sulfur are not mentioned specifically in the scheme of fertility management presented on page 463 because both of these nutrients are taken care of more or less incidentally and usually do not need special attention. For instance, most limes contain considerable magnesium, dolomitic limestone sometimes carrying 40 per cent of magnesium carbonate. Judicious liming, therefore, often will take care of possible deficiencies of this element. Further, mixed fertilizers frequently contain enough dolomitic limestone to counteract their acidifying effects on the soils to which they are applied. It is not uncommon for such a fertilizer to carry 200 or 300 pounds a ton of magnesium carbonate. Moreover, potassium magnesium sulfate as a fertilizer salt is coming into vogue where magnesium deficiencies are suspected. It would seem, therefore, that this element ordinarily is adequately taken care of in the ways mentioned. Nevertheless, it is well to check crops carefully for signs of deficiencies. They are well defined and easily detected.

Considerable sulfur is added to arable soils in crop residues, green manures, and farm manure, the latter carrying perhaps 5 or 10 pounds a ton. Besides this, large amounts often are added in precipitation, the quantity ranging from a few pounds an acre annually to as much perhaps as 100 pounds in extreme cases. Another automatic addition is that absorbed from the atmosphere by the soil. It is thought to at least equal the amount brought down by rain and snow. Moreover, such fertilizers as sulfate of ammonia, sulfate of potassium, and ordinary superphosphate carry appreciable amounts. Since the latter is approximately one-half gypsum, 100 pounds will supply about 12 pounds of combined sulfur, enough for the average crop an acre. In the light of such figures, it would seem that sulfur, except in certain cases, is not likely to be an element that calls for an unusual amount of attention (see page 417). Routine fertility practices should automatically take care of it.

260. *The trace elements*

Trace-element fertilization is a phase of soil management that is destined to great development. The reason is obvious. Our fertility efforts for years have had to do largely with nitrogen, phosphorus, potassium, and lime. Constant cropping with such a one-sided replacement has gradually exhausted the small amounts of available copper, zinc, manganese, and boron below the current needs especially of certain crops, even though their demands are comparatively minute. At present, plant malnutritions due to trace-element deficiencies are becoming apparent wherever crops have been grown for any great length of time. This is especially true in eastern and central United States.

Already crop specialists are familiar with the symptoms of trace-element deficiencies and, as time goes on, the growers themselves will learn them for the relatively small number of crops with which they, individually, are concerned.[1] The fertilizer salts that commonly are used have already been considered (page 420) and gradually the rates of application will be standardized for individual crops and particular soil types. It is especially important to note here that no fertility diagnosis is now complete without a consideration of the trace elements. So long as even one is deficient the crop will be unable to make adequate use of the other nutrients no matter how liberally they are supplied or how favorable environmental conditions may be. A nutrient ration can be just as seriously unbalanced because of the lack of a mere trace of zinc as from a deficiency of nitrogen or potash to the extent of many pounds.

[1] See citations at bottom of page 420.

261. *The effectiveness of the system*

The fertility system as outlined is simple and it is also very flexible. All of the phases are easily adjusted and may or may not be applied, depending on conditions. This is especially true in respect to lime, to potash, and to the trace elements. In any case, however, it will generally pay to add a phosphatic fertilizer to a soil while nitrogen and organic matter almost always need attention.

It is only necessary to refer to the chemical analysis of a representative mineral soil (page 23) and recall what has been emphasized in respect to its fertility needs in order to realize that the scheme as outlined is logical. The figures indicate that the nitrogen and phosphoric acid are low and that the organic matter is none too plentiful in the average soil. The potash content is high, while the lime and sulfur may or may not be critical. With the knowledge now possessed regarding the amount and availability of nutrients and activity of organic constituents, it can be seen that the system is designed to meet any deficiency that may occur and even to forestall, as in the case of the trace elements, an approaching decline. However, it must be borne in mind that the system in its simplest form represents an extensive rather than an intensive type of agriculture and that, as the cropping becomes more intense, a greater and greater reliance must be placed on commercial fertilizers.

A feature of the system worthy of particular attention is the influence of its various phases on the effectiveness of the others. This interlocking is very important in a practical way. For instance, the amount and activity of the nitrogen determines the quantity of humus that can be maintained in a soil. Conversely, organic-matter decay influences the mobility and availability of the nitrogen. The nitrogen-carbon ratio is a recognition of these interrelations. Thus the control of one cannot be attained without almost equal consideration of the other.

Lime affects the other phases of the system in a decided way. Through its influence on the soil microorganisms, lime has much to do with the activity of the organic matter and the availability of the nitrogen. In fact, the vigor with which carbon and nitrogen revolve in their respective cycles is determined in large degree by calcium. Also the addition of lime no doubt liberates potash directly and by speeding up organic decay a very decided indirect influence is effected. The importance of lime in respect to pH adjustment and the efficiency of superphosphate is widely recognized (page 412). Conversely, the potassium and phosphorus by their nutritional effects upon micro-organisms and higher plants not only render the application of lime to soils more efficient but also beneficially influence the activity of nitrogen and organic matter. Although less clearly understood, the trace elements are just as definitely interdependent as the other phases. Thus the proper interlocking of all of these factors, when by chance it is attained, means, in general terms, a well-balanced physiological condition within the soil. This ideal, unfortunately, is seldom realized in practice.

The effectiveness of the system, however, can only be proved by actual field tests covering a long period. While much data are available in this respect, certain experiments at the Ohio Agricultural Experiment Station are especially interesting because they show in a very decisive way the importance of phosphorus supplied by super-phosphate and nitrogen and organic matter carried by farm manure (see Table XLVII).

Table XLVII. Influence of Superphosphate and Farm Manure on Crop Yields of a Rotation of Corn, Wheat, and Clover at the Ohio Agricultural Experiment Station. Average of Twenty-six Years. The Full Treatment Consisted of Crop Residues, Legumes, Lime, Farm Manure, and Superphosphate [1]

Treatment	Average Crop Yield an Acre		
	Corn, Bushels	Wheat, Bushels	Clover Hay, Tons
1. Full treatment	66.2	28.4	2.34
2. Lacking superphosphate	58.9	23.3	1.95
3. Lacking farm manure and superphosphate	36.8	14.2	1.46

Under conditions of good tillage and drainage, corn, wheat, and clover were grown in the order indicated for twenty-six years, a crop of each being harvested every year. Lime was added, usually just before the corn was planted. In the full treatment the corn received farm manure at the rate of 8 tons to the acre reinforced with 320 pounds of superphosphate. The essentials of the system already out-

[1] Williams, C. G., *The Maintenance of Soil Fertility*, Bulletin 381, Ohio Agr. Exp. Sta., 325, 1924.

lined were thus applied to this series of plats: crop residues, farm manure, lime, legumes as a crop in the rotation, and superphosphate. Trace elements probably were not lacking. In the second group of plats noted, superphosphate was excluded, while in the third group both superphosphate and farm manure were withheld.

The deductions from the data presented are so obvious as to need little comment, especially when it is known that lime not only exerts a favorable and cumulative influence on this soil but also greatly encourages the clover, and that legumes tend to increase the yield of the other crops of the rotation. Since the average crop yields of the plats receiving the full treatment were over 12 per cent greater during the last half of the period than the first half, it is difficult to escape the conclusion that the system may, under certain conditions, increase the productivity of certain soils over a period of years.

262. *The importance of a suitable crop rotation in the maintenance of soil productivity*

While the importance of crop residues, farm manure, green manure, legumes, lime, fertilizers, and tillage is fully recognized, few persons realize the benefits that are derived from a suitable crop rotation.[1] The situation arises because the average farmer has no means of gauging the benefits of alternating his crops, while the influence of farm manure or of commercial fertilizer is usually clearly apparent.

A study of the long-continued field experiments in the United States and in England has brought out some exceedingly important facts regarding the benefits of a good rotation.[2] These may be stated as follows:

1. In general, crop rotations have been found to be practically 90 per cent as effective as farm manure and complete fertilizers in increasing the yields of corn, oats, and wheat, and 95 per cent as effective in maintaining the yields of these three major field crops.

2. The benefits of crop rotations do not impair those received from manure and commercial fertilizers. In other words, the effects from

---

[1] Several very good articles dealing with the practical phases of crop rotation will be found in the *Jour. Amer. Soc. Agron.*, Vol. XIX, No. 6, 1927.

See also Weir, W. W., *Soil Science*, J. B. Lippincott Company, Philadelphia, 1936, Chap. XXIV.

[2] Weir, W. W., *A Study of the Value of Crop Rotation in Relation to Soil Productivity*, Bulletin 1377, U. S. Dept. of Agriculture, 1926.

the rotation are more or less distinct and do not in any sense take the place of or render unnecessary the use of farm manure or fertilizers.

3. Compared with manure and commercial fertilizers, the influence of crop rotation is 20 per cent higher on soils containing plenty of lime than those not so favored.

4. On soils long under cultivation, the best results are possible only when a crop rotation containing a legume, farm manure, and commercial fertilizers are used together.

For specific figures respecting the benefits derived from a suitable rotation of crops, reference may again be made to the Ohio Agricultural Experiment Station, although numerous other sources are available. In this experiment corn, oats, and wheat were grown separately and continuously on the same land for thirty years, receiving each year farm manure at the rate of 5 tons to the acre. At the same time these crops were grown in a five-year rotation of corn, oats, wheat, and two years of clover and timothy. The rotation received 16 tons of manure every five years divided between the corn and wheat. Since this would average only 3⅕ tons yearly, it is obvious that the rotated crops were not favored as to artificial fertilization in comparison with those grown continuously. The data are set forth in Table XLVIII.

Table XLVIII.   The Comparative Influence of Continuous Culture and Rotation Cropping upon Yield.   Ohio Agricultural Experiment Station, Average of Thirty Years [1]

Treatment	Crop Yields in Bushels an Acre		
	Corn	Oats	Wheat
Continuous culture	33.8	37.8	19.4
Rotation cropping	51.3	43.7	23.5

The results are so striking that little comment is necessary except to suggest that crops grown in sequence probably utilize the soil nutrients more economically than those in continuous culture, and that the rotated crops without a doubt were greatly benefited by the clover. This legume not only acquires nitrogen from the air, if suitably nodulated, but activates the soil constituents as well.

[1] Williams, C. G., *The Maintenance of Soil Fertility*, Bulletin 381, Ohio Agr. Exp. Sta., 296–311, 1924.

263. *Fertility generalization*

The system so briefly outlined in the preceding pages is merely a group of practices that are designed, when properly correlated, to maintain, or partially maintain, the productivity of a mineral soil. In some cases all of the features are put into operation, in other cases only a few are utilized. Since phosphorus, organic matter, and nitrogen usually need attention, especially in the production of field and vegetable crops, the system is built around their probable deficiency.

In general and dairy farming the utilization of crop residues, farm manure, legumes, and superphosphate is one of the simplest and most satisfactory combinations that can be made of the various fertility factors. Lime may or may not be necessary, while on occasion green manures will be helpful. Whether a complete commercial fertilizer is used instead of, or in connection with, superphosphate will depend on circumstances. Trace-element deficiencies may also need attention. But whatever the combination, its efficiency will be enhanced by a suitable rotation of crops.

With intensive vegetable production the main reliance is usually placed upon complete fertilizers in liberal amounts. With certain other crops an adequate supply of nitrogen and the maintenance of the soil organic matter are the only serious considerations. This is the case with apple production on the medium and heavier types of soil. Again for still other crops, such as tobacco and potatoes, potash and phosphoric acid are the principal concern.

Satisfactory soil productivity is the ultimate objective of soil utilization and the scheme utilized is merely a coordination of practices and manipulations that are designed to attain this objective. Soil-fertility management is, therefore, a practical application of the edaphological viewpoint and should be based on a thorough knowledge of the nature and properties of soils and their relationship to higher plants.

Author Index

Subject Index